THE

FUTURE

OF

PUBLIC

EDUCATION

Myron Lieberman

THE
FUTURE
OF
PUBLIC
EDUCATION

Phoenix Books
THE UNIVERSITY OF CHICAGO PRESS

This book is also available in a clothbound edition from

THE UNIVERSITY OF CHICAGO PRESS

Library of Congress Catalog Card Number: 59-15108
The University of Chicago Press, Chicago & London
The University of Toronto Press, Toronto 5, Canada
© 1960 by The University of Chicago
All rights reserved. Published 1960. First Phoenix Edition 1962
Fourth Impression 1963
Printed in the U.S.A.

To

LEO MOLINARO

with deepest admiration
respect and affection

PREFACE TO THE PHOENIX EDITION

The Future of Public Education was written in 1958–59. Since then I have had good reason to reaffirm some of the views expressed in it and to modify others. For this reason I welcome the opportunity to comment briefly upon them at this time.

The hard-cover edition was widely reviewed, probably more so than I had a right to expect. While most reviews were quite favorable to the book as a whole, it seems to me that few reviewers came to grips with the basic theses set forth in it. My comments about teachers organizations and the reactions to these comments are a case in point.

For one thing, I tried to explain why teachers organizations must be concerned with certain problems typically ignored by trade unions. For example, bricklayers are not required to undergo professional training in institutions of higher education. Teachers are, and for this reason their organizations must be deeply involved in problems of teacher education, certification, and accreditation. On the other hand, teachers organizations will never be effective until they incorporate certain union principles. Unlike fee takers such as doctors or lawyers, teachers are employed by other educators serving in an administrative capacity. For this reason, it is unwise to permit unrestricted administrator membership in professional organizations which represent teachers in matters of employment. The fact that such organizations can and should be concerned about many things in addition to conditions of employment is irrelevant to this conclusion.

In short, what I tried to say was that teachers organizations must incorporate certain features of *both* the fee-taking professions and the trade unions. Nevertheless, I frequently encounter readers who attribute to me or to the book the notion that teachers organizations must be *either* a "trade union" *or* a "professional association." The notion that effective teachers organizations will have to be both seems to me a simple, even obvious thing, but I cannot claim success in getting readers to understand, let alone to accept, this point.

The most important educational event since publication of the hard-cover edition was the election to choose a bargaining agent for New York City's teachers. Conducted in December, 1961, this was the largest white-collar election in our history and was a significant event in public administration as well as in education.

The election itself resulted in a decisive victory for the United Federation of Teachers (UFT), the New York City affiliate of the American Federation of Teachers (AFL-CIO). The UFT received 20,045 votes whereas the NEA-supported Teachers Bargaining Organization received only 9,770 votes in the final tally. In the first three months after the election, the UFT increased its membership from about 7,000 to 12,000 and was making good progress toward its goal of 20,000 members by June, 1962. Thus the election confirmed several important points set forth in the hard-cover edition, to wit:

1. Collective bargaining will soon be widespread in public education.

2. The advent of collective bargaining in public education will provide the AFT with tremendous opportunities and will create severe policy and membership problems for the NEA and its affiliated state and local associations. On the basis of the available evidence, I would say that the NEA has learned nothing from its rout in New York City, undoubtedly the most important setback ever experienced by the Association in its long history.

3. The NEA's poor record in combating racial and religious discrimination will be a serious handicap in its efforts to organize teachers in large northern cities.

4. The future of the AFT lies in its ability to make breakthrough gains rather than in conventional efforts to enrol a few thousand more teachers each year.

The election also suggested that teacher affiliation with the AFL-CIO need not be an insuperable handicap to the AFT in metropolitan centers. As I had pointed out, critics of teacher affiliation with labor have never documented their argument that such affiliation actually compromises teachers in any way. I had also pointed out that experts in public administration generally favor the affiliation of public service employees with national labor bodies. For these reasons, I had rejected the notion that teacher affiliation with the AFL-CIO was wrong in principle or even in practice. I did, however, indicate that teacher objections to affiliation, however invalid in theory or practice, were a major organizing handicap to the AFT.

The New York City election suggests that teacher affiliation with labor can be an asset provided that affiliation is used politically to secure collective bargaining elections for teachers. If the AFL-CIO can get collective bargaining elections for teachers under the proper conditions, teachers are likely to choose AFT locals as bargaining agents. The reason is that such locals will be the only organizations really geared to act as bargaining agents in most communities.

Another important factor bearing on teacher affiliation with the AFL-CIO is the tremendous increase in white-collar employment in recent years. My own thinking assumed that it would be easier to organize teachers into unions after there had been major breakthroughs in other professional and white-collar fields. The New York City experience suggests that the unionization of teachers may provide the stimulus to the unionization of white-collar workers generally. At any rate, given competent leadership the AFT should enrol 250,000 members by 1970. Such a development would bring about changes in every aspect of education.

In retrospect, the major weakness of the book is its failure to deal with the interrelationships between public and non-public, especially Catholic, schools. Since the future of public education is closely related to developments in private education, this was a serious omission, even if no reviewer noted it. Regretfully, I cannot elaborate upon these interrelationships here, but I hope to do so in forthcoming publications.

One last point. Ordinarily, I am regarded as an optimist—a wild-eyed one in some quarters. Nevertheless, in 1959, I did not dream that within three years the New York City teachers would be represented by a bargaining agent chosen in accordance with recognized collective bargaining procedures. New York City employs more teachers than are employed in the 10 smallest states combined or in 43 states taken individually. Thus developments there constitute tremendous progress, even by space age standards, and suggest that the 1960's will be one of the most exciting and fruitful decades in the history of American education.

March, 1962

PREFACE

Some of the material in this book appeared first in *The Nation* and in *School and Society*. I would like to thank the editors of these magazines and the publishers of the many other works quoted throughout the book, for permission to quote from their publications.

In the writing of this book, I have had the benefit of suggestions and criticisms from many sources. In particular, I would like to express my deep appreciation to the following persons, who read all or a part of the manuscript in draft or periodical form and made comments which helped in some way to improve it: Mr. Charles Cogen, president of the New York Teachers Guild, AFL-CIO, Professor Robert Anderson of Harvard University, Professor B. Othanel Smith of the University of Illinois, Dr. Paul Woodring and Dr. Lester Nelson of the Fund for the Advancement of Education, Dr. Robert M. Hutchins of the Fund for the Republic, Dr. James B. Conant, and Mr. Myrl Herman of Washington University. In virtually all of these cases, one outcome was a friendly agreement to disagree on some issues, a fact which should be emphasized because the views of some of these persons are criticized in the book itself. Likewise, there should be no thought that any of these persons necessarily endorses or approves what I have written concerning any organizations with which they are affiliated; quite often the reverse is the case.

The manuscript was also influenced by conversations over the past few years with many persons in school systems, educational organizations, foundations, and institutions of higher education. Since there were so many persons who helped me in this way, I can only hope that a general but sincere expression of appreciation will indicate the depth of my obligation to them. For the final product I alone must and do take complete responsibility. However, my debt to one other person must be recorded; there would be no book at all, let alone a poor one, without the unfailing encouragement and assistance of my wife, Dr. Mary Arthur Lieberman.

November, 1959

CONTENTS

CONTENTS

Chapter I

THE POINT OF VIEW

This book is an attempt to explain and defend a point of view about public education in the United States. The point of view is not crystallized in a label or summed up by a slogan. I am not an advocate of basic education, progressive education, liberal education, the three R's, social adjustment, or stricter discipline in the public schools. I am not going to urge anyone to join a society of the educationally anointed or to subscribe to a magazine which prints only Educational Truth. I shall make no appeal to parents to march on school boards or for Public Spirited Citizens to rise up and clean out the Augean stables of American education. Nevertheless, I believe that public education in the United States is much less effective than it can and ought to be. This book is devoted to explaining why I think so and what I think should be done about it.

Before setting forth my position, I should like to comment briefly upon the contemporary educational situation. Following this, I shall outline the position to be developed in the following chapters, indicating in a general way the points of contrast between this and other analyses of public education. After providing a very general fix on my position, I shall turn directly to the task of relating it to the focal points of current controversy.

To me, the crucial aspect of our educational situation is this: We are at the threshold of a revolution in education, a revolution which will alter drastically every important aspect of education as a social institution and as a profession. In many respects, the directions that this revolution will take are still unclear. Unless the American people, and especially the teaching profession, achieve a better understanding of the problems of public education than they have had in the past, they are not likely to guide this revolution into constructive channels.

I do not predict an educational revolution as a disinterested observer. On the contrary, I will be disappointed if it does not take place. Its absence will reflect upon my capacity as an educational theoretician, but that is not important. What *is* important is the need for such a revolution and the consequences to our society if we do not sense the need for one and carry it out. I have more confidence that an educational revolution is needed than I have that one will actually take place. Nevertheless, what follows is a prediction as well as a hope—and is offered without apologies for either the hope or the prediction.

The future revolution in education may be regarded as having two dimensions. One dimension relates to the fundamental nature of the changes that will take place. There is, of course, no calculus by which we determine whether a change is "revolutionary" or not. Indeed, people often disagree upon whether a particular change in the social order is or is not "revolutionary." At one extreme, changes are so fundamental that no one doubts the propriety of labeling them "revolutionary." At the other extreme, changes are so unimportant that no one doubts their less consequential nature. In between, there are changes that are regarded as "revolutionary" by some people but not by others.

I believe that within the next few decades education in the United States will undergo changes of tremendous scope and magnitude. That is, the changes will affect not only what is taught and how but also such aspects of education as teachers' organizations, professional ethics, teacher education, the theory and practice of teacher compensation, and the many interrelationships between teachers and pupils, parents, communities, and governmental agencies. These changes will be so basic that we will be fully justified in using the term "revolutionary" to describe them.

There is also a temporal dimension to the forthcoming revolution in education. If the federal government were to finance completely the operating costs of private schools, and if it were to do this through a single piece of legislation, such action would undoubtedly be regarded as a revolutionary change in our educational system. On the other hand, local, state, and federal governments frequently adopt legislation which affects the status of private schools. The laws providing for bus transportation at public expense for students in parochial schools are a case in point. It is conceivable that bits and pieces of legislation over a long period of time, perhaps a century or more, would provide for complete governmental support for private schools. Looking back over a century, one might be unable to characterize any particular item as revolutionary, although the impact of all the legislation might be an educational system radically different from that of a century ago.

To generalize from this discussion, at any given time one can, if one peers far enough into the past, justifiably contend that the current state of affairs represents a revolutionary change from a state of affairs in the past. By the same token, one can always correctly predict, by not putting any time limit on the prediction, that there will be a revolution in education. However, merely to assert that our educational system will differ from what it is today, without any indication of the nature or imminence of the changes, is to achieve predictive certainty at the expense of practical value. In this book, the prediction that there will be a revolution in education means more than that, in some remote future, education will be radically different from what it is today. I am asserting that within the foreseeable future—certainly within the lifetime of most readers—there will be fundamental changes in our educational system. Furthermore, in the chapters to follow, I have specifically indicated what I believe will be their nature.

These changes will not take place merely because they are desirable. They will take place as the logical and practical outcome of events and movements which are upon us now. In this respect, to predict their occurrence is analogous to predicting certain developments in the arms race. When the United States produced atomic weapons, its scientists did not know when Russia would also have such weapons. However, that the Russians would develop them within a certain time span was always clear from trends which were obvious to informed persons. Similarly, there are trends which lead to the conclusion that it is no longer a question of whether certain changes in our educational system will occur, but only of when they will occur.

To label a change "revolutionary" is neither to praise nor to condemn it. I believe that the changes predicted in this book will be beneficial to our society. However, they will not be beneficial merely because they are revolutionary. Their beneficent character, if they have any, rests upon other grounds.

The broad framework of our school system was created in and for an era that is fast disappearing. The period in which makeshift compromises can be used to stave off a fundamental overhauling is fast running out. Nevertheless, the fact that a new framework is needed does not by itself settle the question of what is to be its nature and guiding principles. To some extent, these things will be shaped by the impersonal forces that are undermining the current framework. However, once it becomes clear that a new framework for public education must be developed, not one but many alternatives may be suggested. The specific changes I have set forth constitute what I believe to be the best solutions to basic problems that cannot be evaded. The point is, however, that whatever solutions are accepted will constitute an educational framework different from anything we have known in the past.

This assessment, which may be widely disputed, leads directly to the educational position espoused in subsequent chapters. The bare bones of this position are as follows:

1. Public education in the United States is much less effective than the American people, especially the teaching profession, assume it to be. More important, it is much less effective than it can and ought to be.

2. The most important causes of the ineffectiveness of public education are rooted in its anachronistic and dysfunctional power structure.

3. Because most current controversy is concerned with the rightness or wrongness of certain educational policies and not with the power structure within which these policies are made, it is largely irrelevant to the basic problems of education.

4. The basic educational reforms needed in the United States will have to be initiated and carried out by the teachers themselves. It follows from this that the study of teachers' organizations—their programs, leadership, political sophistication, strategy, and tactics—must be accorded high priority by those who wish to bring about fundamental improvements.

5. Appeals to "the public" to solve the problems of education are usually well intentioned, but under present circumstances they ordinarily result in more harm than good to the cause of public education. They will continue to have this effect until the futility of appealing to a diffuse public becomes manifest to educational leadership and until there is established a sensible delineation of the role of the public in the educational enterprise.

To state these convictions is one thing; to defend them is another. The rest of this book is devoted chiefly to the latter task, but I would be the first to insist that this defense is far from complete.

To avoid serious misunderstanding, the reader must always bear in mind the distinction between a claim that proposition X is valid and a claim that the validity of proposition X has been established by a certain set of statements. To be specific, my purpose is to suggest a series of changes which I regard as imperative for the welfare of public education. The arguments for and against each of these changes might well require a book or more. In this one, I have presented only a prima facie case for the proposed changes. My offer to the reader is this: I grant that the arguments in this book are not conclusive. Furthermore, I do not expect the reader to accept conclusions based upon evidence which lies concealed within my nervous system. However, the reader must recognize that the absence *in this book* of conclusive evidence in support of the changes proposed does not justify the inference that such evidence does not exist.

Some kinds of evidence lie in careful scholarship, and only there. Often this evidence is not easily available to the average person, intelligent and public spirited as he may be. There are other cases in which the evidence is all around us, but we do not have the proper "mind set" to recognize it. If you do not consciously entertain a hypothesis, you are not likely to notice the evidence which confirms or disproves it.

Generally speaking, both kinds of evidence are cited in support of the positions taken in this book. At the same time, I have been forced to omit a great deal of the scholarly data upon which my arguments are based. For this reason, I have suggested additional sources for those who may wish to pursue any of these arguments further. My purpose is not to make converts to my point of view but to establish the possibility that this point of view merits further reflection and investigation.

For this reason, it seems to me especially desirable to have the reader test my arguments against the background of his own studies and educational experiences. There are dangers in this procedure. Personal experience can be a very misleading guide unless it is interpreted within a sound theoretical framework. Also, an appeal to personal experience often results in oversimplification, the great curse of educational theorizing. Whether it does so in this case is partly the responsibility of the reader, and perhaps this note of caution will help him to fulfil his responsibility as well as my own.

OTHER EDUCATIONAL VIEWS: SOME
PRELIMINARY COMMENTS

Let me try to locate my position on the spectrum of educational controversy. I hold no copyright on the notion that the situation in public education is not a healthy one. Indeed, if one were to select the most shopworn question in American life today, "What's wrong with our schools?" would undoubtedly be a strong contender for top honors. It would be difficult to suggest more familiar topics than the fifty-seven varieties of progressive education, the fads and frills versus the three R's, why Johnny can't read as well as his grandparents, the underpaid but dedicated teachers, or the need to protect the liberal arts from vocationalism, professors of education, financial impoverishment, and sundry other disasters. The trouble is that these threadbare topics evoke attitudes and arguments which are familiar to everyone. They arouse only the old war horses of educational controversy; everyone else has other fish to fry.

The fact that certain educational problems receive predominant attention in the mass media year after year can be interpreted in different ways. There is a romantic school of thought which holds that certain problems are perennial because of their great importance. Another interpretation is that certain issues are always with us because nobody has come up with a satisfactory solution to them so far. Still another is that any answers to certain educational problems involve an adjustment of conflicting interests; the pressure groups concerned are continually seeking a readjustment to further their own interests. For example, it might be argued that teachers' salaries will always be a problem because of the conflict of interest inherent in any employer-employee relationship.

These and other interpretations may be valid as applied to specific educational problems. Nevertheless, I do not think they provide a satisfactory answer to the question of why we are confronted with so many of the same problems and the same inadequate solutions year in and year out. It seems to me that when a question has been around for a long time and no satisfactory answer to it is in sight, we should begin to question the question instead of the specific answers to it.

This thought prompts me to suggest that the attention given to such old reliables as "progressive education" or "the fads and frills versus the three R's" bears very little relationship to any issues of intrinsic importance. A thoroughgoing skepticism concerning the field of journalism reinforces the suggestion. "Journalists" are not specialists in education, just as they are not specialists in economics, science, government, or any other substantive field of knowledge. Journalists are trained in journalism

—that is, in the methods and techniques of writing news and feature stories. That they should be alarmed about such traditional bogeys as an alleged overemphasis upon methodology when their own training provides a most glaring example of this weakness is ironical but understandable. To assess what is important in a field, one must understand that field. Editors who pontificate about teachers having to be trained in a field in order to teach it adequately seem unconcerned about whether a reporter has to be trained in a field in order to report and interpret it accurately.

It is not that journalists must have a course in methods of teaching in order to report and interpret educational news intelligently. However, they do need a systematic study of the way in which education is financed and controlled, the dynamics of who gets what kind of education, the interrelationships between the local, state, regional, and national organizations which shape educational policies, and the level, direction, and quality of educational research. These are only a few of the subjects which should be studied by persons who exercise the responsibility of informing the public on educational matters. No doubt a reporter can learn some of these things on the job, but the cost in public understanding is too high a price to pay for this way of educating the press. To make matters worse, the level of educational reporting and editorializing in the mass media is not far below the level of these things in the professional literature which most teachers read. In fact, part of the public confusion about education is a direct result of the inability of educators to define clearly just what are the important educational issues.

An issue may be clear, but people may be confused about what to do because the reasons for and against any particular course of action are so evenly balanced. This kind of confusion is often unavoidable. It is really not confusion at all but practical uncertainty. Such a situation differs in kind from one in which the issues are not clear. In the latter, people do not even know what evidence or arguments are relevant to a solution. Education is characterized by many controversies of this kind. Basically, these unclear issues are pseudo-issues, not real ones, because people are not talking about the same thing and therefore cannot be said to be taking issue with each other.

Since World War II and especially since Sputnik, public education has been the subject of considerable discussion. Educators frequently assert that current public interest in education exceeds that of any previous period in history. From reading the mass media and the professional journals, one gets the impression that there is a "great debate" going on. This "great debate" is supposed to be concerned chiefly with the purposes of education; the main issue is commonly thought to be whether the purpose of education shall be intellectual training or social adjustment.

Personally, I am convinced that the so-called "great debate" on education has been mostly irrelevant and that its actual impact on education has been negligible. Without too much oversimplification, we can place the contributions to the debate on a continuum. At one end would be the "critics" of public education. These assert that the public schools have been diverted from their "true" purpose, that they are failing badly, and that drastic changes are necessary to reverse an alleged trend toward educational mediocrity.[1] It is unfortunate but indicative of our educational situation that the phrase "critics of public education" should be widely used to denote a rather specific group. This group consists largely of certain persons who have contended in books, articles, and speeches over the past ten years that the public schools are emphasizing social adjustment to the neglect of their historic and rightful task of intellectual training.[2] The point is that every person who plays a professional

[1] For examples see Arthur E. Bestor, *The Restoration of Learning* (New York: Alfred A. Knopf, 1955); Robert M. Hutchins, *The Conflict in Education* (New York: Harper & Bros., 1953); John Keats, *Schools without Scholars* (Boston: Houghton Mifflin Co., 1957); Albert Lynd, *Quackery in the Public Schools* (Boston: Little, Brown & Co., 1953); H. G. Rickover, *Education and Freedom* (New York: E. P. Dutton, 1959); Mortimer B. Smith, *The Diminished Mind* (Chicago: Henry Regnery Co., 1954).

[2] The organizational focus of the "critics" is the Council for Basic Education, a kind of Progressive Education Association for educational conservatives. The Council is a conglomeration of viewers with alarm who preferred to establish another splinter organization instead of fighting for their point of view within the educational organizations which have the

role in public education should be a critic of it. To label specific individuals or groups as "critics of public education" is implicitly to condemn others, who presumably have lost or neglected their critical faculties.

Ironically, some of the "critics" assert that there is hardly any criticism of public education emanating from the educators themselves. When the latter label a small group as "critics," they inevitably reinforce the very point which the "critics" are making; they are saying in effect that the function of criticism is confined to the "critics." This honors the "critics" more than they deserve and constitutes a gratuitous insult to others who are critical of specific aspects of public education. The tendency to identify the function of criticism with a rather specific group has also been unfair to the latter group. It has given rise to the erroneous notion that the "critics" are opposed to public education per se. On the contrary, the "critics" regard themselves as ardent champions of public education, no less devoted to it than those who (according to the "critics") are unaware of the shortcomings of the public schools.

Every social institution needs criticism. We would hardly regard a person as opposed to legislatures merely because he was critical of the overrepresentation of rural areas in our legislative bodies. Such a person might be an extremely valuable supporter of our legislative institutions, in the sense that he might suggest the corrective measures needed to safeguard their continued existence. Analogously, people who support outmoded and inefficient aspects of public education are not its friends in fact, even though they may be in name and spirit. My point is not that the specific individuals labeled "critics" are the saviors of public education; it is that this way of labeling people can be very misleading. We should be concerned with the specific educational proposals which people make, not with the label they may have picked up along the way.

---

membership and resources to influence the direction of public education. Like the Progressive Education Association, the Council will orbit aimlessly in educational space for a few decades and then wither away, claiming the widespread acceptance of its platform as the reason for its dissolution.

The "critics" are at one end of a continuum; at the other end are those who assert that the public schools are doing a good job on the whole. The person who asserts that everything educational is perfect probably does not exist, any more than the person who asserts that everything about the public schools is bad. However, many people see no need for any sweeping changes in the goals, content, methodology, or control of public education. These people are its "supporters" or "defenders."

The difference between the "critics" and the "supporters" does not lie in their acceptance or rejection of public education per se but in their rejection of certain aspects of the educational status quo. While none of the "supporters" denies the possibility and the need for improvement, the group as a whole is quietistic, except on the need for more money for public education.[3]

Then, as might be expected, there are the middle-of-the-roaders to tell us that things are not as bad as the most severe "critics" tell us nor as good as the "supporters" would have it.[4] The middle-of-the-roaders tend to make this error; they often regard *agreement* that a certain policy is sound as *proof* that it is. People can and do agree upon unsound educational programs; this is a possibility which is not envisaged by some educational conciliators and peacemakers.

This is not a "middle-of-the-road" book for several reasons. First, insofar as there are identifiable schools of educational thought concerning the public school crisis, I am more impressed by the fundamental fallacies they share in common than by the valid points they espouse separately. Second, it is naïve to believe that educational theorizing is not affected by the self-interest of the theorizers, at least as they perceive it. I do not mean that everyone deliberately contends that what is good for

[3] Most of the literature of this group is in periodical rather than book form. Despite his many excellent suggestions for improvement, I would place Dr. Conant in this category inasmuch as he himself rejects the notion that there is need for basic changes in our educational structure. See James B. Conant, *The American High School Today* (New York: McGraw-Hill Book Co., 1959), p. 40.

[4] The best known educator in this category is Paul Woodring. See his *One Fourth of a Nation* (New York: McGraw-Hill Book Co., 1957), and *Let's Talk Sense about the Public Schools* (New York: McGraw-Hill Book Co., 1952).

him is good for the country, but few people keep considerations of self-interest from affecting their consideration of national interest. This is certainly true in the colleges, where professors often visualize a one-to-one relationship between the welfare of their department and the welfare of American society.

One thesis of this book is that in order to achieve substantial improvements in public education, we must first make radical changes in its power structure. It is foolish to suppose that everybody's self-interest will be affected in the same way by sweeping educational changes; to the extent that this is so, it is unlikely that a middle-of-the-road position will make either political or educational sense. The groups whose powers should be diminished are not likely to accept such a development as a sound compromise. In some cases, perhaps they will; in others, they will regard any weakening of their powers as synonymous with the decline of American civilization and resist it accordingly.

Some educational moderates are fond of saying that educational controversy "really" consists of "semantic" differences which would disappear if there were agreement upon definitions. Others see conflict as the result of ignorance and blithely assume that controversy will disappear in the sunlight of more knowledge and understanding. The possibility that more knowledge or a better understanding of other positions may increase instead of decrease controversy is ignored. Nevertheless, increased knowledge may be a cause of, as well as a means of resolving, controversy. A better understanding of the other person's point of view may bring out sharp and irreconcilable differences which were obscured by a less penetrating view.

Agreement upon definitions, more knowledge, and better understanding will invalidate some of the claims which currently fill the air and hence they will also weaken drastically the power of those individuals and groups who rely upon these claims to maintain their position. Because this is so, an approach to educational controversy starting with the assumption that any solutions reached must be acceptable to all sides operates under a handicap likely to prove fatal.

The middle-of-the-roaders want to stress open-mindedness, but this characteristic should refer to one's capacity and willingness to examine all sides to a controversy. It has nothing to do with any a priori judgment about the distribution of truth and error in the controversy. It is as narrow-minded to assume beforehand that truth lies "between" conflicting positions as it is to assume that it lies with one or none of them. Whether a position is extreme in the sense of not being shared by others is not so important as whether it is supported by valid evidence and sound reasoning.

In one sense, I place myself with the "critics" of public education. I am convinced that our schools are not as effective as they should be. I mean by this more than the simple idea that improvement is possible. Improvements are possible in every social institution—our courts, our legislatures, our hospitals, and so on. When I cast my lot with the "critics," I mean to say that the return on our educational investment is too low to be brushed aside by sincere but routine admissions that improvement is possible and desirable. I am asserting that the gap between the achievable and the actual results of public education should be a matter for deep national concern and that this concern must not abate until the gap has been drastically reduced.

"Our schools are not as effective as they should be"—this is a hazy statement. "Effective" according to what criteria? Are all schools or only most schools "not as effective as they should be"? Does the statement refer to all teachers in most schools or most teachers in all schools? Obviously, two people might agree to this statement but upon analysis find that they really did not share the same conclusions about the ineffectiveness of public schools.

My concept of ineffectiveness is this: the public schools do not develop critical thinking, good citizenship, social competence, or creative skills. This statement cannot be applied with equal justice to all school systems, schools, or teachers. If applied to certain ones, it would be a rank injustice. On the other hand, in this book I am not going to try to separate the sheep from the goats in the 50,000 school systems or among the 1,300,000 school teachers in the country. Nor can I give a thorough evaluation of the impact of public education upon every one of the millions of students who attend or have attended public schools.

Clearly, my evaluation of public education is not a model of clarity and mathematical rigor. There is a difference, however, between a generalization which admittedly does not apply to every possible instance and one which is vague and impressionistic. Furthermore, my purpose in stating this generalization is not to lay down a hypothesis to be proved, at least at this particular point. It is to indicate in a crude way the nature of my agreement with some recent critics of public education. When it comes to a diagnosis of *why* public education is ineffective and what should be done to improve it, my views have little in common with those who contend that the liberal arts colleges are a kind of institutional Messiah, come to save the world from anti-intellectualism and the evils of social adjustment. The situation is like one in which two doctors agree that X is critically ill, but one doctor prescribes a bloodletting and the other a blood transfusion. Needless to add, both doctors will have little in common with others who assert that X has only a bad cold or that X is as robust and healthy as the children who eat their Wheaties every day.

Although the point of view set forth in this book is not original with me, it has never been presented systematically to the public or to the teaching profession. What I have to say may give comfort or pain to various groups, but I have no feeling, and certainly no conscious intent, of acting as a spokesman or advocate for anyone else. I hope that I am not making a fetish out of being different. It is simply that no group or organization is advocating the program which I regard as essential for the future of public education. For what it may be worth, this program and its rationale are set forth in the following pages.

Chapter II

WHAT THE PROBLEM IS NOT

The most important educational issue of our time is what should be the purposes of public education. This problem is "philosophical" in nature, in the sense that our answer to it will eventually depend on our vision of the good life and our conceptions of the nature of man, society, truth, ultimate reality, and other philosophical concepts. The determination of the purposes of education is essentially a matter for public rather than professional action.

I wish to dissent from all three of these propositions. The purpose of this chapter is to explain why they are fallacious and how belief in them has been harmful to public education in the United States.

Regardless of whether the determination of the broad purposes of education is *the* major problem of public education, there can be little doubt that most educational theorists think that it is. One of the "critics" writes:

The point I am making is that despite a sometimes fundamental philosophical cleavage, the traditionalists and the modernists believed in content, in a body of subject matter to be taught, but parted company on matters of method. This is no longer the main debate in American education; the controversy today is between those who continue to believe that the cultivation of intelligence, moral as well as intellectual, is inextricably bound up with the cultural heritage and accumulated knowledge of mankind, and those who feel that education's primary task is to adjust the individual to the group, to see that he responds "satisfactorily" to the stresses and strains of the social order.[1]

A recent textbook by four well-known professors of education asks and answers itself:

Why should the teacher know anything about the social role of the school?
First, most of the educational disputes now taking place in many communities center about the essential purpose of the school.[2]

Paul Woodring, a widely known educational theorist who is not identified with any particular school of educational thought, comments:

Today we are engaged in a great national debate over the aims and purpose of education, a debate that has included vigorous criticism of existing schools and of the philosophy of education which lies behind them.

And later, after proposing that "the proper aim of education is to prepare the individual to make wise decisions," he says:

If we can agree on this as our aim, our educational planning will be greatly simplified and the great American debate over education can move on to a profitable discussion of the best means for reaching our goals.[3]

The point of view expressed in these quotations is too common to require further documentation.[4] Nevertheless, despite its wide acceptance in the educational world, I believe that it represents a basic fallacy in our approach to educational problems.

It is true that no *statement* of the broad purposes of education has been accepted by the American people as a whole, but this

[1] Mortimer Smith, *The Diminished Mind* (Chicago: Henry Regnery Co., 1954), pp. 19–20.
[2] William O. Stanley, B. Othanel Smith, Kenneth D. Benne, and Archibald W. Anderson, *Social Foundations of Education* (New York: Dryden Press, 1956), p. 454.
[3] Paul Woodring, *One Fourth of a Nation* (New York: McGraw-Hill Book Co., 1957), pp. 6, 115.
[4] If any more is needed, I suppose that my own advocacy of this position not so long ago should be included. See Myron Lieberman, *Education as a Profession* (Englewood Cliffs, N.J.: Prentice-Hall, 1956), pp. 19–48.

does not mean that there is widespread disagreement about these purposes. There is a difference between agreement with a particular statement of purpose and agreement upon the purposes themselves. It is possible to have either of these things without the other. To the best of my knowledge, the American people as a whole have never agreed formally to a statement of the functions of *any* profession. Nevertheless, the professions are not unduly handicapped by a lack of agreement as to their general purposes. This fact suggests that the absence of any widespread formal agreement on the broad purposes of education must be interpreted very cautiously.

Certainly, there are disagreements concerning the broad purposes of education, just as there are some disagreements concerning the objectives of the medical profession, the legal profession, the engineering profession, the civil service, and many other occupational groups. Sometimes these disagreements present extremely difficult problems for the individual in a given field. Many scientists working on the atomic bomb had grave doubts concerning the purpose of their work. Lawyers are often confronted with situations which force them to decide whether their function is to advance the interests of their client or to see that justice is done. Other examples could be cited. Furthermore, I would agree that in specific instances conflict over the broad purposes of education does constitute a serious problem. My point is that these instances are too infrequent to be regarded as our major educational problem.

Since education is a state and local responsibility in the United States, some people contend that there is no reason why the American people as a whole should agree on its general objectives. Some even go so far as to assert that it would be dangerous to have widespread agreement on the purposes of education. Nevertheless, I believe that the American people are in substantial agreement that the purposes of education are the development of critical thinking, effective communication, creative skills, and social, civic, and occupational competence.

If there is widespread agreement on the broad purposes of education, why do so many people believe that disagreement in this area is so pervasive? The most important reason is the confusion over what are purposes and what are the means of achieving them. In this connection, bear in mind that school subjects are means of achieving certain purposes; they are not the purposes themselves. When we disagree about the inclusion of a subject in the curriculum, the disagreement may or may not arise out of disagreement over educational objectives.

The point of the preceding paragraph is an extremely important one; I shall elaborate upon it on several occasions in later chapters. Here let me suggest a simple example to illustrate the point and to bring out its importance. I believe that one of the objectives of public education is to develop critical thinking. To achieve this purpose, I believe that the study of logic and scientific method should be introduced into the public school curriculum. I also happen to believe that the world history courses so often given at the tenth-grade level are largely a waste of time.

I am not concerned now with defending either of these recommendations. For the sake of argument on the main issue, concede that I am completely mistaken in thinking that the study of logic and scientific method would be more conducive to critical intelligence than tenth-grade world history. I do not see, however, how anyone can question my categorical assertion that I accept and advocate the broad purpose of developing critical thinking. The important issue is whether the study of logic and scientific method would facilitate the development of critical thinking more than the study of world history.

This example suggests that a great deal of argument popularly labeled "controversy over the broad purposes of education" really concerns the means of achieving agreed-upon objectives. This confusion results from the fact that educational theory has not provided a clear-cut demarcation between purposes and the means of achieving them. At this point the reader may ask: "What difference does it make if the disagreement is labeled one of purpose or one of means? Isn't the important fact the one of disagreement, not what it is labeled?" My answer is that in this context, the way we label the disagreement is more important than the fact of disagreement.

Ultimately, the determination of the broad purposes of education is one for our entire society to make. The choice of means is one for the teaching profession to decide. If there is no clearcut understanding of what are objectives and what are means, people think they are arguing about one when they are really arguing about the other. Naturally, as a result of this confusion, people tend to exaggerate the extent of disagreement over purposes. What is more important, this confusion encourages the public to make decisions concerning means which in its own best interests should be made by teachers. *To generalize: it makes a tremendous difference whether we classify a disagreement as one of purpose or as one of means, because the mode of classification has a crucial bearing on who should settle the disagreement.*

Consider again, for a moment, a few sentences from the education textbook already cited:

> In school after school, the teachers and principal are attacked by vociferous groups of citizens who think that the three R's are not given enough time, or that the conventional subjects are neglected, or that the school is not emphasizing moral and spiritual values, or that false and dangerous economic and political doctrines are being taught. . . . Each of these attacks reflects a public concern with what the school is attempting to do. *Each one presupposes that the school should serve one function rather than another—that the role of the school is to teach the fundamental skills and the conventional subjects,* or to develop moral and spiritual character, or to maintain the *status quo* or even the *status quo ante* in economics and politics, and so on.[5]

This quotation illustrates exactly the kind of confusion I am talking about. A controversy over whether "the three R's are not given enough time" is not necessarily a conflict over the function of public education. Such controversy does *not* "presuppose that the school should serve one function rather than another." Assuming that it does so only confuses teachers and laymen alike into exaggerating the extent of disagreement over the objectives

[5] Stanley *et al., loc. cit.* Italics added.

of education and encourages massive interference with academic freedom. If educators themselves tell citizens to debate and settle the amount of time given to the three R's on the grounds that this problem is one of broad purpose, they have in effect abandoned their professional claim to autonomy in this matter. And, in general, academic freedom is muddled away by educators more than it is trampled upon by laymen.

Exaggeration of the extent of disagreement over purposes is compounded by a tendency to assume that people who advocate different subjects in the curriculum necessarily advocate different objectives for education. People often agree on what is purpose and what are means, but then erroneously regard a difference in means as reflecting a difference in purpose. Sometimes it is, but often it is not. Disagreement over the inclusion of a subject may simply reflect differing estimates of its usefulness in achieving an agreed-upon purpose.

Although disagreement over educational purposes is neither the pervasive nor the all-important problem that it is often thought to be, there are some extremely important analytical and practical problems directly related to this problem. In order to effectuate any objective, teachers must develop a set of intermediate objectives which will provide direction for their efforts in the classroom. It is at this point—the point of professional translation of broad purposes into a coherent educational program—that we have some of our major unsolved problems. The failure of the teaching profession to implement certain broad purposes of education has understandably but mistakenly led to the belief that teachers have abandoned these purposes. A failure in performance has come to be regarded as one of intent instead of capability.

For example, one of the objectives of education may be to develop the ability to communicate effectively. However, the first-grade teacher can contribute to this purpose only by setting certain specific goals, such as a vocabulary of so many words or an ability to write the letters of the alphabet, for her students. The English teacher in the high school also contributes to the same broad objective but only by setting intermediate objectives which are different from those set by elementary-school teachers: he works toward such intermediate objectives as an understanding of grammar, an ability to locate sources of information, an appreciation of literary classics, and so on.

Some of the intermediate objectives of the high-school teacher will appear to be the same as those of the elementary-school teacher. For instance, both will accept increasing the pupil's vocabulary as an intermediate objective. In practice, however, the words and concepts taught by one will be different from those taught by the other. Indeed, all teachers should have as one of their broad objectives the development of effective communication. All may contribute toward this objective by increasing the vocabulary of their students. However, each teacher will have a different vocabulary to teach. The history teacher will introduce such new concepts as feudalism or the Industrial Revolution, the physics teacher will introduce such new ones as velocity and ergs, and so on.

The problem here is that the teachers have failed to establish sets of intermediate objectives which would clarify how they propose to fulfil the general objectives of education. The discussion of objectives is usually concerned with the general ones, but this is not where the problem lies. It lies in establishing consistent, defensible, and attainable intermediate objectives which can serve as the basis for evaluating the progress made by the profession.

Let me illustrate this point by examples from other occupations. One of the broad aims of the medical profession is to prolong life. In carrying out this objective, the medical profession has eliminated most communicable causes of death. Of communicable diseases, only tuberculosis and pneumonia are still major causes of death, and the advances made in checking these are impressive. Thus, in 1900 the death rate per 100,000 persons from tuberculosis was 194.4; in 1952 it was only 16.1. In 1900 the death rate per 100,000 persons from pneumonia was 175.4; in 1952 it was 30.5. Again, bear in mind that other communicable diseases have been eliminated entirely or reduced to a negligible factor.

Thus, in carrying out its general purpose of prolonging life, the medical profession has concentrated upon the major causes of death at any given time. Obviously, as some are eliminated, other causes become major. Today, degenerative diseases have largely replaced communicable diseases as the major causes of death, and the medical profession is now beginning to eliminate or substantially reduce the death rate from these. As it succeeds, still other diseases will become major causes of death, and they in turn will be subjected to intensive research with a view to their elimination or substantial reduction.

By thus going from one specific intermediate objective to another, the medical profession has achieved outstanding success in fulfilling one of its broad purposes, the prolongation of life. In the United States, life expectancy at birth was approximately 40 years in 1800, 49 years in 1900, close to 60 years by 1925, and close to 70 years by 1950. Indeed, the success of the medical profession in eliminating one after another of the leading causes of death has led the profession to question whether there are any insuperable biological limits to human life. At any rate, there is every reason to expect greater and greater success in prolonging human life, but always through concrete intermediate goals which lead to the broad goal itself.

Perhaps one other example will be useful. Physicists have as their general purpose the achievement of an understanding of the laws of matter and motion. Their field is usually regarded as encompassing mechanics, heat, electricity, light, and sound. Now, although the general purpose of physicists has remained unchanged for centuries, in recent years they have achieved dazzling success in its fulfilment. For example, when Einstein discovered that $e = mc^2$, he made an enormous contribution to the understanding of the laws of matter and motion. Other physicists have solved one after another of the basic theoretical problems of physics. But the point is that these gains have been achieved because physicists, collectively and individually, have continually set and achieved strategic intermediate objectives which would implement the broad purpose of their profession.

Getting back to education, we see that it too has broad purposes, such as the development of an ability to communicate effectively. Such a purpose is analogous to the general purpose of prolonging life or of increasing our understanding of matter and motion. But whereas doctors and physicists have progressive and feasible intermediate objectives, teachers do not. Therein is a problem of purpose, albeit not the problem which agitates so many of our post-Sputnik philosophers of education.

Let me illustrate what might be done. A student who is capable of earning an engineering degree is ordinarily capable of learning calculus by the time he finishes high school. In practice, such students are not even exposed to calculus until their second or third year in college. Teachers might well accept, as one of their intermediate objectives, the objective of having all students of a certain ability level and career pattern master calculus by the time they have finished high school.

Many interrelated problems would have to be solved to accomplish this intermediate objective. For instance, there are thousands of small high schools which have only one or a very few students capable of learning calculus. Some of these schools have no trained mathematics teachers, and there is little chance that a school system is going to employ a highly paid teacher for a handful of students. Thus, to achieve the proposed objective, it might be necessary to reduce drastically the number of high schools so that the remaining ones could offer appropriate courses with a reasonable teacher-pupil ratio. Obviously, changes in teacher education, in teachers' salaries, in the high-school curriculum, and in many other aspects of education would also be necessary to achieve the suggested intermediate objective. None of these changes is impossible or even impractical, given able leadership.

There are many kinds of intermediate objectives which teachers might set for themselves. Some of them would not involve any improvement in the performance of students. Instead, they would involve only an improvement in the productivity of teachers. Everyone is aware of the fact that maturational factors limit what can be taught to young children. The same student who is capable of learning calculus in the twelfth grade is not capable of learning it in the elementary grades. Of course, when we say that young children cannot learn better or faster, we never know for certain whether we are dealing with a stubborn and eradicable fact of life or with our ignorance of the learning process. In any case, when it is unreasonable to set higher goals for the students, teachers should concentrate upon ways and means of utilizing a smaller number of teachers to accomplish a given educational result. Just as in other fields, productivity may be increased either by a constant labor force which expands its output or by a constant output achieved through a decreasing labor force. In most occupations there are exciting frontiers in both directions. Teachers, however, seem unable to make much progress in either.

It is important to recognize that intermediate objectives should be set by the professions, not by the public. The medical profession is best qualified to decide what specific hypotheses should be subjected to research in order to advance the broad purpose of prolonging life. Surely, physicists are the persons best qualified to decide which particular investigations will deepen our understanding of matter and motion. And in education teachers are, or should be, the persons best qualified to decide what proximate objectives of education should be pursued to fulfil its broad purposes. Unfortunately, while the doctors are making rapid advances in reducing pain and prolonging life, while scientists are exploring the vast reaches of the universe and the nature of the tiniest particles, while our industrialists and our labor force are achieving exciting advances in productivity, in short, while one occupational group after another is soaring to new heights, the teachers seem unable to get off the ground.

Why are the frontiers of public education so static? Why is education lost in a Sargasso Sea, so that from one generation to the next the schools are involved in the same dreary problems with the same dreary kinds of persons advocating the same dreary positions? Partly, I think, because of the misplaced, often pseudo-profound, concern with the broad purposes of education. This concern is the other side of a coin which reveals a shocking unwillingness and inability on the part of teachers at all levels and of all subjects to evaluate their own work.

Are schools today more effective (by any criterion) than they were x number of years ago? This question is important. We cannot evaluate public education without confronting it. Nevertheless, despite the fact that the question is often asked, there is a remarkable lack of systematic reliable data to answer it. The truth is that there is little rigorous evaluation of public education.

We have little evidence to show that the schools today are much more effective than those of an earlier day. Neither do we have much evidence to confirm the belief that there has been a sweeping deterioration in public education. But the important point is that the absence of systematic evaluative data is more remarkable than any conclusion to be drawn from whatever data we have.

An antipathy to evaluation pervades every dimension of the educational enterprise, from the kindergarten to the graduate school. It is reflected in the decline of examinations for a teaching certificate, the fear of any kind of merit-rating for teachers, and the opposition to standardized examinations to test student progress. It is also a cause of the overemphasis upon personality and the downgrading of intellectual competence as a basis for selecting prospective teachers. Personality traits, such as an interest in children, are much more difficult to evaluate than intellectual competence. Reliance upon "personality" as a criterion for evaluating prospective teachers degenerates into reliance upon no criteria at all.

The lack of evaluation in the public schools is the natural and logical consequence of its absence from higher education. Many professors who have been critical of the public schools apparently expect them to apply evaluative criteria which the professors would never dream of applying to their own departments and institutions. For example, in a recent book on the shortcomings of public education, a professor of history points out that (1) the public schools today enrol a much higher proportion of the school age population than they did in previous generations;

and (2) after taking into account the effects of inflation and the fact that the increased enrolments have been most pronounced at the secondary level, educational expenditures per pupil in attendance are much greater today than they have been in the past. The author cites figures to show that educational expenditures per pupil in attendance in 1950 were seven times as great as they were in 1870 and three times as great as they were in 1910. He then makes the following suggestions concerning evaluation:

> It is ludicrous in the extreme to measure the effectiveness of our public schools today by comparing them with the achievements of the wretchedly inadequate schools of previous generations. . . . The present effectiveness of the schools measured against the best that can possibly be achieved, is the *only* valid measure of our educational accomplishment. . . . We must, moreover, measure the achievement of our schools against an even more rigorous standard. Are they giving to the people and to the nation the values that were the promised result of universal education? If the schools are doing their job, we should expect educators to point to a significant and indisputable achievement in raising the intellectual level of the nation—measured perhaps by larger per capita circulation of books and serious magazines, by definitely improved taste in movies and radio programs, by higher standards of political debate, by increased respect for freedom of speech and of thought, by a marked decline of such evidences of mental retardation as the incessant reading of comic books by adults. . . . We should expect school administrators to produce testimonials from employers, professional men, college professors, and officers of the armed services to the effect that young men and women are coming out of high school with sounder intellectual background and greater skill and competence than ever before.
>
> No such claims are being advanced and no such comparisons are being made by the men and women to whom we have entrusted the control of our public schools.[6]

Note that most of the criteria suggested by Bestor are especially appropriate for evaluating the effectiveness of our liberal arts colleges. These colleges enrol a much larger proportion of the population from 18 to 22 years of age than they have in the past. Their level of expenditures per pupil is much higher than

[6] Arthur Bestor, *The Restoration of Learning* (New York: Alfred A. Knopf, 1955), pp. 14, 18–21.

it has ever been. Surely, if they are successfully providing a liberal education, they too should be able to point to "a larger per capita circulation of books and serious magazines, higher standards of political debate," and an increasing number of "testimonials from employers, professional men, college professors, and officers of the armed services to the effect that young men and women are coming out of" (and here let us substitute "liberal arts colleges" for "high school") with sounder intellectual background and greater skill and competence than ever before." [7]

Personally, I doubt whether *all* of the criteria suggested by Bestor are valid for either the public schools or the liberal arts colleges. However, if they are appropriate for one, they are also appropriate for evaluating the other. But there is hardly a hint of this possibility in the prescriptions for educational reform which pour out of the liberal arts colleges. Too many of the professors in these institutions live by a double standard. They are all for evaluation and reform, provided that these things can be confined to the public schools. I do not say this in a "So's your old man" spirit. Despite all the furor over "too many methods courses," let us not forget that most teachers take most of their college training in the liberal arts and sciences. The absence of evaluation in these areas must be regarded as an important cause of the absence of evaluation by teachers in the public schools. Teachers taught by professors who don't practice rigorous evaluation are not likely to practice it themselves.

THE "PHILOSOPHICAL" PROBLEM

We are often told that conflict over the purposes of education is "philosophical" in nature, and that until there is agreement at the philosophical level, there is little hope for agreement at the practical level. Frequently, this idea is expressed in terms of our need for a philosophy of education to provide us with a clear-cut idea of the purposes of education. Having held this point of view myself until a short time ago, I am not in-

[7] For a strong testimonial to the effect that even the best graduates from the best colleges are deficient in the fundamentals of a liberal education, see H. G. Rickover, *Education and Freedom* (New York: E. P. Dutton, 1959), p. 23.

clined to describe its proponents as nitwits. I am inclined, however, to think that they are mistaken and that they tend to confuse rather than to clarify important educational issues.

That educational theorists generally regard the determination of the broad purposes of education as a "philosophical" problem is hardly debatable. A deluge of educational literature, representative of virtually every educational position, can be cited to confirm this point. One author, in criticizing a school board for providing a high-school course designed to train girls to operate beauty shops, says: "Adoption of the course by the county school board was a choice in educational philosophy, and it was presented to the voters as a *fait accompli* but such choices belong to the public that maintains the public school—and to no one else." [8] A former university president writes that "education without a philosophy of education, that is, a coherent statement of the aims and possibilities of education, is impossible." [9]

From the scores of textbooks that echo this point of view, I shall cite only one:

> Part of the function of philosophy of education is to find fault with what we have and to set goals to be achieved. . . . The important role which philosophy has played in the development of education should not be minimized. A statement of purposes provides something to work toward . . . a statement of purpose, a philosophy of education, is needed to guide the invention and to test the tryout of new teaching ideas as they develop.[10]

Sometimes, the same people who believe that the public should determine the broad purposes of education and who regard this problem as "philosophical" will also express the view that it is important for each teacher to have *a* philosophy of education. The difficulty with this point of view is that society, not the individual teachers, should determine the broad purposes of education. To contend that every teacher ought to have "a

[8] John Keats, *Schools without Scholars* (Boston: Houghton Mifflin Co., 1958), p. 8.

[9] Robert M. Hutchins, *The University of Utopia* (Chicago: University of Chicago Press, 1953), p. 52.

[10] Paul R. Mort and William S. Vincent, *Introduction to American Education* (New York: McGraw-Hill Book Co., 1954), pp. 47–48.

philosophy of education," as if every teacher should decide for himself what should be the broad purposes of education which he personally will accept in his classroom, is to be mixed up. It is one thing to have teachers understand the purposes for which schools were established and a totally different thing to have each teacher go off on a tangent pursuant to his private "philosophy of education." Of course, every teacher has the right to advocate that education be devoted to certain purposes not presently accepted in our schools. However, this right is a different thing from the right to substitute one's own purposes for those of the larger community.

A variation on this theme is the practice of having the teachers in a given school or school system formulate their "philosophy of education." Two authorities in the field of educational administration write: "While it is perhaps inevitable that individuals among educational personnel will have a personal philosophy, it is equally true that only one that is representatively and cooperatively arrived at shall be utilized as the foundation for the administrative framework of a school system's or a school's program." [11] But what holds for the individual teacher also holds for all the teachers in a particular school or school system; they do not have the right to substitute their broad purposes for those accepted by our society as a whole.

Like many other terms, the word "philosophy" has more than one legitimate meaning. Nevertheless, the notion that conflict over the purposes of education is "philosophical" would seem strange to most professional philosophers. In professional philosophy today, "philosophical" disputes are distinguished from "scientific" ones. Roughly speaking, philosophical problems are problems of meaning; scientific problems are problems of empirical fact. The question of whether dogs can run faster than horses is of the latter type; there is no way to answer it except by looking to see how fast dogs and horses run. On the other hand, suppose the question is whether there can be a dog who is not an animal. The answer is clearly "No," because part of the

---

[11] Herold C. Hunt and Paul R. Pierce, *The Practice of School Administration* (Boston: Houghton Mifflin Co., 1958), p. 21.

very meaning of "dog" is "an animal with certain characteristics." There would be absolutely no point in looking for a dog who was not an animal; one cannot even imagine such a dog.

I have used simple examples to illustrate the difference between philosophical and scientific questions. Professional philosophers do not argue over whether dogs can be non-animal, any more than scientists argue over whether dogs run faster than horses. As we all know, scientific questions can become technical and complex. Philosophical questions can also; we should bear in mind that mathematics is fundamentally a branch of philosophy. But Plato to the contrary, philosophers are not experts on the purposes of life, and philosophers of education are not experts on the purposes of education.

It is often contended that conflict over the broad purposes of education is "really" rooted in conflict over such complex philosophical issues as the nature of man, the nature of reality, and the nature of truth. For example, Paul Woodring tells us that "A philosophy of education must rest upon a tenable view of the world and of man. It must be consistent with a clear conception of the nature of knowledge, the sources of truth, and a valid ethical theory, and these must be consistent with each other." [12]

The fact of the matter is that the major practical problems of education are not rooted in differences over the nature of man or of society or of reality. Furthermore, we should all be thankful for this fact. These topics have been the subject of irresolvable conflict for thousands of years. Educators would be paralyzed if we had to reach agreement on such ultimate questions in order to operate our schools effectively. Actually, people who have the

---

[12] Woodring, *op. cit.*, p. 31. "I hope to show that the philosophy of education, by which I mean a reasoned and coherent statement of its aims and possibilities, is a secondary subject, dependent on our conception of man and society, that is, upon our philosophy in general" (Robert M. Hutchins, *The Conflict in Education* [New York: Harper & Bros., 1953], p. 1).

For an example of this approach in a philosophy of education textbook, see Harry S. Broudy, *Building a Philosophy of Education* (New York: Prentice-Hall, 1954). According to Broudy, philosophy of education is "the systematic discussion of educational problems on a philosophical level, i.e., the probing into an educational question until it is reduced to an issue in metaphysics, epistemology, ethics, logic, or aesthetics, or to a combination of these" (*ibid.*, pp. 19–20).

most diverse ideas (or none at all!) about such things as the nature of man and the nature of ultimate reality can agree on practical educational questions. And I might also point out that often people who have identical views on these ultimate philosophical questions disagree on practical educational issues.

There are important philosophical problems in education. For example, it is important to clarify the meaning of such educational concepts as "academic freedom," "equality of educational opportunity," and "indoctrination," to cite just a few. Such clarification is a responsibility of philosophers of education, just as the clarification of such concepts as "sovereignty," "representation," and "totalitarianism" is a responsibility of political philosophers. But it is not the particular responsibility of philosophers of education to tell us what should be the purposes of education. They have no special competence to do so. It is time for citizens and educators alike to abandon this approach and to concentrate upon the organizational, technological, professional, legal, and managerial changes which are desperately needed to make public education effective.

These comments cannot logically be taken to mean that the broad purposes of education are unimportant. Water is important to fishes, but it is not a *problem* for them if they are comfortably ensconced in the middle of the ocean. Shelter for my family is important but it may not be one of my problems if I have just paid off the mortgage. To repeat, I am not denying the importance of the broad purposes of education; I am only contending that their problematic character has been greatly exaggerated.

THE PURPOSES OF EDUCATION AS A STRATEGIC PROBLEM

Thus far in this chapter, I have tried to explain why I do not regard conflict over broad purposes as the most crucial problem in American education. I have also tried to explain why the determination of the broad purposes of education is not a philosophical problem. At this point, I should like to discuss these broad purposes from what might be called a strategic point of view. I mean by this that I wish to analyze them from the standpoint of the way in which they are formulated, approved, and modified. Previously, I expressed the view that the public should be the final source of authority for the general objectives of education. But this view says nothing about the way in which these objectives come to be proposed, accepted, or rejected.

To illustrate what I mean by a strategic point of view, consider a situation in which a sick man refuses to consult a doctor. Meanwhile his friends and relatives are arguing over whether he has blood poisoning or an allergy. Suppose we ask, what is this man's problem? Obviously, the nature of his illness in one sense constitutes the most important problem for him. But strategically, the problem is not whether he has blood poisoning or an allergy but how to get him to consult a doctor. Given a solution to this strategic problem, we might expect a rapid solution to the substantive medical one.

Much educational controversy has ignored the strategic problems which must be resolved before we can expect to achieve any worthwhile solution of substantive educational problems. As a case in point, consider the reactions of teachers to the recent wave of criticisms of public education. The teachers often regard themselves as the scapegoats. The public is supposed to set the purposes of education, they say, but it is confused, indifferent, and inconsistent in its thinking. As a result, the teachers are caught between conflicting purposes and pressures. They are supposed to train the mind, to prepare students for college, to eradicate juvenile delinquency, to teach patriotism, the brotherhood of man, how to drive, respect for other points of view, to inculcate good manners and morals, to develop social competence, and so on and so forth. And the public not only expects an underpaid, overworked staff to accomplish all these things but shows little respect or recognition for the achievements of our schools under adverse economic and social conditions.

This is the lament of the teachers. Suppose we concede that there is much truth in it. Despite anything I have said thus far, suppose we agree that the public *is* confused, indifferent, and inconsistent and *does* expect too much for too little. But this fact, if it be a fact, often serves to conceal another aspect of the situation which is not so kind to the teachers. Teachers act as if they are supposed to sit around idly while the "great debate" over the purposes of education goes on. Then when the public has decided what it wants of its schools, it presumably will push a button and the teachers will carry out its mandate.

Even if it be granted that the public is confused as to the purposes of education, still this is not where the *strategic* problem lies. The strategic problem lies with the teachers, their bumbling organizations and their ineffectual leadership. It is their responsibility to provide the ideas and the leadership that would enable the public to think and act its way out of the present crisis. The teachers are in the best position to develop, to formulate, and to gain the necessary public support for the broad educational policies that should guide our people as a whole. Of course, in this process, the teachers must themselves be open-minded and capable of change. But if they continue to play a passive role instead of providing aggressive leadership, they might as well resign themselves to a continuation, even a worsening, of the present state of education.

It may be that I have underestimated the extent to which there is disagreement over the broad purposes of education. It may also be that I do not understand the nature of a philosophical problem and that the determination of these broad purposes is such a problem. Even so, I would insist that this determination is a matter for professional action, from a strategic point of view. In this context, public acceptance is not the prior condition of professional action; it is the outcome of it.

Chapter III

LOCAL CONTROL OF EDUCATION

One of the most important educational trends in the next few decades is likely to be the decline of local control of education. Such a development is long overdue. Local control of education has clearly outlived its usefulness on the American scene. Practically, it must give way to a system of educational controls in which local communities play ceremonial rather than policy-making roles. *Intellectually*, it is already a corpse. At least, I propose to treat it as such in this book. The proper way to treat a corpse is to conduct an autopsy upon it and then bury it promptly. Having done this, we can better understand the rationale for the school system which will emerge from the present chaos in education.

An autopsy of local control reveals several reasons for its demise. In the first place, mobility and interdependence have completely undermined the notion that local communities ought to have a free hand in educating their children. Second, national survival now requires educational policies and programs which are not subject to local veto. Third, it is becoming increasingly clear that local control cannot in practice be reconciled with the ideals of a democratic society. Finally, local control is a major cause of the dull parochialism and attenuated totalitarianism that characterizes public education in operation.

Let us analyze these reasons briefly. In order to do so, consider carefully the following question: *Who* should decide whether the children in a given community should be required to learn to read and write?

Some persons would undoubtedly argue that parents should have the right to raise their children as illiterates if they wish to do so. Most people would probably feel that the public ought to have the right of final decision in this matter. Still, there are many publics: local, state, regional, national, international, and even publics which are not defined geographically. Which of these publics should be authorized to have the last word in the matter?

Until a short time ago, every state had a compulsory education law. These laws took the power to decide our hypothetical question out of the hands of parents and local communities. Recently, however, some states have passed standby legislation which would enable them to abolish compulsory education in order to avoid racial integration in their public schools. States cannot be prevented by the federal government from abolishing public education. There is no way that the federal government can force a state legislature or local community to appropriate money to operate public schools. But what about our basic question—should the decision as to whether children shall learn to read and write be properly regarded as one for local communities or even state governments to make?

The reasons why the power to make this decision was taken away from parents and later from local communities will help us to answer this question. One reason was based upon the concept of fair play for the individual child. There was growing acceptance of the belief that a child's chances in life should not depend upon whether his parents or his local community were willing and able to educate him.

Should a child's chances depend upon whether he lives in a state which is willing to educate him? Certainly not as long as we adhere to the concept of an open society, one in which the individual's chances are not determined by fortuitous factors. As far as the individual child is concerned, the extent to which his state government is willing to provide him with an education is as much a fortuitous matter as the socioeconomic status of his parents or the educational values of his local community.

Consider the problem from a social standpoint instead of an individual one. We are an extremely mobile people. Most of us eventually move away from the community in which we received our education. In the year ending in April, 1958, 30,800,000 Americans changed their residence. Over 11,000,000 moved from one county to another; about half this number moved to a different state. Thus, on the average, every American moves to a different state two times during his life. Under these circumstances, does it make sense to insist that the citizens of one state have no right to insist upon literacy for the children of other states? Today, we plead for federal aid to education in order to equalize opportunities between states. Tomorrow, we could hardly contend that the federal government must stand by idly while a state legislature compounded the inequity by depriving children of an education altogether.[1]

As an abstract proposition, it has always been clear that it is undemocratic to permit educational opportunity to be determined by circumstances of race, geographical location, or economic status. It has also been clear that our national welfare was dependent upon the extent to which individual talents were able to flourish, regardless of their social, economic, racial, or geographical origins. Neither the ideal of equality of opportunity nor the fact of our interdependence is new. What is new is the urgency of these things. Proposals for federal aid to education in order to equalize educational opportunities between states have been ignored by Congress for generations. The same proposals, advanced as a counterpoise to Russian scientific progress, are now regarded as insufficient by panic-stricken congressmen who never supported them on equalitarian grounds.

Some idea of the bankruptcy of local control of education may be seen in the statistics concerning selective service registrants disqualified for failure to pass mental tests. In 1956 the lowest

[1] My argument treats control of education by the states as local control of education. Fundamentally, this identification is sound although people do not now think of control at the state level as local control. It is only a matter of time before they do so, and then the control of education at the state level will go the way of control at the parental and community levels. In point of time, the decline of community control over broad educational policy will precede the decline of state control over it, but the same forces that undermine the one will eventually undermine the other.

rate of rejection for failure was in Montana, where 2.5 per cent of the registrants failed these tests. The highest rate was in Mississippi, where 44.9 per cent of the registrants failed the tests. In ten states, fewer than one out of every twenty registrants failed to pass; in eleven other states, one or more out of every four registrants failed to pass.[2]

The vast differences among the states in the rate of disqualification are not due solely to the differences in the quality of their school systems. A registrant educated in Montana might take his selective service tests in Mississippi or vice versa. The statistics on rejection include the failures to pass because of inherited mental deficiency, and there are other causes for such failure over which the schools have no control. Nevertheless, the differences between the states cannot be explained solely by non-educational causes. Because some states and communities provide a decent minimum education for only a small minority of their children, we must, in all states, draft persons who, for family or occupational reasons, ought not to be in the armed services at all. This is only a small part of the exorbitant price we are paying for local control of education. The intellectual smog that has obscured our grasp of this fact is being cleared away once and for all by such dramatic events as the riots in Little Rock and the Russian conquests of space.

LOCAL CONTROL AND TOTALITARIAN CONTROL

The prevailing point of view is that anything but local control of education, with perhaps a few concessions made to control at the state level, would be a step toward totalitarianism. This view is profoundly mistaken. Our present system of local control is far more conducive to totalitarianism than a national system of schools would be. I know that this statement is not acceptable to the overwhelming majority of the American people, including the teachers, but I am willing to stand on it.

The assertion that our educational system tends toward totali-

[2] NEA Research Division, *Research Bulletin*, XXXVI, No. 1 (February, 1958), 29.

tarianism seems absurd on its face. A totalitarian system is one which develops a massive uniformity of outlook. It is based upon a policy of intellectual protection for a point of view that cannot stand the test of free discussion. We have a multitude of schools of all denominations or no denomination at all. Among the teachers and students in our public schools, there are adherents to every major political, economic, and religious point of view. What could be further from totalitarianism than this?

In most states the purposes and the content of education are left to local school boards to determine. Undoubtedly, there are some constitutional limits to the purposes for which communities may operate public schools. However, these limits have never been spelled out, and there is great latitude in what a community might require of its schools. Since the purposes of education are set forth locally, the predominant groups in the community tend to establish purposes which accord with their particular religious, political, economic, or social points of view. As a practical matter, therefore, local control results in the same kind of intellectual protectionism that characterizes schools in totalitarian countries.

The basic problem is not that communities define the purpose of education to be the acceptance of the Protestant faith or unswerving devotion to the single tax or the inculcation of the tenets of the Democratic party. Some communities have not blinked at adopting purposes as sectarian as these, but this is not where the problem lies. Even where a community accepts the most liberal educational purposes for its public schools, its interpretation of what intermediate objectives and what educational programs fulfil these purposes may have the same stultifying effect as outright adherence to a sectarian purpose. Every pressure group is for the general welfare, but each has its own version of what measures do in fact promote the general welfare. Similarly, every pressure group is for a liberal or a democratic education, but has a special version of what intermediate objectives and what educational programs lead to this result.

What is crucial is that, at the local level, it is relatively easy for a preponderant group to enforce a policy of intellectual protectionism for its sacred cows. Thus the white majorities in

Southern communities exclude instruction that is critical of racial segregation. Communities in which fundamentalist sects predominate exclude instruction critical of evolution. Some communities have prohibited the study of the United Nations or of UNESCO. Ours is a heterogeneous country, but in most communities the predominant racial, religious, economic, or political groups are able to veto whatever in the school program displeases them.

Looking at our system as a whole and seeing the existence of public schools teaching diverse doctrines, one might infer that our schools are free. We do not readily recognize the totalitarianism implicit in our situation because not all schools protect the same dogmas. Nonetheless, a diversity of schools based upon intellectual protectionism for different dogmas does not constitute a "democratic school system." At least, it does not do so if "democratic" refers to the education actually provided in these schools instead of to the legal structure which encourages a variety of one-sided programs.

The diversity of our undemocratic schools is not the only factor which maintains the fiction that we have a democratic school system. No matter how successful a group may be in excluding certain facts and ideas from the public schools, television, radio, and other mass media are almost certain to expose students to these facts and ideas. The power structure of American society is such that no single group is able to enforce or to indoctrinate its dogmas on the population as a whole. People look at this situation and say "Our schools have kept us free." They should say "Our freedoms have survived our schools."

THE MYTHOLOGY OF LOCAL CONTROL

Many persons believe that public education was not made a federal responsibility in the Constitution because the founding fathers feared the potentialities for dictatorship in a federal school system. Actually, education was not included as a federal function in the Constitution because the idea of free public education had not even occurred to the founding fathers. At the time of the American Revolution, the concept of universal public education was receiving attention for the first time and then only from a few frontier thinkers. Our decentralized school system was not an inspired stroke of genius but a historical accident, resulting from the fact that the ideal of free public education for all became widely accepted only long after the American Revolution.

Our schools have never been an important foundation of our free society. Our freedom is partly due to a separation of powers which enables us to transact public business reasonably well while avoiding excessive subjection to government officials. Perhaps for this reason we tend to regard the diffusion of power over our schools as an essential element of our free society. But adherence to the general principle that we must avoid excessive concentration of power does not automatically justify every separation or diffusion of it. Everything depends upon the circumstances—what powers are involved, who is to wield them, and so on. It is preposterous to think that merely because their political genius was expressed through a constitution embodying a remarkably successful separation of powers, the founding fathers would align themselves today with the supporters of local control of education.

People are seldom aware of the non-public character of public education. They tend to regard it as a legal concept and to neglect it as an educational concept. However, the ideal of public education means more than having some governmental unit—local, state, or federal—provide the funds to operate schools. Public education has a referent in the quality of education as well as in its financial basis. The qualitative referent is an education in which the search for truth is carried on regardless of what empires topple, interests collapse, or heads roll. Without this, public education is a delusion, as dangerous as the notion that mere government ownership of the means of production will automatically result in their operation for the public welfare instead of for private interests. The socialization of a service at any level of government is no automatic guarantee that the service will be performed in the public interest. The "new class" should have ended all of our illusions on this score.

Public schools, then, are not necessarily infused with a public spirit. Likewise, the fact that a school is privately controlled does not mean that its program is necessarily sectarian in character. The program of some privately controlled institutions such as Harvard is more free of parochial limitations than the programs in most publicly controlled institutions. In short, we cannot assume anything about the educational program of a school merely from a knowledge of whether the school is publicly or privately controlled.[3] Nor can we infer that the educational program of a school is undemocratic merely because the school is locally controlled or that it is democratic merely because the schools are part of a national system. The relationship between the legal status of a school and the quality of its educational program is never one of strict logical implication.

The system of legal controls under which schools operate is only one factor which serves to shape their educational programs. However, it is an extremely important factor. Because a national system of controls is more likely to broaden the purposes of education and to preserve the professional autonomy of teachers, it is much more likely to provide a truly liberal education than a multitude of totalitarian systems under local control. It is a striking fact that in England, which has a national system of education, the teachers are on record as being opposed to local control of education precisely because they fear that it would undermine their professional autonomy.[4] Meanwhile, teachers in the United States, who lack any substantial measure of professional autonomy, continue to act as if local control must be maintained inviolate lest academic freedom (which they do not possess) be imperiled.

The decentralization of our schools is often justified by an

---

[3] The notion that private education per se is superior to public education is assiduously cultivated by private school interests at all levels. It is a myth insofar as it pretends to be a generalization or even a statement of probable tendency. This myth results in outright tragedy at the elementary and secondary levels if parents assume that exorbitant fees automatically purchase educational advantages not available in the public schools.

[4] Educational leaders in England are very outspoken in their view that any trend toward giving local boards of education increased control over the financing of education would be a threat to the freedom of the teaching profession. See Sir Ronald Gould, "The Teaching Profession," *The Concept of Professional Status* (London: College of Preceptors, 1957), p. 42.

appeal to the experimental nature of this situation. We supposedly have fifty state school systems, each of which is free to try something different from the others. Each state has delegated considerable power to local school boards, which supposedly multiplies the experimental possibilities. This is thought to make for progress, since each state and each system is not only free to try something new but is free to benefit from the experience of other systems.

There is no doubt that some change for the better occurs in this way. Nevertheless, such enormous decentralization cannot be justified on the grounds that the different school systems constitute a vast pool of educational experimentation. The different schools do not constitute experiments except in the loosest sense of the word. They do not operate under conditions carefully controlled for purposes of analysis and comparison. They just operate.

Much of the experience of different systems is valuable only on the premise that education should be a state or local responsibility. A school board may indeed be interested in how another community put over a school bond campaign. But if funds came from the federal government, the experience of this or that school system in raising money would be academic.

The truth is that local control of education has obstructed rather than facilitated educational research. By and large, only large urban systems allocate funds to research. Even in these cases, the research is generally limited to problems that are of local concern. Very few school systems support any research that is even theoretically of more than local interest.

Educational research is supposed to be a function of our universities, but they also have a tendency to concentrate on local problems. Thus a university will make a study of population trends in a nearby community which desires to know where to build its new schools. Few universities devote any substantial effort to research on teaching and learning which would be of universal interest.

Educators have not learned from the development of industrial research. In industry, most research is conducted by corporations with a monopoly or near monopoly of the market for a particular product. These firms can support research intended to have a national impact because they stand to benefit from it. On the other hand, little research is conducted from private funds on products whose ownership is diffused. For example, individual farmers are generally unwilling to support research from their private funds because they would be adding substantially to their own cost of operation, while the results of the research would be immediately available to all farmers whether they had contributed to it or not.

We have much the same problem in education. Why should a particular school system support research which is for everyone's benefit? If we do not expect an individual farmer to support basic agricultural research from his own funds, neither should we expect him to support an educational research program in his local schools from local funds. The federal government supports basic research in agriculture because of the clearly evident futility of waiting for the small operator to do so. The same policy can and should be followed in education.

The U.S. Office of Education, a branch of the Department of Health, Education, and Welfare, has conducted research on certain administrative problems for many years. However, it was not granted funds for research in the art and science of teaching until 1956. In that year, $3,000,000 was made available by Congress for grants in various fields of education. The National Defense Education Act passed by Congress in August, 1958, included an appropriation of $18,000,000 over a four-year period for research on the educational use of radio, television, and audiovisual aids. It is likely that larger amounts for educational research will be appropriated by Congress in the future. But as long as education is primarily a state and local responsibility, educational research will never receive the support it ought to have. Local communities and state governments will never adequately subsidize research which is clearly universal in application.

How much money ought to be spent on educational research? Public education is a $15,000,000,000 enterprise. Enlightened practice in large-scale industry and government is to spend 3 to 6 per cent of the total budget for research. In education, this would call for an expenditure of from $450,000,000 to $900,000,000 annually. In fact, it is unlikely that the country is spending more than $25,000,000 a year from all sources for educational research.

The suggestion that it is realistic to think in terms of a twenty-fold increase in expenditures for educational research will be considered a pipe dream by most educators. Nevertheless, such an increase would still leave expenditures for educational research at a conservative level even if we are now spending only $25,000,000 annually for this purpose. Those who blanch at my proposal should remember that we are currently spending well over $300,000,000 annually for medical research. A report submitted to the Secretary of Health, Education, and Welfare in the summer of 1958 by a distinguished advisory committee of medical educators and research executives calls for increasing our expenditures for medical research to the point where the nation will be spending a billion dollars a year for such research by 1970. Foundations which are currently supporting educational research might well support studies and action programs designed to develop more adequate sources of funds on a national basis. It does not take such studies, however, to realize that educational research has been neglected under our system of local control of education.

In this connection, it is interesting to note that one of the most persistent and most pathetic arguments against a national school system is that such a system would not permit experimentation in the schools. The assumption seems to be that centralized administration is necessarily non-experimental or that it necessarily insists upon uniformity down to every detail. Actually, several federal departments which have centralized administration also subsidize programs of research which dwarf anything we have ever seen in education. The departments of Defense and Agriculture illustrate the possibilities.

If the present structure of American education is not conducive to the support of research, it is well designed to obstruct the utilization of it. On this subject, we need only to compare the lag between the discovery and the application of knowledge in education and the lag in other professions.

In the legal profession, important developments such as Supreme Court decisions are taken into account by all lawyers within a very short period of time. When the Bureau of Internal Revenue makes a ruling which affects a substantial number of tax returns, the accountants generally absorb it within a matter of months. Everyone is familiar with the short period of time between the discovery of an effective polio vaccine and its use by doctors everywhere. In education, however, the lags between discovery and practice are scandalous. These lags are reflected in what is taught as well as in how teachers teach their subjects.[5]

The average person is little aware how long it takes for important new knowledge to be reflected in the public school curriculum. The diffusion of teacher education and of the curriculum is so great that it often takes decades before teachers realize the need to add or delete a subject or to make radical changes in the content of an accepted subject. Even after this hurdle has been passed, tens of thousands of school boards must be persuaded that these changes are desirable. "Go ye therefore and persuade all those who are affected by the decision"—thus reads the Word in textbooks on school administration. The Curriculum Committee of the PTA, the school board, the parents, the students—all must have a voice in a decision which affects them. An infinite number of banana peels lie between the professional decision to modify the curriculum and actual practice in the school.

THE BREAKDOWN OF LOCAL SUPPORT
FOR PUBLIC EDUCATION

The case against local control of education becomes more compelling when we consider the practical problems involved in introducing basic changes that require heavy expendi-

[5] The need for drastic revision in the mathematics and physics curriculum of the public schools is discussed in Howard F. Fehr, "The Mathematics Curriculum for the High School of the Future," *Teachers College Record,* LIX (February, 1958), 258–67, and the articles on the Physical Science Study Committee in *Science Teacher,* XXIV (November, 1957), 316–29; and *Harvard Educational Review,* XXIX (Winter, 1959), 1–36.

tures. In recent years, our high schools have been severely criticized for their real or alleged neglect of science. For the sake of argument, suppose that we required every high-school student who has the ability to do college work to take three years of physics during his high-school career. At this point, consider only the practical problems involved in implementing this recommendation. How would we get from the status quo to a situation in which all these high-school students take three years of physics? Regardless of whether this particular change is desirable, consider its implementation solely from the standpoint of the difficulties of making any basic curriculum reforms under the present system.

There are over 21,000 high schools across the country. In 1956, only 12,000 of these schools offered one full year's work in physics. As late as 1954, 50 per cent of all schools having tenth-grade pupils did not offer physics at all. These were usually the smaller schools, but it is interesting to note that only one-fourth of all high-school students in 1954 took as much as one full year of physics before graduation. We are thus confronted by thousands of school boards which have seen fit to offer one year's work or none at all in physics.[6] Each board must now be persuaded, one by one, to make drastic changes in its curriculum. Since it is unlikely that the additional work in physics will simply be added to the present curriculum, each board must make its own decision about what subjects shall be reduced or eliminated. Each board must decide what to do with the teachers in subjects to be eliminated.

Even assuming that most school boards could be convinced that more work in physics is desirable, can they be persuaded to implement such a change? If a school is to offer three years of physics instead of one or none, extensive remodeling would almost invariably be required. There would have to be substantial expenditures for new laboratory equipment and supplies. Just how substantial these would have to be is evident from a survey

[6] I do not mean to suggest that there is one school board for each high school. Actually, the number of school districts is over twice as large as the number of high schools, even though many districts include more than one high school.

made in March, 1957, by the NEA's Research Division, which covered the needs for instructional equipment in high-school science and mathematics classes. More than half the schools responding to the inquiry from the Research Division reported that they did not even have direct electric current in their physics laboratory. Less than 15 per cent of the schools reporting had a calculator available for mathematics courses. Only one school in five had a graph board in every mathematics classroom; about two out of every five did not have a graph board in any mathematics classroom. The report indicated that 57 cents was the average per pupil expenditure for supplies and consumable equipment in science classrooms.[7]

Before most high schools could offer three years of physics, local school boards would have to adopt salary schedules much more attractive than the prevailing ones. Even though physics is now offered for only one year in the majority of schools which offer it at all, there is already a large and growing shortage of physics teachers.[8] It would be pleasant to think that school boards which have heretofore balked at making minimal expenditures for physics instruction will suddenly be inspired to vote the necessary taxes for an adequate program. Unfortunately, the odds are overwhelmingly against such a development.

Under our present system of financing education, the states and local communities supply over 95 per cent of the funds for public education. Our nation spent a total of $14,827,550,000 for public education in 1957–58. Of this total, about 3 per cent came from federal sources, 40.8 per cent from the state governments, and 56.2 per cent from local sources. On a state-by-state basis, there are wide variations in the relative amounts supplied by local, state, and federal sources. In Alaska, 14.7 per cent of

[7] NEA Legislative Commission, *The Hidden Need: Basic Instructional Equipment for Schools* (Washington, D.C.: National Education Association, nd.). See also n. 8 below.

[8] The National Defense Education Act passed by Congress on August 23, 1958, provided an appropriation of $300,000,000 over a four-year period for science equipment. It will be interesting to see how long it takes for Congress to recognize the futility of waiting for local school boards to institute salary schedules high enough to attract reasonably competent science and mathematics teachers.

the total expenditures for public education came from the federal government, whereas only 0.5 per cent of the total spent in New Jersey were from this source. Also in 1957–58, Delaware raised 88.2 per cent of its school revenues at the state level and 10.3 per cent at the local level. At the other extreme, Nebraska raised 6.9 per cent of its school revenues from state sources and 89.5 per cent from local sources.[9]

In general, the trend has been for local sources to provide a decreasing percentage of the total expenditures for public education. Expenditures by the state governments tend to constitute a much larger percentage of the total, while the percentage from federal sources has been increasing but at a much slower rate than that coming from the state governments. There are several reasons why this structure is not working and can never be made to work.

In the first place, some states have four to five times as much taxable wealth, on the average, as other states. The differences between school districts are even greater; some school districts have several hundred times as much taxable wealth as others. Ability to support education has also been studied in terms of what educators call "personal income payments per pupil enrolled," that is, the total income received by the residents of a state divided by the number of pupils enrolled in its public schools. In 1956–57, "personal income payments per pupil enrolled" amounted to $17,432 in Delaware and $3,754 in Mississippi. Needless to say, there were even greater differences between the richest and the poorest school districts.

For many years, authorities on school finance have pointed out that the poorest states and school districts usually devote a higher proportion of their resources to education than do the wealthier ones. Theoretically, one might argue that this is not very significant because all states and school districts should be making a greater effort to support education. However, this argument overlooks many important considerations relating to our tax structure. One such consideration is the competitive aspect of state and

[9] Data from Research Division, *Estimates of School Statistics* (Washington, D.C.: National Education Association, 1959).

local taxation. In New York City, there is a concentration of high incomes unequaled anywhere in the country. Nearly 20 per cent of all internal revenue is collected in New York State. Thus it would appear that New York City, which is permitted to levy an income tax but does not, and New York State, which does levy an income tax, could easily have the very best schools in the nation. The difficulty is, however, that many high-income persons and corporations would move if tax rates were raised substantially. This is why it is often fallacious to criticize states and communities for not raising taxes; if they did so, they would lose people and businesses to areas less concerned about education. The need for, and justice of, federal taxation for education would thus remain even if there were substantial equality in wealth and revenues among all states and school districts. The fact that a federal tax cannot be evaded at the expense of children in a particular school district is one of the most compelling reasons why we must move toward an educational system financed by the federal government.

Still another factor makes it very unlikely that an adequate educational system could be financed without massive federal support. School districts have been forced to raise most of their funds (54 per cent in 1953–54) by means of the property tax. Unlike most other taxes, property taxes must usually be submitted to popular vote. As is usual in this type of situation, the people who are badly hurt by a substantial tax increase are more effective politically than the diffuse majority which benefits from the increase. The result is that an increasing number of bond issues for school funds are being defeated in communities sympathetic to public education. Here is some indication of the rising (and often justified) tide of resentment against such discriminatory taxation.

The need for federal support of public education, if not for a federal system, is also related to the way in which the federal government supports non-educational activities. In the new highway program, for example, the federal government will spend $9.00 for every dollar appropriated by the state governments. Obviously, this will result in a bigger share of the state dollar being spent on highways. And, in general, states are tending to appropriate funds for projects which will receive substantial support from the federal government. Thus the only way that education can compete for funds, even at the state level, is for the federal government to assume a much larger share of the educational budget.

THE CENTRALIZATION OF PUBLIC EDUCATION: PRELIMINARY CONSIDERATIONS

The preceding discussion has by no means covered all the practical difficulties inherent in our present system of educational controls. To continue with our hypothetical change for a few more paragraphs, bear in mind that more and better physics teachers in high schools require more and better physics teachers in institutions of higher education. However, our colleges and universities are already confronted by serious shortages of qualified physics teachers. In the United States, there are about 1,200 institutions of higher education which train teachers. Who will see to it that a sufficient number of these 1,200 institutions will have enough money to retain good physics professors and adequate supporting facilities?

If the high schools drop certain subjects to make room for additional physics courses, the colleges which prepare teachers must do likewise. What are the colleges going to do with their faculties and their facilities for training teachers in the subjects no longer taught in the high schools? There is no assurance that the colleges will produce teachers prepared to teach three years of high-school physics just because the high schools would like to have such teachers. In fact, the colleges are not even producing enough physics teachers to offer one year of high-school physics. Many colleges are able to keep going only because they enrol large numbers of prospective teachers for inexpensive subjects. They would be devastated if required to increase their offerings in physics and decrease them in such inexpensive subjects as history and speech.

Perhaps these complex problems can be solved within the

framework of local control of education. Somehow, we might just muddle through the last half of the twentieth century with an eighteenth-century educational system. The chances are, however, that the practical sense of the American people will be forced to assert itself and that they will develop a centralized school system while simultaneously reaffirming their faith that any such system is un-American.

It is difficult to predict the form which centralization will take. It is possible that centralization may take place while much of our present educational structure is formally left intact. To understand this, bear in mind that a national system of education is not necessarily the same thing as a federal system of education. A federal system would be one in which the schools were operated by the federal government. However, education might continue to be the legal responsibility of states and local communities, while it also became substantially similar over the country as a result of non-governmental pressures.

The point can be illustrated by the situation in medicine. Legally, medical education and licensure are controlled by the various state medical boards. In actuality, these state boards are so dominated by the American Medical Association that we have a national system of medical education. There are some variations from state to state, but nothing compared to the chaos in teacher education and licensure. There are other occupations wherein the legal control of professional training and entry is a state function but wherein the activities of national professional organizations and accrediting agencies have brought about a national system of professional training and licensure.

The same possibility exists for elementary and secondary education. That is, even though education at these levels may continue to be the legal responsibility of state and local governments, various organizations and social pressures may force the different states and communities to adopt the same basic educational program. Under these circumstances, it would make sense to speak of an educational system that was national but not federal.

It is unlikely that in the next few decades we shall have a

federal school system covering the entire country. Such a development would occur only if the failures of states and communities to carry out their educational responsibilities were to be brought home dramatically to the American people by some such event as the abolition of public education in the South. I am convinced, however, that we are about to move rapidly toward a national system of education. What is certain is not the form but the fact that we shall have a much more centralized system of education in the future than we have had in the past. The idea that the present chaos in education is the price one has to pay for living in a democracy, or the even more nonsensical notion that the prevailing educational chaos is one of the foundations of democracy, will linger on but without any real force in our society.

Unquestionably, the most important barrier to a centralized system of public education is the notion that any such system would be "totalitarian" or "undemocratic." We are warned that a centralized system would provide an opportunity for one particular group, say a political party, to seize control of the schools, and by indoctrinating its point of view, maintain itself in power. Since this line of reasoning is undoubtedly the basis of our fear of a centralized school system, I wish to consider it at some length in this and the following chapter.

Those who think along these lines usually point to Soviet Russia to illustrate the dangers of a centralized system of education. But it should be obvious that one cannot assume that a centralized system per se is more likely to be totalitarian than our own. England, France, and the Scandinavian countries all have national systems. In all of these, there is less political interference with teachers than there is in the United States. Put positively, there is more freedom to teach and to learn in all of these national school systems than there is in the overwhelming majority of schools in the United States.

In the United States, how would any particular group, be it political, religious, or economic, achieve such complete control of all schools that it could produce a generation of unthinking disciples? To develop such a generation would require complete control of our mass media. This in turn would presuppose fairly complete control of the government. Any pressure group which could achieve such controls would have no need to control the schools. Indeed, it could safely permit schools to operate as they do now, preparing generations of civic illiterates who firmly believe they have fulfilled the highest obligations of citizenship when they have flipped a lever in a voting booth.

We already have many schools supported by the federal government. What evidence is available indicates that the teachers in these federal schools have more, not less, freedom than teachers elsewhere. For example, there is as much or more academic freedom at Howard University, which is supported by federal funds, than there is at the overwhelming majority of institutions of higher education.

People are opposed to a centralized system of schools for many reasons, not all of them noble ones. Some of the opposition comes from private school interests which would not share in the federal funds which will undergird such a system. We need private schools, but the arguments which some private school spokesmen make against federal aid or a federal school system are unrealistic. Private educational institutions whose *raison d'être* is to keep the faithful from being exposed to heretical points of view oppose federal aid to education on the grounds that such aid would mean mass conformity and indoctrination. The free and independent mind which these institutions claim to nurture is what some of them fear above everything else.

Nonetheless, it must be conceded that many people have a gnawing fear of a centralized school system which is quite unrelated to any thought that their particular points of view might not survive in such a system. These people do not fear for their points of view in an atmosphere of intellectual freedom. They would not exclude a fair presentation of other points of view in the schools even if they had the power to do so. Their fear is for the integrity of the system, not for the fate of their particular views on political, economic, religious, racial, or other controversial issues.

Ironically, these fears often are based upon experiences with local control. Every inadequacy of a local board reinforces rather than weakens the fear of a federal system. Under the present system, the worst blunders are confined to a limited area. What would happen, people ask, if a national school board or federal school administrator were to engage in the educational follies which characterize some local school boards?

The answer is that it would be a calamity, but the more we centralize our school system (up to a point, of course), the less likely it is that such a calamity will occur. The crucial point is that at the national level, no one group has the kind of power to interfere with the educational program that one sees every day under a system of local control. The rabble rousers who can successfully frighten a large city school system like that of Los Angeles into dropping an essay contest on the United Nations would not have a chance in a federal school system. Nor would the more powerful pressure groups be able to shape the educational program to their own ends. None has sufficient power by itself to do this. Each would be watched and checked if necessary by all the others if it attempted any massive interference with the educational program or with educational personnel. Since no non-professional group would have the power to dictate the educational program or personnel policies, and since teachers would not be subject to local censorship, the teachers would be free to discuss points of view which are now proscribed by local boards of education.

The fact, if it be a fact, that no pressure group would be able to dominate a centralized system might not sound very appealing. Would the integrity of such a system rest upon a balance of power among large national pressure groups, all of whom would subvert the school program to their own ends if they could? If so, what assurance is there that tomorrow, or the day after, the balance of power will not change so as to provide one of these groups, or a combination of them, with the opportunity they seek?

If by "assurance" is meant an ironclad guarantee, of course there is none. We are choosing between practical alternatives, not between mathematical solutions, one of which is the perfect answer. It is local control of education which provides a greater opportunity for national pressure groups to dominate the educational programs of the public schools, on a *national* basis. The reason is that local school boards are unable to withstand the pressures which can be generated by powerful national organizations which know what they want from our schools. However, there is another factor which seems to me to clinch the case for a centralized school system, at least insofar as the criterion of academic freedom is concerned. This factor is the impact which centralization is likely to have upon teachers' organizations and the role which they would play in protecting the integrity of a centralized public school system.

Chapter IV

PUBLIC AND PROFESSIONAL

DECISIONS

Within the foreseeable future, local communities will no longer determine what subjects are to be taught or what textbooks and teaching materials are to be used in the public schools. Because this power will be taken away from local communities, it will also be taken from parents, PTA's, citizens' committees, veterans' organizations, and other individuals and groups which currently exercise their power over the curriculum through local school boards. The purpose of this chapter is to explain why authority over the curriculum will be taken from local school boards, with whom this authority will be lodged, and how these developments relate to the alleged dangers of a centralized school system.

At the present time, the power to decide what subjects should be offered rests primarily with local boards of education. In some states, certain subjects are required by state law. In other states, local school boards have unlimited freedom to determine the curriculum. In still other states, a state government may make its financial support to local school districts contingent upon compliance with state regulations concerning the curriculum. Legally, local boards are free to go their own way in this type of situation. Practically, they seldom do so.

Of course, in approving curriculums, local boards must give some thought to a variety of pressures. The curriculum policies of accrediting agencies must be respected. Otherwise, students will not be given credit for their work when they transfer to other schools or apply for admission to college. The colleges exert heavy pressure on the public school curriculum through college admission requirements. The effect of such requirements varies from community to community. A community in which a high proportion of graduates goes on to college will be more responsive to college admission requirements than a community from which no one goes on to college. However, granting the existence of these and other pressures, it is the local school board which ordinarily has the final word on what subjects are to be taught in its schools.

The history of spelling as a school subject illustrates why this is a harmful procedure. For a long time, spelling was offered as a separate subject. Just before 1900, a number of studies indicated that the time devoted to spelling soon reached a point of diminishing returns. That is, beyond a certain period of time, students did not learn to spell appreciably better by devoting more time to the subject—two hours a day devoted to spelling did not seem to produce appreciably better spellers than fifteen minutes devoted to it.

As a result of such studies, proposals were made to reduce the amount of time devoted to spelling as a separate subject. The reaction to these proposals was often uninformed and foolish. Many people thought a new breed of teachers, opposed to spelling, had taken over. Actually, the proposals were made by educators who fully accepted the objective of developing good spellers but who also were critical of the traditional way of achieving this purpose. Nevertheless, proposals to change the amount of time devoted to spelling had to run the gauntlet of every school board whether or not they knew or cared particularly about the evidence on the subject.

We have similar problems today. English as a school subject usually includes two subject matters, grammar and the study of English literature. With respect to grammar, evidence indicates that its formal study is not as important as the extent to which a person is accustomed to hearing and reading good grammar in his daily life. Furthermore, although time should be set aside for the study of grammar, there is some question as to the best distribution of time. The typical way of teaching grammar is to have students write essays which are corrected by English teachers. Instead of regarding grammar as a separate subject called "English," it may be better to put more emphasis upon grammar as it is used in all subjects. The history or geography or science teacher ought to insist upon good grammar as much as the English teacher.

If there were more emphasis upon good grammar in *all* subjects, teachers might reasonably decide to devote less time to English as a *separate* subject. Their purpose would not be to undermine high standards of grammar and composition but to achieve high standards in a more efficient way. Nevertheless, no matter how clear and convincing the evidence, can anyone doubt the public reception that would be accorded proposals to reduce the amount of time devoted to English as a school subject? Undoubtedly some school boards would approve the change. But many others would not, or would not until the teachers had spent more time in persuasion than they do in research. The businessmen, reading only the conclusion and not the evidence or the rationale for it, would be up in arms. The schools are already turning out illiterates, and here is a proposal to reduce the time devoted to English! Some proponents of private education, never too squeamish about the basis of their criticisms of public education, would point to the proposal as proof positive of what they had been saying all along about the public schools. Nor can much help be expected from our newspapers, few of which publish any research reports relevant to the educational proposals that receive wide publicity.

Actually, there is no need to use hypothetical examples to illustrate the folly of according non-professional boards of education the power to set the curriculum. Thousands of school systems do not offer any foreign language. This is not as foolish as the thousands of others which offer a foreign language for only one or two years. There is no real point to the study of a foreign language unless the students acquire the power to use it. Such power cannot ordinarily be acquired in less than three or four years of study. Nevertheless, only a very small number of school systems offering foreign languages provide more than one or two year's work in the languages they offer.

Strictly from the standpoint of efficiency, it does not make sense to force the professional employee to justify his every means to reach an end which everyone accepts. If there were a serious question whether teachers should develop students who can read and write clearly, that would be one thing. But if there is agreement on the purpose, then it is the task of the professional to evaluate the means employed. He is not paid just to be in the classroom; part of his job is to keep abreast of current research in his field. It also does not make sense to expect school boards, which are non-professional bodies, to keep up with all the research in all subjects. Common sense calls for placing the decision-making power over the curriculum with the persons who are being paid to know more about it than the layman does.

The notion that most school boards are satisfied to accept professional advice concerning the curriculum is not warranted by their performance to date. What advice educational personnel give school boards is heavily influenced by their need to cater to the prejudices of these boards. In many communities, the teachers dare not recommend curriculum changes which are professionally sound because the changes are not politically expedient.

A common technique employed by superintendents is to organize a committee of the school board or a citizens' committee on the curriculum. Such committees are used to study and recommend changes in the curriculum, and they usually include some teachers or have teachers assigned to work with them. Eventually, the committees often make the same recommendations which the teachers would have made immediately. But the whole procedure is unfair and inefficient. If the citizens differ from the teachers, the latter naturally feel that their professional expertness has been disregarded or called into question. If the citizens always accept the views of the teachers, the citizens inevitably come to feel they are being used for window dressing.

Sometimes the rationale for including lay citizens on curriculum committees is that this is the way to prevent "excessive professionalism." The non-professionals are supposed to act as watchdogs on the teachers, who might otherwise abuse their professional autonomy. However, the practice of including lay citizens on agencies designed to answer professional questions rarely works well, either in education or in other professions. The public interest is almost invariably better served by leaving professional questions to the professionals. I say this in the full knowledge that some public school personnel have made indefensible curriculum proposals. The curriculum that must be justified to a larger professional community will often be much different from the one which must be justified to a board of non-professional persons.

Many prominent critics of public education believe that public school personnel are responsible for introducing trivial subjects past the unsuspecting guard of school boards. The school boards have allegedly been taken in by the professional pretensions of their superintendents and curriculum experts. No diagnosis could be more fallacious. The "modern" school administrator believes that public opinion determines what is professionally defensible. Nothing could be further from the minds of most school administrators than a firm determination to provide a curriculum that is professionally defensible, regardless of public opinion. School administrators ought to try to shape public opinion concerning the curriculum, but, in fact, school administration in the United States is degenerating precisely because school administrators *ask* instead of *tell* the public what should be taught in the schools. It is their catering to public opinion, not their attempt to ignore it, that should be criticized.

Virtually all of the "what's wrong with public education" books end with a clarion call for citizens to attend PTA and school board meetings to achieve this, that, or the other reform. Such appeals have a certain plausibility; in the mind's eye, we can see an aroused citizenry resolutely marching on the school board to safeguard the education of children. In reality, the citizen-watchdogs often turn out to be PTA mothers, professional Legionnaires, people who want the school bus to stop closer to (or farther from) their homes, young men on the make politically, and other groups and individuals with assorted axes to grind. Most have a sincere interest in the welfare of public education, but this interest gets so intermixed with their private interests and their hobby horses that the net result of their participation is not especially beneficial.

The quality of the recent books on public education varies a great deal. Good or bad, none of the books has made a dent in the status quo.[1] The significant thing about them is not their impact, which has been virtually nil. It is that regardless of their educational position, the authors uncritically accept the thesis that educational reform is, in the first instance, a matter for public instead of professional leadership. The appeal to a diffuse citizenry to save our schools is futile, not because the schools do not need saving but because most worthwhile educational reforms will have to be initiated and carried out by the teachers. Books that urge citizens to exercise a closer rein on curriculum and methodology merely reinforce the absence of professional autonomy in public education; in doing so, their impact, if they have any, is to make it more difficult to carry out needed educational reforms.

[1] I am referring to such books as Irving Adler, *What We Want of Our Schools* (New York: John Day Co., 1958); Arthur Bestor, *The Restoration of Learning* (New York: Alfred A. Knopf, 1955); James B. Conant, *The American High School Today* (New York: McGraw-Hill Book Co., 1959); Alfred Lynd, *Quackery in the Public Schools* (Boston: Little, Brown & Co., 1953); Robert M. Hutchins, *The University of Utopia* (Chicago: University of Chicago Press, 1953); John Keats, *Schools without Scholars* (Boston: Houghton Mifflin Co., 1958); H. G. Rickover, *Education and Freedom* (New York: E. P. Dutton, 1959); Mortimer Smith, *The Diminished Mind* (Chicago: Henry Regnery Co., 1954); and Paul Woodring, *One Fourth of a Nation* (New York: McGraw-Hill Book Co., 1957). The one possible exception might be Dr. Conant's book. However, this book was published only after Dr. Conant had worked with school boards all over the country on his findings and recommendations for action. It is as accurate to think that Dr. Conant's prestige and organizational spadework made his proposals effective as it is to think that the logic of his position is responsible for their impact.

PROFESSIONAL AUTONOMY IS NOT
UNDEMOCRATIC

Quite frequently, the supporters of professional autonomy in education are thought to be persons who have an authoritarian bent. Be this as it may, there is nothing undemocratic in the proposal that teachers and not school boards should decide the subjects to be taught. However, the reasons why people think the proposal is undemocratic are not difficult to understand. The relevant cliché here is that the public should determine what should be taught, and the teachers should determine how to teach whatever it is that the public wants taught. Like most educational clichés, this one has just enough plausibility to stay alive despite the abuses to which it leads.

The crux of the matter lies in the words "what" and "how." The public determines *what* to teach in the sense that it sets the broad purposes of education. The fallacy lies in regarding the *what* as a list of subjects instead of a set of purposes. "Teachers should teach students to communicate effectively" is one thing. "Teachers should teach penmanship one hour per day in the sixth grade" is something else again. The first statement is one of purpose, which should be made by the public; the second is a statement of the means to be employed and should never be legislated by a non-professional agency.

At any time, research may justify changes in the time devoted to a subject or the grade levels at which it is taught. This is why it is foolish for a state legislature to prescribe the curriculum. It is like legislating that drug X must always be employed to cure a certain illness. Imagine the predicament that doctors would be in if they had to have a new law passed every time they wished to employ a new and better drug for this illness.

The other side of this coin is the confusion over *how* in "how to teach." If people were clear that the public should determine the broad purposes of education, then it would be understood that "how to teach" refers to subjects as well as teaching methods. When we say that a doctor knows how to cure, we do not mean to limit the *how* to a bedside manner. We mean it to include the substantive knowledge which the doctor applies to achieve a desired end.

The public expects the medical profession to prolong life and to reduce physical pain. No one in his right mind assumes that the public should decide what drugs should be used and that doctors should decide only how to apply them. Absurd as this would be, it is exactly analogous to the notion that the public should determine the subjects to be taught and teachers should decide how to teach them. "How to teach" should be interpreted to mean "how to achieve the goals set for the profession by the public." It would then be clear that non-professional determination of the curriculum is a threat, not a safeguard, to our democratic institutions.

How does one know what purposes the public has set for education? At the local level, the school board can state what they are. The state legislatures can do this at the state level. There is no inherent reason why Congress cannot and should not do this at the national level. In fact, we are likely to get a much better statement of purpose from Congress than we are from a local board.

Theoretically, it is possible for the American people to accord the schools a very narrow purpose. Instead of saying that one of the purposes of education is to develop an understanding and appreciation of our democratic heritage, they might say that the purpose of education is to insure that every student can recite the Bill of Rights from memory. We would regard such a statement of purpose as a mistake. Our thought would be that what the people specified as an end (memorizing the Bill of Rights) should have been regarded only as a means to a larger end. Whether memorizing the Bill of Rights is the best means to this end should be left up to the teachers to decide.

Still, it is logically possible that the American people could define the purposes of education in such a way that the curriculum would not be a matter for professional decision. I hope this will not happen, but it remains a possibility. No matter how often it is pointed out that memorizing the Bill of Rights should be regarded as only a means, and not a very effective one at that, people might insist that this is what they want their schools to accomplish above all else.

It should be clear, however, that the danger of having such narrow purposes decreases as we have a larger and larger community set the purpose. In particular localities, people might insist the purpose of education to be the rejection of the theory of evolution, or an understanding of the history of Oklahoma, or an appreciation of the importance of dairy products, to cite only a few things that have been prescribed by state laws. But, at the national level, such narrow purposes would be manifestly unfeasible.

In the abstract, practically everyone agrees that our schools should teach students to think critically in important areas of concern—politics, economics, international affairs, and so on. What subject matters and what teaching methods will develop such critical thinking? You cannot develop critical thinking if the students and teachers cannot criticize anything. Teachers who are serious about developing critical thinking must have the freedom to be critical of points of view learned at home, in the community, at church, and so on.

A teacher who wishes to develop critical thinking in the area of international relations must stimulate students to analyze the concept of sovereignty. I do not say the teacher should persuade students that national sovereignty is outmoded or even that what was good enough for McKinley's day is not good enough for ours. These are conclusions which a student might or might not reach after he has studied the matter. The point is that if the teacher does his job properly, some students may get the idea that national sovereignty is not the unmixed blessing that the local American Legion post makes it out to be.

The development of critical thinking, of an understanding and appreciation of our democratic heritage, of dedication to the truth wherever it may lead—these purposes take precedence over any particular political, economic, racial, religious, or social point of view. This means that in principle no point of view should be above analysis and criticism in the public schools. However, as things stand, teachers do not have the power to act on this principle.

In the long run, we must see to it that non-professional determination of the curriculum is as unthinkable as non-professional determination of the techniques of brain surgery. In the short run, the solution is to resist non-professional interference in every way possible while working toward a system in which such interference would be impossible. However, there is no thought that individual teachers should seek martyrdom. The problem is essentially one of institutionalizing professional autonomy rather than leaving it to heroic individual defenders to protect. And it should go without saying that there is a difference between non-professional interference with the curriculum and non-professional advice concerning it. My contention is that teachers should have the power to decide what subjects are to be taught. This does not mean that teachers would be justified in ignoring every suggestion from non-professional sources or in adopting a "To hell with the public" point of view.

If teachers should decide what subjects should be taught, then clearly they should decide what instructional materials should be used in teaching these subjects. The power to determine the choice of instructional materials is in fact the power to determine the subjects. Nevertheless, some people persist in the view that the school board should decide on teaching materials.

The absurdity of having school boards, parents, or citizens' committees evaluate and pass on the fitness of instructional tools is most clearly reflected in controversies over "subversive" materials. It is or ought to be obvious that instructional materials are neither subversive or non-subversive in isolation. The Constitution can be utilized for subversive purposes, just as the *Daily Worker* can be used to expose the nature of the Communist party.

Suppose a high-school history teacher decides to have his class study whether the Communist party in the United States is or is not a tool of Russian foreign policy. What materials should he use in the classroom? He should have the official statements of Russian foreign policy and those of the Communist party in this country. For the latter purpose, he would need copies of the *Daily Worker*. By reading them, students could see for themselves how the Communist party in the United States did in fact follow every turn and twist of Russian foreign policy.

All this seems reasonable enough—or does it? I doubt whether a single public school teacher, superintendent, or school board in the country would dare to order such materials, even though they provide the most devastating information on the Communist party obtainable anywhere. The teachers are not going to take any chances with a school board which, if it is typical, divides instructional materials into such ridiculous categories as "subversive" or "patriotic." And the board is not likely to "take any chances" on a teacher who requests such materials. SCHOOL BOARD APPROVES *Daily Worker* IN THE SCHOOLS—a millennium of explanations would not undo the damage of one such headline.

In a country where the professional autonomy of teachers cannot be violated with impunity, it is respected. Where it is respected, newspapers do not print such headlines. Both the public at large and the teachers would be amused by them. In fact, a situation giving rise to such a headline would never arise where teachers had professional autonomy. What would be news would be the foolishness of some non-professional agency in classifying instructional materials as "subversive" or "non-subversive."

Fundamentally, the confusion between public and professional decisions in education is one aspect of our failure to clarify the role of the expert in a democratic society. As a result of this failure, we count noses to answer questions which should be settled by reference to experts, and we rely upon experts to answer questions which should be settled by counting noses. In education, the first type of mistake is the most prevalent. Public education developed in the United States in the absence of a teaching profession. Teachers simply accepted without question the idea that the community had the right to decide subjects, instructional materials, and methods as well as the broad purposes of education. Teachers often questioned whether the community was exercising its rights wisely, but they never questioned the legitimacy of these rights.

The precarious employment position of public school personnel, especially school administrators, is another important factor contributing to the absence of professional autonomy in education. Superintendents are often hired on a year-to-year basis. Few have contracts running for more than two or three years, and practically none has tenure. This being the case, few superintendents are going to insist upon their professional autonomy when they know that such a stand may cost them their jobs.

What is worse, the exposed position of superintendents inevitably weakens their support for the professional autonomy of teachers. Suppose a teacher uses a textbook which the school board regards as subversive. Since the superintendent has to please the board, not the teachers, to hold his own job, he is not likely to take the attitude that instructional materials are strictly a matter of professional autonomy. He is much more likely to tell the teacher to drop the textbook. This will, of course, be done in the name of democracy. The elected representatives of the people have the right to say what goes on in their schools; if they have said that *Robin Hood* tends to justify stealing from the rich to give to the poor, we must drop *Robin Hood*—or else.

The real tragedy in this situation is that superintendents and teachers accept it as the way things ought to be. Those who submit curriculum proposals to their school boards are not fuming inwardly at their lack of professional autonomy. In their own eyes, they are following the democratic process when they permit, even encourage, school boards to tell them what subjects to teach and what instructional materials to use. Thus a power structure and an ideology which antedates any serious thought of teaching as a profession is precisely what stands in the way of its becoming one today.

Schools of education, and especially their departments of educational administration, have propagated the notion that public school personnel should not make an important change in the curriculum without first securing community support. This counsel is typically labeled a "democratic theory" or a "democratic philosophy" of education. Advocated as it usually is without any conception of professional autonomy, its effect has been to make any insistence upon autonomy appear undemocratic to the teachers themselves. In all seriousness, the damage has been even worse. The concept of professional autonomy has been eliminated from the consciousness of teachers. In effect, the schools of education tell teachers they are "professionals" while simultaneously undermining the independence which is an essential ingredient of professional status.

Much of the opposition to determination of the curriculum by teachers is due to certain misconceptions about the rationale for professional autonomy. First, it should be emphasized that the justification for taking authority over the curriculum away from local boards and giving it to the teachers is not that the teachers are always right or that the school boards are always wrong, even on admittedly professional matters. Professional autonomy does not result in the absence of error but in the reduction of it.

Opponents of professional autonomy often point to particular instances wherein teachers have made indefensible curriculum decisions. Such instances are cited to justify the denial of teacher control over the curriculum. Such reasoning demolishes only the nonexistent position that perfection is the rationale for professional autonomy. It is like saying that laymen should prescribe drugs because doctors make mistakes.

This brings me to a related point. Professional autonomy does not mean the absence of any control over the professional workers. On the contrary, it means that controls requiring technical competence are exercised by persons who possess such competence. To be specific, if the issue is whether a teacher is choosing appropriate instructional materials, the issue should be settled by persons competent to judge this, not by irate parents or American Legion posts or even intelligent and responsible school boards. Professional autonomy, then, does not imply the absence of all controls. On the contrary, it logically calls for the development of a wide range of professional controls. These are often much more rigorous than those exercised by lay boards.

People tend to think that giving professional autonomy to public school teachers is tantamount to turning over public business to private interests. Actually, it amounts to turning over public business to the kind of public employees most likely to conduct it properly. It can safely be stated that more unwarranted inferences have been drawn from the fact that teachers are publicly employed than from any other single fact about public education. Teachers should not control entry to teaching, should not determine the subjects taught or the instructional materials to be used, should not be permitted to bargain collectively, should not have the right to strike, do not need to formulate and enforce a code of professional ethics—the list of *non sequiturs* that invariably follows the "point" that teachers are public employees constitutes a fairly complete catalogue of what's wrong with American education.

When the average citizen thinks of himself as an employer, he tends to think of public servants as a group that should be servile. The public (which is "I") puts up the money, so "I" have the right to tell teachers what to teach. But it is not an unqualified good for employers, public or private, to be able to coerce their employees. Surely, we can learn this much from what is going on in other parts of the world. When the private patient says to his physician: "Restore me to health, but I shall tell you what drugs to use and the dosage," the physician is ethically obligated to withdraw. The reason is that the physician cannot take responsibility for the health of his patient under such circumstances. The same reasoning would apply in the case of a publicly employed physician—he would be obligated to withdraw from employment wherein he had to submit to lay interference in professional matters.

This is the way teachers should regard the matter. If school boards prescribe subjects and teaching materials, the teachers should withdraw as employees on the grounds that it is not in the interest of their client, the public, to permit it to make professional decisions. Teachers cannot accept responsibility for educational outcomes under such circumstances, any more than physicians can accept responsibility for medical outcomes when laymen tell them how to diagnose and what to prescribe for the sick. It is not in the public's interest as an employer to insist upon lay control of professional matters. The teachers have no moral obligation to acquiesce in the actions of any employer, public or private, who violates their professional autonomy; on the contrary, their obligation to the public interest is to resist such action with all their might.

THE SIGNIFICANCE OF PROFESSIONAL AUTONOMY IN A CENTRALIZED SCHOOL SYSTEM

There are many other misconceptions concerning professional autonomy in public education. However, instead of going into all of them at this point, I should like to relate the analysis to the decline of local control of education and to the possible dangers of a centralized system of schools.

Considerations of national security and fair play require an unprecedented educational effort in this country. Many states and communities will not make this effort—some because of last ditch opposition to integration, some because they are too poor, some because they do not put a sufficiently high priority on educational needs, and some for other reasons. Meanwhile, the national stake in good education will become much more urgent in the near future. The problem then becomes how to reconcile the national stake in an adequate educational system with state and local options to have an inadequate system. Such options, heretofore taken for granted as in the national interest, will inevitably be recognized as contrary to it in the near future.

Every argument made for federal aid to education will gain added force as the disparity between imperative educational needs, on the one hand, and state and local efforts, on the other, grows wider and wider. Consider these arguments: federal aid is needed to equalize educational opportunity, to insure that we have an adequate supply of trained manpower, to equalize financial responsibility as well as educational opportunity, to eliminate the tensions and conflicts resulting from large numbers of uneducated citizens in a mobile society, and so on. If states refuse to strengthen their schools, if they weaken them, if they abolish them altogether to stave off integration, do all these reasons for federal support for education become invalid?

The answer is that they do not. If there is no state or local school system, or if such as exists does an inadequate job even with federal aid, every argument for federal aid becomes an argument for a national system of education.

In the near future, the American people will realize that they have been misled by both proponents and opponents of federal aid to education. The proponents have argued for federal aid on the grounds that some states and communities simply do not have the resources to support good schools. The opponents have opposed federal aid on the grounds that states and local communities do have the financial ability to support good schools. However, the idea that federal aid to education should be dependent upon the ability of states or communities to support education will soon be recognized for the hoax that it is. Some children in wealthy communities are being denied a decent education because their communities refuse to support their schools adequately. Is the national loss any less than if these children had been denied an adequate education because their communities were too poor to provide it? Is it any less unfair to the individual child to let him be deprived of an education because his community refuses to tax itself than to let him be deprived of it because the community has no resources to be taxed? The answers to these questions must be to place the national welfare and the equities of individuals above the financial condition or educational caprice of states and local communities.

As the pressures for a national school system continue to grow, many thoughtful people will take a new look at the problem of federal controls. As they do so, they will become aware of certain basic changes in our society which bear upon the problem at hand. When our nation was founded, the American people were a much more homogeneous group, in terms of their occupations, than they are today. In 1789, over 90 per cent of the people made their living directly or indirectly from farming. At that time, therefore, the problem of avoiding an excessive concentration of federal power required a geographical, rather than an occupational, distribution of power.

Today, however, the problem of avoiding an excessive concentration of federal power must be solved in occupational rather than geographical terms. A cotton farmer in Mississippi has more interests in common with cotton farmers in neighboring states than he does with engineers or teachers or grocers in Mississippi. Thus he attempts to advance many of his major interests through his occupational group rather than through state or local communities. I do not wish to oversimplify this process, but the distribution of power among occupational groups has tended more and more to overshadow its distribution among geographical groups. When the people of a state take important action, usually they are strongly influenced by the attitudes of occupational organizations.

As occupational specialization increases, so does our interdependence. As our interdependence increases, the regulation of occupational affairs becomes more and more a federal instead of a state function. And as this happens, it becomes apparent that avoiding an excessive concentration of federal power requires the development of powerful occupational organizations. Thus a larger and larger portion of industry and commerce has become interstate rather than intrastate. There is more and more regulation of industry and commerce at the federal level. But the factor that stands in the way of arbitrary federal action is the emergence of occupational autonomy and strong national organizations of employers and employees.

These considerations are appropriate to education, and especially so because it is or should be a profession. A profession is an occupation which possesses some kind of expertness. It is in the public interest to accord the professional worker the autonomy to make the decisions which require this expertness. This is why it is undesirable to have non-professional control over the curriculum in any school system. We already have a tremendous amount of non-professional control over the curriculum, a fact which should not be ignored in assessing our present way of doing things. If a centralized system of education places the power to decide curriculum content with appropriate professional persons, it will be a great improvement over the present system.

In asserting the need for professional controls in a centralized system, I do not mean to contend that *all* professional decisions, such as those relating to the content of the curriculum, should be made at the national level. Some professional decisions should be made at state or local levels. Others should be regarded as the prerogative of the individual teacher. The same point should be made with respect to non-professional educational decisions. Some of these decisions should be made at the national level, others at state or local levels, and still others should be made by parents or students.

Regardless of whether a decision is professional or non-professional, the extent of state, local, or individual option to make the decision must be decided in the first instance at a more inclusive level. This is only common sense. The American people as a whole have made national defense a federal concern. It would be senseless to permit individual citizens to decide for themselves whether the country was at war or whether they should bear arms in its defense. Nevertheless, within the limits of national policy, we permit individuals to choose their branch of military service or to enlist in the regular army. In education, there is an urgent need for a clear-cut, comprehensive national policy outlining the educational decisions to be made at the national level and those to be made at state, local, or individual levels.

Our chief concern should be the way in which professional opinion is recognized and articulated in a centralized educational system. For example, the fact that some educational decisions may be made by federal officials is not important per se. What is important is who are these officials, how are they appointed, what specific decisions do they have the power to make, to what extent is their tenure dependent upon satisfying professional opinion, and so on. We must not attempt to settle concrete questions of power and authority in education by generalized appeals to the virtues of a particular level of control.

At present, there is confusion in every direction. The line between professional and non-professional educational decisions has all but disappeared. The main result of this has been a tremendous amount of professional decision-making by non-professional agencies. In addition, the emphasis upon local control has given local school boards the power to make all sorts of non-professional decisions which should be made by non-professional agencies at state or national levels.

It must be clearly understood that both professionalization and centralization can be overdone. There is no pat formula by which we can classify decisions. Each must be evaluated on its own merits to determine whether it is professional in nature and also whether it should be made at the national, state, local, or individual level. We will never make educational sense until we stop using phrases like "local control of education" or "federal control of education" or "academic freedom" as substitutes for clear thinking about the decision-making structure of education.[2]

For example, there has always been *some* federal control over public education, which, like any activity of state or local government, must be carried on within the limitations set by the Constitution. All the furor over racial integration in the schools should not blind us to the fact that the Supreme Court has been deciding such issues as whether or not children in public schools must salute the flag in school, must be released for religious instruction, or must sing Christological Christmas carols. And although some may have questioned the wisdom of its decisions, no one has seriously questioned the Court's constitutional right, its duty even, to make *a* decision on these matters.

Under our present system, people are accustomed to having pressure groups of every kind and description shape the school program to their own ends. They presuppose that the same policy would prevail under a centralized system. Obviously, if the educational program in a centralized system were to be placed under congressional control, or under the control of a politically dominated national school board, the ensuing political

[2] For a more thorough analysis of this point see Myron Lieberman, *Education as a Profession* (New York: Prentice-Hall, 1956), chap. IV.

melee could be disastrous. But the way out is to realize that the problem is not which public—local, state, or national—should establish the educational program, but how to make certain that it is in the hands of the teachers, where it belongs. Once the American people understand the occupational dimension to the distribution of power in our educational system, they will have overcome a major psychological barrier to a centralized educational system.

It is not just a question of whether a more centralized system would be better *if* it were characterized by professional autonomy. The crux of the matter is that centralization itself will hasten the establishment of professional autonomy in education. In the long run, the integrity of public education in a centralized system can and must be protected by the rise of a teaching profession. Nevertheless, it is not altogether germane to fear centralization because the professional organizations of teachers are abysmally weak at the present time. Centralization will dramatize the weaknesses of teachers' organizations and put in motion the forces that will eliminate these weaknesses. Centralization and professionalization are inevitable, not in spite of what people think but because enough people will eventually think long enough and hard enough about public education to realize that no other policy makes sense.

Chapter V

THE MYTH OF THE TEACHING PROFESSION

Education has been bypassed by the professional revolution which has done so much to transform our society. However, such a revolution cannot be delayed much longer in education. Even if the teachers are content to work with a nineteenth-century personnel structure, the facts of modern life will compel them to abandon it.

According to the present personnel structure in public education, all public school teachers are members of the same profession. Since teachers really constitute a number of highly diverse occupational groups, the policy of treating every teacher as a member of the same profession leads to a superficial and self-defeating unity among them. It is as if we were to lump together the directors of General Motors and laborers on the assembly line and call them both "automobile manufacturers." For most purposes, the use of a common occupational label would tend to cover up important differences rather than to reveal basic similarities between the two groups. This is precisely what has happened in education as a result of the policy of treating all teachers as members of the same profession.

The tendency to regard all teachers as members of the same profession has resulted in more than semantic confusion. It has lowered the quality of education and all but nullified the development of a strong teaching profession. For this reason, we must develop educational policies that frankly recognize the basic differences between various kinds of teachers. To be specific, instead of regarding teachers of all grade levels and all subjects as specialists within a single profession, we must regard them as a cluster of related but different professions. This cluster must work together in the schools just as doctors, nurses, psychologists, pharmacists, dietitians, and therapists work together in hospitals. But the present situation in education is as absurd as the situation would be in medicine if all the medical occupations just mentioned were labeled "doctors" and treated as specializations within the same profession.

In order to understand the harmful consequences of regarding all teachers as specialists within the same profession, we must first analyze professional specialization in a general way. What determines whether two occupations should be regarded as specializations within the same profession or as two separate professions? If we are clear on this point, we shall be in a better position to appreciate the need for drastic changes in the teaching profession.

To clarify the problem, compare two persons who are in different occupations with two persons who work in specializations within the same profession. The first situation can be illustrated by A and B, who are both salesmen. A sells refreshments at baseball games. B sells electronic computing machines, the cheapest one selling for $250,000. The second situation can be illustrated by X and Y, who are both lawyers. X is a specialist in corporation law. Y is a specialist in the law of wills and trusts. Why do we think of A and B as members of different occupations although both are "salesmen" and of X and Y as members of the same profession despite their specialized interests?

In the case of A and B, the category "salesman" reveals superficial similarities but covers up basic differences. It takes no formal training to sell refreshments at baseball games, but to sell enormously complex electronic computers does require a considerable amount of specialized training. B must have a background in mathematics and engineering. As a person dealing with the top executives of large corporations and government agencies, he must have a thorough grasp of data-processing systems. In short, B is a mathematician or an engineer who sells. There is nothing in common between A and B in such matters as their training, the organizations to which they belong, the occupational literature they read, the conditions under which they work, the social and economic status of their jobs, and so on. To regard them as members of the same occupational group because they both sell would be patently absurd.

The situation with respect to X and Y is much different. They have a substantial amount of common training. If their professional training was at all divergent, the divergencies represented only a small portion of their total education. Although X and Y may belong to a few different occupational organizations, they also share membership in city, state, and national bar associations. To some extent, they read the same professional literature. They are governed by the same governmental and professional agencies and work under the same code of ethics. There is no inherent difference in their social and economic status, as there is in the case of A and B. In short, although there are differences between X and Y, we are referring to basic occupational similarities in referring to both as "lawyers."

In the case of our two salesmen, nobody is fooled by the common label. The very fact that "salesmen" covers so many diverse groups who sell inhibits us from making any judgments about an individual because he is a "salesman." For this very reason, salesmen who must have a technical background and who operate at the upper echelons of industry try to appropriate some other label (e.g., sales engineer) to distinguish themselves from the huge undifferentiated mass of "salesmen." Persons at the bottom of the sales group are only too glad to use the broad label "salesman" to cover up their specific place in the hierarchy of salesmen.

Now the situation in education is that basically diverse groups do use the same label, to wit, "teacher." However, unlike the situation with respect to salesmen, people are misled by the common label "teacher" into according the same treatment to these diverse occupational groups. These groups have two characteristics in common; they teach and they work in the same building. But these common characteristics are extremely superficial. They can be compared to the similarities between a man who sells at a cigarette counter and one who sells electronic computing machines in the same building.

To illustrate what happens when we regard all teachers as members of the same profession, I wish to analyze briefly some aspects of the increased attention being given to driver education in secondary schools. I have selected driver education for this purpose because it is probably the fastest growing subject in American high schools. A study conducted by the NEA in 1954 indicated that 47 per cent of our high schools had some kind of offering in this area; about 80 per cent of these schools offered driver education as a separate course or devoted an equivalent amount of time to it.[1] To simplify the analysis, I shall consider the impact of this growth only upon high-school teachers of physics.

Physics teachers and driver-education teachers are supposed to be specialists within the teaching profession. In the overwhelming majority of school systems, both kinds of teachers are paid exactly the same salary so long as they have the equivalent amount of training and years of teaching experience. They belong to the same local, state, and national educational associations. (They may, of course, also belong to organizations limited to teachers in their field of specialization. However, such organizations for specialized groups coexist with the comprehensive organizations for all the practitioners in all the professions.) At the state level, the requirements for licenses for both groups are regulated by the state education department. On the surface of things, it appears that these two groups of teachers represent specializations within the same profession. What is wrong with this situation?

It does not take professional training to teach people how to

[1] NEA Research Division, "The Status of Driver Education in Public High Schools," *Research Bulletin*, XXXII (April, 1954), 55–56.

drive a car safely. Most of us learned how to drive from relatives or friends who were not licensed teachers of driver education. Our "teachers" simply passed on a skill which required very little formal education to learn or to teach. This is borne out by the fact that it has never been deemed necessary to insist upon a college degree for people who operate private driving schools. Such schools are ordinarily permitted to operate without any governmental regulation whatsoever, in the same way that private language, music, or dancing schools are conducted.

Perhaps the most conclusive evidence in this matter is in the amount of specialized training actually taken by teachers of driver education. The 1954 NEA study of driver education included a summary of the specialized training of driver-education teachers.[2] Of the driver-education teachers, only 32.4 per cent had had a one-week intensive course, and 14.5 per cent had no special preparation in driver education at all. Only 12.6 per cent had one full semester course (that is, not a summer-school course) in driver education.

When it comes to physics teachers, the situation is altogether different. The person who has had only a one-semester course in physics cannot teach physics to high-school students—and everyone knows that he cannot. The physics teacher needs a considerable amount of specialized training; the driver-education teacher needs so little specialized training that it is unrealistic to accord him the same professional recognition.[3]

Bear in mind, however, that in the overwhelming majority of school systems, physics teachers and driver-education teachers are accorded the same financial and professional recognition. They are paid the same, and they participate equally as faculty members and in the professional organizations of teachers at local, state, and national levels. Obviously, one possible result of these policies is to upgrade the status of driver-education teachers. Such upgrading has happened to some extent. And if

[2] *Ibid.*, p. 67.

[3] It is true that the specialized training of teachers includes more than their training in the subjects they teach. However, it is difficult to believe that teachers of driver education need to study much of anything besides driver education to do their job properly.

the only effect of the inclusion of driver education teachers within the teaching profession were to upgrade their status, perhaps no particular harm would be done. However, let us analyze what happens in practice when driver education is included in the teaching profession.

First, what are the academic and intellectual standards for the occupation of teaching going to be, now that we have added driver education to it? It takes less intellectual ability and training to teach driver education than to teach physics. Ostensibly, this need not matter. Standards for becoming a driver-education teacher could be maintained at such a high level that such teachers would be on a par with the physics teachers. In practice, however, the inclusion of driver-education teachers in the teaching profession is certain to depress the standards for the teaching group as a whole.

As a general rule, the larger an occupational group becomes, the more difficulty it has maintaining high standards for entry. In the instant case, if the intellectual standards for a teaching certificate are maintained at the level required for good physics teachers, it becomes impossible to recruit enough teachers of driver education. The result is that standards are lowered to the point where it becomes possible to recruit an adequate supply of both kinds of teachers. This weakens the quality of physics teaching and the professional status of physics teachers.

The deterioration of the teaching profession as a result of the inclusion of subprofessional teaching groups can be a rather subtle process. We want teachers who can do a good job of teaching their subject. However, our notions of what constitutes good teaching can and do vary, and they depend in part on the available supply. Thus in teaching fields characterized by extreme shortages, there is a tendency to revise downward our idea of what constitutes good teaching. Conversely, in areas where there is an oversupply of teachers, we raise our standards. The supply of teachers for a given subject thus affects our notion of the appropriate minimum level of competence a teacher should have. In this way, deterioration of the quality of teachers is often hidden by lower standards.

If we lower the standards for teaching a particular subject, then teachers who were unsatisfactory according to the old standards may be satisfactory according to the new ones. Thus whether it takes as much ability to teach driver education as it does to teach physics depends upon what standards we accept for a good job of teaching each subject. By insisting upon extremely high standards for driver-education courses and very low ones for physics courses, we might produce a situation in which there was no significant difference in the ability required to teach one subject or the other.

Despite the difficulties of comparing the intellectual abilities required to teach different subjects, it should be obvious that more intellectual ability and training are required to teach high-school physics than to teach driver education. Bear in mind that the intellectual abilities and training required to teach a subject bear a functional relationship to the performance expected of the students. We could insist upon very rigorous requirements for teachers of driver education. We might require them to have a Ph.D. degree and ten years of safe driving experience and to be able to disassemble and assemble automobiles blindfolded. But we would quickly agree, I think, that these requirements would be absurd. The reason is that they would not be reflected in the results which driver-education teachers achieve in their teaching. True, the requirements might make some difference, but the difference would not be enough to justify the requirements. It would be like requiring a janitor to have a master's degree in sanitary engineering.

Sooner or later, we come to a point where the benefits to be expected from additional formal training are not worth the costs to the individual and to society. There is no simple way to determine where this point lies. It varies from one occupation to another. Sometimes it is very difficult to decide the cutoff point. But, conceding all this, it must be clear that we are overtraining the driver-education teacher by requiring him to take four to seven years of higher education, whereas we are not overtraining the physics teacher by these requirements.

These comments most definitely do not mean that every high-school physics teacher is intellectually superior to every driver-education teacher. My supposition is that as a group the physics teachers are intellectually superior to driver-education teachers but that there is some overlap between the two groups. The crux of the matter is, however, that this overlap has been achieved by overselecting and overtraining driver-education teachers and underselecting and undertraining physics teachers.

THE INTEREST-IN-CHILDREN MYTH

Most people believe that the common characteristic of good teachers is their desire to work with children. The majority of teachers, school administrators, and schools of education share this view. In most education textbooks, the teacher's attitude toward children is commonly stated to be the most important characteristic of good teachers.

The truth is that a person's attitudes toward working with children are a relatively useless criterion of his success as a teacher. What is most important, and here I am speaking primarily but not exclusively of high-school teachers, is the teacher's knowledge of and interest in the subject he teaches. This is an unpleasant truth in many places. It is a truth which has been misunderstood in the liberal arts colleges and ignored in the colleges of education. It is a truth that may be misinterpreted. But it is a truth that must and will be clearly recognized in the near future.

Several tests have been devised to use in counseling students about their choice of careers. These tests have been constructed from studies of the interest patterns of people who have been successful in a particular occupation. These studies indicated that there are rather common patterns for persons in particular occupations. For example, forest rangers will tend to be more interested than the average person in some things and less interested in others. If a person shares the same interests as successful forest rangers, there is some basis for thinking that he might well consider becoming a forest ranger. Similarly, if a person's interests appeal to few forest rangers, then there is considerable doubt whether the choice of a job as a forest ranger would be appropriate for that person.

The research of Strong, who was a pioneer in the field of vocational interests, is of particular relevance. In the early years of his work, Strong assumed that the interests of high-school teachers, principals, and professors of education would be similar. Later, he came to the view that:

> The theory upheld by most departments of education that all teachers should be interested in teaching young people first and only secondarily interested in their subject matter may possibly be a worthy ideal. But the facts of the case are that these two types of men [high school social science and mathematics-physics teachers] have quite different interests. . . . The same situation holds true with respect to women high school teachers . . . Evidently teaching per se, like managing per se, is less significant than the specific kind of teaching or managing.[4]

It can be stated categorically that the point of view expressed by Strong is now the accepted point of view in vocational counseling, though not in the schools of education themselves. In assessing a person's potentialities for becoming a good teacher, vocational counselors today give more weight to a person's interest in a subject area than they give to his interest in working with young people.

These comments should not be interpreted to mean that a person's attitudes toward children are completely irrelevant to his success or failure as a teacher. The point is that insofar as teaching is concerned, the key consideration usually is whether the person has a strong interest in his subject field. Granted, some people who have a strong interest in a particular subject would make poor teachers because of their negative attitude toward children. However, as a rule, persons with the necessary subject-matter interest and ability regard the school as one of many environments in which they can fulfil this interest. "Working with children" is generally not the decisive factor, one way or the other.

Let me explain the point in a different way. Suppose that from all the persons who have the necessary interest in physics to be good physics teachers, we choose one hundred at random. If this

---

[4] Edward K. Strong, Jr., *Vocational Interests of Men and Women* (Stanford, Calif.: Stanford University Press, 1943), p. 161.

is done, only a small number, perhaps twenty-five at most, will be unfit for high-school physics teaching because of their disinterest in or negative attitude toward children. On the other hand, suppose that from all the persons who have a strong interest in working with children, we again select one hundred at random. Suppose also that from this number, we wish to exclude those who would not be good physics teachers because of their insufficient interest in physics. This time, we would have to exclude a very substantial portion of the group, perhaps seventy-five or more.

In other words, a person might be unfit for teaching either because of a lack of interest in working with children or a lack of interest in the subject. At the high-school level, however, it is the subject factor which most often rules the person out. The emphasis upon interest in children is misplaced—not because the prospective teacher does not need it, but because its absence is seldom the reason why people are poor teachers. It is the same mistake that characterizes concern with loyalty of teachers. Of course, teachers should be loyal to their country, but it is not reasonable to say that loyalty is what you are looking for in teachers, when only one teacher out of a million is disloyal. Loyalty is important, but it is not selective in this context. Similarly, an interest in working with children is important, but it is not much of a selective factor in assessing whether or not people will make good teachers.

I do not wish to contend that the interest tests currently in use are infallible or even that they are of very great value. They are, however, widely used in vocational counseling and they seem to serve a useful purpose, so long as they are used with good sense. In most universities, the training of guidance and vocational counselors is a function of the department of education. It hardly behooves these departments to question the value of the tests at this late date merely because they implicitly contradict the dogma that a strong interest in working with children is the chief criterion of a good teacher. The surprising thing is that the departments of education should be the last instead of the first to abandon this dogma.

Consider the problem from the standpoint of recruitment. If teaching required the same ability level, regardless of subject, and if a strong interest in children were the common denominator of teachers, it would be surprising to find extreme shortages in some fields and a surplus in others. This is what we do find, and the reasons should be obvious. The college student who has the ability and interest to be a physics teacher is the same person who has the ability and interest to be a physicist in private industry. There is no particular reason why he should enter teaching if his salary as a teacher is going to be substantially lower than it is in industry.

THE ECONOMICS OF A UNITARY PROFESSION

The worst consequence of regarding every person who teaches in public schools as a member of the same profession is that this policy weakens the quality and quantity of instruction in areas where good teachers are most urgently needed. The present crisis in high-school physics is an illustration of this fact.

If we accept the view that teaching should compete with other fields, we should be in a position to offer physics teachers starting salaries of $6,500 to $7,500 with good prospects of making $10,000 within five years and opportunities for outstanding persons to make $25,000 to $50,000 a year before retirement. Actually, the highest salary schedules for teachers in the entire country do not even begin to compete with this salary range. In New York City, which has a moderately high schedule, the top salary for a classroom teacher with a Ph.D. degree and thirty years of teaching experience is $8,700—about $2,500 more than starting salaries for persons with a bachelor's degree in physics. No wonder the potential physics teacher turns his back on a teaching career.

To get more and better physics teachers, we must provide substantial increases in their salaries. However, since the overwhelming majority of school systems pay all teachers the same amount regardless of the subject taught, they find it necessary to raise the salaries of all teachers just to attract those who are most needed. And as might be expected, school systems are refusing to pay all teachers the salaries needed to attract good physics teachers. The result is a shortage of physics teachers, a shortage that will become more acute as long as we adhere to the fiction that all teachers are members of the same profession.

Consider what happens when a school budget is presented to a school board. The addition of driver education has increased the total budget, thereby making it more difficult to get approval of higher salaries for physics teachers. The more teachers there are, the more difficult it becomes to increase their compensation. This helps to explain why the uncritical accretion of more teaching specializations has had a disastrous effect upon the economic status of those teachers who should be getting paid at a professional level. To raise the salaries of all teachers a few per cent a year makes a substantial difference in any school budget. This is why the inclusion of a new subject is a matter of the greatest importance to the teaching profession.

In addition to increasing the total budget, and thereby making it more difficult to pay any teacher a professional salary, the addition of subjects like driver education has a harmful effect on the public's attitude toward the teaching profession. A school board is not going to pay teachers $10,000 a year to teach adolescents how to drive safely. The fact that these salaries must be paid to get good high-school physics teachers is never going to overcome the public aversion to overpaying the driver-education teacher. In short, the teacher who should be paid as a professional is bound to suffer when his salary is geared to salaries for teachers who do not require professional training.

Teachers ought to be the first to scrutinize critically proposals to expand educational offerings, since they are the first victims of unwarranted educational inflation. Nevertheless, teachers are currently the chief advocates of educational inflation in our society. They wish to add innumerable subjects, increase the services offered, extend education for all downward to the nursery level and upward to the graduate school—and they lament their economic and professional problems! The crucial point, however, is that quite apart from the welfare of teachers, or of some teachers, what the country needs is not so much more and better teachers in general but more and better teachers in specific areas of instruction. Of course, it is always good to have better teachers, regardless of grade level or subject. Certainly, all teachers should be striving to improve their teaching. But it is time to confront the possibility if not the fact that certain of our efforts to improve teaching at all levels and subjects have actually weakened it in some of the most important areas of instruction.

Note that the problem must eventually plague the colleges as well. If there are to be high-school teachers of driver education, there must be college professors to teach the prospective high-school teachers what and how to teach in driver education. And so the entire process is repeated at the college level. Professors of physics are bound to suffer when college budgets include professors of driver education, their secretaries, their offices, their supplies and equipment, and so on. The inclusion of professors of driver education (usually labeled professors of safety education) has the same adverse effects upon the social and economic status of physics professors as the inclusion of driver-education teachers has upon high-school physics teachers, and for exactly the same reasons.[5]

It is as if medicine and nursing were combined in one profession. Obviously, to secure enough physicians and nurses, it would be impossible to adhere to present standards for admission to medical school. The desperate need for nurses would force medical schools to lower their standards for entrance and for graduation in order to produce an adequate supply of the two specializations. If admission standards were lowered to accommodate a larger group, then the standards to pass each course would also be lowered because of the lower caliber of the student body. Inevitably, standards for graduation would also be lowered. As this happened, public expectations and attitudes vis-à-vis the medical profession would change and public respect for it would

[5] The devastating effect of proliferating courses in higher education upon the economic status of professors is set forth in Beardsley Ruml and Donald H. Morrison, *Memo to a College Trustee* (New York: McGraw-Hill Book Co., 1959).

decline. People could not pay physicians as well as they do now because they would also have to pay nurses similar fees. For these and other reasons, the inclusion of nurses would destroy the medical profession as we now know it. True, the nurses might be better off, just as the driver-education teachers are better off as a result of the false unity which regards them as the professional equals of physics teachers. But make no mistake about it, society as a whole would suffer along with the "real" physicians from any such movement to treat medicine and nursing as a single profession.

In many cases, it is difficult to say whether a certain kind of work should be regarded as a specialization within a profession, albeit the easiest and the one with the least prestige and economic rewards, or as a subprofessional occupation not to be included at all. Technically, the policy of according physics teachers the same treatment as driver-education teachers might be regarded as an inequity *within* the teaching profession. It might be argued that the shortage of physics teachers is due to the fact that their economic status is tied not to that of a subprofessional group but to that of a different specialization within the same profession. Perhaps my analogy should have been to a hospital which insisted upon hiring surgeons, the highest paid medical specialists, at the same salary as anesthesiologists, the lowest paid specialists. If the hospital wanted to get good surgeons, it would have to overpay the anesthesiologists. If it insisted on paying only the salary needed to get good anesthesiologists, it would go without surgeons or perhaps with less able ones.

Now a single salary schedule does result in inequities between some teaching groups which should rightfully be considered as specializations within the teaching profession. However, this fact has not been overlooked in proposing to exclude driver-education teachers from the teaching profession. Embarrassing as it may be, we must face up to the fact that many teaching fields currently regarded as specializations within the teaching profession should be regarded as outside the profession altogether.

In advocating the exclusion of certain kinds of teachers from the profession, I do not wish to minimize the importance of what these groups teach. The severest critics of driver education as a school subject agree that safe driving is important. However, its importance is not the only factor to be considered in deciding whether or not to include it in the curriculum. Its proponents think that if students who take driver education have a lower accident rate than students who do not, this justifies its inclusion in the curriculum. This is an erroneous, or at least an oversimplified way of judging the matter. Perhaps the time and money that go into driver education could accomplish more for safe driving if devoted to stricter enforcement of the traffic laws or better examinations for drivers' licenses. We must also consider what students could be studying instead of driver education. Perhaps our society would be better off if students accelerated their technical or civic training during the time they devote to driver education.

I can summarize my analysis here by saying that the functions of the school system need not be identical with the functions of the teaching profession. Since the schools bring together all the children, it may make sense to provide certain health and welfare services through the schools, or to use them whenever we must deal with all children. But whenever this is done, we should not deprofessionalize education by enlarging it to include every group that works in the school.

THE EDUCATIONAL PROFESSIONS

The breakup of education as a single profession will involve much more than the exclusion of certain fields from "the teaching profession." I doubt whether it makes sense to think of "the profession" merely as an entity from which subprofessional and semiprofessional groups have been excluded. It makes more sense to think of education as a cluster of professions, which include many that are of equal status. For example, science and mathematics teachers might constitute one profession and social science teachers another. There need be no invidious distinctions between them; it might simply be the case that although the same minimum level of intellectual ability is needed for both, the training for them is so different that it is unwise to lump them together.

Anyone who adheres to the notion that teaching is a unitary profession ought to consider current certification requirements. For example, in the state of New York, the permanent certificate for both elementary and high-school teachers requires a master's degree. Elementary teachers are required to have thirty-six hours of education courses and high-school teachers twenty-four hours. A minimum number of credit hours for each high-school teaching field of specialization is also specified. Both certificates require a certain distribution of courses outside the field of education.

Now insofar as the state requirements are concerned, it is quite possible for elementary and high-school teachers to get a permanent certificate without taking one course in common. This statement is not even restricted to those courses which are part of the professional training of teachers. It is, of course, unlikely that this will occur during the entire five-year period of higher education required for permanent certificates, but the state requirements leave it as a theoretical possibility. As a matter of fact, we could add a school principal and a school superintendent to this example and the statement would still hold—insofar as New York state certification regulations are concerned, it would be possible for all four of these persons to get permanent certificates without having taken one professional course or one course of any kind whatsoever in common. And yet elementary teachers, secondary teachers, principals, and superintendents are supposed to be members of the same profession!

Even this situation does not fully reveal the extent to which present certification policies are inconsistent with the view that all teachers and school administrators are members of the same profession. It is possible for two high-school teachers to receive permanent certificates without having taken so much as one course, professional or otherwise, in common during their five years of study. And in other specialized areas, such as elementary education, the amount of work which must be taken in common by all prospective teachers is negligible.

These comments are in no way intended as a criticism of the certification requirements for teachers in New York State. On the contrary, the more defensible these requirements are, the more they demonstrate the hollowness of a teaching profession that includes teachers of all subjects and grade levels. The New York certification requirements are typical of those prevailing elsewhere. There are few if any states in which teachers of different subjects and grade levels are required to have a significant amount of common training. There are many states in which even teachers of the same subject and grade level need have very little common training or none at all.

We cannot continue to have it both ways. If teachers of different subjects and grade levels are really members of the same profession, then this fact must be reflected in their training. In medicine, law, architecture, and other professions, most of the training program is taken by all practitioners, regardless of specialization. Specialized or elective study constitutes only a small portion of the total program. On the other hand, if current certification policies for teachers are at all correct, education is really a host of professions instead of a single profession with many specializations.

The more one analyzes current certification policies, the clearer it is that they are inconsistent with the notion of a comprehensive teaching profession. In medicine, law, dentistry, pharmacy, architecture, and practically every other profession, the practice is for the appropriate state agency to issue one certificate, regardless of specialization. A lawyer does not get a license to practice criminal law or corporation law; he gets a license to practice *law*. Specialization is chiefly a matter of employer-employee relations; it is not something regulated by a professional license. Thus the professionals identify themselves chiefly as members of the profession as a whole, not with a particular segment of it. In education, the tendency is to have a multitude of certificates which limit the holder to specific areas. This is more consistent with the view that education is a group of separate professions than it is with the view that it is a single profession.

How many different teaching professions should there be? Clearly, there should not be one for each subject. It is just as harmful to create separate professions which should be merely specializations within a profession as it is to ignore basic differences between professions. There is already overspecialization in some areas of education and we must constantly be on guard against the establishment of educational requirements that bear little or no functional relationship to the work involved. Education is not the only field in which unnecessary educational qualifications have been established for certain kinds of work, but it is well on the way toward being one of the worst offenders in this respect. (In this connection, for example, I question the growing trend to require a substantial amount of course work in educational administration for positions in that field.)

In the long run, we should expect the teaching professions to be built around subject areas. There will be border-line cases in which it will be difficult to decide the professional status of teachers of a particular subject. At the secondary level, there will be a few professions of co-ordinate status. There will also be a few of varying status, their number depending upon the functions which are assigned to the schools.

Perhaps the most fundamental change will be the development of elementary education as a separate profession. Historically, elementary education was so regarded until the 1940's. It was not only different but somewhat lower than high-school teaching in social and economic status. Elementary teachers were naturally unhappy about this situation. They emphasized the importance of good teaching during the first years of school. The Freudian emphasis upon the crucial early childhood years was enthusiastically indorsed by the elementary teachers; the cult of the child never carried so far in the high schools as it did in the elementary schools.

However, the most potent factors tending to equalize the training and compensation of elementary and secondary teachers probably had little to do with the functional requirements or importance of the two fields. Elementary teachers far outnumbered secondary teachers in local, state, and national teachers' organizations. As a result, these organizations inevitably came to advocate the elimination of salary differentials between the two groups. This development coincided with the need for more elementary teachers immediately after World War II. For this reason, school boards found it expedient to accept a single salary schedule, since by doing so they were able to meet their immediate needs for more elementary teachers.

As previously pointed out, in most states elementary and secondary teachers are already members of different professions insofar as certification requirements are concerned. All that needs to be done is to recognize this fact in other aspects of education. The United States is now the only major country in which the two groups are placed on an equal footing within the same profession. Partly as a result of this policy, the professional status of high-school teachers in the United States has suffered a drastic decline in the past fifty years. It is questionable whether substantial improvements in secondary education can be achieved if every improvement accorded high-school teachers must be accorded the elementary teachers as well.

Twenty-five years ago, only a handful of states required elementary teachers to have a bachelor's degree. Today, most states require it. However, the higher requirements for elementary teachers have resulted in substantial increases in their nonprofessional, not in their professional training. And this in turn suggests that the effort to treat elementary and secondary teachers as specializations within a single profession is not based upon actual job requirements in these two fields.

Perhaps it is true that we need to strengthen drastically the education of teachers at all levels. However, the non-school demand for people who can teach well in high school is far greater than the non-school demand for those who can teach well at the elementary level. In the days when a pool of unemployed was taken for granted, there was a plentiful supply of teachers for any level or subject. In an economy geared to full employment, the effort to attract enough good high-school teachers by conditions of employment geared to the elementary group is almost certain to fail.

Before leaving this subject, let me add a few important qualifications to my comments thus far. First, if we took the various kinds of teaching positions currently in existence, I am certain that elementary teaching should not rank lower in its professional standards and requirements than *all* secondary teaching positions. To put the matter in another way, the occupational differences between certain secondary teaching fields are as great or greater than the differences between elementary and secondary teaching. In fact, I would argue that it is fallacious to compare elementary with secondary teaching per se; the particular kind of secondary-school teaching that is involved makes a considerable difference. For that matter, I am not altogether certain that elementary teaching as such should be regarded as a homogeneous field from an occupational standpoint. My other main qualification is that this entire discussion could be invalidated by the development of a personnel hierarchy built around the teaching of a single subject. Let me turn briefly to this last possibility, since it may upset quite a few of our present policies relating to educational personnel.

THE TEAM CONCEPT

Up to the present time, the emergence of different professions has been discussed solely in relation to the various teaching fields of specialization. Thus it was suggested that teachers of science and mathematics might constitute one professional group, teachers of the social sciences another, and so on. At this point, let us consider the possibility of a professional hierarchy *within* a single subject rather than *between* teachers of different subjects.

My analogy here is again to the medical situation, wherein the doctor is the head of a medical team which includes nurses, psychologists, pharmacists, dietitians, and other specialists. The latter groups are not specializations within the same profession; they constitute a hierarchy of professions which operate under the direction of the doctors. I believe it is possible to introduce such a personnel hierarchy into education. Such a development would change the teaching profession in a revolutionary way.

For illustrative purposes, consider an elementary school which requires twenty teachers. Since superintendents usually prefer teachers who have graduate degrees, let us assume that all twenty have a master's degree. It might be possible to provide a better education for the children in this school with three teachers holding a Ph.D. and seventeen holding a bachelor's degree. (This is an arbitrary breakdown which I am using merely to illustrate the possibilities of a hierarchical structure.) Let us suppose that the persons with Ph.D. degrees are the "teachers." They are the educational equivalent of physicians. The persons with bachelor's degrees are the educational equivalent of nurses. Let us call them "assistant teachers" or "auxiliaries." They work under the direction of the "teachers," who have seven years of training. Without making any unreasonable assumptions about the situation, we can visualize a number of ways in which a staff of three "teachers" and seventeen "auxiliaries" might be more effective than one comprised of twenty teachers each with a master's degree.

1. It would provide for a higher level of technical competence in the school itself. For example, one of the Ph.D.'s could be an expert in the teaching of the basic skills. Another might be an expert in child growth and development, and in the diagnosis and treatment of psychological and physical blocks to learning. The third might be a person with considerable training in certain subject-matter fields, whose responsibility it would be to supervise curriculum planning. Or one of these "teachers" might be a person with training in arts and crafts and in teaching them in the elementary school. These "teachers," each with seven years of training, would be available in the school to help with any problem requiring expert diagnosis and treatment.

2. A good deal of the professional training for elementary teachers is often given in schools of education, far removed from any children or classrooms. Some of this training could be shifted to the school systems with great profit to everyone. This will be apparent if we consider present training programs. The average elementary teacher takes about eighteen semester hours of work in elementary education; certainly the average is not much more than this and it is possibly less. This means that each prospective teacher takes the equivalent of six courses carrying a credit of three semester hours per course. Now the typical professor of elementary education teaches three or five courses per semester.

Thus it is not unreasonable to suppose that elementary teachers currently receive their professional training from no more than two to four professors.

Bear in mind that the "teachers" in our hypothetical school will have academic and professional training which is at least equivalent to that possessed by professors of elementary education. This means that each "teacher" is able to teach the equivalent of two to four courses. In other words, the three "teachers" in our example would encompass more technical expertness in the field of elementary education than the typical elementary teacher is currently exposed to during her entire program of professional training. If each "teacher" were to teach the "auxiliaries" the equivalent of two courses, the latter would have the equivalent of eighteen semester hours of college work.

One might raise certain objections: for example, the typical elementary school will not have the library facilities which are available at a college. But facilities for scholarly study are not needed to learn to teach every practical skill. For that matter, many subjects in medical school are taught with reference to a single textbook and practically nothing else. Similarly, one might object that the "teachers" could never find time to teach the "auxiliaries." However, school systems could employ the "teachers" and "auxiliaries" on an eleven or twelve-month basis, rather than for nine or ten months. Part of the work of the "auxiliaries" would be studying under the direction of "teachers," perhaps before and after the school term. Classes could also be held for the "auxiliaries" during the school year. Instead of rushing off for an extension course on elementary methods, taught in a university classroom without a child in the building, the "auxiliaries" could be taught on the job by persons who would also be around to supervise their classroom work. In other words, the "auxiliaries" would receive some of their training as a regular part of their duties.

3. Since there are only three "teachers" who are recognized from the outset as professionals, they could easily be paid $10,000 to $20,000 a year. This would enable the schools to attract top quality personnel who would have completed a program of

professional training as long and as rigorous as that which is required for any other profession.

4. Turnover would be largely confined to the people with four years of training—those at the "auxiliary" level. This is the level at which turnover comes in other professions. The existence of the professional hierarchy would reduce its damaging effects, which would come chiefly in the lower echelons.

5. The high salaries paid the "teachers" would make it possible to attract more men into elementary teaching.

6. The hierarchical plan would cost less despite the higher salaries paid the "teachers." In the first place, there would be no need to pay all twenty persons a "professional" salary. Nurses and technicians do not receive and do not expect to receive salaries equal to those paid doctors; similarly, the "auxiliaries" would not expect to be paid as much as the "teachers." As a matter of fact, it would probably be less expensive to have three persons with seven years of training plus twenty with four years of training than it would be to have twenty each with a master's degree. That is, a hierarchical personnel structure may require more persons but still provide better education at less cost than the present system.

7. Although the hierarchical plan would provide for a higher level of technical competence in the school, it would represent a substantial saving in the over-all cost of professional training. The conventional way of staffing the school calls for twenty teachers, each with five years of college training. This comes to a total of one hundred years of college training. The suggested plan calls for seventeen teachers with a bachelor's degree (68 years of training) plus three teachers with a doctor's degree (21 years of training), or a total of eighty-nine years of college training.

Note that we could add two more "auxiliaries" and still be operating with less *total* training (ninety-seven years) but a higher level of specialized training in the school. If any hierarchical structure could reduce the total amount of time devoted to higher education, the savings to our society would be enormous. Any unnecessary prolongation of higher education represents a double loss—the expense of the unnecessary education and the loss of the productive labor which both professors and students would otherwise render.

This three "teacher" and seventeen "auxiliary" plan is illustrative only; my basic argument for a professional hierarchy would not be invalidated merely because this particular arrangement might prove less effective than our present one. Certainly, the possibilities for developing a new personnel structure are not limited to elementary education. My own conviction is not that the particular hierarchical arrangement I have suggested is the answer, but that we will develop a personnel structure in education radically different from the prevailing one. How many skill levels it will have, and what will be the proportions of professional, semiprofessional, and subprofessional personnel, are matters for research and experimentation.

Whenever I have suggested to teachers that one of our educational frontiers is the development of a hierarchical personnel structure, the character of their objections has tended to confirm my conviction that such a structure is feasible. I have been told that it is undemocratic, that there would be no way for "teachers" to work with the "auxiliaries," that Dr. Smith, who has a Ph.D. in the teaching of reading, knows less about it than Miss Jones, who does not even have a bachelor's degree, and so on.

One of the most common reactions is that it is all right to have teacher aides but they must not be permitted to teach. The assumption is that teaching is always the professional part of the teacher's job. This is questionable. In medicine, there are situations in which the difficult task is diagnostic, and the work after diagnosis may be as simple as giving the patient a pill. On the other hand, there are situations in which the diagnosis is obvious even to a nurse, but the action called for requires the highest levels of professional skill and judgment. As a practical matter, therefore, one cannot say that the medical aides should never do any diagnosing or that they should never do any medicating. The only limitation that makes sense it that whatever role they are given be appropriate to their training and experience.

Similarly, there are educational situations in which diagnosis is extremely difficult but "teaching" quite simple. For example, it might be very hard to diagnose a reading difficulty but relatively easy to supervise the remedial action needed once the diagnosis becomes clear. There are other situations in which diagnosis may be relatively simple (e.g., grading and scoring standardized tests may indicate certain academic weaknesses) but the teaching required after this point may require the highest level of skill and expertness. People who "know," before any systematic experimentation with professional teams designed to teach a single subject, that teacher aides must never be permitted to teach are not showing the open-mindedness expected of good teachers. And, in general, the intellectual level of the objections to a personnel hierarchy in education shows clearly that teachers have never even considered a personnel structure different from the prevailing one.[6] This gives me hope that when they do think about the matter, something much better will emerge from the present situation.

[6] The hostile reactions of teacher organizations to the teacher aide project in Bay City, Michigan, illustrate this point. In brief, this project was designed to find out whether a teacher with an aide could teach a large class as effectively as two teachers assigned separately to classes of regular size. Teacher organizations should be the first to propose and support such projects; instead, their negative attitude toward the very idea of experimentation in this area has been rather poorly disguised as criticism of the research design and alleged results of the Bay City project.

Chapter VI

THE MISEDUCATION OF EDUCATORS

Let me begin my discussion of teacher education with a confession of avoidance. I am not going to argue for or against the proposition that teachers take too many methods courses and too few courses in their subject fields. One reason is that I am bored by the stale and sterile academic wrangling over this red herring. Such genuine issues as are occasionally involved in this controversy will be better understood if we begin with the genuinely important problems of teacher education.

The most important problem in teacher education is this: Who should determine the content and duration of programs of teacher education? I grant that the decision-making authority, whoever it rightfully may be, will be confronted by many difficult questions. Under any structure there will be disagreements, just as there are disagreements about medical and legal and engineering education. Such disagreements are fruitful, however, only when they can be raised and settled within a sound decision-making structure. Teacher education lacks such a structure.

Most of the current controversies over teacher education are carried on apart from any thoughtful consideration of who ought to have the operating power to resolve them. It is the neglect of this issue that is primarily responsible for the perpetual chaos and confusion in teacher education. Once this issue is settled on a sound basis, we will see the orderly resolution of current controversies in this area. But unless and until it is properly settled, we might as well resign ourselves to a continuation of sterile bickering on the subject.

Let us analyze briefly how decisions concerning the education of teachers are made at the present time. This is difficult to do because the decision-making structure in teacher education is so diffuse. Every state has its own procedure, and the variations among and within states are almost beyond description. In a brief discussion, the most that can be achieved is to convey some idea of the chaos that prevails in this field.

The most common procedure is for the state legislature to delegate to a state board of education the power to prescribe the requirements for a teaching certificate. These state boards are usually non-professional bodies, appointed by the governor, and serving without pay. The certification requirements they prescribe vary widely from state to state, but whatever they are, teacher-training institutions must respect them in planning the content and duration of programs of teacher education.

Quite frequently, the legislatures set forth special requirements which the state boards of education cannot abolish or modify on their own authority. Thus some state legislatures have required applicants for a teaching certificate to have a course in the history or the constitution of their particular state. Some have required prospective teachers to take a loyalty oath. In still others, there is a legislative requirement that an applicant for a teaching certificate be a citizen, or that he have applied for his first papers.

There are also states in which the legal responsibility for prescribing the requirements for teaching certificates rests with the chief state school officer, most commonly known as the superintendent of public instruction or the commissioner of education. Frequently, it is the responsibility of this officer to recommend the requirements to the state board of education, which has the power to approve or to reject these recommendations.

There is tremendous variation in the extent to which the requirements are spelled out by the state authorities, whoever they may be. For instance, in Colorado, a prospective teacher of English needs only twelve semester hours in the "area of English" and only five in the specific subject taught (English, speech, drama, etc.) to qualify for a teaching certificate; in Kentucky, a prospective English teacher needs forty-eight semester hours in the area and thirty in the specific subject field. The requirements in other states vary between these limits.[1]

Note, however, that the course requirements laid down by the state authorities seldom go beyond specifying the required total number of hours in the subject taught, in general education, and in education courses. Thus it is usually up to each teacher-training institution to decide what specific courses will be used to meet the state requirements. This gives them a great deal of operational control over programs of teacher education.

For purposes of illustration, we may note that as of 1957 there were fifteen states which required 24 semester hours of English for a permanent secondary certificate to teach English. Now, in each of these states, it is the responsibility of the teacher-training institutions to decide what courses in English will be used to meet the 24-hour requirement. There is considerable variation among institutions on the courses actually utilized for this purpose. Such variations frequently exist even between teacher-training institutions within a particular state. In fact, students at the same institution preparing for the same license often fulfil the state requirements by course patterns which differ from student to student.

The same pattern holds with regard to the requirements in general education or in education courses. That is, despite a state regulation requiring a certain number of hours in these areas, the training institutions usually decide which courses will in fact be used to meet the state requirements. The over-all result has been sheer chaos, and even within a given state, let alone when any two states are compared, there is no assurance that the teachers who have met identical state requirements have actually had very much training in common.

Sometimes the discretion accorded the teacher-training in-

[1] W. Earl Armstrong and T. M. Stinnett, *A Manual on Certification Requirements for School Personnel in the United States* (Washington: National Education Association, 1957), pp. 29–30.

stitutions even goes beyond the freedom to decide what courses will be used to meet the state requirements. In some states, such as Nevada and Washington, the number of semester hours required to teach academic subjects is not spelled out. Instead, the state requires that the teacher shall have a "major" in the subject, and the number of hours required for a major is left to the teacher-training institutions to decide.[2]

The chaos with respect to course requirements for a teaching license is paralleled by chaos with respect to the method of selecting or appointing the state authorities which set the requirements. Even when there are similarities in title between these authorities, there are often wide divergencies in the ways in which they are appointed or elected. A state superintendent of public instruction may have substantially the same power to regulate teacher education in each of three different states. In one state, he may be chosen in state-wide elections, in another, he may be selected by the state board of education, and in still another, he may be appointed by the governor. Similarly, state boards of education may have identical powers to determine the content and duration of teacher education, but from state to state there are the widest divergencies in the constituencies and in the methods of selecting members of the board. In some states, various state officials are ex officio members; in others, there are certain limitations on who can be a member. Some states expressly exclude teachers from the board; others expressly include one or more educators. In some states, appointments are made on a geographical basis, whereas in others there is no geographical restriction or distribution required by state law.

We can summarize the situation in this way: From state to state, the power to regulate the requirements for a teaching certificate is haphazardly divided between legislatures, boards of education, education departments, superintendents of public instruction, and teacher-training institutions. The policies adopted by each of these agencies are often shaped by chance factors which should have no influence at all on teacher-education. In

[2] *Ibid.*

other words, when we take into account not only who makes the decisions affecting teacher education at the state level but also the processes by which these persons acquire their positions, it becomes clear that there is neither rhyme nor reason to the way in which teacher education is controlled in the United States.

But who *should* control it? Let me approach this question first from a professional point of view. In other professions, the practitioners themselves exercise the decisive role in shaping programs for their own training. Entry to the profession is controlled through state board examinations, and the professional schools must offer a curriculum that will enable their graduates to pass these examinations. The scope of the examinations is so broad that the professional schools have little discretion to offer electives or to require subjects not required by the state boards. The crucial point, however, is that the state boards which prescribe and evaluate the examinations are controlled directly or indirectly by the practitioners of the profession concerned.

Professional control over professional training takes different forms from state to state and from profession to profession. Sometimes it is indirect and depends more on the pressure which the profession can bring to bear upon state authorities and schools than it does on any explicit mention of practitioner control in the laws regulating professional training.

On many occasions, teachers have asked me why teachers must control entry if teaching is to be regarded as a profession. The question is really like asking why a bridge player has to take thirteen tricks to make a grand slam. The fact that teachers think they are asking a question of fact instead of a question of meaning is in itself a reflection of their widespread naïveté concerning professionalism. By definition, an occupational group is a profession only when it controls entry to that occupation. To ask whether teachers should control entry to teaching is tantamount to asking whether teaching should be a profession at all; to oppose teacher control of entry while advocating that teaching be a profession is to be confused.

One might argue that if expertness is the criterion, then we should leave professional training to the faculties of the professional schools. We cannot do this because it is necessary to have some check upon the schools themselves. This check is supplied by the state board examinations controlled by the practitioners. The very purpose of these examinations is to make sure that the self-interest of the schools does not thwart the public and professional interest in high standards of professional training. Granted, the practitioners are also affected by the standards of professional training for their profession. However, the self-interest of the practitioners is usually served by high standards, whereas the self-interest of the institutions offering professional training is often served by low standards. The state board examinations controlled by the practitioners provide a very necessary safeguard against commercialism in the professional schools.

What about commercialism on the part of the practitioners? Many observers regard control over entry largely as an attempt by professional groups to enhance their own economic position by limiting the supply of persons eligible to practice the profession. This point of view is not supported by past experience with professional controls (despite some popular prejudices against the American Medical Association in this regard). It is undebatable that there are some needless or questionable requirements for entry to many occupations. What is debatable is (1) the extent of such requirements, (2) the extent to which they would be eliminated by removing occupational control over entry, and (3) whether the harmful consequences of unnecessary restriction due to professional control outweigh the harmful consequences of permitting laymen to regulate entry into a highly complex and essential social service.

Probably the reason why most people, including most teachers, reject teacher regulation of entry is the fact that teachers are publicly employed. It is thought that this would permit public decisions to be made by a private group. The fact that most teachers are publicly employed supposedly indicates that the public has a stronger interest in the requirements for teaching than for medicine. But this fact is irrelevant. It is in the public interest to place the control of professional training in the hands of those who are best equipped to decide what is required for successful practice. This is the basic issue. Surely, it would not make sense to turn control of medical education over to plumbers and salesmen if and when most physicians are publicly employed. The analogy is appropriate; given a reasonable projection of present trends, most physicians will be publicly employed within a few generations.

Parents are every bit as concerned about the competence of doctors for their children as they are about the competence of teachers. Indeed, the final irony here is that while teachers argue for non-professional control of entry and for financing educational services from public funds because teaching is so important to society, doctors insist upon professional control of entry and a non-governmental system of financing medical care for the same reason. Of course, even if people were more concerned about the quality of teachers than about the quality of doctors, it would still make little sense to argue that the proper way for them to express their concern is by having laymen decide what doctors must study in order to be admitted to practice.

Certainly, the dangers of unjustifiable occupational protection are no greater among publicly employed professions than among privately employed ones. Unjustifiable restrictions upon the supply of doctors would be as harmful as unjustifiable restrictions upon the supply of teachers. If anything, not to be able to get a doctor when one is needed is a more serious calamity than not to be able to get a teacher. The point is, however, that there is absolutely no difference in the economics of the two situations. If the supply of doctors is restricted for the benefit of the doctors, citizens pay higher medical fees. If the supply of teachers is restricted for the benefit of the teachers, citizens pay higher taxes.

To summarize, one cannot show a single danger in professional control of admission to a publicly employed profession that is not present in a situation of private employment. By the same token, the benefits that accrue to the public from professional control in fee-taking professions would also be reflected in the publicly employed professions as well. Insofar as entry is concerned, it should not make the slightest difference whether the profession being licensed is publicly or privately employed.

THE MYTHOLOGY OF TEACHER EDUCATION

As things actually work out, programs of teacher education are a hodgepodge which reflects the irrational controls to which they are subjected. This hodgepodge has been rationalized by the teacher-training institutions as "the freedom to experiment" with different programs. In fact, serious experimentation in teacher education is practically at a standstill. Even more important, the extreme diffusion of controls over teacher education has created a situation wherein it is practically impossible to place the education of teachers on a professional basis. This comes out most clearly when we consider the claims and counterclaims made by various types of colleges which prepare teachers.

Professors in teachers' colleges contend that these institutions are ideal for teacher training because, unlike the universities, they concentrate upon training instead of research. This is a completely antiprofessional point of view. The best professional schools, whether they be in medicine, engineering, dentistry, psychology, or anything else, are located in the universities which are centers of research. The best physicians, the best engineers, the best professionals in any field, are trained in institutions where the professors are advancing the frontiers of knowledge in the basic disciplines of the profession. The medical professors who are carrying on the most advanced research in the cause and cure of illness are going to produce better physicians than those who concentrate on teaching. For that matter, a physician could not become a medical professor, at least in a first-rate medical school, unless he were advancing the science of medicine.

Teachers should be trained only in institutions where the professors are engaged in research in the subjects studied by the teachers. If a student is going to be a chemistry teacher, he should be trained where the professors of chemistry are engaged in the study of problems in their own field. Likewise, he will be better trained if his professors in subjects which he will utilize but not teach, such as educational psychology, are engaged in significant research.

Of course, if teacher education is to be conducted on a professional basis, it must be taken away from the four-year liberal arts colleges as well as from the teachers' colleges. Furthermore, it should be taken away from them for the same reason that it should be taken away from the teachers' colleges. The four-year liberal arts colleges also lack the research orientation which an institution must have to be an adequate center for professional training.

I do not wish to give the impression that nobody in a teachers' college or liberal arts college ever does any research, nor do I mean to suggest that every professor in every university is engaged in research, constructive or otherwise. But the point is that the university is designed for research, or should be, at any rate. The existence of particular individuals who do not implement the university ideal does not alter the basic case for placing the education of teachers in the university setting, where it belongs if it is to be genuinely professional.

The squabbling over what type of institution is best equipped to train teachers is generally carried on with the most naïve assumptions concerning the professional aspects of teacher education. Professors of education have been prone to argue that the professional portion of teacher education is to be found solely in the education courses taken by prospective teachers. This is fallacious on at least two grounds. First, a teacher's professional training includes his specialized training in the subject he is to teach. In the second place, many education courses are not professional courses at all.

For example, the course labeled "Introduction to Education," which is probably the most widely offered course in education, should hardly ever be regarded as a professional course. Practically all colleges require students to take a course in political science. However, nobody regards introductory courses in political science as professional training, to be studied only by political scientists. Similarly, students are often required to take an "Introduction to Economics," in which they are supposed to acquire some insight into our economic system. Again, nobody contends that such courses are professional in nature, to be taken only by prospective economists. By the same token, I do not believe that a course which involves the introductory study of our educational system should be regarded as a professional course in education.

The fact that certain education courses are not professional must be interpreted carefully. One should not infer from this fact that these courses should not be taken by prospective teachers. Prospective teachers should be required to study our educational system. Indeed, I think it makes sense to require *all* students to study it, just as it makes sense to require all of them to study our political and economic systems. But I am equally convinced that that study of education at this level is no more professional than the courses in political science or economics which are required of all students. What puzzles me is to hear so many "academic scholars" talk about the crucial importance of education and then restrict its study as much as they possibly can. To label such academicians "confused" is to take the most charitable interpretation of their actions. At any rate, as long as professors in departments other than education persist in the untenable position that only prospective teachers should take courses in education, and not even then if it can be helped, the mistaken tendency on the part of professors of education to classify all education courses as "professional" will continue.

While many professors of education delude themselves that a teacher's professional training consists of his education courses, professors in other areas exhibit an equally naïve view of the basic principles of education for other professions. It is common to hear complaints outside departments of education (and sometimes within them) that state certification regulations interfere with institutional autonomy. Of course they do—but not as much as they should. To read all the complaints about the fact that there are state requirements for a teaching license, one would never suspect that the curriculum in other kinds of professional schools is not determined by institutions of higher education but by the state boards which control entry to the professions.

All this is not said to justify any particular certification requirements. On the contrary, I think most of them are indefensible. But the point is that many individuals, especially in higher education, do not grasp the full implications of their argument that teacher education ought to be largely the province of each institution which trains teachers. This argument may be sound, but it cannot be reconciled with the notion that teaching is a profession.

It may make sense to accord institutional autonomy to the liberal arts college, which we might justifiably permit to set its own requirements for a degree. But professional schools are supposed to operate on an altogether different basis. Here, the major concern is not with the student so much as it is with the future clients of the professional worker. In the professional school, what the student wants to study, or even what the institution would like for him to study, must give way to what the student must know and be able to do in order to carry out his professional tasks effectively. Experience shows rather conclusively that it is as unsound to permit each institution to set the requirements for professional training as it is to permit individual students to set them through an elective system.

It is true that even in professional schools students have some choices. Most notably, they can choose their area of specialization, if the profession lends itself to specialization. But even in these situations, the state boards or extralegal professional boards will frequently determine what the student must study to be proficient in his specialty. In education, every teacher is a specialist; there is no such thing as general practice. Although a qualified student should be entitled to choose his own special field, neither he nor the institution should have much discretion to determine the content of programs of teacher education. If there are rigorous state board examinations covering the minimum essentials for successful teaching, teacher-training institutions can be given considerable freedom to develop their own programs. However, this is not likely to be a major practical concession, since few institutions will find it feasible to require much more training than is necessary to pass the state board examinations.

Teacher-training institutions will object strenuously to this point of view, but they must be ultimately overruled. Their argument is that we must wait until specific patterns of teacher education prove their worth before we require all teachers to take them. The rejoinder must be that the present diffuse and dysfunctional structure of teacher education makes it all but impossible to develop better patterns or to have any pattern gain acceptance against the vested interests which would be swept away by a system of professional controls. To delay changing the present structure until we get better programs of teacher education is unrealistic. We are unlikely to get the better programs until we change the structure.

INTEGRATING THEORY AND PRACTICE

Common usage often classifies education courses as either "theoretical" or "practical." The basis of the distinction has never been too clear. The most common interpretation seems to be that "theoretical courses" are the ones with little or no classroom application whereas "practical courses" supposedly are useful in the classroom. This interpretation has had unfortunate connotations. It suggests that theory is not practical and that what is practical is devoid of theoretical content.

The "theoretical-practical" distinction should not be used to refer to the results of courses but to the context in which they are taught. Some courses, such as those in mathematics, are theoretical in the sense that their content is a body of theory. They are also practical in the sense that they are useful in application to professional problems. However, they need not be taught in a practical context; students do not have to practice manipulative skills to grasp their content.

There are other courses which are both theoretical and practical, in the sense just described, but which do require a practical context to be taught effectively. To go outside the field of teacher education, a course in surgery, like one in mathematics, has theoretical content and is certainly useful in practice. However, unlike mathematics, it must be taught in a context of application. In order to learn theory as well as skills, the prospective surgeon must be taught where there are cadavers, sick people, instruments, machines, drugs, and other accouterments. However, this fact does not mean that surgery has no theoretical content.

Good programs of teacher education should include both theoretical and practical courses as I have described them. For example, a prospective teacher should take courses in mathematics and education. The mathematics courses are purely theoretical in the sense that they need not be taught in a practical setting. But what about education courses?

Some education courses require a practical context, others do not. There are still others which would be difficult to classify. Some might be improved by having the theoretical content taught in a practical context, but the need to teach them this way may not be clearly decisive. It is in these courses that the instructor may require a few field trips or assign projects which involve some practical experience.

Let me illustrate: Courses in the history of education need not be taught in a practical context. They can properly be classified as theory courses, according to the usage I have proposed. Most courses in methods of teaching should be taught in a practical context. Prospective chemistry teachers should be taught methods of teaching chemistry while they have an opportunity to observe the subject being presented to the kinds of students they will eventually teach. Their opportunities for observation, and perhaps even for trying out what they learn in a methods course, should not be deferred until a later time.

In the actual structure and sequence of education courses, little attention is typically paid to the need to teach certain courses in this way. Prospective teachers take most of their courses at a college of education, far removed from the kinds of classes they are supposed eventually to teach. Occasionally an instructor may require some observation of schools as part of a course, but this is usually sporadic, even in the courses where practically all the teaching should be done in a practical context.

Student teaching is commonly thought to make up for the absence of demonstrations and applications in other parts of the teacher-education program. For this reason, most states require a period of student teaching for a certificate, the amount varying from state to state, grade level to grade level, and subject to subject. Nevertheless, it is doubtful whether student teaching, as it is currently taken by prospective teachers, is really of much help to them. It is usually undertaken after all other education courses have been completed or during the semester when the student teacher is completing his course work. This procedure cannot make up for the sterile way in which the other education courses are taught. Prior to the time they take their student teaching, prospective teachers have taken courses in methods, educational psychology, tests and measurements, and others in which the content requires a practical setting to be grasped effectively.

The failure to teach certain education courses in a practical context has more serious consequences than the student's failure to acquire methods and techniques. Even the theoretical content of many education courses cannot be thoroughly understood as long as they are taught apart from demonstrations and applications. Therefore, when the prospective teachers come to their period of student teaching, they have already forgotten whatever theory they may have learned in previous education courses. The effort to integrate theory and practice during student teaching fails, not because the theory is erroneous (although this is often the case) but because the students never really grasped the theory or the skills and techniques which they were supposed to have learned.

Note also that deferring the student's practical experience until his period of student teaching eliminates most of his opportunities to discuss this experience with his instructors in a systematic and fruitful way. Since he will have finished most of his course work prior to the student teaching period, the prospective teacher brings the questions generated by student teaching to the supervising teacher or the director of student teaching. These people, however, are not usually the specialists to whom his questions should be directed.

My point may also be made by an attempt to visualize how professional training in other fields would be conducted if it followed the pattern of teacher education. If the procedures currently followed by education students were followed in medicine, medical students would study anatomy, surgery, obstetrics, and other medical subjects chiefly as textbook courses. They would see no broken limbs in the surgery course, no women in labor during the obstetrics course, and no mentally ill persons during the psychiatry course. They would be told about medical principles and techniques, but all or practically all firsthand experience with sick persons would be deferred until their internship.

Of course, one shudders at the thought of what this would do to medical education. When a medical professor explains the principles, techniques, and drugs required to keep patients alive during an operation, he does not confine his activities to talking about these things. He makes sure that his students are confronted within the day or week with concrete illustrations of them. However, if medical education were like teacher education, there would be very little integration of theory and practice in the medical courses themselves. The demonstration and applications exemplifying the content of the course would be deferred, not just for days, weeks, or months but for years. In such an event, the medical students would have forgotten most of what they had learned, or were supposed to have learned, by the time they began their internship.

Teacher education should be changed to make it accord with sound principles of professional training. This will require an end to the practice of deferring practical training until the period of student teaching. A much larger measure of practical training must be included in some (but not all) of the courses which precede student teaching or teacher internships. Teacher-training institutions must put aside the notion that they can teach theory in one course, practice in another, and have the prospective teacher splice them together properly during a period of student teaching.[3]

The fact that practical experience is deferred to the period of student teaching might not be so unfortunate if it also were not bungled so badly. The student teacher usually works under the supervision of a regular teacher. The university director of student teaching or one of his assistants usually visits the student a few times during the months of practice. Even under ideal conditions, this is an unsound arrangement. Although an effort is made to get good supervising teachers, this often turns out to be a hit-or-miss proposition. The supervising teachers are generally not paid for their supervision; hence many look upon the task of overseeing student teachers as an unnecessary interruption of their work. The choice of supervising teachers frequently depends on a chain of fortuitous factors—what school systems are available, whether the principals and the teachers are interested in having any student teachers, where the student teacher lives, how far the participating school is from the college of education, what teachers are available at the times which the student teacher can spare from his other subjects, and so on.

Going back to our medical situation again, note that the very same professor who gives the lectures also supervises the practical demonstrations and applications. This fact eliminates the possibility that differences in theoretical orientation between the person giving the course and the person supervising the practical experience will leave the student without any orientation whatsoever. Even with the best of intentions, it may be very difficult for the supervising teacher to know what was taught by the professors of education, just as it is impossible for the professors to get more than a fleeting glimpse of the supervising teacher at work.

The fact that the practical demonstrations and applications and the supervision of the prospective teacher's practical training are

[3] Robert M. Hutchins has long contended that the institutions of higher education should provide the theoretical training and the professions the practical training needed for incoming members of a profession. In my opinion, this point of view overlooks the extent to which a practical context may be desirable, or even essential, to learning the theory which the professional man should know. See Robert M. Hutchins, *The University of Utopia* (Chicago: University of Chicago Press, 1953), p. 40.

not handled by the same persons who provided the theoretical content is a basic weakness of virtually all teacher-education programs. The professors are never sure of what the supervising teachers are going to do. The activities of the supervising teachers may or may not illustrate the points which the professors were trying to make in their college courses. The result is that there is little articulation between the practical experience gained in student teaching and the college courses which supposedly provide the theoretical basis for that experience.

This problem is compounded by the fact that the teachers responsible for day-to-day supervision of student teachers usually do not possess the same amount of training as the professors who give the courses. It is as if medical professors were to teach the courses and then turn over the supervision of interns to medical technicians. It does not make sense to leave the supervision of the trainee's practical experience in the hands of persons who have less training than those who teach the theory.

Many classroom teachers, especially those who supervise student teachers, would take strong exception to these comments. They would contend that the teacher-training institutions frequently send out student teachers who know a lot of unworkable theory and nothing else. They would argue that the lack of articulation between the supervising teachers and the college professors is due not to the fact that the former have an inadequate theoretical orientation but rather to the fact that the professors of education have forgotten, if they ever knew, what it was like to teach in elementary and secondary schools.

I have a great deal of sympathy with this point of view. After all, it is only what might be expected under a system where the professors of education only talk about teaching but no longer have to do any work themselves below the college level, even for demonstration or research purposes. The situation is as if upon becoming a professor of surgery, a medical professor never conducted another operation in his life. Yet the fact is that those professors of education whose responsibilities include instruction in the art and science of teaching in elementary or secondary schools rarely teach again at these levels once they have assumed their professorial positions. It should be no surprise that what they have to say becomes divorced from some of the harsher realities of the classroom. I would suggest as evidence for this the fact that classroom teachers are rarely as permissive as they were urged to be by some professors of education. The teachers simply could not retain control of their classrooms while permitting their students the freedoms which were advocated by the professors.

Student teaching is often regarded and justified as a kind of internship, comparable to that which is undertaken by future doctors before they enter medical practice. In this connection, it is interesting to note that internship programs are being abandoned by the medical schools. In 1956, only one medical school still required an internship for an M.D. degree. The medical schools have found internships inefficient, and for the same reasons that student teaching is ineffective in teacher education. All too often the future doctor would take his internship at a hospital where the supervisors were not acquainted with the training program in the medical school. Often the supervising doctors did not know as much as the interns they supervised. Many hospitals used interns as cheap labor and had no systematic training program for them. Frequently there was little articulation between the internship and the courses taken in the medical school. If the intern was confronted by a situation which led him to question something which he was taught in medical school, it was too late to raise the issue with the professor who was responsible for teaching it.

The solution in medical education has been to introduce more practical experience in the courses in the medical school, where the same persons could present theory and supervise practical demonstrations and applications. I believe we must accept substantially the same solution to the problem of integrating theory and practice in teacher education.

At the present time, teaching internships are a growing practice in teacher education. The internship ideal is viable, and under certain conditions its widespread adoption could be a boon. Unfortunately, too many programs of teacher education labeled "internships" are such in name only. The quality of these programs varies considerably. Many amount to nothing more than taking some education courses simultaneously with paid teaching. They reveal little or no articulation between the courses taken in the university and the school experience that would make them meaningful.

Actually, some internship programs have really gone off the deep end in their uncritical notions of articulating theory and practice. They have operated as if such subjects as "history of education" need to be integrated with practice in the same way as courses in "methods of teaching." However, it is as unwise to try to teach every course in a practical context as it is to teach none of them this way. On the whole, the content of a history of education course lies in a good university library. It should be sought there, without naïve attempts to teach it in a practical context. We must scrutinize each subject matter, whether in an education course or not, to evaluate the extent to which it must be taught in a practical context to be learned effectively.

These comments are relevant to the issue of whether future teachers should take their professional courses as undergraduates or whether these courses should be deferred until the student has acquired a bachelor's degree or completed preprofessional training. In most professions, students devote their full time first to preprofessional studies. When these are completed, regardless of whether they include a bachelor's degree, the students devote their full time to studies in the professional school. Training in law, medicine, and dentistry illustrates this point. Personally, I favor this policy, partly because the professional school needs the full day to do its job properly. It seems difficult to believe that our best professional schools could operate effectively if they had students for only half the day, even if the students were enrolled in these schools for twice as many semesters as they are now. There is also the fact that studies taken during the undergraduate years, especially the freshman and sophomore years, are hardly regarded as professional by the outside world.

Many people in teacher education would accept this analysis. The trouble starts when they add to it the unwarranted notion that all education courses are "professional." The result is that courses like "Introduction to Education," which should be taught to freshmen and sophomores as a part of a general education sequence, are postponed to the fifth year, where they look rather anemic compared to fifth-year work taken by law or medical students. Furthermore, the policy of deferring all education courses to the fifth year results in a situation wherein this year is often pre-empted by education courses, making it difficult for students to take graduate work in their field of specialization.

On the other hand, the situation is not necessarily improved by the inclusion of education courses in the undergraduate program. All too often, the courses so included are the ones which should be deferred to the period of professional training. Thus many schools give courses in methods of teaching early in the undergraduate years. By the time the student goes out to teach, he has forgotten whatever he might have learned in the methods courses. The period between the end of professional studies and the beginning of professional practice should be as brief as possible.

FACILITIES FOR TEACHER EDUCATION

Most current thinking about teacher education is concerned chiefly with changing the course requirements for a teaching certificate. "Reforms" usually consist of juggling the course requirements to accord with the prejudices of whoever happens to be in the saddle at any given time. Other aspects of teacher education, such as its need for more adequate facilities, are not receiving the attention which they deserve.

Teacher education should have available schools which are geared to that purpose without sacrificing any educational rights or privileges of students. Many teachers' colleges and schools of education established laboratory schools partly for this purpose. These laboratory schools were also established to provide research facilities for professors interested in studying children and how they learn. In most laboratory schools, however, the research function has all but disappeared. For this reason, these schools are not the advanced centers of teacher education that they were originally supposed to be.

The basic weaknesses of the typical laboratory school are clear from comparing its operations to those of a teaching hospital. The teaching hospital is deeply interested in the most difficult and unusual cases, for such cases are the most valuable from the standpoint of research and experimentation. On the other hand, the student body in most laboratory schools is bright and well behaved. In many institutions, the laboratory school has an unusually large percentage of faculty children, so that it takes on the character of a private school. I know of more than one school where this fact created special problems because the teachers in the laboratory school were in the same academic department as the parents of the children in their classes.

Some laboratory schools try to enrol a "normal" school population, a procedure which is questionable on at least two grounds. In the first place, a student body representative of the population as a whole is practically never found in any particular school. And, in the second place, unusual children or classes often provide the best illustrations for learning how to teach average ones. At any rate, because of their lack of a research orientation, their fear of tough cases, their tendency to assume utopian conditions of employment for the future teachers, and their use of demonstration teachers with less than the top level of training, the laboratory schools are but another illustration of the way in which teacher education apes the appearance while avoiding the substance of professional training.

The fact that many teacher-training institutions do not have any laboratory schools at all, and that existing laboratory schools are not being used effectively in training teachers, emphasizes the need to reconsider the relationships between public school systems and teacher-training institutions. In recent years, the Fund for the Advancement of Education has been supporting programs of teacher education in which public school systems play a much more active role than they have in the past. In these programs, school systems are being encouraged to provide financial assistance to teaching interns, to make available staff time for teacher education, and to work co-operatively with teacher-training institutions in the selection, training, and evaluation of prospective teachers.

These efforts are a step in the right direction. There is no doubt that public school systems must develop closer relationships with teacher-training institutions for the sake of better teacher education. At the same time, however, I have come to believe that one hard fact severely handicaps most of the efforts to bring about a really effective working relationship between school systems and teacher-training institutions: there is no unified control of public education and teacher education. The result is that the institutions which train teachers do not have enough control over the schools to develop a first-rate program of teacher education. Communities support their schools to educate children, not to train teachers. The public school systems are geared to this purpose, and teacher education must be adjusted to it.

Most school systems are willing to accept student teachers, although not necessarily on the conditions that are best from the standpoint of teacher education. When a school system is asked to do more than this, the school board is likely to raise several objections. "Why," they will ask, "should we provide our money, staff, and resources to train teachers who will not necessarily come into our system anyway?"

For various reasons, some school systems are willing to do more for teacher education than to accept student teachers. They provide paid internships for prospective teachers, release some staff time for working with teaching interns and with personnel from teacher-training institutions, and participate extensively in the selection and evaluation of prospective teachers. They recruit able new teachers, provide recognition for their own outstanding teachers, or have related purposes in authorizing such extensive participation in teacher education.

Nevertheless, teacher education cannot be effectively reorganized without some basic changes in the legal and administrative relationships between school systems and teacher-training institutions. The extent of financial participation by school systems in teacher education is still an open question. The main problem here is to make sure that the school systems get a reasonable return on their investment. Aside from this difficulty, public school personnel are acutely sensitive to community reaction to teachers in training. Parents want their children taught by experienced teachers, not by student teachers or interns. Even if the children are learning as well as they would under their regular teacher, it may be very difficult for public school administrators to convince parents of this or to resist parental requests that the regular teachers take over.

Simply put, the dilemma is that teacher-training institutions must be able to control some schools for training purposes, but such purposes are secondary to those for which the communities support the schools. The solution to this dilemma will have to be similar to the solution reached in medical education, where teaching hospitals are used to train future physicians. The patients in these teaching hospitals generally receive better treatment than they do in ordinary hospitals. The services performed by medical students are closely supervised by outstanding professor-physicians who are always available for emergencies which are too much for the students. The professor-physicians check the medical progress of patients so that no patient actually suffers from being used for educational purposes.

If teacher education were to follow this example, the pupils in the schools used to train teachers would be better off educationally than pupils in other schools. The teacher-training schools would have the best teachers and the most up-to-date facilities, so that the pupils (as well as the student teachers) would be taught at the frontiers of the science and art of teaching. Although the student teachers and interns might do a substantial amount of teaching, the professor-teachers would closely evaluate the progress of pupils to insure that the latter do not suffer because they are being taught as part of a teacher-training program.

The necessary arrangements could be worked out with school systems in several ways. For example, a community might sign a contract permitting a teacher-training institution to operate a particular school, paying the institution what the community would ordinarily pay to operate that school. A community which needs a new school might make an agreement with a teacher-training institution whereby the latter built and operated the school with some reimbursement from the community. The institution would have to provide the additional funds needed to make the school an educational showcase; however, it would be reimbursed for the costs which the school system would otherwise have to pay from its own funds.

This practice has already been established in medical education. Cities often pay medical schools a certain amount to operate a hospital, which is then used by the medical school for teaching purposes. The medical school puts up additional funds to insure that the hospital will provide the very latest in medical care. I know of no important reason why a similar procedure cannot be worked out in teacher education. Such a procedure would give communities a strong practical incentive to support teacher education.

As I have suggested, one of the problems of teacher education is the development of a corps of teachers who have a high degree of theoretical training and who can also do the demonstration teaching in elementary and secondary schools. These teachers must be key members of the university faculty. Teacher-education responsibilities should not be superimposed on teachers whose primary responsibility lies to a school system. We must also give up the practice of having prospective teachers "supervised" by university personnel who spend each day in a different school with a different student teacher and a different regular teacher. There must be supervising professor-teachers devoted to teacher education on a full-time basis. The load for such persons could be one demonstration class and one class of student teachers, with the rest of their time devoted to research and experimentation.

Anyone who thinks that the basic reforms needed in teacher education consist of adding or deleting certain courses is only deluding himself. The basic reforms needed are structural, not curricular. Important curricular reforms are needed, but they will follow, not precede, the structural reforms. We must develop a new system of controls over teacher education, including an examination system interposed between graduation from a teacher-training institution and the receipt of a teaching certificate. Teacher training must be confined to institutions which have the resources to carry it out on a professional basis; this calls for a drastic reduction in the number of institutions which train teachers. The authority to issue teachers' certificates must be vested in educational authorities who are responsive to professional opinion. The requirements for a teaching certificate must not be enacted into state legislation but must have the force of law. The certification structure should be flexible, so that it is not necessary to get an act of the state legislature every time professional opinion supports a change in the certification requirements. As for the current controversy over whether teacher education is putting too much emphasis on "how to teach" at the expense of "what to teach," I can only say again that it is a sad and pitiful thing to see this treated as a basic issue in teacher education.

Chapter VII

WHY LIBERAL EDUCATION DOES
NOT LIBERALIZE

Public education, teacher education, and liberal education are so intertwined that a discussion of one quickly involves analysis of the other two. Thus far, however, liberal education has been largely ignored, at least by name, in the preceding chapters. Let us try to analyze what it is and how it relates to public education.

Like progressive education, liberal education suffers from an overdose of definitions. As I view it, the idea of liberal education has a great deal in common with the idea of public education proposed in previous chapters. The common core of these ideas is an education that extends the horizons, that relates to basic ideas and problems, that develops the ability to think, that heightens sensitivity and perception in areas of deep human concern. When I refer to liberal education, I refer to a kind of education which is sabotaged in public schools when students are not allowed to analyze the beliefs which prevail in their homes and local communities.

Historically, the task of inculcating a liberal education has been the responsibility of the "liberal arts college." This college is not necessarily a separate institution of higher education. It can be a separate college in a multipurpose institution, such as a state university, which also includes professional schools, research institutes, and other administrative units.

We must never overlook the distinction between liberal education as an ideal and the liberal arts college as an institution. Criticism of the institution is not necessarily criticism of the ideal. In this discussion, at least, such criticism is intended only to implement that ideal. I raise this point because some critics of liberal education as it now operates have been unjustifiably accused of being hostile toward the ideal of liberal education. This is like saying that a person is opposed to representative government merely because he criticizes the overrepresentation of rural areas in the state legislatures. Still, in the present climate of educational controversy, one cannot be too careful; if you do not say specifically that you believe in motherhood and patriotism, someone is likely to infer that you are against these things.

Whether or not public education and liberal education should be regarded as ideological twins, there is widespread agreement that teachers ought to be liberally educated. Whether they are is something else. The most obvious way to assess the actual extent of their liberal education is to see how much of their total academic program is in the liberal arts. Unfortunately, we can make only guesses on the subject. There are differences in the amount and kind of academic work taken by teachers from state to state, institution to institution, subject to subject, grade level to grade level, and teacher to teacher. Sometimes courses classified as in the liberal arts by one institution are classified as professional by another, or vice versa.

Granting all the difficulties in making an estimate, I would say that about 80 per cent of the academic work of classroom teachers has been in the liberal arts. This estimate is probably a little low for secondary teachers and it may be somewhat high for elementary teachers. In both categories, there will be many individuals who have either a much higher or a much lower percentage of their total program in the liberal arts. Nevertheless, I do not believe that any conclusion reached in the following discussion would be invalidated by the exact figures, whatever they may be.

If about 80 per cent of the academic work of teachers is in the liberal arts, the effectiveness of public education will be closely related to the effectiveness of the liberal arts colleges. Indeed, our concern here should not be limited to the effectiveness of the liberal arts college in preparing future teachers. Its impact upon all who pass through it is a matter of the utmost importance to American education.

One's first thought is apt to be the difficulty of evaluating the influence of liberal arts colleges. There are so many of them, with so many variations in resources, staff, and student body, that one hardly knows where evaluation is to begin. One of the most common procedures has been to test students before and after their attendance at a liberal arts college. Sometimes the students are tested at various intervals during their college careers and after graduation. The idea is to see what changes have taken place in the values and intellectual habits of the students during their college years.

To spell this out a little more, an entering freshman will have certain political, economic, religious, and cultural ideas. He will have certain reading habits relating to the number and quality of books, magazines, and newspapers he reads. He will have a certain stock of information about the world and his place in it. It seems reasonable to assume that if the liberal arts college is doing its job, there will be some basic changes in the values and intellectual habits of students during their four years in a liberal arts college. We should not expect every student to change his point of view on everything, but we certainly should expect that every student will have changed his position on some crucial issues by the time he graduates. Also, we should expect some changes in the intellectual habits of the students after four years of college. For instance, we should expect changes in what they read or in the kinds of radio and television programs which engage their interest.

Before analyzing the results of these "before and after" studies, bear in mind one possible weakness in them. One might find certain changes in students during their years in college, but how is one to know that the changes are due to the influence of the college itself? After all, some people who have never attended college broaden their horizons, acquire new tastes, or change their reading habits.

Unfortunately, it is not possible to compare each college graduate to an identical twin who did not attend a liberal arts college. But rather strenuous efforts have been made to approximate this situation by utilizing a matched-pair technique in which an attempt is made to set up two groups which are as much alike as possible; the only difference between the groups is that one attends a liberal arts college and the other does not. Then the activities of the two groups are compared over a period of years.

To illustrate this procedure, we might take X, who is a high-school graduate about to enter a liberal arts college. He will have a certain grade record, scholastic aptitude, religion, political outlook, socioeconomic status, interest inventory, physical makeup, and so on. The researcher puts X in one group. He then tries to find another person, Y, who is like X in all these respects, but who does not go on to college. Of course, the very fact that Y is not going to college indicates that there may be important differences between him and X, but the researcher tries to keep these differences to a minimum.

Now if the liberal arts college is having an impact upon its student body, there should be differences between the X's and Y's as the years go by. The Y's will not all be growing up in the same environment while the X's are attending college. Some will be in non-academic environments conducive to intellectual growth, some will not. Nevertheless, we should certainly expect substantial group differences between the X's and the Y's—differences in vital information, in ability to think clearly, in awareness of social issues, in reading habits, in participation in civic and cultural activities, and so on.

What, then, do the studies show? They show that the impact

of the liberal arts colleges on the values and intellectual habits of their students is negligible.[1] Regardless of curriculum, location, or reputation, the liberal arts college typically does not produce any profound changes in its student body.

Of course, some students do change their views and values. But to say that they change while attending college is not to say that they change *because* they are attending college. In short, the changes are not more numerous or more fundamental than we would expect if the students had not attended a liberal arts college at all. In the words of the Jacob study:

> This study has not discerned significant changes in student values which can be attributed directly either to the character of the curriculum or to the basic courses in social science which students take as part of their general education.
>
> For the most part, the values and outlook of students do not vary greatly whether they have pursued a conventional liberal arts program, an integrated general education curriculum or one of the strictly professional-vocational options. The more liberally educated student may take a somewhat more active interest in community responsibilities, and keep better informed about public affairs. But the distinction is not striking and by no means does it occur consistently among students at all colleges. It does *not* justify the conclusion that a student acquires a greater maturity of judgment on issues of social policy or a more sensitive regard for the humane values because he had a larger dose of liberal or general education.
>
> Even fundamental revisions of the formal content of the curriculum designed to confront students more forcefully with problems of personal and social conduct and to involve them in a searching examination of value issues rarely appear to have brought about a marked difference in students' beliefs and judgments, let alone their actual patterns of conduct. Nor is there solid evidence of a delayed reaction or "sleeper effect." The alumnus of several years exhibits no unusual trademarks identifying the character of his undergraduate curriculum.[2]

The conclusions of the Jacob study, as well as of practically every other major study which has tried to assess the impact of

[1] The most recent summary of the evidence is to be found in Philip E. Jacob, *Changing Values in College* (New York: Harper & Bros., 1957). I have confined my quotations on the impact of the liberal arts college to this book because it takes into account, and is consistent with, previous studies on the subject.

[2] *Ibid.*, pp. 5–6.

the liberal arts college, are not new. They have never been a surprise to persons who believe that the educational claims of liberal arts colleges ought to be evaluated just as rigorously as the educational claims made for the public schools. However, most people find it difficult to believe that an educational institution to which so much obeisance is paid can in fact be so ineffective. Rigorous evaluation of its own effectiveness ought to be an integral part of the operation of every liberal arts college. In practice, however, it is much more convenient to take its effectiveness, and hence its mode of operation, for granted.

This unwillingness to face the facts is most clearly reflected in the claims which are made for the liberal arts college by its professional supporters. Many a college president has cited a host of alumni prominent in business and the professions as proof of the virtues of a liberal education (at his institution, of course). This evaluative technique has even been reduced to an exact science by taking the number of alumni listed in *Who's Who* as the criterion of institutional excellence.

It is no accident that the above technique is embraced most enthusiastically by certain Ivy League colleges. The competition to be admitted to these colleges is based upon prestige considerations which have nothing to do with their alleged educational superiority; it is essentially like the competition to be pledged to a powerful fraternity. The very fact of being pledged is a strong indication that owing to the wealth, power, and prestige of the pledger's family, his chances in life are far above the average. And just as it is not fraternity life that enables him to "succeed" later on, so it is not his attendance at a prestigeful liberal arts college that does it either. His later "success" is due primarily to the factors that enabled him to attend such a college and pledge such a fraternity in the first place. A college which caters to students from rich and powerful and prestigeful families should be able to cite more than rich and powerful and prestigeful alumni as proof of its educational effectiveness.

Interestingly enough, the same kind of fallacious argument is often used to "prove" the value of public education. The fact that the average high-school graduate earns more than the average non-graduate is often cited to demonstrate the value of a high-school education. The possibility that the same factors which enabled certain students to complete high school would, independently of their attendance, enable them to achieve a higher than average level of income is quietly ignored. The higher average income of high-school graduates vis-à-vis non-graduates is undoubtedly due at least in part to several factors other than what they learned in high school, such as their higher average intelligence, the higher average socioeconomic status of their families, and so on. The existence of a high correlation between graduation from high school and later success does not establish a cause-and-effect relationship.

Even if such a relationship were established, we would have to evaluate it carefully. If large corporations employ only college graduates for the positions which lead to the top, the college graduates are bound to show up better than the non-graduates regardless of the ability of the non-college group. If a sizable number of large corporations prefer graduates from certain colleges, such as the Ivy League colleges, then the graduates of the preferred colleges are likely to be economically more successful than graduates of the same ability from non-preferred colleges.

It is true that the firms involved believe that they will get superior personnel in this way. However, even if such a result were established, it would not necessarily prove the *educational* superiority of the preferred colleges. It might prove only that a higher percentage of superior students enrolled in certain colleges for reasons that had nothing to do with the educational program of these colleges. The corporations might well be justified in their recruitment procedures while erroneously attributing the superiority of their personnel to the educational programs of the preferred colleges. Essentially, it is the old story of faith in a fact creating the fact. If employers believe attendance at a particular college is valuable, and therefore require it, then such attendance does become valuable even if the educational program of that particular college is in fact no better, even if it is worse, than the educational program of other institutions.

Obviously, the technique of citing a long list of successful alumni is not equally useful to every liberal arts college. This fact may help to explain why the last-ditch defense of so many liberal arts colleges often lies in an appeal to ethereal considerations. The values of the liberal arts college are said to be not subject to measurement, or to objective analysis of any kind. "We develop moral and spiritual values," the argument runs. "Even though these goals are not subject to measurement, they are the most important part of man's cultural and spiritual heritage."

The trouble with this point of view is that it makes evaluation completely impossible. Whatever the liberal arts college is supposed to accomplish must eventually be observable in somebody's behavior. If there is no observable behavior which can fairly be attributed to the college program, there is no basis for assuming that the college is liberalizing its student body. The same intangibility which is cited to defend the liberal arts college also demolishes its claim to be achieving anything.

Indeed, how could a professor know whether he was successful as a teacher except through what his students write, say, and do? It is absurd to have a student take thirty to forty courses, in each of which he is presumably evaluated according to some observable standard of judgment, and then contend that the objectives of the college program as a whole are so intangible that student behavior affords no clue to the success or failure of the college. And it must be pointed out that the burden of proof here is on the liberal arts college. It accepts the student, encourages him to spend four years of his life under its tutelage —and for what? Certainly not for objectives which are so intangible that nobody can ever know whether or not they have been accomplished.

It is always an interesting experience to challenge liberal arts graduates on the values of the education they have received. I have done this in graduate courses many times and the patterns of response are fairly predictable. Invariably the students assert that the average college graduate makes more than the average non-graduate. Of course, this assertion is true, but as previously pointed out, one cannot infer from it any educational superiority of the liberal arts colleges. But aside from this, it is interesting that graduates should fall back so quickly upon an economic justification for the kind of education they have received.

When pressed for new ideas they have acquired in college, the students rarely respond with a substantive answer. They "know" they have broadened their outlook, met so many different kinds of people, and learned to adjust—but practically never can you get them to set out in clear analytical language an idea they have acquired. Indeed, it can be a shattering experience to listen to these graduates evaluate their college experience. Girls whose only interest in a grade was its role in sorority life tell you in earnest tones that they have learned so much just from the different people they have met in college. These same girls live their entire college careers in sorority houses from which girls of unlike religion, race, socioeconomic status, or social values are rigorously excluded. Listening to their defense of college life, one would never realize that intellectual and social conformity are predominant characteristics of the liberal arts college—that is, if one could ignore their comments on social problems or intellectual issues.

There comes a time when the students finally grasp the question which has been put to them. They realize that they are being asked a very simple thing—what new insights do they have which can reasonably be attributed to their liberal arts program? As a rule, there are none, but the students stubbornly refuse to accept this conclusion, even when they are unable to offer proof to the contrary. "Do you mean to say," they ask, "that we have wasted all the time we were in college?"

Of course, they have not wasted it. They have landed the husband or secured the necessary polish or degree without which they cannot get a good job. But, intellectually speaking, the liberal arts college has failed to do a job. As Jacob puts it in discussing the impact of a college education upon student values:

Changes are rarely drastic or sudden, and they tend to emerge on the periphery of the student's character, affecting his application of values rather than the core of values themselves.

To call this process a *liberalization* of student values is a misnomer.

The impact of the college experience is rather to *socialize* the individual, to refine, polish, or "shape up" his values so that he can fit comfortably into the ranks of American college alumni.[3]

The situation with respect to the liberal arts college reminds me of student reaction to a well-known philosophy professor in a midwestern university. This professor was an avowed atheist who made it a point to tell his classes that he had an affirmative belief in the non-existence of God. Nevertheless, he was unable to get students to believe that he was really an atheist. The students would merely nudge each other, secure in the belief that the old boy was just spouting atheism to stir up some class discussion. The students "knew" that underneath it all, he believed in God like everybody else. Similarly, if you tell students that there is no strong evidence to indicate that the liberal arts college is liberalizing, their reaction is that you are just saying this to stir up some class discussion. The students may not have any evidence to contradict the assertion, but they retain a sublime faith that such evidence exists.

The ineffectiveness of our liberal arts colleges is too pervasive to be solved by tinkering with their course structures. From college to college or even within the same college, students take a wide variety of courses in virtually every conceivable sequence. The results are consistently unimpressive. In its insistence that even fundamental revisions of the liberal arts curriculum have no discernible impact upon the values and intellectual habits of students, the Jacob study only echoed the results of other major studies devoted to this problem.

THE IMPACT OF LIBERAL ARTS
COLLEGES ON PUBLIC EDUCATION

There is a tendency in some quarters to regard the public schools as a deleterious influence upon the liberal arts colleges. The colleges are supposedly fortresses of high academic standards and intellectual training which are being overwhelmed

[3] *Ibid.*, p. 4. It would seem that the large number of professors in liberal arts colleges who are worked up to a fever pitch over an alleged emphasis upon social adjustment in the high schools have plenty of homework to do.

by the illiterate, undisciplined graduates of the public schools. If you think of education at one level primarily as the foundation of education at a higher level, it seems logical to regard any weakness in elementary or secondary education as a cause of the same weakness at the college level. But this way of looking at the matter often overlooks the reverse, the impact of higher education upon elementary and secondary education.

Actually, there is a reciprocal influence between all levels of education. That is, what is done at each level has some influence on what is done at the others. The tendency to regard each level as preparatory for the next is valid in certain contexts and for certain purposes, but we must not overlook the influence of the higher levels of education upon the lower ones. The graduate and professional schools have had a tremendous impact upon the undergraduate colleges; the undergraduate colleges have always been greatly influential in shaping the policies of the high schools; and so on. With the exception of professors in the graduate schools, the teachers at one level of education almost always receive at least some of their training at higher levels of education. Equally important, the examples provided by higher education in terms of such things as academic standards and professional sanctions have had a lasting influence on these things in elementary and secondary education.

It is with these thoughts in mind that I suggest a long and hard look at the impact of higher education, especially of the liberal arts colleges, upon elementary and secondary education. The interrelationships between the various levels of education make it unlikely that major weaknesses in any one of them do not have some roots and causes in others. This is particularly true of public education; my conviction is that every major weakness of public education has its roots in higher education, and especially in the liberal arts colleges. For example, overemphasis upon athletics, social graces, and "adjustment," the favorite whipping boys of our contemporary custodians of culture, are strictly hand-me-downs from the liberal arts colleges.

We may take the development of football as a case in point. Intercollegiate football made its first appearance in November,

1869. The first game was between Princeton and Rutgers. The emphasis accorded football by our leading liberal arts colleges is suggested by the rosters of the first All-American teams: it was not until 1894 that the most authoritative All-American team, the one selected by Walter Camp, included anyone not from Yale, Princeton, or Harvard. In that year, one player from the University of Pennsylvania was chosen by Camp for his annual All-American team. The building of stadiums instead of classrooms, the recruitment and glorification of athletes instead of scholars, the marching bands and the cheerleaders, the practice of recalling the alumni on a day set aside for athletics instead of for intellectual achievement and stimulation—these things originated and flourished in liberal arts colleges long before they became a part of the high-school scene.

Likewise, the current outcry against education for "life adjustment" comes with poor grace from the liberal arts colleges. While their presidents are extolling the intellectual life upon their campuses, their admissions officers may often be found looking for "good all-around students" instead of "just bookworms." More than one "A" student from Brooklyn has been denied admission to an institution which allegedly emphasizes the intellectual life on the grounds that he "would not adjust satisfactorily" to life at a particular college. Others have been turned down because of the college's alleged need for a "better geographical distribution" for its student body.[4] And we might also note the fact that our undemocratic and anti-intellectual fraternities and sororities were established in liberal arts colleges. They flourished there and eventually became a disruptive and miseducational influence upon our public high schools.

I should not wish to condemn liberal arts colleges today for the mistakes that they made generations ago. Some colleges have

[4] "Professor Henry Steele Commager, of Columbia and Amherst, was discussing the problem of students anxious to get into the *best* colleges. He said that colleges prefer students who would give the school a geographic, social and scholastic balance. One dean of admissions told him: 'If we wanted to, we could have our entire student body composed exclusively of students who all have "A" averages, all from Westchester, and all studying to become doctors'" (from Leonard Lyons' column in the *New York Post*, August 19, 1958).

adopted various measures to eliminate or check the undesirable trends just mentioned. If a professor or an administrator in a liberal arts college criticizes public education, we should evaluate these criticisms according to the logic and evidence which support them, not according to the critic's institutional affiliation. The point is, however, that many of the reforms needed in public education will be delayed, or will not take place at all, unless and until these same reforms are made in liberal arts colleges. It is futile to expect high schools to stress intellectual achievement if the liberal arts colleges do not.[5]

Indeed, much of the pointing with alarm at public education by professors and administrators of liberal arts colleges constitutes sheer effrontery on their part; their own institutions are often directly responsible for the evils which these academicians find in the public schools. For instance, recently I read about a high-school basketball player who was besieged with offers from over a hundred colleges. The pressure upon him had become so great that he finally announced that his choice of college would be made at a press conference in a few weeks. Press conferences called by high-school athletes to announce their choice of college are rare, but intensive recruitment of these athletes by liberal arts colleges is not. And yet who ever heard of these colleges making a similar effort to enrol outstanding high-school scholars? Perhaps the public schools have ceased to stress intellectual achievement, but to whatever extent this criticism is valid, the liberal arts college bears the major responsibility. It has provided most of the education of the teachers. The educational policies governing most of the public school population are set by school board members who graduated from a liberal arts college. And by its own example and influence, the liberal arts college sets the standards and climate for the public schools.

[5] It is illuminating that the more education people have, the more likely they are to regard social adjustment as the most important function of education, and the less likely they are to regard mastery of school subjects as most important. Persons with some college education are five times as likely to regard social adjustment as the most important function of education as are people with only a grammar-school education. See *The Public Looks at Education* (Report No. 21 [Denver: National Opinion Research Center, 1944]), p. 15; and also Myron Lieberman, *Education as a Profession* (Englewood Cliffs, N.J.: Prentice-Hall, 1956), p. 31.

Regardless of the origins of non-academic activities in our educational institutions, it would be futile to try to eliminate all of them in either our colleges or our public schools. Furthermore, I question the wisdom of such a policy even if it could be put into effect. If intercollegiate athletics could be abolished overnight, our institutions of higher education would not thereby become beehives of intellectual activity. What is needed is not so much a de-emphasis upon non-academic activities but a new and effective emphasis upon the intellectual aspects of education.

This is not just a play on words. There is no need to abolish the activities and ceremonies which honor non-academic achievers. The task is to find ways of doing this for intellectual achievers as well. There is also a need for better ways of according prestige to intellectually outstanding teachers. Because athletic coaches in the public schools are in the public eye more than teachers, they are better known and have better chances of getting administrative positions. This is undesirable because it leads to a situation wherein the persons least qualified academically tend to get the key leadership positions. However, this problem will not be solved by the abolition or de-emphasis of interscholastic athletics. It will be solved when other teachers achieve positions of respect in their communities. If teachers were really intellectual leaders, if their opinions were important to the community at large, and if they had their own ways and means of becoming public figures, they would not feel any need to de-emphasize non-academic activities.

At the present time, the academic posture toward many non-academic activities is tinged by frustration and jealousy. Occasionally, a diffuse resentment against the higher financial rewards and greater public recognition accorded football coaches finds expression in a speech or article which receives wide publicity; there is no easier way to achieve a reputation as a crusading intellectual than to lead a "Down with football" movement on the campus.

One professor who achieved immediate if fleeting fame by this tactic explains his crusade in this way: "My only charges against football were that football was becoming symbolic of anti-intellectualism (a fact which nobody questioned during the entire hullabaloo), and that football has practically nothing to contribute to the purposes of a university." [6] Aside from the likelihood that much of what the professors themselves do "has nothing to do with the purposes of a university," the rationale for crusades of this type is dubious. Oxford and Cambridge were competing in rowing matches long before our own universities were participating in football, yet the excellence of these English institutions of higher education is rarely challenged. I have never seen it suggested that they must raise their intellectual level by abolishing rowing, which presumably has as little to do with the purposes of a university as does football.

Instead of baying in the manger, the professors should set high academic standards in their courses, departments, and institutions. They need only insist upon these things and they can blithely ignore what students do outside the classroom. Whether a student plays football, joins the glee club, or attends a beer party nightly should be of no concern to the professors, individually or collectively. On most campuses, non-academic activities do not replace the intellectual life; they flourish because there is no such thing as intellectual life on these campuses in the first place.

PUBLIC AND PRIVATE EDUCATION

As I have been using the phrase, "liberal arts college" denotes public as well as private institutions. However, one frequently hears glowing references to the educational virtues of the *private* liberal arts colleges. The phrase has a kind of double-barreled effect; liberal arts colleges are supposed to be more liberalizing than other kinds, and private colleges are supposed to be superior to public ones. For public relations reasons, the latter thought cannot always be expressed bluntly; it is something which the other fellow (especially if he is a donor or foundation executive) should infer without your having to spell it out for him. I would like to suggest that the educational superiority of private education per se is a myth. There are good

[6] Wade Thompson, "My Crusade against Football," *The Nation*, CLXXXVIII (April, 1959), 314.

private schools at every level of education, but there is no evidence for believing that private schools per se are better or are likely to be better than public schools.

Regardless of whether they are public or private institutions, most liberal arts colleges are unable to secure adequate financial support without sacrificing their intellectual integrity. I have been in state universities where "radicals" were expected to lie low so that they would not endanger the university budget. Faculty coffee breaks were often devoted to discussing whether a faculty member had the right to make public pronouncements that might jeopardize the budget—or, if he had the right, whether he ought to exercise it. Donors take the place of legislatures in privately supported liberal arts colleges, but the result is still professorial subservience to outside pressures.[7]

As in the case of the public schools, there is wide variation from one liberal arts college to another in the dogmas and prejudices which receive academic immunity. But the closer one analyzes the situation, the more apparent it becomes that public schools and liberal arts colleges suffer from the same maladies. The fallacious notion that "He who pays the piper must call the tune," which has done so much to weaken public education, is generally accepted in higher education; the professors may not believe that it is right but they obviously don't know what to do about it. As long as they have been unable to develop independent sources of power and financial support which would do away with their mendicant status, the inability of elementary and secondary teachers to do so should be no surprise.[8]

The fact is that all types of educational institutions have found

[7] For an excellent analysis and criticism of the view that private colleges are more free than public colleges from non-academic interference, see Harold W. Stoke, *The American College Presidency* (New York: Harper & Bros., 1959), chap. IV.

[8] "I believe that the educators of America are largely responsible for the present confusion in and about education. They have felt obligated in my day to seek for money, first, last, and all the time. They have always supposed, I think erroneously, that money could be obtained only for activities that harmonized with the interests and opinions of those who had it" (Robert M. Hutchins, *The University of Utopia* [Chicago: University of Chicago Press, 1953], pp. 83–84).

it necessary to make unprofessional accommodations to their sources of funds. This fact underlies a few comments I wish to make concerning private schools below the college level. They have cultivated the idea that there is something especially liberalizing about private education below the college level. This claim should be examined carefully.

At the elementary and secondary levels, there is undoubtedly a great deal of overlap in the quality of public and private schools. My judgment is, however, that the quality of private non-parochial elementary and secondary education is widely exaggerated. I do not say this on the basis of carefully controlled evaluations of private schools (which are badly needed, by the way) but on the basis of the fact that private schools are not ordinarily subject to the same degree of state supervision as is public education.

The majority of private schools are Catholic parochial schools. Where such schools flourish, it would often be political suicide to insist that they meet the same standards as public schools. An important illustration of this is the fact that although all the states require *public school* teachers to meet certain minimum standards for a teaching certificate, only ten states require *all* elementary teachers to meet these standards and only seven require *all* secondary-school teachers to meet them.[9]

Note that the private non-parochial schools are in a much different situation than are the parochial schools. Both kinds may enjoy freedom from public supervision, but the parochial schools are part of a larger system that provides its own safeguards. I do not believe that these safeguards are as effective as those prevailing in the public schools, but this is an impressionistic judgment which it is unnecessary to argue at this point. The important thing is that there is some centralized supervision of parochial schools which is not present in the case of private

[9] W. Earl Armstrong and T. M. Stinnett, *A Manual on Certification Requirements for School Personnel in the United States* (Washington, D.C.: National Education Association, 1957), p. 40. Seventeen states require private elementary-school teachers and twenty-one require private secondary-school teachers to have a state certificate if the private school desires to be accredited.

independent schools at the elementary and secondary levels.

It is true that the controls over public education exercised by the states (and extralegal professional associations) are not very rigorous. There is a vast amount of poor education going on in public schools that do conform to state requirements. Nevertheless, although these requirements vary from state to state, they ordinarily make it more difficult to operate schools that lack adequate staff, facilities, equipment, supplies, sound instructional programs, and other things essential to a good education. The state controls do not generate a high level of education, but they put a floor (with many holes in it, to be sure) under public education.

Let me cite a recent experience to demonstrate what can happen in the absence of state supervision of private schools. In a university where I worked, a man 58 years of age applied for admission to our teacher-education program. This man was a retired postal employee who had attended college on a part-time basis prior to his retirement. He had recently been awarded a bachelor's degree in mathematics with honors, and he wanted to teach this subject in high school. In view of this man's outstanding intellectual achievements and his obvious strength of character and personality, he was encouraged to go into teaching despite the fear that he might have a difficult time getting a teaching position because of his age. This turned out to be the case; the man could not get a position in the public schools. As a result, he finally accepted a job in a private boarding school in a nearby state.

A few months later, he came to me, asking whether it would be ethical for him to resign in the middle of the year. He cited the following conditions in the school as the reasons why he wished to sever his connection with it as soon as possible:

1. Teachers taught academic subjects for which they had no preparation whatsoever.

2. Although the school claimed to have an outstanding guidance program staffed by trained personnel, it actually had no such program and no trained personnel in this area. This was especially shocking because the school enrolled an unusually

high percentage of problem children—those who were emotionally disturbed and those who were just dumped there by their parents.

3. There was practically complete staff turnover every year, not only because of the low salaries and unpleasant conditions, but because the school administration was apparently not anxious to have anyone learn too much about its operations.

4. Teachers often were forced to teach more than one subject at a time in the same room, skipping back and forth between two groups of pupils.

5. Students were charged outrageous prices for personal and educational services, some of which were nonexistent.

6. Parents were assured that the graduates of the school would get into college. The headmaster always encouraged the staff to give high grades to fool parents and admissions officers; he even changed grades submitted by instructors to achieve this goal. The students who got into a reputable college quickly flunked out; others were enrolled in colleges which apparently existed to meet the needs of private schools such as this one.

7. Students were abused mentally and physically; "tortured" would not be too strong a word to describe some of the things that were done.

What happened after this teacher told me about his situation is instructive. I called the state education department where the school was located to inquire about the extent to which there was state supervision of private schools.[10] In answer to my query, I was told that the state education department was helpless; the only state regulations pertaining to private schools were the following:

1. They must keep Standard School Registers if children from seven to fifteen years of age inclusive are in attendance, and also make an annual report to the State Department of Education.

2. They must be providing the required courses of instruction in citizenship and must file a copy of such courses annually with the secretary of the state Board of Education.

[10] When I set forth the conditions without naming the school, the official to whom I was talking assumed that I meant another school in the state!

3. Secondary schools which accept pupils whose tuition is paid out of public funds must be approved for that purpose specifically.

4. The medium of instruction and administration in all public and private elementary schools shall be the English language and not more than one hour in any school day may be given to instruction in any one language other than English.

5. Their buildings must conform to state laws governing safety and sanitation.

It does not take much thought to realize that these requirements provide virtually no protection for children in private schools. The requirement that not more than one hour a day be devoted to a foreign language is absurd, but it applies to public school pupils also. The value of these regulations is suggested by the following: Although a course in "the duties and responsibilities of U.S. citizenship" is required under regulation 2, there is absolutely no requirement relating to the preparation of the teacher giving such a course. No matter how inadequate such a teacher might be, there was no legal basis for state intervention to protect the pupils.

I cite this example for a reason. Wherever there are no educational standards enforced by an agency that has the power to apply powerful sanctions, some institutions will go to virtually any lengths to stay in business. This applies to every level of education, but it is more difficult to swindle the public and the students in higher education. At the elementary and secondary levels, the students are not able to protect themselves; if there are no others to do it for them, we can expect the worst. To this extent, I would modify my earlier statements to the effect that public and private educational institutions reveal the same weaknesses. In a sense, they do, but we must also recognize what is likely to happen as a result of the sweeping absence of safeguards in private education.[11]

---

[11] I have selected an extreme example which may be very unfair to the vast majority of private schools. However, shortly after writing this chapter, my attention was called to two recent publications dealing with elite private schools, the top fifteen in the country. These schools (and many others, I am sure) are far superior in every way to the private school I have just

LIBERAL EDUCATION AND THE STUDY OF
EDUCATION

Education is the major activity of one-fourth of our population. For this reason alone, the curriculum of the liberal arts college might be expected to clarify important educational problems. Who ought to be given what kind of an education? Who is receiving an education? How is and how ought education to be financed? What are the proper limits of professional decision in the educational system? What are, and what ought to be, the scope of community and parental decision in our schools? Surely a rigorous study of such educational problems ought to be as conducive to a liberal education as the study of our political or economic systems, not to mention the trivia which are part of the curriculum of most liberal arts colleges.

Reasonable as this idea might seem to the non-academic mind, it is not obvious to most professors. In our liberal arts colleges, the professors continue to croak "vocationalism" at the idea of education courses even for teachers, and to act as if a course is liberalizing only to the extent that it has nothing directly to do with man's work or his immediate problems. The schools of education have compounded the confusion by their insistence that every education course is "professional." Since all education courses are "professional," none is presumably a proper part of liberal education.

The entire controversy over education courses is a remarkable illustration of the capacity of college professors to confuse words with things and institutions with ideals. Instead of regarding

---

described. However, the publications indicate rather forcefully that even the best private boarding schools are overrated as educational institutions and that they should not be regarded as models for the public schools to emulate. See Vance Packard, *The Status Seekers* (New York: David McKay Co., 1959), chap. xvi; and E. Digby Baltzell, *Philadelphia Gentlemen* (Glencoe, Ill.: Free Press, 1958). I am also indebted to Mr. David Merrall, vice-president of one of the better private secondary schools in New York City, for the suggestion that the private schools in the National Council of Independent Schools are reasonably free from the characteristics of the worst private schools. I hope the suggestion is well taken, although at the present time I am not well enough informed either to indorse or to criticize it.

liberal education as an ideal and then evaluating courses according to their capacity to contribute to this ideal, professors have come to regard liberal education as something that can occur only in courses which are under the jurisdiction of the liberal arts college. There is no basis in theory or fact for this identification; it is purely gratuitous. Nevertheless, on most campuses it has the force of Holy Writ.

It is common today to read of the need for greater emphasis upon the liberal arts in teacher education. We are told over and over again that we require "a massive transfusion of the liberal arts." The people who talk this way generally hold to the position that our teachers are poorly educated, but they persistently ignore the fact that a large part of the training of most teachers consists of subjects in the liberal arts categories. Another fact often ignored is that our liberal arts colleges produce more high-school teachers than our teachers' colleges. If our high schools are as bad as the professional liberal arts college advocate would have us believe, one might begin to question whether a massive transfusion of the liberal arts is really the answer. Perhaps a massive exposé would be more appropriate.

The antagonism toward the study of education even for teachers, let alone as an essential part of a liberal education, has implications for the layman's attitude toward education as well as for teacher education. Offhand, it might be supposed that it is chiefly the less educated citizenry which is responsible for violations of academic freedom. In practice, the possession of a B.A. degree seems to give people a strong feeling that they ought to tell teachers what and how to teach. If anyone doubts this, he need only peruse the educational backgrounds of school boards which engage in the crudest interference with the professional autonomy of teachers.

And, after all, why should they not interfere? They have been told over and over again by the country's leading champions of the liberal arts that teaching is not a profession, that it requires very little specialized preparation. Indeed, according to a former president of the University of Chicago, "All there is to teaching can be learned through a good education and being a teacher." In context, Hutchins clearly meant that all the education a person needs to be a teacher is the same general education that everyone ought to have, that no professional training of any kind is required for teaching.[12] If this is the case, it is difficult to understand why the public should not rightfully interfere with the content and methods of teaching, since they would know as much about these things as the teachers.

Paradoxically, Hutchins has acquired a reputation as a staunch defender of academic freedom. In fact, his statements on this subject are among the best that have been made:

> Academic freedom is simply a way of saying that we get the best results in education and research if we leave their management to *people who know something about them.* Attempts on the part of the public to regulate the methods and content of education and to determine the objects of research are encroachments on academic freedom. . . . The democratic view that the state may determine the amount of money to be spent on education and may regulate education and educators by law has nothing to do with the wholly undemocratic notion that citizens may tell educators how to conduct education and still less with the fantastic position that they may tell them how to live, vote, think and speak.[13]

Of course, this rationale for academic freedom is completely inconsistent with the notion that teaching requires no special training whatsoever. It hardly makes sense to urge that we leave education and research to people "who know something" about these things and, at the same time, to argue that a good general education suffices to be a teacher. Thus while the schools of education contend that teachers are professionals and then advocate lay-professional relationships that are the essence of antiprofessionalism, an influential segment of our liberal arts

[12] Robert Maynard Hutchins, *The Higher Learning in America* (New Haven: Yale University Press, 1936), p. 56. In a recent discussion Dr. Hutchins asserted that my interpretation of what he had written was not correct. I am happy to know that he no longer holds to the view I have ascribed to him, but I invite anyone to check the source to see whether I have quoted him correctly and with due regard for the context. And after all, it is his published views, not those he holds privately, that have had the most influence on American education.

[13] *Ibid.,* p. 21. Italics added.

faculties insists that teachers are not professionals, and yet that they ought to have professional autonomy!

The refusal of liberal arts colleges to regard the study of education as a liberal study is partly responsible for some of the strange views of public education that seem to be endemic in these circles. I have read statements, made in utter seriousness, that the shortage of mathematics and science teachers in our high schools is due to the fact that potential teachers of these subjects balk at having to take a flock of methods courses for a teaching certificate. One even hears this in liberal arts colleges which do not require a single education course of their own mathematics and science instructors but which are experiencing serious difficulty themselves in recruiting instructors in these areas.

The irony of the situation is that the hostility toward the study of education in liberal arts colleges is simply a case of academic man cutting off his own nose to spite his professorial face.[14] In the past fifty years, the professors in liberal arts colleges have suffered a sharp social and economic decline. The prospects are that their situation will deteriorate even further. Yet of all occupational groups, the professors have the best opportunities to study their occupational problems and to build a deep and lasting case for public understanding and support. Instead of utilizing this opportunity, they have rejected it out of hand.

If educational problems are not sufficiently important to be included in the liberal arts curriculum, if they are not worthy of serious research by at least some of the professors in liberal arts colleges, it should come as no surprise that the graduates of these colleges are not particularly interested in the problems of the colleges. Granted, another course is not the solution to

[14] The governing body of the American Association of University Professors is its Council. Members of the Council are elected from ten geographical regions of the country. Two persons are nominated and one is elected from each region. A professor long active in the AAUP and one in whose integrity I have the utmost confidence told me that in order to get a Negro elected to the Council, it was decided to run him against a professor of education. I later wrote to the national office of the Association and discovered that the first Negro elected to the Council had in fact been elected over a professor of education—and had also failed to attend any Council meetings!

every problem. Still, who but themselves do professors in liberal arts colleges have to blame for public indifference to fundamental educational problems?

THE FUTURE OF LIBERAL EDUCATION

The liberal arts college is supposed to develop a common intellectual framework and a lifelong commitment to intelligent modes of behavior. For a long time, the curriculum set forth to achieve these goals was dominated by the study of ancient languages, literature, and history. By common consent, these studies precede specialized education for professional or managerial careers. In recent years, professional training has increased in duration, creating strong pressures to keep the period of preprofessional training to a minimum. Although preprofessional training is supposed to be devoted to liberal education, it actually shows a growing emphasis upon subjects related to professional work. Despite all the warnings that we must not neglect the humanities, they are declining in importance, even in the liberal arts college itself.

These movements are still in their early stages, but they have thoroughly frightened the professors in the humanities. Many of them are clutching at straws to bolster their position. Science, they say, can give us knowledge only of means. It can be used to destroy men as well as to enrich them. Men must know the purposes and the values of life or their scientific studies will be used destructively. The humanities are the subjects which tell us the purposes and values of life, hence they should be the heart of the liberal arts curriculum.

This philosophical bunk is regarded as a profound truth by many professors of every subject threatened by the increasing emphasis upon science and mathematics in the liberal arts curriculum. At the same time, however, intelligent people in all walks of life are finding it increasingly difficult to take seriously the claim that professors in the humanities know more than anyone else about the purposes and values of existence. Of course, the idea that a certain group has special insight into these things is not new. Plato's concept of the philosopher-king was based on it. However, philosophers have learned a great deal since (as well as from) Plato, including the futility of the claim that philosophers or any other academic group are experts on the purposes and values of life. Philosophy itself, by the way, is one of the more productive disciplines erroneously classified in the humanities; it is amusing to hear these pretentious "philosophical" defenses of the humanities that would be rejected out of hand by professional philosophers.

The need to develop well-rounded individuals, whole men instead of narrow specialists, is another lead-weighted life preserver for most of the humanities. To produce well-rounded individuals, you must have a well-rounded curriculum—that is, one scattered over as many fields as possible. Thus we get the game of academic musical chairs whereby every department is given a required course or two. The more departments that get into the act, the more whole and well rounded the student.

When elementary teachers talked about "teaching the whole child," this was an occasion for uproarious laughter in the higher echelons of liberal education. Although the idea was never clearly defined, it was based upon sound educational considerations, such as the need to utilize the emotional, aesthetic, and physical as well as the intellectual components of learning. It was never based upon any need to keep the academic peace or save a few subjects from extinction. Nevertheless, it was and is ridiculed by the same professors who think "the whole man" is the answer to the world's most pressing problems. Upon closer inspection, "the whole man" turns out to be the college student who has been exposed to a smorgasbord academic program. Quite often, the smorgasbord program includes a number of smorgasbord survey courses which emphasize "the broad view."

What the future holds for liberal arts colleges is difficult to say. Even if they should retain their present form, their curriculum is likely to be increasingly dominated by the professional schools. How long they can go on without drastic change is problematical. It is questionable whether the liberal arts college can continue to maintain the fiction that subjects like speech, English, and history are genuine disciplines, and that those who teach these subjects are members of the same profession as those who teach physics, chemistry, mathematics, philosophy, or economics. The liberal arts college, even more than the high school, is composed of disparate elements that bear no inherent intellectual or organizational relationship to one another.

Historically, the public schools have followed rather than led the colleges. Nevertheless, we may see a change in the historical pattern. Many educational reforms may come first in the public schools and then trickle upward to the liberal arts college. This is especially likely in the area of employer-employee relationships; the American Association of University Professors lags hopelessly behind those organizations of public school teachers that are beginning to pay serious attention to collective bargaining and teacher control over entry.

Instead of trying to assess the future of the liberal arts college, perhaps we should concentrate upon something infinitely more important, the future of liberal education. Liberal education is too important to be abandoned because our present ways of implementing it are not effective. Perhaps it is time to abandon, or at least scrutinize, the idea that liberal education belongs primarily to late adolescence. We might then try to create an educational structure that will articulate our educational resources with the major problems confronting our society. A liberally educated person is one whose education is continuous, but I question whether continuous education can be achieved by a few years of college which are supposed to be an educational generator for the rest of the student's life. The liberal arts college simply does not provide its graduates with enough momentum to overcome their lack of any organic relationship to our educational resources.

It is a mistake to think that liberal education can disregard concrete circumstances of time, place, people, and events. Whether or not education is liberal in effect depends as much upon these factors as it does upon the content which one seeks to teach. To be specific, if the American people are confronted by grave issues of foreign policy, how can we synchronize their understanding of the issues with their hour of decision upon them?

This basic educational problem will not be solved by the course-jugglers in the liberal arts colleges. More evening courses will not solve it either. Basically, the problem is how to make our occupational organizations, our service clubs, our political parties, and our religious and cultural organizations more effective educational agencies. Thus far, we have not found the structural keys to liberal education. We are, in fact, just beginning to look for them seriously. Pathetic ventures such as the Great Books program must be seen in context as a primitive effort to develop continuous liberal education. If failures such as this do not discredit the ideal of universal and continuous liberal education, we will eventually discover the ways and means to implement the ideal effectively. But the first and most important step is to grasp the fact that our present institutional means, to wit, the liberal arts college, is not getting the job done.

Chapter VIII

EMPLOYER-EMPLOYEE RELATIONSHIPS

IN A PUBLIC PROFESSION

The twentieth century has been a period of fundamental changes in employer-employee relationships. For the most part, these changes have been confined to private employment and are just now beginning to be reflected in public employment. However, their widespread introduction into public employment, including public education, is a practical certainty.

Before analyzing these changes, I wish to discuss briefly two attitudes that have obstructed clear thinking on employer-employee relationships in education in the past. First, there is the attitude that any policy associated with unions is inappropriate for a professional association. The second is that any policy which is helpful to a privately employed occupational group is inappropriate for a publicly employed one. These two attitudes must be completely dispelled if we are to understand the future of the teacher as an employee.

There are differences between unions and professional associations. There are also similarities between them. Unfortunately, people are often confused on the points of similarity and dissimilarity. The important thing is that in evaluating the appropriateness of a policy for public education, we not be misled by superficial similarities or dissimilarities between unions and professional associations.

To illustrate, suppose we are considering whether a certain practice which has worked successfully for unions should be adopted by teachers. It is a *non sequitur* to think that a "union practice" cannot be successful because "teaching is a profession." Our interest should be in the conditions that led to the success of this practice and whether these conditions prevail in education. We must always be interested in *relevant* conditions. To adopt a policy in public education merely because it has proved successful in other occupations would be equally foolish unless the conditions justifying the policy in the other occupations also prevail in education.

The logic of this point applies to policies followed in the professions as well. A policy which has proved successful in other professions would be good for education only if the conditions which led to its success elsewhere also prevail in education. By the same token, policies which were not successful in other professions may be successful in education if the conditions causing failure elsewhere are not present in education.

Let me restate the point in a different way. Education is a unique occupation. So is medicine, flagpole sitting, and every other occupation. But even unique occupations may have important similarities with others. We should never, therefore, assume that the experience of any other occupation is inappropriate for education merely because "education is unique." Neither should education blindly follow the experience of other occupational groups merely because there are general similarities among them.

To illustrate this point, let me quote from a recent publication of a teachers' association in New York City:

> During October, we were asked to attend a hearing . . . regarding the institution of a union dues check-off system for teachers. This was opposed by the BTA on the grounds that teachers consider themselves professional people who are opposed to any deductions from their salary checks, and who wish to pay their dues to any organization personally and at times and in the manner determined by themselves alone. Our opposition to the plan was duly noted at the hearing.[1]

[1] *The Brooklyn Teacher,* February, 1958, p. 2.

This illustrates how a false professionalism can mislead teachers. In the first place, public employees must always give their consent for any direct deduction of dues from their salary checks. For this reason, the reference to choosing personally the time and place to pay dues misses the point—why not choose the time and place indicated by the check-off? Since acceptance of the check-off is always voluntary in public employment, it is foolish to contend that teachers would lose their freedom by paying their dues through a check-off. It would mean only that they would have chosen to exercise their freedom in this way.

The fact that the check-off is more common among unions than among professional associations has nothing whatsoever to do with professionalism. The reason that most professionals do not pay their dues by a check-off is not because of their opposition to this practice in principle. Most professionals are fee-takers; hence there is no feasible way to check-off their dues. For this very reason, most professional organizations devote a great deal of their resources to collecting dues, resources which could otherwise be devoted to promoting the interests of their members. Hence it is to the interest of the members, regardless of whether the organization is a "union" or a "professional association," to facilitate the collection of dues.

The snobbery toward unions revealed in the quotation is made even more ridiculous by the fact that some professional groups which are on salary do accept the check-off. Many non-union teachers' associations collect their dues in this way. As a matter of fact, the check-off will soon be almost as common in public employment as it is now in private employment. This change will help considerably to strengthen organizations of public employees, including teachers' organizations which are more concerned with organizational efficiency than with avoiding "union" practices.

Because of the attitudes just discussed, teachers are an extremely backward group in the area of employer-employee relations. I mean by this much more than the fact that teachers are not doing very well in terms of salaries and working conditions. I mean that their entire approach to employer-employee problems is outmoded. There will be no basic improvement in teachers' salaries and working conditions until the teachers themselves develop a new framework of employer-employee relations in education. This new framework must be accompanied by new concepts of the teacher as an employee, new attitudes toward the strategy and tactics of securing adequate conditions of employment, and new concepts of what are adequate conditions of employment.

One of the first objectives of teachers should be to end legislative determination of their conditions of employment. The teachers must realize that state-wide minimum salary laws, or state-wide tenure laws, perhaps the two dearest legislative objectives of every state teachers' association, are anachronisms. Teachers should not spend another cent toward securing these objectives by legislation.

To understand why this is so, let us examine the current strategy employed by teachers to improve their conditions of employment. This strategy is a simple one. The major effort is made at the state level. The state teachers' associations strive for legislation setting minimum levels of teacher welfare. Local school systems are free to exceed these minimums but not to go below them. For example, states may legislate minimum salaries for teachers; school districts are free to pay more than the state minimums but may not pay less.

This strategy can be extended to other aspects of employment. State legislation may require school districts to give tenure to teachers after a certain period of time, to require a fair hearing for teachers who are being discharged, to contribute to a retirement system, and so on. In each case, local teachers' associations are supposed to try to improve upon the state-wide minimums mandated by the legislatures. By and large, this is the strategy that has been employed by teachers during the past fifty years. Efforts to secure federal aid do not alter it in any essential way.

What is wrong with this strategy? First, consider the problem at the state level, using state minimum salary laws to illustrate the weakness of the entire procedure. When teachers do succeed in establishing state minimum salary laws, the minimums are rarely substantial when enacted. Substantial or not, the minimums quickly become irrelevant in an inflationary and expanding economy. Ours is an economy in which an occupational group must steadily increase its income merely to maintain its relative position vis-à-vis other occupational groups. As a practical matter, state legislatures are not able to make the continual adjustments in conditions of employment which are necessary to protect the position of public employees. This is one reason why conditions of public employment typically lag behind those in private employment.

State legislatures usually meet every year but they are not in session for long periods of time. In addition to setting minimum salaries for teachers, they are under constant pressure to set minimum salaries for many different kinds of state employees, many kinds of municipal and county employees, and many kinds of private employees in intrastate commerce. Time-consuming as this is, it is only part of the tremendous legislative jam that confronts every session of state legislatures. Legislation concerning roads, hospitals, higher education, welfare agencies, parks, conservation, and other areas must be considered during these sessions.

I have said that even the state minimum salary laws which are helpful when passed soon become irrelevant. The fact is that most of them are of little value when passed. Few communities can get good teachers at the minimums set by the states. In Iowa, which has had a minimum salary law since 1913, the legal minimum salary for a beginning teacher with a master's degree was $810 per year as of September, 1958. In North Dakota, which has had such legislation since 1905, the legal minimum for such a teacher was $1,350 per year. These states provide the most extreme examples, but there are many others.[2]

Why can the minimums not be raised every year or every few years in order that teachers may keep pace with other groups? A legislature cannot sit every year as a salary-setting agency for

[2] See NEA Research Division, "State Minimum-Salary Laws," *Research Bulletin,* XXXVII (February, 1959), 8–12.

hundreds of different kinds of employees. It is too busy. Any legislation that affects so many people in so many different ways as minimum salaries for teachers must undergo interminable hearings. From one year to the next, different legislators and different parties with different commitments are in power. Every change requires another round of hearings, subject to all the changing elements that pervade a state legislative body.

What has been said concerning minimum salary legislation obviously applies to other state legislation relating to teacher welfare. The legislation is always too little and too late. Even so, the state teachers' associations fall back exhausted once they have achieved it. By the time they have pulled themselves together for another assault upon the legislature, conditions have usually become so bad that school systems have to improve them, regardless of legislation, just to get a teacher in every classroom.

The futility of legislative determination of conditions of employment is recognized by the overwhelming majority of authorities in the field of public administration. Not all of them have specifically discussed the role of legislation in public education. Those who have are convinced that it is as outmoded a way of resolving employer-employee relationships in this field as it is in other areas of public employment.[3] Every criticism that applies generally to legislative determination of the conditions of employment applies with equal or greater force to public education. If the teachers cannot learn this much from their continuing failure to improve their economic position, they deserve a seat in the corner with a dunce cap on their heads.

Actually, emphasis upon state legislation has been an unwise strategy quite apart from the frustrations inherent in legislative determination of conditions of employment. As previously pointed out, state appropriations in many important areas are supplemented by federal appropriations.[4] This has not been true in the past in education. Thus the state dollar goes farther in other fields than it does in education. For this reason teachers

---

[3] See Morton Robert Godine, *The Labor Problem in the Public Service* (Cambridge, Mass.: Harvard University Press, 1951), and Sterling D. Spero, *Government as Employer* (New York: Remsen Press, 1948).

[4] See the discussion on pp. 49–50.

should give federal aid for teachers' salaries the very highest strategic priority. Such aid should be in large enough amounts to provide a strong incentive for state legislatures to appropriate funds for public education. This will not happen unless the federal government assumes a much bigger share of the costs of public education than is currently contemplated by Congress.[5]

COLLECTIVE BARGAINING
IN PUBLIC EDUCATION

What will replace the present framework for resolving the conditions of employment in education? The answer is collective bargaining. Predictions are risky and perhaps foolish, but I would guess that collective bargaining will be the established mode of resolving employer-employee problems in education in most of the states within a generation.

What is collective bargaining? In federal legislation, it is defined as:

. . . the performance of the mutual obligation of the employer and the representatives of the employees to meet at reasonable times and confer in good faith with respect to wages, hours, and other terms and conditions of employment, or the negotiation of any agreement, or any question arising thereunder, and the execution of a written contract incorporating any agreement reached if requested by either party, but such obligation does not compel either party to agree to a proposal or require the making of any concession.[6]

At the present time, school boards in most of the states are legally free to ignore the duly chosen representatives of the teachers if the boards so desire. Note that collective bargaining imposes an affirmative obligation on employers to recognize the representatives of the employees and to negotiate with them as such. In the absence of such a requirement, the employers are

[5] The National Defense Education Act, passed by Congress on August 23, 1958, does provide some incentives for the states to spend more on education, since it provides for matching federal funds for certain educational expenditures. However, teachers' salaries constitute about two-thirds of the total cost of public education, and this act did not provide any federal funds for such salaries, except for teachers who undertake certain kinds of advanced study.

[6] Labor Management Relations Act, 1947, sec. 8 (d).

really free to deal with each employee as an individual. Teachers must secure legislation that would *compel*, not merely *permit*, school boards to negotiate with their representatives.

For collective bargaining to take place, both sides must make proposals and counterproposals in good faith. However, they are not required to accept any specific proposal or make any specific concession. It might appear that one or the other side might continually make unreasonable proposals and thereby frustrate the collective bargaining process, but this is not really a difficult problem to resolve in practice. Whether parties are bargaining in good faith is a question of fact, and it is usually clear whether it exists or not.

The rationale for collective bargaining is that although neither side is required to accept a proposal or make a specific concession, it is likely that the parties will agree upon conditions of employment if they are required to bargain in good faith about them. In other words, it is based on the theory that if the parties are forced to adhere to certain procedural requirements, they will ordinarily agree on the issues that are the subject of negotiation. In education, this would mean that a school board would not be unlawfully delegating any of its discretionary powers concerning conditions of employment merely because it was compelled to bargain with teachers about them.

Collective bargaining will come first between local teachers' associations and local school boards. In its early stages, the boards will be permitted but not required to bargain with teachers. Then laws will be passed requiring local boards to recognize the representatives of the teachers and to bargain with them in good faith concerning conditions of employment. For reasons to be explained shortly, these laws will then be changed to provide for collective bargaining at the state level. At this stage, the legislatures will delegate to the state superintendent of public instruction the authority to negotiate conditions of employment with the representatives of state teachers' associations. These negotiations will be conducted annually or biennially as they are in industry. The agreements reached will be subject to legislative approval, but this will be a much simpler process than the attempt to have the legislatures enact into law all the provisions of such an agreement. The persons who negotiate for the state legislatures will have a good idea of their limits, just as the persons who negotiate for large companies have a good idea of what they can and cannot concede in negotiations.

It is likely that this procedure will eventually be put into practice at the national level. Representatives of the national teachers' organizations will meet with appropriate representatives of the federal government to negotiate conditions of employment. The agreements reached will be subject to congressional approval. These agreements will not attempt to state precisely the exact terms of employment for every public school teacher in the country. Some of the conditions of employment may be spelled out at the federal level, others may be left to collective bargaining at regional, state or local levels.

It should never be assumed that merely because bargaining takes place at the national level, the resulting agreement must provide for exactly the same conditions of employment in every part of the country. This point is also relevant to bargaining at the state level, which may well result in intrastate differences in conditions of employment. In industry-wide collective bargaining, differentials for people in different regions doing the same kind of work are not uncommon. There is no reason why this practice cannot be accepted in public employment when it is desirable to do so. Even now, administrators of federal projects coming under the same federal agency do not pay the same wages for the same work in every state. They are accorded the discretion to negotiate for certain kinds of employees at prevailing wages. Of course, federal educational administrators would not have a prevailing wage rate in private employment to use as a yardstick in negotiating with teachers. But the illustration does show that there could be flexibility in a federal system.

I am not contending that teachers of the same subjects and grade levels in different parts of the country ought to be paid differently, nor am I contending that they ought to be paid the same. I am merely pointing out that there is no inherent reason why teachers' salaries would have to be the same the country over if they were determined by collective bargaining at the national level.

Collective bargaining can be introduced into public education in so many different ways and with so many different qualifications that it may be foolhardy to predict its lines of development. Nevertheless, I should like to explain why bargaining will be carried on at successively higher levels of government, until there is collective bargaining by teachers at the national level.

At the present time, teachers are an extremely weak occupational group. They have no control over entry to teaching at the state level and are unable to bargain collectively at the local level. They are also handicapped by the fact that there is only one employer for teachers in most communities. Whenever there is only one employer for a particular service, the absence of any competition gives the employer an enormous advantage in setting the conditions of employment. In most occupations, a person can change employers without having to move to another community. Obviously, the fact that teachers cannot do so weakens their position. Then too, the presence of large numbers of women who are ready to leave their housewifely tasks and become teachers at any time tends to keep teachers quiescent.

Nevertheless, there are other factors favorable to teachers which they have never used properly. Within a given community, the school board is the only employer, but on a state level, there are hundreds of employers and only one state teachers' association. Thus, at the state level, the power situation is reversed, or could be. Where there is a multitude of employers and only one employee organization, the latter usually has an excellent opportunity to force any one employer to be reasonably accommodating. For this reason, teachers will have an unparalleled opportunity to gain the balance of power vis-à-vis local school boards when collective bargaining is introduced at the local level.

Let us suppose that a state legislature has authorized collective bargaining in local school systems. The state teachers' association might then set a minimum salary which would be binding upon all of its local associations; none could agree to work for less. If a community refused to pay its teachers this minimum, it would have a real fight on its hands. The state association could establish a defense fund to support teachers in the community affected. All institutions of higher education and teacher-employment agencies would be alerted not to refer any applicants to the system until the dispute was settled. Since acceptance of employment in the system during the duration of the dispute would be unethical, new teachers would not be likely to wish to step into the breach. Under these circumstances, the community would soon find the money if it did not already have it.

Collective bargaining will be much more effective in improving the conditions of employment in education if it is accompanied by teacher control over entry. Such control is necessary to prevent public authorities from winning every dispute by licensing a horde of housewives and throwing them into the breach caused by a community's unwillingness to pay its teachers a decent salary. Actually, control over entry is the more important of these two strategic objectives if a choice must be made between them. The point is, however, that with able leadership, the balance of power would shift from local school boards to the state teachers' associations. Local communities would take care before challenging the power of an organized and determined state group.

To understand what will happen next, we may again turn with profit to industrial experience. When a union became so strong that it was able to impose its will upon individual employers, the employers combined so that they could not be coerced individually. And this, I think, will happen in education. Local communities which are no match for a powerful state teachers' association will inevitably come to favor a state-wide approach to conditions of employment. Inevitably, the approach will be state-wide not only in terms of the applicability of the agreement but in the source of funds to implement it. And the same process, in attenuated form, will add to the pressures for collective bargaining at the federal level, when a powerful national organization of teachers puts pressure upon individual states.

At the state level, if not at the local, collective bargaining in public education will become multiple bargaining. I mean by this that there will eventually be other groups represented at the bargaining sessions besides the teachers and the administrators who negotiate for the state government. There will be need for technical representatives to advise on the costs of various proposals. It may be feasible to have representatives of the legislature as observers during the bargaining sessions so as to provide informed leadership in that body when its approval is required. Precautions must be taken to prevent the teachers and administrators at the state level from entering into an agreement which is unfair to the taxpayers or to other groups which must be paid from public revenues. There are cases wherein employers and employees in a particular industry have made agreements which satisfy both sides at the expense of other groups in the economy. One reason for insisting upon legislative approval of basic agreements reached in collective bargaining in the public service is to prevent such an occurrence. Other precautions, requiring the systematic representation of several groups, will also be necessary.

These considerations also suggest a reason why collective bargaining in public education is bound to come, regardless of current attitudes toward it. In modern society, competition between individuals has been largely replaced by competition between groups. People who work in an occupation which has little group strength are bound to lose out in such a situation. For this reason, they will eventually turn to collective bargaining whatever their prejudices against it. Collective bargaining enables large occupational groups to advance their interests much more effectively than they could as individuals. This is as true in public as it is in private employment.

The weakness of individual negotiation where there are large numbers of persons doing the same work for the same employer has long been apparent. In recent years, however, there have been basic changes in the nature of the groups which bargain with each other. We can take the history of collective bargaining in the field of coal mining as an example. First, there was bargaining between individual miners and the owners of a particular mine; then between all the miners in a mine and the owners of that mine; then between all the miners in all the mines under one owner and that owner; and finally between all the miners in all the mines and a council of all the owners in the industry. We can see this pattern in one field after another. There is, therefore, a tendency for the most important economic decisions to be made at the national level, not only at the bargaining tables but in Congress, in the executive branch of the federal government, and in many other ways.

The upshot of this trend is to make the strength of the national organization the crucial factor in the determination of economic position. This is true even when the national organization is not a party to the actual negotiations between employers and employees. An occupational group which is not tightly organized, which does not exert any real power at the national level, will lose out in the struggle for economic position. To be specific, if teachers do not bargain as a group, it is extremely unlikely that they will improve their relative economic position regardless of how many sputniks the Russians send flying into space. Furthermore, if teachers continue to make their main effort at state and local levels while most other large groups make theirs at the national level, the economic position of teachers will continue to deteriorate. For even where the national organization is not a party to the direct negotiations between employers and employees, its influence, or lack of it, will be reflected in the ability of its state and local groups to gain their objectives. In self-defense, therefore, the teachers will have to organize and bargain at successively more inclusive levels, until they find themselves bargaining at the national level. But it will make a world of difference whether the teachers take this step as a last desperate resort or whether they have the foresight to take positive action now in this direction.[7]

TEACHER REPRESENTATION UNDER
COLLECTIVE BARGAINING

One of the most important problems which must be solved to make collective bargaining successful in public employment is the organizational basis of teacher representation. In industry the wisest policy has been to have the majority organization represent all the employees. Bargaining with two or more organizations is usually not a successful policy. Each of the competing organizations refuses to agree to anything to make sure that it does not settle for less than the other. Since the organizations are competing for members, their leaders tend to outpromise one another, thus building up impossible demands on the employers. Sometimes the employers play off one organization against another, thereby keeping them all weak. In other situations the employers often have no way of telling which of two or more competing organizations really represents employee sentiment.

On the other hand, a single organization which includes highly disparate levels and kinds of employees is almost certain to result in arbitrary treatment of some employees. For example, in New York City it would seem hardly feasible to have the same organization represent beginning teachers in the elementary schools and the high-school principals. The first-year teachers need only a bachelor's degree; they are paid $4,500 per year (in 1959). The high-school principals are experienced professional employees. All have at least a master's degree and many have doctoral degrees. They receive $15,600 per year after five years of satisfactory service.

What we have here is the old problem of craft versus industrial unionism, only this time in an educational instead of an in-

[7] The best brief treatment of many of the points raised in this section are set forth in John K. Galbraith's *American Capitalism: The Theory of Countervailing Power* (Boston: Houghton Mifflin Co., 1956). This book could be read with profit by all teachers.

dustrial context. Anyone who thinks this problem is of no concern to educators should consider the following news story:

> A bill which would make the High School Teachers' Association the sole bargaining agent for teachers in the senior high schools will be introduced in Albany shortly by Sen. Harry Gittleson and Assemblyman Lentol. The measure was drafted today by the law firm of Bennenson and Israelson, counsel for the HSTA.
>
> Under the proposed bill the State Labor Relations Board would have power to determine any controversy in connection with the representation of teachers in the senior high schools. The Board of Education would be called on to recognize, as the representative of the high school group for collective bargaining purposes, any organization which has the majority of these teachers as its members.
>
> The bill further calls on the school board to negotiate such matters as employment, working conditions and salaries with the selected organization, and provides for the employment by the board of an impartial arbitrator to settle any disputes that may arise.
>
> The measure provides that while the proposed plan is in effect, "no teacher subject to its provisions shall have the right to strike, whether or not such right is preserved by law or otherwise recognized for employees of the state or other employes of the city." [8]

Four days after the publication of this item, the following story appeared in a different New York City newspaper:

> Mayor Wagner is considering the issuance, in the next few weeks, of an executive order giving civil service unions many of the rights enjoyed by unions in private industry. The proposed order also would set up more systematic machinery for the adjustment of labor disputes in city departments. . . .
>
> The proposed order would guarantee the right of municipal workers to join unions of their own choosing and to bargain collectively through those unions. However, it would rule out any form of compulsory union membership for those who did not want to join.
>
> Unions designated by a majority of the workers in an appropriate bargaining unit would get exclusive bargaining rights. However, minority groups would retain the power to present to city officials the views and requests of their members. . . .

[8] *New York World-Telegram and Sun,* January 9, 1958, p. 29. Legislation requiring school boards to confer with representatives of the majority organization of teachers has already been passed in Minnesota and Wisconsin. However, these laws do not specifically require "collective bargaining" between teachers' organizations and school boards although they do require school boards to meet with the representatives of the teachers.

Under the projected city plan, a majority union would be informed of the minority views and would conduct all negotiations affecting those views. The minority groups would be barred from participating directly in the official machinery set up by the city for the adjustment of grievances.

The determination of the appropriate unit would rest with the Labor Commissioner. He would decide whether the unit should include a whole department, several departments or various classes of workers of subdivisions within a department. . . .

The yardstick would be the grouping best calculated to assure workers the fullest freedom of union selection consistent with the efficient operation of the public service. . . .

Labor disputes that could not be settled through direct talks between departmental heads and the unions representing their workers could be carried to [the Labor Commissioner's] office. The executive order would grant him flexibility in resolving the dispute. . . .

The program would apply initially to an estimated total of 110,000 workers in departments directly responsible to the Mayor.[9]

The solution to the problem of representation will probably be along the lines suggested by these news stories. Within the educational system as a whole, there will be established broad categories of employees: professional, administrative, custodial, semiprofessional, clerical, skilled labor, unskilled labor, and perhaps a few others. Each job in the schools will be included in one of these categories. Within each, there will be elections to determine the employee organization or organizations to bargain for that category. Collective bargaining cannot be carried on effectively if all employee groups, regardless of size, are accorded equal representation. It is possible that there will be exclusive recognition of the majority organization, as in private industry. However, at first, there is more likely to be a plan whereby organizations within each category are accorded representation according to their size. Such a plan would eliminate splinter representation while giving important minority interests an opportunity to gain recognition and expression.

Within the professional category, important differences between groups of teachers will be reflected in the bargaining

<hr>

[9] *New York Times,* January 13, 1958, pp. 1, 41. Executive Order 49 embodying these recommendations was issued by Mayor Wagner on March 31, 1958.

situation. For example, certain kinds of high-school teachers may choose one organization and elementary teachers may choose another. There may be a third organization which attempts to represent both groups. Eventually, there may be two or three major groupings by grade level or subject area.

Undoubtedly, it will take considerable experience to determine the appropriate units of organization. Since future developments may change the personnel structure of education at any time, it will always be necessary to avoid dogmatic adherence to a given form of representation. For example, the accepted point of view is to regard both elementary and secondary teachers as members of the same profession and the same employee group. However, as the first news item illustrates, many high-school teachers do not wish to be included in the same group as elementary teachers. They believe that high-school teaching should be paid more than elementary teaching. Since there are invariably more elementary than secondary teachers in comprehensive teachers' organizations, such organizations rarely favor a differential for high-school teachers.

Conflict between elementary and high-school teachers over a single salary schedule was primarily responsible for a resurgence of interest in the High School Teachers' Association in New York City in 1947. Until that time, the high-school teachers had enjoyed a higher salary schedule. When this differential was eliminated, the high-school teachers could not get the existing comprehensive organizations to work for its restoration. As a result, many of them split off in order to work within an organization composed entirely of high-school teachers.[10]

There is a way to protect any substantial minority of teachers within a comprehensive organization. The organization could, on its own initiative, provide for the representation of any group which would otherwise feel that its interests were being sacri-

---

[10] As things stand now, the teachers in New York City are fragmented into more than seventy organizations because they have not learned how to provide adequate protection for minority interests within the structure of a comprehensive teachers' organization. One would be hardpressed to find a more overorganized group, or one weaker for its size, than the 40,000 New York City teachers.

ficed in the mass. If the minority were assured of some representation at the bargaining table, it would not have to secede to protect its interests.

For instance, a comprehensive teachers' organization could provide that a certain number of its representatives be chosen by high-school teachers. A procedure similar to this was adopted by the United Automobile Workers when many skilled workers in the UAW became increasingly dissatisfied with their lot. These workers felt that too much emphasis was being placed on improving conditions for unskilled and semiskilled workers and that more emphasis was needed on maintaining the differentials between themselves and other types of workers. To meet their criticisms, the UAW adopted a constitutional amendment giving skilled workers the right to disapprove a proposed contract if it was not satisfactory to them.[11]

Thus, if certain interests are not adequately represented within an organization, they will seek such representation outside it. The ever present threat of independent outside representation will force comprehensive organizations to give some recognition to minority groups. This kind of problem clearly exists in education. All the syrupy speeches at teachers' meetings maintaining that everyone who works in the school is a member of one big happy family cannot sweep this fact under the rug.

TEACHERS AND SCHOOL ADMINISTRATORS IN A COLLECTIVE BARGAINING SITUATION

One of the important effects of collective bargaining in public education is likely to be a clarification of the relationships between teachers and school superintendents. Currently, it is customary for superintendents to belong to the local education associations which represent the teachers as employees. This has always placed superintendents in an awkward position. As the chief executive officer of the school board, a superintendent

[11] See "Contracts and Negotiations," *Constitution of the International Union, United Automobile Workers*, adopted at the April, 1957, Convention in Atlantic City, N.J., sec. 3, art. 19, pp. 51–52.

is clearly a managerial employee. Nevertheless, in most school systems he is also regarded as the spokesman for the teachers in a community. The result is that the superintendents are placed in a position where they are expected to represent both sides in matters pertaining to conditions of employment.

Some educators have contended this is as it should be. The superintendent supposedly rises above his partisanship for one or the other side to advocate what is fair for both. In practice, however, the superintendent's tenure in a particular community depends upon his pleasing the school board rather than the teachers. It does not take much imagination to realize that the teachers are gravely handicapped by this situation. The inclusion of managerial representatives in an employee organization is prohibited by law in private industry.[12] This is necessary to prevent employer domination and to insure that the representatives of the employees will in practice advance their interests instead of those of the employer.

The domination of teachers' organizations by school administrators was largely responsible for the formation in 1916 of the American Federation of Teachers, a union affiliated with the AFL-CIO. The AFT excludes superintendents and places a number of other restrictions on the inclusion of administrative personnel in its membership. However, the AFT is numerically overshadowed by the National Education Association, which has over 600,000 members. The NEA has always favored the inclusion of administrative personnel in the same organizations as classroom teachers despite the fact that some of its affiliated local education associations are restricted to classroom teachers. The NEA has taken the position that to exclude administrators from a teachers' organization would mean adopting a trade union practice which may be appropriate in industry but has no place in a profession.

The advent of collective bargaining in public education is likely to present the NEA with some very difficult questions of

[12] Technically, it is prohibited only if the employee organization seeks the jurisdiction of the National Labor Relations Board. However, most large employee organizations find it to their advantage to do so.

policy and practice. Obviously, if collective bargaining is to be prevalent in education, it becomes important whether the representatives of management—in this case, the school superintendents—are excluded from the employee organization. Certainly, it is just as important to protect the integrity of employee organizations in public as it is in private employment. It is precisely the lack of this protection that makes a mockery of trade unions in the Soviet Union. In that country, employee organizations are dominated by the government, that is, by the employer. For this reason, they are of very limited value in protecting the rights and working conditions of their members.

Authorities in the field of public personnel administration agree that when it comes to the need to protect employee organizations from employer domination, there is no valid distinction between public and private employment. The experience of organizations of postal employees in the United States bears this out. In the early 1900's, many postal employees joined AFL postal unions in order to get rid of administrator-dominated organizations. Since then, the problem has come up in scores of other organizations of public employees, and the solution has always included forbidding membership to or weakening the influence of administrators within the employee groups.

The fact that some of its own local associations exclude educational administrators is usually ignored by the NEA. Such exclusion is thought to be justified only because, in the communities affected, the school administrators did not treat the teachers kindly. The NEA has also ignored the fact that the American Association of University Professors excludes from active membership persons whose duties are half time or more administrative in character. This exclusion is even more rigid than the exclusion of school administrators from the American Federation of Teachers. Thus we have the paradox that administrators of public institutions of higher education are excluded from the organizations of professors, but the administrators of public school systems are not excluded from organizations of public school teachers. If such exclusion is necessary to protect the integrity of the AAUP as an employee organization, it would seem equally necessary in the case of organizations of public school teachers.

In defense of NEA policy, it is contended that local associations in other professions are open to all members of the profession. This is true, but it overlooks basic differences between education and these other professions. Physicians do not stand in an employer-employee relationship with one another; therefore, there is no need to exclude doctor-administrators from the local medical associations. Likewise, the practitioners in other professions are so seldom in an employer-employee relationship with each other that a policy of excluding employer-professionals would hardly make sense in a community-wide organization of professionals.

Even though most physicians are fee-takers, some are hospital administrators. It might be argued that if my point of view were sound, it would at least require the exclusion of hospital administrators from the local medical association. The fact that this is not done supposedly shows by analogy that the union point of view on administrator membership is unsound in a professional association. However, there are good reasons for not excluding medical administrators from local associations, reasons which do not apply to educational administrators.

A local medical association is not an employee organization; a local teachers' organization practically always is. A local medical association does not represent all the physicians in negotiations with a single employer, who is represented by a physician-administrator. Such a situation would call for the exclusion of the physician-administrator who negotiates conditions of employment on behalf of the employer. In other words, where an employer-employee relationship does exist between members of the medical profession, an employee organization can be organized, and it can exclude the employer-professional; but there would be no point to excluding the physician-administrator from a local medical association which does not bargain with anybody and which has no reason to do so.

In fact, where the situation confronting physicians is similar to that confronting teachers, the physicians do engage in collective bargaining. In some communities, the costs of medical services are borne largely by the health funds of unions. Because so many of their prospective patients are covered by the union's health fund, physicians who are not approved by the medical administrator of the union have no chance to practice successfully in these communities. Furthermore, the fee schedule set by the union has a strong influence on the economic position of the physicians. In these communities, therefore, the physicians must come to terms with the union in somewhat the same way that teachers must come to terms with a school board. In both cases, there is little realistic hope of professional employment other than from the one major employer.

In these communities, where the physicians are dependent upon one employer just as are the teachers, there is a growing tendency toward collective bargaining between physicians and the unions. The physicians as a group negotiate conditions of employment, even though this is technically still a matter for individual doctors and patients to decide. What is even more interesting is the fact that more and more physicians are specifically calling for collective bargaining as the best procedure to determine fees, schedules, and other conditions of employment in such situations.

Another factor in the medical situation which lessens the need to exclude physician-administrators from the medical associations is the tight control over entry which is exercised by the medical profession. This puts the individual physician in a much stronger bargaining position than the individual teacher. Administrator domination is not a serious problem in the medical profession because the individual physician is not dependent upon a particular employer in the community. The teachers, having only one employer, and lacking any effective control over the supply of teachers, lack the power to bring the employer to reasonable terms. In short, physician-employees are in an incomparably stronger position than teacher-employees; hence administrator domination of medical associations is less likely than administrator domination of educational associations.

The problem of administrator membership in teachers' organizations involves much more than the status of school superintendents in local associations. Principals will want some organizational medium to protect their own interests. What will be the status of principals—should they be regarded as managerial employees, as another kind of teacher, as a craft union within the employee organization, or as an independent employee group? Perhaps it is a mistake to think of principals as a homogeneous class of educational employees. Note that in industry, the label "foreman" actually covers a wide range of supervisory personnel. Some have very little supervisory or managerial responsibility, others have a great deal. One must look to the occupational situation, not the label, to determine their status in an intelligent way.

Similarly, there are basic differences between the principalship of a New York City high school and that of a small rural school. In the former, the principal is a powerful administrator who supervises a school with 3,000 students and perhaps 250 teachers. The principal of a small rural school may teach most of the day, supervise as few as 3 teachers, and be a mere rubber stamp for the county superintendent of schools. A high-school departmental chairman in New York City has more administrative responsibility than many principals in small rural schools. For this reason, it is difficult to propose any inflexible dividing line between managerial personnel and other employees. As long as collective bargaining is conducted from school district to school district, there will be variations in the constituency and the framework of the teachers' organizations.

The impact of collective bargaining upon administrator membership in teachers' associations is difficult to predict. The possibilities are numerous and depend upon factors which cannot be assessed very well at this time. For example, the extent to which teachers are successful in achieving control over entry to teaching will have important repercussions in their membership policies. The more rigorous this control and the more it forces communities to compete for teachers, the less danger will exist of administrator domination of teachers' associations and the less need there will be to exclude administrators from these associations.

Although there are many possible solutions to the problem of administrator domination, the National Education Association has yet to make any constructive contribution toward a sensible solution. The NEA admits that there has been some administrator domination in the past but treats all suggestions that the problem still exists as a trade union criticism beneath the dignity of professional teachers to answer. This attitude must give way to one which is more in accord with occupational realities. Some restrictions will have to be placed upon administrator membership in the organizations which bargain on behalf of teachers. There is, of course, no reason to restrict administrator membership in professional organizations which do not have any bargaining functions.

COLLECTIVE BARGAINING IN PUBLIC
EDUCATION: PROBLEMS AND
PROSPECTS

The preceding analysis has not touched upon many of the objections that will be raised against collective bargaining in public education: that it would require an unlawful surrender of the discretionary powers of school boards; that it would lead to strikes by teachers; that it would unduly hamper school administrators; that it is out of place in public education because education is not carried on for profit; that it would threaten the stability of government; that the public would never stand for it; and so on. None of these objections has any real merit.[13]

The advent of collective bargaining in public education will raise many genuine problems in addition to the few which have been discussed. It will be important to develop a structure that permits individual grievances to be handled promptly and fairly in the schools where they arise, but without placing unwarranted restrictions on school administrators. There need be no fear that teachers would abuse effective grievance procedures, for to do so would be to jeopardize the continued existence of these procedures. There must be a clarification of what is properly subject

[13] These objections, as well as many other points discussed in this chapter, are analyzed in detail in Myron Lieberman, *Education as a Profession* (Englewood Cliffs, N.J.: Prentice-Hall, 1956), chap. xi.

to bargaining. However, problems like these are already being solved every day in the largest and most complex enterprises, both public and private. There is no reason to believe that they cannot be solved in education.

Many people believe that the recent Russian successes in science and technology will automatically redound to the benefit of teachers in the United States. The public, it is thought, is now willing to provide adequate conditions of employment for teachers.

This point of view is a delusion. Nobody is going to bestow anything upon the teachers, national crisis or no national crisis. The teachers will have to fight for their place in the sun, and they will have to be much better fighters than they have been in the past. It is doubtful, to say the least, that a suddenly aroused public is going to cut down on its liquor, cigarettes, and television sets in order to pay its teachers more.

Recent events have provided teachers with a great opportunity to reverse their occupational decline. At present, the teachers are muffing this opportunity, chiefly because they regard it merely as an opportunity to get better salaries or fewer classes or more sick leave. They must realize that to struggle in the same old way for the same old objectives, different only in the higher amounts of money requested, is to insure failure. The opportunity and the task ahead is to transform the entire framework of employer-employee relations in education.

Collective bargaining will not only be a change in the way teachers negotiate their conditions of employment. It will be an orderly way of channeling the ideas and energies of teachers into their work. It will mean that the professional opinion of teachers as a group will receive consideration, not at the whim of school boards or administrators, but as a respected part of the educational enterprise. Collective bargaining may be advocated initially as an economic measure, but its ultimate justification will lie not so much in what it will do for the teachers as in what it will do for American education.

Chapter IX

TEACHERS' ORGANIZATIONS: A LOOK AT THE RECORD

The foremost fact about teachers' organizations in the United States is their irrelevance in the national scene. Their futility in protecting the public interest and the legitimate vocational aspirations of teachers is a national tragedy, much more dangerous to our democratic institutions than the excessive power wielded by such familiar bogeys as "Madison Avenue," "labor bosses," "captains of industry," "military high brass," and the like. Because their organizations are weak, teachers are without power; because they are without power, power is exercised upon them to weaken and to corrupt public education.

Let me illustrate the justification for these statements first by a brief analysis of the National Education Association (NEA), the largest organization of school teachers in the United States. The NEA has over 600,000 members, most of whom are public school teachers. Although it was founded in 1857 as "The National Teachers Association," much of its growth in membership is a recent phenomenon. By 1907, fifty years after the founding of the NEA, there were only 2,332 members. Gains were small until 1918, when a trend toward teachers' unions spurred school superintendents into an all-out campaign to enrol teachers in the NEA. Membership jumped from slightly over 10,000 in 1918 to more than 118,000 in 1922. Except during the depression, membership increased steadily, but the largest gains have come in recent years. From 1952 to 1957, the average annual gain in membership was close to 40,000 per year.

At the Centennial Convention in 1957, NEA dues were raised from five to ten dollars per year. This action resulted in a moderate decline in membership. However, NEA dues are still much less than the prevailing dues in most national professional organizations. Its huge membership enables the NEA to support a budget ($6,927,000 in 1957-58) larger than that of any other professional association.

The size of the NEA is partially reflected in its complicated organizational structure. The NEA has thirty departments, devoted to such diverse fields as school administration, retired teachers, school secretaries, higher education, audio-visual instruction, and art education. The departments vary considerably in membership, prestige, and power. Much of the power in the NEA rests with the American Association of School Administrators (AASA), an NEA department whose membership consists largely of school superintendents. Despite the fact that its membership is only slightly over 10,000, the AASA is far more powerful than the Department of Classroom Teachers, which enrols 70 per cent of the Association's membership. There is ordinarily no requirement that one be a member of the NEA to be a member of a department, or vice versa. Thus, although the NEA works closely with the departments, the latter are often quite autonomous; they have their own membership and dues structure, permanent staff, and programs. This fact is frequently overlooked. A recent example was the widespread criticism of the NEA when the executive secretary of the Department of Secondary School Principals urged the members of his department to cancel their school subscriptions to *Life* magazine because of certain articles in it alleged to be unfair to American education. The NEA was widely and unfairly accused of advocating unethical practice in this case.

In addition to the thirty departments, there are twenty-four permanent commissions and committees operating under the nominal control of the Representative Assembly, a delegate body of about 6,000 members. There is also a Board of Directors (77 members), an Executive Committee (11 members), and a Board of Trustees (5 members), whose main function is the selection of the chief permanent officer of the Association, the Executive Secretary. There are thirteen Headquarters Divisions which operate under the Executive Secretary, who is assisted by five assistant executive secretaries and a business manager. The presidency is chiefly a ceremonial office and, by long tradition, goes to a man one year and a woman the next. The twelve vice presidencies are also largely ceremonial; their chief purpose is to reward the faithful with prestige and a few trips during the year. However, beginning in 1958, the first vice-president automatically became president the following year. The total NEA staff of about six hundred is housed in a new $9,000,000 structure completed in 1958, in Washington, D.C.

A less impressive picture of the NEA emerges from a consideration of its recruitment techniques. Although many teachers join freely, there has long been a great deal of compulsory membership in the NEA. A few years ago an official of the American Federation of Teachers, the only serious organizational threat to the NEA, suggested to me that NEA membership would be cut in half if superintendents would stop forcing teachers to join the NEA in order to get or keep their jobs. This is very probably an exaggerated estimate, but the practice of coercing teachers to join the NEA is still widespread in many states.

It is practically impossible to assess the precise extent of compulsory membership. The chief reason for this is that teachers are generally not in a secure position from which to publicize or protest the practice. In many communities, teachers have no tenure and do not dare to protest against compulsory membership. In some states, teachers are still forced to join the NEA despite explicit state laws forbidding the practice of requiring membership in a teachers' organization as a condition of employment. Even in Oklahoma, which has such a law, I have met teachers who informed me that their superintendents did not even bother to suggest membership; the deductions for NEA dues were made without any prior discussion with the teachers. Since teachers have no tenure in Oklahoma, most of them are afraid to protest such coercion. A teacher who is not rehired may find it very difficult to prove that his dismissal was due to his opposition to joining the NEA.

It is really a most remarkable thing that many school boards make, or permit their superintendents to make, membership in the NEA and its affiliated state and local associations a condition of employment for teachers. The requirement that the teacher join these organizations is often included as a part of the employment contract signed by the teacher. In other areas of public employment, there would be a tremendous outcry if public employees were forced to join a particular organization as a condition of employment. The reader need only imagine the reaction in his own community if the city administration should require all publicly employed carpenters, plumbers, and electricians to join the AFL-CIO as a condition of employment.

The public administrator, like the administrator in private industry, usually prefers a weak employee organization or none at all. Only in education do we find a large body of public employees openly required to join an organization as a condition of employment. The reason for this is that school administrators dominate the NEA and its affiliated associations. Ironically, compulsory membership in teachers' associations is most common in rural areas, where there is the most pronounced anti-labor sentiment. The superintendent and the board of education would be horror-stricken, if they stopped to think about the matter, to realize that they had instituted "a closed shop"— and without even the approval of the employees!

THE NEA AS A PROFESSIONAL ORGANIZATION

The NEA prides itself on being "the largest professional organization in the world." This may be so. But what about its effectiveness? What has it accomplished since it was founded more than a century ago?

This is not an easy question to answer. Many factors influence the quality of education and the status of the teaching profession. In particular cases, it may be impossible to ascertain the relative influence, for good or evil, of all the forces that try to shape educational policies. If teachers' salaries are low, it might seem unfair to blame the NEA, which is struggling to raise them.

On the other hand, NEA programs must be evaluated in terms of their effectiveness as well as in terms of their purposes. If teachers' salaries are low, it does not make sense to absolve the Association of responsibility because it tries, albeit in vain, to win higher salaries from an apathetic public. An important test of any occupational organization is its effectiveness in overcoming public apathy. If educational facilities throughout the country were reasonably adequate, we would expect most of the credit to go to the NEA even though other agencies might also have played a role.

But if facilities are not adequate, we should not absolve the NEA of responsibility merely because it has "fought for better schools." Its adequacy as a teachers' organization must be measured by its success in overcoming opposition, not by reference to what it would like to see done in the absence of opposition.

In order to analyze the NEA's record, we should be clear about the kinds of objectives which professional organizations strive to achieve. Traditionally, the term "professional" has been applied to occupational associations which protect clients from incompetent or unscrupulous practitioners. There are several ways by which an association can accomplish this objective. Usually it tries to secure control of admission to the profession, then to set standards which protect the public. For example, admission to the medical profession is in the hands of state medical boards, composed entirely of doctors. In most states, the medical association controls appointments to these boards. This situation was made possible only by the vigorous support given to the state associations by the American Medical Association, the national association of doctors.

A professional association can also work for high standards in the educational institutions which provide professional training. It can either upgrade or eliminate the professional training program in schools which have inadequate programs. It may also set high standards for membership (as distinct from admission to the profession), thus providing the public with some means of distinguishing the competent from the incompetent practitioners regardless of what public authorities do. In addition, it can formulate and enforce a code of ethics which subordinates the welfare of the practitioners to the welfare of the public.

Let us consider first the NEA's record concerning standards for entry to the teaching profession. With all due regard to variations from region to region, state to state, institution to institution, occupation to occupation, and person to person, the over-all picture is clear. As a general rule, teaching requires from one to five years less preparation than other professions. Many institutions have no program of selective admission, or only a nominal one, for entry to teacher education. The quantitative and qualitative standards for graduation from programs of teacher education are typically much lower than they are for medicine, law, engineering, and other acknowledged professions. The lower standards for admission to and graduation from programs of teacher training are paralleled by the decline, amounting to an almost complete disappearance, of public machinery to test the adequacy of professional training. The use of written examinations for a teaching license, a common practice fifty years ago, is practically extinct today. Such examinations are still common in other professions, and the trend is to extend their use wherever possible. In short, for the country as a whole, there is not a single step toward the teaching profession for which the standards are set as high as they are for a similar step in other professions.

The NEA deplores low standards for teaching. In fact, the standards are low because teachers have no control over them, and they have no control over these standards because the NEA does not believe in it. Since 1921 at least, the NEA has advocated non-professional control of the state boards which set the standards for teacher certification. The NEA has maintained this policy despite the fact that professional control over entry has always preceded the establishment of high standards in the acknowledged professions. This explains why every professional association except the NEA is attempting to expand its control over entry.

The really ominous fact is that in a growing number of states, teachers are *excluded by law* from the boards which control entry to teaching. To appreciate the professional decline to which the NEA is currently leading the teachers of this country, one must realize that other professions are still moving to strengthen their control over such boards. Indeed, since control over entry is a criterion of professionalism itself, the NEA's policy on this issue is essentially an antiprofessional one.

The sad truth is that NEA policies are responsible for—or unable to remedy—a situation in which the public cares less about the competence of teachers than it does about the competence of any other professional group. The basic purpose of certification, or licensure as it is called in other professions, is to protect the public from incompetent and unscrupulous practitioners. As previously pointed out, in the overwhelming majority of states, only public school teachers need be certified; those who teach in non-public schools are generally not required to satisfy any state-imposed requirements. This is in striking contrast to the prevailing situation in other professions, where there is not one set of standards for publicly employed professionals and a different set, or none at all, for privately employed ones. The protection of the public requires that *all* professionals establish their competence. This is true for physicians, attorneys, dentists, and every other profession. The NEA's desire for higher standards for teachers is sincere, but the major barrier to higher standards is its own support for, or indifference to, non-professional control of admission to teaching.

The status of professional ethics in education is another remarkable example of the NEA's preoccupation with the appearances of professionalism while it ignores its substance. The NEA has had a "Code of Professional Ethics" since 1929. Up to the present time, its Committee on Professional Ethics has formally tried exactly one person for unprofessional conduct. This took place in 1946, when Dr. William H. Johnson, the superintendent of schools in Chicago, was expelled from membership in the NEA. Johnson himself did not even bother to appear or to answer the charges of corrupt and dictatorial administration which were the basis for the Committee's action.

Since less than one-third of the teachers in the country were NEA members at the time, the punishment accorded Johnson seems rather innocuous. Nonetheless, the educational journals of the day hailed Johnson's expulsion as a historic occasion, marking the beginning of an era in which teachers would assume corporate responsibility for their professional conduct. In fact, however, the NEA's Committee on Professional Ethics merely reverted to its traditional role of issuing pious platitudes about the child, home, community, country, and profession. As with so many other NEA agencies, its main function seems to be in providing some of the faithful with a few trips each year at NEA expense.

The absence of any enforcement of the NEA's Code of Professional Ethics is more understandable when one reads the Code itself. It is a confused ragbag of platitudes and contradictions which would be quite dangerous if its enforcement were taken seriously. For instance, Section 1, Principle II, of the Code asserts that "a teacher will adhere to any reasonable pattern of behavior accepted by the community for professional persons." This presumably means that it is unethical for a teacher in Mississippi to condemn racial segregation. Section 3, Principle III, states that "the teacher will discuss controversial issues from an objective point of view, thereby keeping his class free from partisan opinions." The Committee has not yet explained how a teacher can "discuss controversial issues" while simultaneously "keeping his class free from partisan opinions." [1]

The absence of NEA leadership in developing and enforcing a code of professional ethics for teachers is reflected in the apathy of the NEA's affiliated state and local associations on this matter.

[1] For a more detailed analysis of the NEA Code of Professional Ethics with some suggestions for improving it, see Myron Lieberman, *Education as a Profession* (Englewood Cliffs, N.J., Prentice-Hall, 1956), chap. xiii.

The activities of these associations in the area of professional ethics usually consist of adopting the NEA Code, framing it, and then promptly ignoring its existence. The majority of teachers have probably never read the NEA Code; in fact, many teachers are not even aware that any such code exists.

TEACHER WELFARE AND THE NEA

There is no hard and fast line which divides "professional" activities from those designed to advance the welfare of teachers. Adequate salaries are desirable from a broad social point of view as well as from the teachers' point of view. But for purposes of analysis, it is illuminating to consider what NEA leadership has accomplished for the American teacher.

Such an analysis is difficult to make in a few paragraphs because the trends have not affected all educational groups in the same way. Thus from 1904 to 1953, the real income of principals and teachers in large city high schools actually declined, whereas the real income of elementary teachers increased during this period. In general, however, teachers have either suffered an absolute decrease in real income since 1904 or their real income has increased at a much slower rate than has real income in other occupations. Certain groups of elementary teachers constitute the only important exception to this statement.

Since 1929 at least, the average annual salaries of public school personnel have remained very close to the national average for all employed persons. In 1929, the average teaching salary was $1,400 and the average for all employed persons was $1,405. By 1957, the average teaching salary was $4,450 and the average for all employed persons was $4,190. Between 1929 and 1957, the average annual teaching salary was higher than the average for all employed persons in nineteen years, and in eight years it was lower. However, during this period there was never a substantial difference between these two averages.[2]

[2] Most of the data in this and the preceding paragraph is taken from NEA Research Division, *Economic Status of Teachers in 1954–55* (Washington, D.C.: National Education Association, 1954); and Beardsley Ruml and Sidney G. Tickton, *Teaching Salaries Then and Now* (New York: Fund for the Advancement of Education, 1955).

The 1950 Census gave data on 1949 incomes for eighteen professional occupations requiring at least a bachelor's degree. In twelve of these, the average income was at least 50 per cent above the average for all employed persons. Teaching ranked fifteenth among these professional occupations; in 1949, the average income of teachers was only 14.1 per cent above the median income of all employed persons, including part-time workers. As late as 1957–58, 25 per cent of all classroom teachers received an annual salary of less than $3,500. Also during 1957–58, 46,000 teachers were paid less than $2,500, a figure which is $1,690 less than the average for *all* employed persons, including persons employed only part-time, during 1957.[3]

Although there is no authoritative definition of a "professional level of income," it is usually taken to be two to three times the average annual income of all employed persons. On this basis, it is clear that the NEA has made no progress toward securing a professional level of income for teachers during the past fifty years. But even this statement does not bring out the actual extent of the NEA's failure to advance the interests of teachers. The failure of teachers to improve their salaried position relative to other occupational groups really represents a major decline in their economic status. The number of days worked per year has declined in every major occupation except education, where it has increased from 147 in 1904 to 182 in 1953. Furthermore, the number of hours worked per day has increased in education but decreased in practically all other occupations.

It should also be noted that the fringe benefits in industry are increasingly superior to those in education. Most collective agreements in industry provide for severance pay for employees who must be released for no fault of their own. Such provisions are urgently needed in education, where, for instance, the consolidation of school districts or desegregation often reduces the number of teachers needed. Nevertheless, there is no severance pay for teachers, no matter how long their service. The typical employ-

---

[3] I have taken the data in this paragraph from NEA Legislative Commission, *Teacher Shortages and Teacher Salaries* (Washington, D.C.: National Education Association, 1958).

ment agreement in industry includes grievance machinery according employees a full measure of protection against arbitrary and capricious changes in the conditions of employment; the typical teaching contract is completely silent on these matters. The only dimension in which teachers still enjoy some superiority over other occupational groups is in the matter of vacations, but this gap is being steadily narrowed from both directions, with longer vacations in industry and shorter vacations in education.

The NEA does work for teacher welfare, but its programs are low in aim and weak in execution. Politicians are well aware of the fact that NEA support or opposition is irrelevant at the polls. One need only compare the NEA's record with that of the American Medical Association to appreciate this. In 1950 the Truman administration attempted to pass a compulsory health insurance bill which was opposed by the American Medical Association. To defeat the legislation, the AMA raised $3,000,000 by assessing every one of its members $25.00. Compulsory health insurance, financed by federal funds, has been dormant ever since the Association's campaign against it.

Regardless of one's attitude toward the legislation killed by the American Medical Association, there can be only respect for the forceful way in which the Association achieved this legislative result. If the NEA could assess every member $5.00 and pour the resulting $3,000,000 into a vigorous, well-planned campaign for federal support of teachers' salaries, every member would get back this assessment many times over within a short time. But the NEA is incapable of moving with vigor and imagination, even when confronted by the most serious problems and challenging opportunities.

Some NEA apologists always take the attitude that the Association does its good deeds behind the scenes. It is allegedly not interested in headlines, and therefore one should not condemn the NEA for the fact that its activities are not in the public eye. For a long time I felt like an uninitiated ignoramus, criticizing the NEA only because I was not privy to innumerable good deeds which, for some unexplained reason, had to remain confidential. Unfortunately, the steady and continuing decline of the teaching profession are public facts which require public analysis.

Of course, the NEA does perform some valuable services for teachers. If a local association desires a credit union, the NEA will help to organize it. The NEA's information and research services are prompt and thorough. Many NEA publications are extremely useful. The teacher who plans a trip will get all the help he desires from the NEA's Travel Service.

Nevertheless, while freely conceding the existence of these and other worthwhile activities, it is necessary to face up to two basic facts about them. The first is that these constructive results have been achieved largely in areas which are peripheral to the basic problems of the profession. Second, even in these useful but peripheral services, the NEA often reveals a shocking inability to act on principle.

For example, the NEA Travel Service sponsors tours to Arab countries from which Jewish teachers are excluded. Despite many protests against this practice, the NEA's Executive Committee continues to permit its Travel Service to continue to sponsor these tours. The excuse given is that it is not the NEA but the countries involved which are responsible for the discrimination. On this line of reasoning, the NEA might just as well abandon the policy (adopted after one of the few successful revolts in NEA history) of meeting only in cities providing satisfactory accommodations for all delegates, regardless of race. The NEA could meet in Mississippi and contend that any inconvenience suffered by Negro delegates was due to discrimination by Mississippians, not by NEA agencies.

Every occupational organization undoubtedly has some redeeming features. However, we need to know more than the simple fact that there are good and bad aspects to the NEA. If we are to act intelligently with respect to the NEA, we need an understanding of its specific accomplishments and failures. In this context, it would be most naïve to equate mechanically NEA successes and failures. On the basic professional issues, the NEA has been a dismal failure. A general who loses an army to gain a few yards of barren land is not a success. Neither is an occupational organization which dissipates the funds and energies of hundreds of thousands of teachers for limited, even picayune, results.

STATE AND LOCAL ASSOCIATIONS

Education in the United States is largely a function of state and local government. This fact emphasizes the need for strong teachers' organizations at the state and local levels.

Let us first consider teachers' organizations at the state level. The state teachers' associations (or state education associations, as they are frequently called) vary widely in membership, resources, programs, and leadership. It must be obvious, however, that these associations share responsibility with the NEA for the condition of education in the United States today.

The lack of professional control over admission to teaching, the low standards for teaching certificates, the existence of substandard programs of teacher education, the declining professional and economic status of teachers, the absence of professional autonomy, the superficial attention to professional ethics —all these and other indications of professional failure constitute a reflection upon the state education associations as well as upon the NEA. Most of these associations have never put up a real fight for the most basic principles or the most elementary vocational objectives appropriate for teachers. They are habituated to begging for crumbs instead of fighting for loaves; more often than not, they get the back of the hand from the state legislatures.

As for the local education associations affiliated with the NEA, not even the NEA's own studies venture the claim that they typically wield any real power in their communities. Occasionally an outstanding individual stimulates a local association into significant action, or conditions degenerate to the point where the local association must act or perish. Exceptional individuals and circumstances are, however, an inadequate answer to an organizational need which is always present in every community. As it is, most local associations are not taken seriously, even by their own members. The fact that their dues are seldom more than a dollar or two a year affords some indication of the character of their programs.

A 1948 study of local associations made by the NEA's Research Division indicated that their programs were usually devoted to problems of teacher welfare, such as getting higher salaries.[4] This finding should have embarrassed quite a few NEA adherents, who are always criticizing teachers' unions for being preoccupied with teacher welfare. Of course, the fact that local associations devote most of their attention to salary problems does not mean that teachers are more mercenary than other vocational groups. It means only that they are less efficient in achieving their economic goals. It is typical of local education associations to dissipate their energies in futile efforts to improve their conditions of employment. Other than this, they give teas for new teachers in the fall and retiring teachers in the spring, and perhaps listen to a few travelogues in between.

TEACHERS' UNIONS

To understand the history and prospects of teachers' unions in the United States, it is necessary to make a few additional comments about the NEA. The NEA was founded by school superintendents and has always been dominated by them. Partly for this reason, it has never developed a vigorous program to improve the economic status of teachers. Even after 1900, an influential segment of NEA leadership believed that emphasis upon teacher welfare was unprofessional and beneath the dignity of the Association.

Under these circumstances, it was inevitable that the teachers should seek an organizational medium devoted to advancing instead of stifling teacher welfare. Many came to feel that unions were the answer, and in 1916, teachers from New York, Chicago, Gary, Scranton, Oklahoma City, and Washington, D.C., combined to form the American Federation of Teachers (AFT). Soon after its formation, the AFT was issued a charter by the American Federation of Labor. It is currently affiliated with the AFL-CIO.

[4] NEA Research Division, "Local Education Associations at Work," *Research Bulletin,* XXVI (October, 1948).

The founders of the AFT were not always hostile to the NEA. Many of them believed that the two organizations should be complementary. It was thought that the NEA would be devoted to the science and art of teaching and the AFT would be devoted to improving the economic status of teachers. However, within three years after it was founded, the AFT had more teacher members than the NEA. From 1916 to 1919, its membership increased to over 10,000. Frightened by this unexpected development, the NEA launched a powerful counterattack, beginning in 1920. Superintendents forced teachers to join the NEA and its affiliated state and local associations. Teachers were also forced to sign employment contracts in which they agreed not to join unions. School administrators found it easy to carry out these policies in the anti-labor climate which followed World War I.

By 1927, membership in the AFT had dropped to 3,500. Then, under the impetus of the depression, membership began to rise slowly. Just prior to World War II, the AFT was forced to expend most of its energies in expelling a Communist faction operating chiefly out of a few eastern locals. After the expulsion of the Communists (some of whom then joined the NEA, according to AFT leaders), the AFT again entered upon a period of steady growth. In 1958, its membership was slightly over 55,000.

The founders of the AFT shared the popular view that public school teachers should not be permitted to strike.[5] To make up for the loss of power resulting from the relinquishment of this right, it was thought that teachers needed powerful allies to overcome the strong industrial, commercial, and real estate lobbies that usually opposed higher taxes for educational purposes. The labor movement seemed a natural ally. The vast majority of wage earners could not adequately finance the education of their children by private expenditures. Union leaders such as Samuel Gompers had long been aware of the fact that equality of educational opportunity could be realized only through higher taxes upon the more favored economic groups. For these reasons, teacher affiliation with the labor movement appeared to be a

[5] The 1958 Convention passed a resolution calling upon teachers to work for the right to strike.

practical means of securing a wide base of support for the objectives of the teachers.

This rationale helps to explain why AFT publications generally put more emphasis upon the activities of other unions than they do upon the activities of professional associations; for instance, they constantly refer to the success of other unions which have utilized collective bargaining. At the same time, however, the AFT has completely ignored the need for teacher control over entry to the teaching profession. This is a surprising failure in view of the fact that many unions as well as professional associations have realized the importance of job control in raising standards of service. The shortsighted "professionals" in the NEA are quite mistaken in thinking that teachers should not soil their professional hands with tough collective bargaining, but the AFT is at least as shortsighted in its failure to understand that certain policies of the fee-taking professions, such as occupational control over entry, must be incorporated into the programs of teachers' organizations.

The failure of the AFT to advocate teacher control over admission to teaching has nothing to do with the charges often made against the Federation that it is "unprofessional." As a matter of fact, the reasons why most teachers refuse to join the AFT have little or nothing to do with the criticisms which can justly be made of it. For instance, teachers' unions have been opposed on the grounds that, as public employees serving all the people, teachers should not affiliate with any particular segment of the population. It is alleged that affiliation with the labor movement would compromise teachers in their daily work.

This, of course, is not an argument against teachers' unions as such but only against their affiliation with the labor movement. But in any case there is no reason why a teacher's affiliation with the AFL-CIO should compromise his work any more than his affiliation with any religious, political, or social organization which takes a stand on broad social issues. Authorities in the field of public personnel administration agree that this objection to affiliation with the labor movement by public employees has little merit. In fact, decades of experience with public employee unions affiliated with the labor movement have shown that affiliation is to be desired rather than feared as a matter of social policy. Parenthetically, it might be noted that although it is not officially affiliated with other groups, the NEA has on several occasions shown the most extreme partiality to certain non-educational organizations, such as the American Legion.

AFT supporters defend their affiliation with the AFL-CIO on two contradictory grounds. First, they argue that affiliation enables the AFT to secure the support of practically all organized labor for AFT objectives. This contention naturally raises the question whether other unions in the AFL-CIO can force the AFT to take an action opposed by the teachers. The AFT's answer is that it, like other federations in the AFL-CIO, is autonomous. It cannot be forced by other federations in the AFL-CIO to support policies opposed by the teachers. This defense of affiliation is valid, but it materially weakens the case for affiliation. As a practical matter, other unions in the AFL-CIO support AFT policies only to the extent that these other unions independently favor such policies. It is true that most unions in the AFL-CIO usually support AFT recommendations concerning education. However, it is doubtful whether affiliation is an important factor in securing such support.

Second, and more to the point, affiliation is really based upon the discredited assumption that the interests of teachers coincide with the interests of other unions in the AFL-CIO. Actually, with or without affiliation, other unions support or oppose AFT policies as they see fit. Furthermore, many organizations not affiliated with the AFL-CIO support such AFT objectives as federal aid to education.

Even if its affiliation with the AFL-CIO has been helpful to the AFT in some ways, it has also been a serious organizing handicap. Although affiliation does not compromise the teachers individually or collectively, many teachers think that it does and are lost to the AFT for this reason. But regardless of their logic or lack of it, there is no inherent reason why 1,300,000 teachers should need affiliation with the AFL-CIO any more than 200,000 physicians or a like number of lawyers should need it. Affiliation was attractive when teachers' unions were founded because the teachers were weak. However, their future lies in developing independent sources of power, not in continuing to rely upon the largesse of other occupational groups. It seems to me that AFT supporters have concentrated so hard upon answering invalid objections to affiliation that they have never given much thought to other objections which do have merit.

It must be emphasized that the preceding comments referred to teacher affiliation with the labor movement, not to the desirability of teachers' unions as such. However, many arguments against teachers' unions which are decisive with the teachers themselves make no sense whatsoever. Thus it is often contended that teachers should not form unions because teachers should not have the right to strike. However, the right to strike and the right to unionize are two different things entirely; it is quite possible to have one without the other. The same holds for the desirability of striking and the desirability of unionizing. The view that the strikes are a necessary adjunct of unionization is completely mistaken.

Ironically, the AFT has a very specific constitutional prohibition against strikes, whereas the NEA's constitution has nothing to say in the matter. Personally, I believe that teachers should have the legal right to strike, since they are morally obligated to withdraw their services under certain conditions.[6] Perhaps most people do not share this view. The point is, however, that many unions of public employees have constitutional provisions prohibiting strikes.

Probably the most important deterrent to teacher membership in the AFT is the reluctance of teachers to become identified with blue-collar workers. Teachers are one of the most white-collar-conscious groups in our society. They like to think of themselves as "professionals," a category higher than "union workers." AFT leaders do not like to admit that the idea of joining a "union" is repugnant to most teachers, but AFT pub-

[6] For a more thorough analysis of this issue, see Myron Lieberman, "Teachers Strikes: An Analysis of the Issues," *Harvard Educational Review*, XXVI (Winter, 1956), 39–70.

lications never cease to pound at the theme that a union can be "professional."

In any event, the statistics concerning membership tell the story. In 1959, more than forty years after it was founded, the AFT enrolled less than 5 per cent of the teachers in the United States. It has been making small gains in recent years, but they are insignificant in the over-all picture. In 1957, the NEA increased its membership by 44,000, whereas the 1957 total membership of the AFT was only about 55,000. As a result of an increase in dues from $5.00 to $10.00, NEA membership declined during 1958–59. Nevertheless, it still has over ten times as many members as the AFT.

Some union leaders have finally realized that the label "union" is damaging in organizing white-collar workers. The latter are asked to join "associations" or "guilds" instead of "unions." AFT leadership, however, is dominated by professional liberals who simply cannot accept the fact that the war cries of traditional unionism will never organize the teachers. AFT spokesmen continually refer to NEA locals as "company unions." The analogy may be sound in principle, but the reference to NEA locals in these terms is poor strategy. Teachers simply do not wish to be labeled as members of a union, and organizing strategy that emphasizes the terminology of unionization is bound to fail with them.

While teachers shy away in droves from the AFT for the most superficial reasons, the criticisms which can legitimately be made of the organization go unnoticed by members and non-members alike. Among these criticisms are the AFT's neglect of teacher control over entry, its adherence to outmoded strategies of gaining welfare objectives, its uncritical attitude toward single salary schedules, its blind adulation of the labor movement, its refusal to study and profit from the experience of the fee-taking professions, and its failure to provide for the specialized teaching interests of its members. The AFT is a courageous organization. Usually it is much quicker to act on principle, even at some risk to its own organizational strength, than is the NEA. Its sympathetic attitude toward the labor movement has enabled it to see the need for many policies which are badly needed in public education. Nevertheless, the organization would have to undergo basic changes in program, strategy, and leadership to do the organizational job that is needed today in American education.

Teachers do have much to learn from the labor movement. They also have much to learn from the fee-taking professions and from other organizations of public employees. Furthermore, teachers have interests in common, as well as some that conflict, with each of these groups. To be successful, teachers' organizations must be much more sophisticated about the lessons to be learned from these groups, and the points of common and conflicting interests, than they have been in the past.

A teachers' organization which is not affiliated with labor, which is free both from administrator domination and also from an unimaginative and unproductive hostility toward administrators, which aggressively advocates teacher control over entry to the teaching profession as well as collective bargaining, which is ready to take a new look at such shibboleths as local control of education, which is adamant on such matters of principle as the elimination of racial segregation from public education, which takes the lead instead of dragging its heels in the introduction of such things as educational television or a new personnel structure in education—such an organization might well replace the NEA as the predominant teachers' organization in the United States. In any case, the development of a teachers' organization along the lines suggested is one of the most important educational needs of this generation.

Chapter X

THE PROFESSORIAL EXAMPLE

Apart from the professional apologists for the AFT and the NEA, there is little dissent from the conclusion that existing teachers' organizations are a feeble lot. What are the reasons for this situation?

The organizational situation of the teachers of teachers, and the influence of their example, is undoubtedly a large part of the answer. This calls for a brief analysis of the American Association of University Professors (AAUP), the national organization of college professors.

Although commonly regarded as both a "professional" and an employee association, the AAUP fulfils only a few limited functions of either type of organization. At best, it fulfils these in a most cursory way. The AAUP sets forth certain principles relating to faculty participation in policy-making, tenure, and academic freedom, but these are guides only. The Association exerts no control over admission to college teaching. It enforces no educational standards for institutions of higher education. The AAUP itself exercises no corporate responsibility for the competence or the professional conduct of professors. No professor has ever been expelled or suspended from the AAUP for unethical conduct, nor are any likely to be in the foreseeable future. Politically, it is doubtful that the Association has even nuisance value. If Congress or a state legislature has ever paid any attention to the AAUP, the incident has escaped my attention.

The weakness of professorial organizations is most pronounced at the state level. When state legislatures consider appropriations for higher education, including those for professorial salaries, the professors are seldom represented before the appropriate legislative bodies. State organizations of professors exist in only one-third of the states, hence the professors ordinarily lack even the machinery to present their views on a state-wide basis to state officials.[1]

The case for or against state legislation affecting professors is usually argued by college and university administrators. These administrators are not active members of the AAUP, and according to AAUP regulations, they cannot be. Active membership is prohibited to persons whose duties are half-time or more administrative in nature, on the grounds that the interests of such persons are likely to conflict with those of the professors. To be represented on crucial issues by persons conceded to have interests which conflict with their own is a striking commentary on the practical sense of the academic community.

At the local level, the influence of AAUP chapters varies a great deal from institution to institution. In most cases, however, local chapters have little influence. They do not ordinarily enrol a majority of the faculty, and they lack official status in dealing with college and university administrators. Their dues are nominal and their programs correspondingly trivial.

AAUP conventions, publications, and programs devote more

---

[1] The following comment about meetings of state and regional associations of the AAUP is illuminating: "Rarely, or never, have questions of salaries, for example, or closely related financial matters, been discussed. This may have been well, for it may be predicted that a state conference is destined to failure if it permits itself to become a pressure group, or attempts to discuss salaries and financial matters in cases where some of the institutions concerned must compete for appropriations from the state legislature. The chief value of state conferences would seem to be the opportunity for informal discussions and the interchange of ideas. A decision to act should seldom be the outcome of a state conference; such decisions should be left to the individual chapters" (James Holladay, "The Role of Regional Meetings in the Work of the Association," *American Association of University Professors Bulletin*, XL [Autumn, 1954], 448). The author of this remarkable invitation to occupational suicide served as first vice-president of the AAUP during 1957–58.

attention to individual cases relating to tenure and academic freedom than they do to any other type of problem. This preoccupation may speak well for the AAUP's devotion to principle, but it is hardly a testimonial to its effectiveness as a professional organization. During its existence, the AAUP has failed to advance any broad welfare interest of the professors. I do not mean to imply that the advancement of these interests is or should be the only objective, or even the major objective, of the Association. Its primary objective should be the protection of the public interest in matters relating to higher education. Nevertheless, the advancement of the welfare of professors must also be one of its basic and legitimate responsibilities. This responsibility need not conflict with its responsibilities to the public. It is in the public interest that there be a strong organization devoted to the welfare interests of the academic profession. But what does the record show?

Consider briefly the economic fortunes of the professors since the founding of the AAUP. Shortly after it was established in 1915, the United States entered a period of inflation brought on by World War I. It was not until 1932 that college professors were able to achieve salary levels which accorded them the same purchasing power that they enjoyed prior to World War I.[2] From 1940 to 1957, the purchasing power of faculty salaries declined again. During this period, the professors lost about $2 billion of real income because their salaries failed to keep pace with rising prices. Furthermore, the rest of the population was experiencing an increase in real income during this period. The professors would have had to earn from $5 to $6 billion more than they did from 1940 to 1957 to have gained their proportional share of the nation's rise in real income during this period. To put it in individual terms, there was an average loss of $30,000–$36,000 per faculty member as a result of the inability of professors to maintain their relative economic position from 1940 to 1957.

The income level of college professors is extremely low in view

[2] Seymour E. Harris, "Faculty Salaries," *American Association of University Professors Bulletin*, XLIII (December, 1957), 590. Most of the data cited in my discussion of the economic status of professors is taken from this article.

of their long average preparation (typically, seven years of education beyond high school). The mean pay of all college professors in 1955–56 was $5,200. This was only 33 per cent more than the national average for all employed persons, regardless of ability or educational attainments.

When the income of professors is compared to the income of groups whose training is substantially equal to that of the professors, the differences are quite substantial. The $5,200 mean pay for all college teachers in 1955–56 was about one-third of the average net income of physicians in private practice in the same year. Fewer than one professor in every two hundred was paid more than $14,000 in 1955–56 whereas 57 per cent of all physicians earned $15,000 or more in that year. While the differences are not so great in the case of lawyers and dentists, these groups also enjoy a substantial economic superiority over professors.

The economic decline of the professors is not questioned by the AAUP. On the contrary, the decline has been accepted as a reason to give higher organizational priorities to improving the economic status of professors. However, the AAUP's program for achieving this objective hardly inspires confidence that the Association will be more successful in the future than it has been in the past in this regard.

Essentially, the program consists of a scale by which to grade the salary schedule at each institution of higher education. Institutions which pay full professors a minimum of $14,000 get an "AA"; institutions which pay them a minimum of $12,000 get a "A," and so on, until at the lower end of the scale, institutions which pay full professors as little as $5,250 get an "F." Other academic ranks are also graded in the same way.[3]

As a minor detail in a program to achieve higher salaries, the practice of giving institutions letter grades according to their salary schedules would not be objectionable. Unfortunately, the grading plan appears to be the major plank in the AAUP's "program" to improve the economic status of professors. Its futility

[3] For an explanation of the way in which the grading plan is supposed to work, see "Grading of Academic Salary Scales," *American Association of University Professors Bulletin,* XLIV (March, 1958), 214–36.

is obvious just from a realization of the short shrift it would get in other occupations. Imagine Walter Reuther telling the United Automobile Workers, "Fellows, General Motors gets a "B" this year and Ford gets a "C." I am sure that Ford will be striving to raise its grade to "B" in the years ahead so you men working for Ford should not feel that your national organization has let you down."

It is quite possible that the use of the grading scale may retard higher salaries rather than improve them. The strategists in the AAUP assume that institutions which receive low grades will be encouraged to raise their salaries. Although this may happen to some extent, the grading scale is likely to have an adverse effect upon salaries at the top of the scale. If an institution is at the top of the scale, its trustees and administrators may use that fact as an excuse not to raise salaries. Not that this is my fundamental criticism of the grading proposal; the whole business is so naïve and so completely ignores the crucial role of organizational pressure and power that its crashing failure can be taken for granted.[4]

The inability of the AAUP to exert effective pressure is not the sole cause of the economic decline of the professors. However, many of the other causes could be eliminated or mitigated by a reasonably alert professional organization. For example, the AAUP gives little serious attention to ways and means of increasing the productivity of professors. It typically bases its appeals for higher salaries upon the increases in the cost of living during recent years. On the other hand, economists generally believe that salary increases should be tied as much as possible to increases in the productivity of occupational groups, not to increases in their cost of living. An alert professional organization would be active both in increasing the productivity of its members and in making certain that they received a fair share

---

[4] Between 1940 and 1950, non-academic salaries in institutions of higher education increased 110 per cent, whereas academic salaries increased only 54 per cent. At least one well-known economist has interpreted this fact as evidence that the organizations of professors are weaker than the organizations of janitors and other non-academic employees. See Harris, *op. cit.*, p. 587.

of the benefits of their increased productivity. The AAUP has been practically useless along both of these lines.

The AAUP has no status as a bargaining agent for the professors. Administrative authorities are not legally compelled to negotiate with the AAUP about anything. The fact that administrators and boards of regents frequently consult with AAUP representatives is not too important. It makes a considerable difference whether an employer is compelled (by law or by the organizational strength of the employees) to negotiate with employee representatives or whether the employer talks to employee representatives as a matter of charity. The difference, of course, is reflected in the quality of the agreements reached. Employee organizations which compel recognition from the employer achieve greater gains than those which have no recognized legal status as bargaining units and which are too weak to compel employers to recognize them in this capacity.

THE AAUP, TENURE, AND ACADEMIC FREEDOM

The real tragedy of the AAUP is not that professors have fallen behind the Joneses. It is the AAUP's shocking incapacity to protect the integrity of higher education. The industrial worker needs free speech, but it is not as a rule necessary for him to do his job. Again speaking in broad terms and allowing for much qualification, the industrial worker is concerned functionally with physical processes, not conflicting ideas. On the other hand, the professors who formed the AAUP specifically recognized that their jobs often required a frank treatment of new and upsetting ideas. Yet the fact is that the typical industrial worker has more freedom on the job to speak his mind freely than the overwhelming majority of college professors who require such freedom to do their job properly.

If the state of academic freedom seems better today than it did during the heyday of the late Senator McCarthy, the reason is not in what the AAUP has done. It is that a combination of factors over which the AAUP had no control, such as the decline and death of the senator, helped to mitigate the cruder forms of interference with academic freedom. The fact that a demagogue like the late senator from Wisconsin can throw the academic community into great turmoil indicates how weak academic freedom really is in the United States.

The fallacy of supposing that academic freedom is growing stronger merely because one particular threat to it has subsided is apparent from the situation in the South. In many Southern institutions of higher education, academic freedom on matters relating to racial segregation has all but disappeared. The professors in these institutions realize that all the local, state, and national branches of the AAUP are too weak to protect individual professors who criticize racial segregation, either in their role as citizens or in the legitimate exercise of academic freedom.

Because many professors tolerate the most extreme violations of academic freedom in order to keep their jobs, it is a grave error to evaluate the AAUP's record with respect to tenure and academic freedom merely by reference to the cases which become matters of controversy. Indeed, even in cases where unjust dismissal actually occurs, the professors involved are often unwilling to appeal to the AAUP for help. They may believe, and with good reason, that the AAUP is incapable of restoring them to their positions. Since an appeal to the AAUP may destroy a professor's chances of securing a position elsewhere, appeals are not often made. Thus few tenure cases officially arise, because the AAUP is so weak an organization.[5]

[5] ". . . I was dismissed from a university after several years service as an assistant professor. I was informed that my department was overstaffed, but an additional instructor was employed in that department for the next academic year. What the real reason was I do not know to this day. I submit that such things are outrageous, but they are not very rare. A similar case was investigated by Committee A of the American Association of University Professors, but far more numerous are the cases that are never reported by the victims. They conclude, as I did, that they will have a better chance to get back into academic life if they avoid publicity" (E. H. Sturtevant, "Selection and Retention of Faculty Members," *American Association of University Professors Bulletin,* XXV [October, 1939], 421). I quote this statement not for the evidence it bears but for the common-sense reasoning it represents. For a systematic study of the extent to which academic freedom has been impaired without any protest or action by the professors, see Paul F. Lazarsfeld and Wagner Thielens, Jr., *The Academic Mind* (Glencoe, Ill.: Free Press, 1958).

A DIAGNOSIS

Why has the AAUP never developed a broad and realistic program to promote the welfare of college professors? What has prevented it from becoming a powerful occupational organization, serving effectively to protect the integrity of higher education and at the same time to advance the welfare of the professors?

Paradoxically, one reason for its failure to protect academic freedom is that the organization is devoted chiefly to this purpose. Thus its appeal is largely confined to those who already have a strong interest in the matter. Many professors see little sense in joining an organization which is preoccupied with academic freedom and which is not particularly effective even in this limited area.

The AAUP's failure to grasp the fundamental importance of recognition is also part of the explanation for its unimpressive record. As things stand, each chapter of the AAUP must devote a great deal of its time and energy to achieving an integral place in the structure of employer-employee relations at its institution. The AAUP seems content with a strategy which calls for an institution-by-institution approach to achieve this objective. But success, if achieved at all, is due to the efforts of outstanding individuals or to the friendly attitudes of particular administrators, and when these people disappear, the influence of the chapter does also. Professors refuse to join because the chapters have no assured status, and the fact that they do not join makes it more difficult for the chapters to achieve such status.

The institution-by-institution approach to recognition can be compared to the industrial scene before the New Deal, when every union had to devote most of its energies to force employers to negotiate conditions of employment. If recognition were assured, the chapters would be free to concentrate upon professional and economic problems instead of organizational ones. This goal can be achieved in different ways. One way would be to give the highest priority to legislation that would require college administrators to negotiate with the duly chosen representatives of the professors on matters of employment.

This strategy will seem absurd to many professors. After all, it presupposes that professors have to become a pressure group and get into the political arena like everyone else. It presupposes also that it is futile to wait for society to bestow wealth and power on academic man; he will have to fight for these things or go without them. This is not a pleasant thought, especially since professorial political incompetence has long been characteristic of American politics. Of course, this fact cannot be conceded, publicly at least, by the professors. The evils of becoming a "pressure group" provide a face-saving rationalization for their political incapacity.

The alleged evils of being a pressure group frequently find expression in the long-standing controversy within the AAUP over whether it is or ought to be a "trade union." As is the case within the NEA, the professors find it necessary to formulate elaborate and wholly gratuitous distinctions between their activities and those of "trade unions." The distinctions reveal little understanding of unions, but what is more important, professorial strategy is weakened by the requirement that it be different from that adopted by blue-collar workers. How much it is weakened can be seen from the following incident. A friend of mine who was a delegate to the 1959 AAUP Convention told me that her expenses were shared equally by her chapter and her university. While she was in the office of the university president prior to the convention, he urged her to go to the convention and "put some guts" into the Association. Imagine a president of a coal company paying the expenses of a miner to the annual convention of the United Mine Workers and urging the miner to "put some guts" into the UMW! As the saying goes, "We should live so long!"

The professorial compulsion to avoid the appearance of trade unionism is reflected in the following paragraphs in a report recently issued by the AAUP's Committee Z on the "Economic Status of the Profession":

ALLEGED TRADE-UNION PRACTICES

The Committee is aware of the unfavorable reactions which its program has aroused in several quarters. Members of administrations and governing boards of colleges and universities have expressed themselves, sometimes in angry words, concerning the "trade-union practices" to which the AAUP is supposed to have resorted.

The comparison of our activities with trade-union practices might by many members of the profession be interpreted as a recognition of the effectiveness of our activities; some might even accept it as a flattering comparison; others may resent it, reject it, or be embarrassed. Be this as it may, we should note at least one essential difference between trade-union methods and the methods employed in our program. Trade-union pressure achieves its greatest effectiveness by utilizing some monopolistic or bargaining advantages; our methods, however, involve nothing but publicizing three indexes of salary payments for each institution. Public knowledge of prices or wages paid is one of the prerequisites which economists regard as essential for the functioning of a free competitive market. The quest for public information on the salary conditions at different institutions can certainly not be considered an improper demand.[6]

Another important reason for the weakness of the AAUP at all levels is that local chapters cannot count upon immediate and effective support from the national organization in a time of crisis. This is apparent from a consideration of the feeble sanctions employed by the AAUP. These sanctions are more appropriate for a ladies' aid society than for a professional organization.[7] For example, when the gauntlet is thrown down to the AAUP by an institution of higher education and an issue must be resolved by an all-out test of strength, the most drastic action taken by the AAUP is a vote to censure the administration of the institution concerned. Such action, often taken years after the event which precipitated the controversy, has been the limit of AAUP action

---

[6] "Report of Committee Z to the 45th Annual Meeting" (Washington, D.C.: American Association of University Professors, 1959), p. 15. Duplicated material.

[7] I wrote this sentence before attending the 1959 annual national convention in Pittsburgh. In their reliance upon wrist-slapping statements of censure instead of deeds and their fear of using, or appearing to use, pressure tactics, the delegates at that meeting were nothing if not enfeebled. The atmosphere was really not much different from that of an NEA convention.

in cases involving the most fundamental opposition to the Association's policies.

In censure cases, the professorial victim often suffers a severe setback, regardless of his innocence in the matter. Of course, not all grievances are carried to the point where they involve a vote of censure by the national organization. Some are settled on a basis favorable to the professors but without publicity by the national office. Nevertheless, these cases do not justify a belief that the AAUP has been an effective professional organization. The conditions confronting the academic community as a whole are too unsatisfactory to accept such a conclusion.

Some of the most basic reasons for the weakness of the AAUP are rarely discussed in academic circles. Professors have yet to face up to the fact that it is unrealistic to regard all college teachers as members of the same profession. Failure to confront this issue and to take the organizational steps required by a realistic answer to it are a basic cause of the weakness of the AAUP.

If you ask a medical professor his occupation, he is more likely to think of himself as a physician than as a professor. True, he is both, but the relative emphasis is crucial. The professor physician is more likely to be interested in the American Medical Association than in the AAUP. Likewise, the chemistry professor regards himself as a chemist and the American Chemical Society as his professional organization. The mathematics professor regards himself as a mathematician and gives his organizational priorities to the American Mathematical Association.

In short, most professors are primarily interested in organizations which concentrate upon developments in their fields of specialization. There is, however, a vast difference between the various specialized organizations to which professors belong. The medical professor need not worry about the weakness of the AAUP because the American Medical Association has a very effective program to protect the independence and economic status of physicians. Furthermore, physicians need not be professors. They can make out very well apart from any university connection. Thus the universities are forced to bargain with individual physicians who wish to teach, and to respect the autonomy of the medical professor. However, the AAUP is irrelevant as far as this outcome is concerned. On the other hand, most professorial organizations are study organizations and only that. And since professors tend to join them instead of the AAUP, they really have neither a professional nor an employee organization.

We may use history professors to illustrate this point. They regard the American Historical Association as their "professional" organization. Now whatever the American Historical Association may be, by no stretch of the imagination can it be regarded as a professional organization. According to an Association publication, "The American Historical Association welcomes to its membership anyone who subscribes to its purposes"—and pays $7.50 in dues. The Association sets no standards for admission to teaching history or being a "historian." It exercises no control over the training of historians. It neither formulates nor enforces a code of professional ethics. It is at most an organization of people interested in history; it is no more "professional" than a society of stamp collectors. The very fact that history professors pompously refer to the American Historical Association as their "professional" organization tells us a great deal about the organizational naïveté of these academicians.

The same analysis applies to the various regional and state historical associations. Only persons hard up for status symbols would dream of calling them professional organizations. Note, however, what happens when history professors concentrate their organizational activities upon these associations. The various historical associations do not represent the professors as employees. Only a small minority of professors at each institution teach history. University administrators are not going to negotiate separately on conditions of employment with each history department, and, indeed, the history professors themselves do not advocate that they should. The upshot is that the "professional" associations of history professors have no impact whatsoever on conditions of employment for history professors. Equally important, these associations are completely devoid of the professional controls and sanctions which might give individual history professors a measure of bargaining power and occupational protection vis-à-vis their employing institutions.

We can summarize the situation in this way: A truly professional organization is concerned with both the work of the profession and the conditions of employment of its membership. Some professors, such as those in medicine, are members of non-academic professional organizations which effectively serve these two kinds of interests. Most, however, confine their organizational activities to such organizations as the American Chemical Society, the American Physical Society, the American Historical Association, the American Sociological Association, and so on. The programs and activities of these organizations are devoted exclusively or in large part to a field of knowledge; they have practically no impact upon conditions of employment in higher education.

The AAUP is supposedly the comprehensive organization of professors which *is* concerned with conditions of employment. However, since the AAUP has no subject divisions or sections, it lacks one of the basic appeals of a professional organization. Some professors divide their time and energy between the AAUP and their subject organizations, but this is an inefficient procedure. Because many do not join the AAUP at all, or because those who do join divide their organizational energies between several incomplete organizations, the AAUP is fatally weakened as a professional and as an employee organization. The employing institutions dictate to a disorganized group of individuals instead of negotiating with strong organizations of professionals.

These comments about the AAUP are not intended to excuse the weaknesses of organizations of public school teachers. Nor are they intended merely to show that certain problems confronting teachers below the college level are also prevalent in higher education. It is the causal relationship in the situation that is important. Teachers tend to look to professors for leadership; when the latter are so incapable of solving the kinds of problems which concern teachers also, professorial leadership becomes a case of the blind leading the blind.

A PRESCRIPTION

The organizational mess in education can be cleaned up; to think otherwise is to despair of the future of American education. In order to clean it up, we must first dispel two basic misconceptions concerning the dynamics of educational reform.

I have already alluded to one of these misconceptions. This is the notion that because certain issues are for the public to resolve, the teachers are absolved from responsibility for the decisions made by the public. This misconception is based upon a formalistic instead of a strategic conception of the relationships between a profession and the public it serves. Having discussed this point at some length in previous chapters, I shall not elaborate upon it here.

The other misconception is not as obvious, but it is more pervasive. This is the notion that school systems and institutions of higher education are in the best position to initiate and carry through needed educational reforms. The people who are subject to this misconception are aware of the need for educational leadership. The trouble is that they overemphasize leadership by educational administrators and neglect the crucial role of organizational leadership.

Education textbooks, especially those in school administration, resound with appeals for educational statesmen. It is clear from the context, however, that superintendents or principals are expected to fill this role. A heavy emphasis upon instructional leadership also stands out in educational literature; I would estimate that of all the books and articles on the subject of educational leadership, less than a hundredth part is focused directly upon leadership in teachers' organizations.

The same mistaken emphasis prevails in higher education. This is apparent from such things as the pattern of foundation grants. Enormous sums are granted to strengthen educational institutions; very little is spent to strengthen educational organizations.

The foundations have made some grants to educational organizations for the avowed purpose of raising their level of effectiveness. For example, in November, 1958, the Fund for the Republic made a $10,000 grant to the Academic Freedom Fund of the AAUP. The money is to be used for investigations of alleged violations of academic freedom, the support of professors whose means of livelihood have been cut off in such cases, legal expenses, and appropriate publicity. These are worthy causes but thoroughly typical of the tendency to concentrate upon a few visible cases while the entire academic community sinks deeper into the abyss.[8]

What must be done? Some things have been pointed out, or are implicit in the preceding discussion; others will be suggested in subsequent chapters. At this point I would like to make a proposal that goes beyond any specific area where reform is needed. The proposal is applicable to all major educational organizations, but I shall use the AAUP for illustrative purposes.

The AAUP should draft, or cause to be drafted, a proposal for a thorough, critical, no-holds-barred evaluation of itself. Regardless of who drafts the proposal, it should provide that the evaluation not be under the control of the organization; it should be conducted under other auspices with the consent and co-operation of the AAUP. The evaluation should cover every important aspect of the Association—its goals and goal-setting procedures, dues, membership requirements, publications, personnel, business procedures, relationships with local chapters, legislative programs, state and regional groups, national conventions, strategy and tactics; in short, the Association has to be put through a wringer. This is not likely to happen if the organization itself controls the evaluation.

The evaluation should be prospective as well as retrospective; that is, it should be programmatic. For example, from the evaluation there might emerge sound proposals that the present $8.00

---

[8] Frankly, it is difficult for me to understand why the Fund for the Republic should have made this grant. The professors ought by this time to be able to fight their own battles and take care of their own wounded. If they cannot, the foundations ought to help them discover and eliminate the reasons for their incapacity. But it is not the business of a foundation to provide support for routine cases which should be an organizational responsibility.

dues be raised to $50.00 or even $100. These proposals would be accompanied by specific suggestions as to the way the money should be spent and the results to be expected.

The evaluation, including action proposals, should become the Association's agenda for the next few years. If the evaluation is carried out as suggested here, a number of vested interests in the Association are going to get hurt. I do not mean the paid staff necessarily, but many points of view long advocated and followed in the organization will have to be abandoned. This fact underlies the need for outside evaluation; whatever recommendations emerge will have a better chance of being accepted if they come from expert but disinterested sources.

The important task is to get a program accepted by the membership as a basis for action. Presumably there will have to be modifications of the proposals emerging from the evaluation, but the directions to be taken should be fairly clear. The re-education of the membership can be achieved through the *American Association of University Professors Bulletin,* special publications, and local, regional, and national meetings. To speed up this process, there should be a series of Institutes on Educational Leadership held at leading universities throughout the country. These institutes should be designed to re-educate chapter and regional leaders on the findings and recommendations of the evaluation. They should not presume to make chiefs out of Indians but to give the present leadership at local, state, and regional levels a new conception of what their organizations can and should do.

A program of the kind just outlined should be designed to change our image of professorial organizations in a relatively short time. Such a program would not cost more than a few million dollars at most; even if it were to cost this much, the amount would be small compared to those the foundations are currently pouring into rearranging and integrating courses, institutional self-surveys, and the other dry wells of foundation drilling. I am convinced the money can be raised if and when the AAUP makes a genuine effort to get it for this purpose.

These comments concerning the need for and the strategy of

organizational reform in higher education apply with equal force to organizations of public school teachers.[9] Some schools of education must challenge the present emphasis on strengthening school systems and concentrate upon strengthening teachers' organizations. Needless to say, however, "strengthening" teachers' organizations is not the same thing as helping them to enrol more members to pay more dues to be thrown away on the same old objectives.

In order to strengthen their organizations, educators must demand and support a level of leadership higher than that prevailing. They must get rid of the leadership that has led them to the current impasse and must put in positions of power and responsibility leaders who will produce results. This is not unreasonable; results *can* be achieved with able leadership.

Contemporary educational leadership reminds me of a basketball coach described to me by a friend. When his team was losing badly at the half, the coach's half-time counsel was, "Make those baskets!" This advice was about as helpful as advice to teachers that they deserve higher salaries. Higher salaries for teachers are not a program—they are one of the objectives of a program. Mere reiteration that teachers should receive higher salaries or have better training or be accorded more respect does not constitute leadership worthy of teacher support. Leadership consists of finding ways and means to achieve these objectives.

Unfortunately, the record shows not only a steady decline of the teaching profession but also that the full-time leaders of state and national teachers' organizations are practically never fired, no matter how little their organizations accomplish. In teachers' organizations, it seems that nothing succeeds so well as failure.

Let me illustrate what must be done in terms of the state teachers' associations. The executive secretaries of these associations are the authorized spokesmen for the teachers. These spokesmen should command the utmost respect, by virtue of both their position and their personal qualifications. Their position should

[9] The NEA recently employed a private consulting firm to make a survey of itself. The results were some improvements in the business operations of the Association, but the survey did not really come to grips with the more basic problems of organizational goals, strategy, and achievements.

be regarded as of equal or greater importance than the presidency of a major university or the top educational job in the state government. Furthermore, the qualifications and rewards for this position should be consistent with this point of view.

In fact, teacher leadership at the state level is often tragically weak. Teachers who would hire the very best lawyer to be their advocate in a legal case show the most shortsighted reluctance to hire the most effective occupational advocate that money can buy. A conservative estimate of the difference between effective and ineffective state leadership would be several hundred dollars per year per teacher. This being the case, a salary of $50,000 a year would be cheap for a really able leader of a large state teachers' association. In a state like New York, such a salary would amount to less than fifty cents per year per teacher if all teachers belonged to the association. This kind of salary is needed to attract and support top caliber leadership, but only one of the state associations pays as much as $25,000 to its chief executive. The teachers, who do so much talking about the importance of our investment in human resources, are the least inclined to make such an investment out of their own pockets.

Instead of waiting for scattered individuals in scattered organizations over the country to take a few timid steps to remedy this situation, there must be launched a massive nationwide effort to create a new concept of this position. I recognize the enormous difficulties involved, including the obvious threat to many of the present leaders. There are states in which the teachers would be well advised to retire their present officers on full salary in order to get on with the job. But once the teachers grasp the importance of organizational leadership, they will find the ways and means of getting it.

In conclusion, let me affirm my conviction that the weakness of teachers is a catastrophe for the country as well as for the teachers. The educational world is full of professional liberals who are always ready to denounce the power of the American Medical Association, the American Bar Association, the National Association of Manufacturers, the AFL-CIO, and other occupational organizations. Meanwhile, the educators are helpless to protect the integrity of their own work or their own legitimate vocational interests. Whatever abuses of power may justly be attributed to such organizations as the American Medical Association, one must question whether the country would be better off, medically or otherwise, if the AMA were as weak as the AAUP, the NEA, or the AFT. Conversely, if the country is not so well off educationally as it ought to be, our educational organizations must bear the major responsibility for this situation. It is time to put aside the cliché that the public is only getting what it deserves—that is, what it is willing to pay for—in the field of education. Our concern should not be with the public but with the educational organizations which fail to provide leadership that will be respected and followed by the public.

Chapter XI

THE STRATEGY AND TACTICS OF
EDUCATIONAL CHANGE

It is unrealistic to expect the public to initiate basic educational reforms or to provide the driving force needed to effectuate them. Intelligent non-professional action is essential at certain stages, but the major and enduring responsibility for improving our schools lies with the people who work in them.

This view calls for a reassessment of current strategy designed to improve education. My analysis will deal first with this strategy, which in my opinion misconceives the role of the public in bringing about educational improvements. It will then move on to some suggested changes in the role to be played by the public. The last part of the chapter will be devoted to specific problems of strategy confronting the teachers. These problems are important to everyone, since they involve the nature and limits of occupational action in areas of fundamental public concern.

To illustrate current strategy for achieving educational improvements, and my criticisms of this strategy, I propose to analyze the development and implementation of the "Conant report." [1] The background of the report is as follows: Dr. Conant was approached by the Carnegie Corporation to see whether

[1] James B. Conant, *The American High School Today: A First Report to Interested Citizens* (New York: McGraw-Hill Book Co., 1959).

218

he had any interest in returning to the field of education after completing his duties as ambassador to the Federal Republic of Germany. Pursuant to the discussions between Dr. Conant and representatives of the Carnegie Corporation, the latter made a grant to the Educational Testing Service to enable Dr. Conant to study certain problems relating to comprehensive high schools in the United States. In Dr. Conant's own words, "comprehensive high schools" are those "whose programs correspond to the needs of *all* the youth of the community."

Dr. Conant did not attempt to conduct a broad survey of American high schools generally, or even of comprehensive schools. His overriding interest was to ascertain

> whether, under one and the same roof and under the same management, it is possible for a school to fulfill satisfactorily three functions: Can a school at one and the same time provide a good general education for *all* the pupils as future citizens of a democracy, provide elective programs for the majority to develop useful skills, and educate adequately those with a talent for handling advanced academic subjects—particularly foreign languages and advanced mathematics? The answer to this question would seem to be of considerable interest for the future of American education. If the answer were clearly in the negative, then a radical change in the structure of American public secondary education would be in order. . . . On the other hand, if the answer is in the affirmative, then no radical change in the basic pattern of American education would seem to be required.[2]

Note that if Dr. Conant were able to locate at least one comprehensive school satisfactorily fulfilling the functions he deemed appropriate for them, he would be able to provide a definitive answer to his basic question. The existence of one such school demonstrates that it is possible for a comprehensive school to fulfil these functions. (Actually, Dr. Conant regarded eight of the 103 schools visited by him or his staff as adequately fulfilling these three functions.)

Dr. Conant's report was published in February, 1959. A major part of the report is a series of twenty-one recommendations for improving public education. The range of these recommendations is indicated by some of their headings: "The Counseling

[2] *Ibid.*, p. 15.

System," "Required Programs for All," "Ability Grouping," "English Composition," "The Academic Inventory," "Homerooms," etc. In some cases, the recommendations made under these headings are very specific. For example, Recommendation 6 reads:

The time devoted to English composition during the four years should occupy about half the total time devoted to the study of English. Each student should be required to write an average of one theme a week. Themes should be corrected by the teacher. In order that teachers of English have adequate time for handling these themes, no English teacher should be responsible for more than one hundred pupils. . . .[3]

We thus have the following situation: A man who is a distinguished scientist, an outstanding university president, a successful diplomat, and a devoted supporter of public education in and for our democratic society is liberally supplied with funds to enable him to study a basic problem of American education. He carries out the study and writes a report which receives unprecedented publicity; approximately 200,000 copies of it were sold or otherwise distributed within six months after it was first published. For the most part, the educational recommendations in the report would improve public education. Although I disagree with some of them and admit incapacity to evaluate others, nothing that I have to say depends upon any criticism of the educational recommendations in the report. The report itself is intelligent, reasonable, and without a trace of the hobby-horsing or ax-grinding that characterizes most books on education written for the general public. It comes at a time when it is difficult to get men of Dr. Conant's stature seriously involved in the problems of public education. What, if anything, is wrong with the situation?

Perhaps nothing—as I have described it thus far. But let us look at the way in which the report is being implemented. According to Dr. Conant: "When I first planned the study, I had in mind formulating my conclusions in such a way that they could be presented in various states to the citizens committees concerned with supporting good public education." And later he states, "Since, however, the school boards, almost without excep-

[3] *Ibid.*, pp. 50–51.

tion, do have a great degree of freedom in managing the local school, I have addressed this report *in the first instance to school board members.*" [4]

In attempting to implement the recommendations emerging from his study, Dr. Conant met with school boards and citizens' committees over the entire country. He also worked with various professional organizations, but the focus of his persuasive efforts was on the school boards.

What would have been the reaction to the procedure followed by Dr. Conant if someone had utilized it in higher education? Surely, Dr. Conant would have been the first to protest if, while he was president of Harvard, the trustees had notified him that they wanted certain changes in the curriculum and in "the requirements for admission to advanced courses" put into effect at the beginning of the school year. Presumably, these things are a professional prerogative at Harvard. I see no reason why they should not be so in public education as well—and this brings me to one of my reasons for thinking that the net impact of the report may be harmful despite the merits of its educational recommendations. The procedures used to implement the report reinforce the prevailing notion that school boards ought to decide professional matters, such as what subjects should be offered and at what grade levels.

The matter of professional autonomy is not confronted squarely in the report. Those comments which do relate to it are rather ambiguous. We read that:

Other recommendations [those not involving a budgetary increase] concern the details of school organization and curriculum; in the first instance, these recommendations belong in the province of school administrators. . . . Some of the recommendations listed below can be put into effect at the beginning of the school year without upsetting in any way the morale of the teaching staff. Other recommendations, however, can be effective only if a majority of the teachers are convinced of their wisdom. . . . I have in mind particularly the controversial subject of ability grouping, any recommendations in regard to marking or grading, and the requirements for admission to advanced courses. [5]

[4] *Ibid.*, pp. v and 9. My italics.
[5] *Ibid.*, pp. 43–44.

These comments are not too clear, since there is no explicit statement of what curriculum matters are for the school board to decide and what are "details" for the professional staff to decide. Furthermore, the need for school boards to convince the teachers of the wisdom of certain changes raises some interesting questions. Teachers should be persuading school boards of the need for changes in class size, ability grouping, and requirements for admission to advanced courses; is there not something amiss when the persuading on these matters is the other way around?

To change the curriculum, persuade those who have the power to change it—the school boards. In this sense, Dr. Conant's procedure is sound; there is no point in persuading the teachers first, since they could only recommend action to their school boards. But if you believe, as I do, that our most serious curriculum problems flow from the fact that teachers do not have the operating power to make the professional curriculum decisions, then you do not try to bring about changes by means of a strategy that reinforces the prevailing antiprofessional power structure of public education.

To clarify this point, consider two of the proposals in the report. Its major recommendation calls for the elimination of small high schools. Dr. Conant states: "I should like to record at this point my conviction that in many states the number one problem is the elimination of the small high school by district reorganization." Later, he says: "I can sum up my conclusions in a few sentences. The number of small high schools must be drastically reduced. Aside from this important change, I believe no radical alteration in the basic pattern of American education is necessary in order to improve our schools. And "Unless a graduating class contains at least one hundred students, classes in advanced subjects and separate sections within all classes become impossible except with extravagantly high costs . . . [;] the same conclusion has been reached by a committee of the American Association of School Administrators." [6]

The fact that small schools are wasteful and that their consolidation ought to be given very high priority has been a re-

[6] *Ibid.*, pp. 38–40, 77–78.

curring theme of textbooks in secondary education and school administration for decades.[7] However, before analyzing the implications of this fact, let us look at one other proposal and Dr. Conant's comments concerning it. Recommendation 18 reads in part as follows:

The school board should be ready to offer a third and fourth year of a foreign language. The guidance officers should urge the completion of a four-year sequence of *one* foreign language if the student demonstrates ability in handling foreign languages. . . . The main purpose of studying a foreign language is to obtain something approaching mastery of that language. And by mastery is surely meant the ability to read the literature published in the language and, in the case of a modern language, to converse with considerable fluency and accuracy with an inhabitant of the country in question.[8]

Dr. Conant then makes the following comment:

I have met no teachers of foreign language who felt that anything approaching mastery could be obtained by the study of a foreign language for only two years in high school, nor have the students felt that two years of study had given them any real working knowledge of the language . . . [;] the foreign language teachers with whom I talked were almost unanimous in agreeing that two years were quite insufficient and that a very small residue, if any, was left in the student's mind after such an exposure.[9]

Dr. Conant does not claim originality for these recommendations. Indeed, it is precisely because they are not original with

[7] See R. Emerson Langfitt, Frank W. Cyr, and N. William Newson, *The Small High School At Work* (New York: American Book Co., 1936), esp. pp. 42–61; William M. Alexander and J. Galen Saylor, *Secondary Education* (New York: Rinehart & Co., 1950), pp. 196–99, 474–75; and Rudyard K. Bent and Henry Kronenberg, *Principles of Secondary Education* (3d ed.; New York: McGraw-Hill Book Co., 1955), pp. 97–102; and Paul R. Mort and Walter C. Reusser, *Public School Finance* (2d ed.; New York: McGraw-Hill Book Co., 1951), pp. 582–86. Literally dozens of other textbooks as well as scores of articles in educational journals also emphasize the need to eliminate the small school. A recent yearbook of the American Association of School Administrators was devoted largely to the problem of eliminating schools or school systems which are too small to operate efficiently. See American Association of School Administrators, *School District Organization* (Washington, D.C.: American Association of School Administrators, 1958).

[8] *Conant, op. cit.,* p. 69.

[9] *Ibid.,* p. 69.

him that the attention given them demands our own attention. John Gardner, president of the Carnegie Corporation, says about the report: "If the reader . . . is in the mood to roll up his sleeves and say 'precisely what can we do tomorrow morning to improve our schools?' this is the book." [10]

In view of the fact that the major recommendations of the report have been made for years by professional educators, it seems to me that some important questions are going unanswered —perhaps because unasked—in this situation. Take Mr. Gardner's reader who is "in the mood to roll up his sleeves" and go to work "tomorrow morning to improve our schools." Why were his sleeves not rolled up ten or twenty years ago, when the reforms now recommended by Dr. Conant were first made by the professionals in his community? Is it desirable, is it necessary, that school boards should have to be convinced by an outside figure of great prestige to carry out reforms advocated by the overwhelming weight of professional opinion in their own community?

Mr. Gardner goes on to say: "Hundreds of thousands of Americans all over the country are concerned about their schools, wondering what to do about them, seeking answers, hoping for guidance. Mr. Conant has provided that guidance." [11] I yield to no one in my estimate of what one man can do, in education or any other field. Nevertheless, I am skeptical of the man-on-horseback approach implicit in the preceding quotation. I suggest that a fruitful course for a foundation to follow would be to analyze the reasons why those proposals in the Conant report long advocated by professional opinion should have lain dormant through the years. For what it is worth, my own view is that the strategy of implementing educational reforms exemplified by the Conant report has so weakened the power and prestige of educators that what they say no longer counts.

The dangers of this strategy will be more evident if we pay due regard to the specificity of the recommendations in the re-

[10] *Ibid.*, pp. x–xi.
[11] *Ibid.*, p. xii.

port. The report points out that it takes three or four years of study to master a foreign language. This can change. Teachers may find it feasible to provide short periods of intensive study which materially shorten the over-all time needed to master a foreign language. The ease of travel to foreign countries, international television, or new developments in teaching may also have this result. In short, it may be that two years will be deemed sufficient for the mastery of a foreign language. But if so, where will Dr. Conant be? He specifically points out the probability that some of his recommendations may need revision in five or ten years. But this misses the point. If school boards do not *now* accept the recommendations of their professional staff concerning the amount of time needed to master a foreign language, what reason is there to believe that they will be more willing to accept such recommendations in the future?

The Conant report is an eloquent plea for the continuation and strengthening of comprehensive schools on the grounds that such schools are an essential bulwark of social cohesion in the United States. It is nonetheless clear that Dr. Conant himself is (or was) far behind professional opinion on the extent to which these schools lack social cohesion and contribute to the stratification of American society. He writes:

> Somewhat to my surprise, I found that almost without exception those students elected to the student council or as officers of the class were in the group of the more academically able students who were preparing to go on to college. Such was the case in each of these schools, although the reader must remember that this collegebound group was always in the minority.[12]

Now this is itself a surprising statement. Educational research going back at least twenty years has demonstrated that college preparatory students tend to monopolize class offices and other prestigeful positions far out of proportion to their numbers. These students are also favored in grading, in discipline, and in the various academic, musical, and literary contests which characterize large comprehensive schools. These points are made in

[12] *Ibid.*, p. 18.

many textbooks in the sociology of education and in secondary education. Principals of comprehensive high schools always expect to encounter this phenomenon.[13]

The favored position of children from the upper classes in comprehensive schools obviously weaken Dr. Conant's thesis that such schools are a sort of melting pot for children from different social classes. The children from different socioeconomic classes may be together physically in the comprehensive school, but they are not necessarily getting to know and like one another better as a result.

These considerations do not necessarily invalidate the ideal of a comprehensive school. In my opinion, they only point to specific problems which must be solved in order to effectuate the ideal. But the fact that the country's leading supporter of comprehensive schools was so obviously unaware of important data bearing upon the ineffectiveness of these schools suggests the dangers and the futility of relying upon one man, no matter how outstanding, to provide "the" answers to complicated educational problems on a hit-and-run basis. The question, therefore, still remains—how can we articulate professional opinion in the structure of public education so that it is reflected in practice within a reasonable period of time, and what strategy should be followed to achieve this goal?

[13] Examples of research studies which bear directly upon this point are David Wright, "Participation in Extra-Class Activities According to Economic Status" (master's thesis, Stanford University, Calif., 1937); Elizabeth J. McElroy, "Participation in Extra-Curricular Activities as a Welfare Phenomenon" (master's thesis, Stanford University, Calif., 1937); Harold C. Hand, *Principal Findings of the 1947–48 Basic Studies of the Illinois Secondary School Curriculum Program* (Springfield, Ill.: Office of the Superintendent of Public Instruction, 1949); and A. B. Hollingshead, *Elmtown's Youth* (New York: John Wiley & Sons, 1948). The last reference, which devotes considerable attention to the phenomenon which surprised Dr. Conant, is one of the most widely read books in the country in the fields of sociology, adolescent development, and education. For an example of a textbook in secondary education which deals very specifically with the domination of school offices by children from the upper classes, see Harold C. Hand, *Principles of Public Secondary Education* (New York: Harcourt Brace & Co., 1958), pp. 99–104.

THE STRATEGY OF SCHOOL-BY-SCHOOL IMPROVEMENT

Let me turn next to another strategic fallacy in the Conant report. This fallacy may be more pervasive among the public at large than among educators, but I believe that it overwhelmingly characterizes the strategic thinking of both groups. I refer to the faith in a school-by-school approach to educational reform. In Dr. Conant's words:

> The improvements must come school by school and be made with due regard for the nature of the community. Therefore, I conclude by addressing this final word to citizens who are concerned with public education: avoid generalizations, recognize the necessity of diversity, get the facts about your local situation, elect a good school board, and support the efforts of the board to improve the schools.[14]

The plausibility of this advice, especially for parents, is obvious. The individual parent is most interested in the education of *his* child at *this* time in *this* school. Furthermore, he cannot go to Washington or to his state capitol to remedy shortcomings in his school system. His interest may be great, but his individual circumstances render such action prohibitive. Since he can affect the school system attended by his children more easily than he can a state legislature or Congress, he tends to focus his educational efforts on the local school boards. These agencies alone provide immediate results.

The school-by-school (or community-by-community) strategy rests upon the assumption that local school boards have the power to bring about basic educational reforms. Unquestionably, they have the legal power to bring about some of them. But they do not have, nor are they likely to have, the operating power to bring about many of the important reforms which are needed.

We have already discussed (in chapter iii) the various reasons why it is no longer possible to rely upon local (and state) sources of revenue to finance the rising costs of public education. Even where substantial sources of revenue are physically located within a school district, they are frequently not available for educational

[14] *Ibid.*, p. 96.

purposes because of features of the tax structure not subject to local control. Furthermore, there are many communities which just do not have sufficient revenue.

The limitations of the community-by-community approach are also obvious from the standpoint of teacher education. There is a nationwide shortage of teachers in several crucial areas. This problem cannot be solved on a system-by-system basis—the various systems are simply dividing up the scarcities. No single system, except possibly the very few largest, can affect the over-all supply and demand situation. Raising salaries in one system to get certain kinds of teachers, e.g., physics teachers, merely creates a shortage of such teachers in other systems. Furthermore, raising salaries means raising taxes, and this brings us back to the financial plight of most school districts.

School boards are political creatures of the state legislatures, which can eliminate, expand, or modify the powers of these boards at any time. Some legislatures and constitutions have placed a ceiling on the tax rate that can be levied for the public schools. No matter if all the citizens in a particular district are willing to double their taxes for schools, they cannot legally do so. They must first get action at the state level to be able to act at the local level.

The limitations of the community-by-community approach constitute one of the major problems in reorganizing small school districts in order to get schools large enough to be efficient. As Dr. Conant himself points out, where such reorganization depends on a majority vote in all the districts to be reorganized, it is often rejected by the voters of one district. This is likely to happen if one district does not possess resources commensurate with the number of children it would contribute to the consolidated district. The citizens of the wealthier districts do not wish to pay higher taxes for the education of the children from the poorer districts. Clearly, this problem can be solved only by adopting a broader strategy than the community-by-community approach to educational reform.[15]

[15] In general, some type of mandatory legislation is needed at the state level to expedite the consolidation of small and inefficient school districts.

I do not wish to underestimate what a good school board can do. Neither do I wish to exaggerate it. When the standard advice given to those who work for better education is to concentrate on electing and supporting good school boards, I feel most strongly that the potential of these agencies to improve public education is being vastly overrated.

It is no answer to point to what an exceptional school board has achieved. Our attitude toward school boards must be based upon what we can reasonably expect them to be and do, given a wide range of circumstances affecting their membership and their freedom—both legal and practical—to take action. Strategy should take into account what exceptional people do, but can it be sensibly based upon the assumption that everyone will be exceptional? Suggestions that citizens "get the facts" and "elect a good school board" have been made for a long, long time in American education, and the results are not impressive.[16]

For these and other reasons, I disagree with the belief that the most important election for the education-minded citizen is the local school board election. In the short run, and for rather limited goals, sometimes; in the long run, the educational views of governors, state legislators, Congressmen, and presidents are more important than the views of local boards. A governor who realizes the need for a new framework of educational controls in his state is more important than a hundred school boards, good, bad, or indifferent. A president who is aware of the national stake in public education and is prepared to take whatever federal action is necessary to protect that stake is more important to the future of public education than thousands of school boards.

Why not work for all of these things—education-minded school boards, legislators, governors, and presidents? By all means, let us do so. But let us also be clear that the priorities lie where the power lies. When you advise people to work for better schools

See American Association of School Administrators, *School District Organization* (Washington, D.C.: American Association of School Administrators, 1958).

[16] See Neal Gross, *Who Runs Our Schools?* (New York: John Wiley & Sons, 1958).

by telling them to concentrate upon their local situation, you direct their energies to the most visible but not necessarily most important agency of educational reform. School systems operate in a context which limits what can be achieved on a purely local basis. Failure to understand this context is the reason for the sincere but misguided faith that people have in the possibilities of local solutions to educational problems.

My criticism of a community-by-community strategy should not be interpreted to mean that I favor a policy of citizen inaction. The usual modes of citizen support for public education are inefficient, sometimes even harmful, but citizen participation and support is essential for its improvement. If, for example, the citizen is a member of the American Legion, he can resist Legion pressure on the school board to conduct misguided essay or athletic contests. He can try to get his local post to end the Legion's systematic interference with American education on a national basis. Similarly, in their churches, unions, professional and trade associations, and other affiliations, citizens can resist the efforts of these organizations to achieve a favored place in the schools. At the same time, they can enlist the aid of these organizations in developing an effective system of public education.

To the superintendents who ask, "What should we teach?" they can say, "If *you* don't know, we'll hire someone who does." They can participate intelligently in school board elections; they can help even more by making constructive educational policy an important criterion of fitness for high political office. They cannot do this unless they know what is constructive; here, teachers' organizations and liberal arts colleges have failed badly. In any event, whether the citizens do these things, or many others that might be suggested, depends primarily upon what the teachers do. For this reason, let us turn to some of the strategic problems which the teachers must solve to lead the way.

THE MERGER OF THE AFT AND THE NEA

The first thing teachers should do is put their own organizational house in order. This will require a merger of the

AFT and the NEA. All teachers can and should help to achieve this goal. To do this, they must understand why this merger is essential and the basis upon which it could be accomplished. They can then support leaders who will work toward the merger and remove from office those who wish to continue the present unproductive stalemate between the two organizations.

Some educational writers have expressed the view that the competition between the two organizations is a good thing. This point of view overlooks the realities of organizational competition. With two competing organizations, attention is devoted to belittling the opposing organization instead of concentrating on the constructive work that needs to be done. The efforts of teachers are dispersed, and outsiders play one group off against the other. Quite frequently, the competition has the most disruptive effects upon a school faculty or upon the administration of a school system. A single organization by no means eliminates all organizational problems, but it is usually better than the existence of two or more competing organizations.

With imaginative leadership in either organization, the present unproductive stalemate might be ended. There is certainly a logical and constructive basis for merger. Essentially, there are two basic issues which divide the two organizations. One is the fact that the NEA has no restrictions upon administrator membership. The other is the AFT's affiliation with the AFL-CIO. It seems to me the proper resolution of these issues is so apparent that only organizational inertia and the existence of vested interests in the present situation serve to perpetuate it.

On the side of the AFT, there must be a recognition that the policy of affiliation with labor has reached a dead end and must be abandoned. Whether the AFT has the courage to face up to this fact is an open question.[17] With some AFT members, affiliation with the labor movement has become a sacred cause instead of a means to be evaluated according to its utility in facilitating certain ends. Some members of the AFT have been passed over

[17] Personally, I have often wondered what AFL-CIO leaders think privately about the AFT's affiliation with the AFL-CIO. It is difficult for me to visualize any advantages to the AFL-CIO in having 55,000 teachers affiliated with it.

for promotion because of their loyalty to the organization. Many were active in the long and bitter struggle during the late 1930's and the early 1940's to expel a Communist faction. People who have been identified for many years with an organization and who have risked a great deal for it cannot be expected to abandon it casually. Indeed, I am not advocating that they abandon it at all, except under certain conditions. It is at this point that some educational statesmanship from the NEA is badly needed.

As much the larger of the two organizations, the NEA might take the attitude that any merger must be on its terms. However, such an attitude would be a grave strategic mistake. The concessions to be made in a merger cannot be based solely upon the size of the organizations to be merged. They must take into account the logic of the arguments involved and the direction of events. Grant practically every criticism made of the AFT, but you cannot escape the fact that the organization has endured because of its adherence to a principle that must eventually be recognized in teachers' organizations generally. As employees, teachers must have organizations reasonably free from domination by school administrators.

Freedom from administrator domination is not just a matter that concerns two competing teachers' organizations. It is, or ought to be, a matter of fundamental public policy. Teachers' organizations, like those of most other government employees, must be free from administrator domination. Unless such a policy is adopted and implemented, there is a danger that this country will drift into a totalitarian state. It does not make sense for the government to protect the integrity of employee organizations in private industry by restricting managerial membership in them and then fail to provide the same protection for organizations of public employees.

The odd part of the situation in education is that approximately one-fourth of the local associations affiliated with the NEA already do exclude administrative personnel. Some of these associations have an even more rigid policy to this effect than do some of the local unions in the AFT. The point is that minimal restrictions upon administrator membership are required of every local federation affiliated with the AFT. On the other hand, the NEA has no national policy to this effect. It will accept affiliation by local associations whether or not they have any such restrictions.

The problems of effecting a merger would be most difficult where an NEA local permits unrestricted administrator membership. Yet even in these cases, there is no insoluble problem if common sense and a respect for occupational realities are present. Actually, most school superintendents are more interested in the publications and activities of the American Association of School Administrators than they are in those of the NEA. Other kinds of administrators, such as high-school principals, are frequently more interested in the specialized associations devoted to their kind of work than to the NEA. Administrative personnel need not give up their professional affiliation with the NEA at the national level, but they should get out of local associations which represent the teachers as employees. In the long run, this will be to the advantage of administrators as much as teachers. No one should be fooled by the thought that these administrators are usually not very active in the local associations. Administrative personnel do not have to be very active to destroy the effectiveness of a local employee organization.

The fact of the matter is that the AFT has itself never grasped the implications of its policies relating to administrator domination. In some communities, it has become necessary for the teachers to designate an organization to represent them in negotiations with the school board. In such elections, teachers have been allowed to name a local education association which allows free and unrestricted membership to the managerial employees of the school system. This situation should be prohibited as a matter of public policy. The worker in private industry cannot choose between an organization which includes managerial employees and one which is free of them; neither should teachers be allowed to choose between the employer-dominated teachers' organizations and organizations free from such domination. Nevertheless, the AFT does not make any systematic appeal to school boards and state legislatures to exclude organizations permitting unrestricted administrator membership from the ballot in elections to decide which organization shall represent the teachers.

For the NEA to procrastinate any further in recognizing the importance of this issue could be disastrous. Collective bargaining is coming in public education, and it will require independent teacher organizations. If the NEA persists in its present policies, it is possible that the AFT will make substantial gains as collective bargaining becomes more widespread. And if AFT membership increases, it will mean the development of many more vested interests which would be opposed to a single teachers' organization. The difficulties of merging the two organizations will be increased many times over, and they are bound to dissipate their energies in fighting each other. This is why no greater mistake could be made by the NEA than to assume it should ignore the AFT merely because at this time it is approximately twelve times as large.

The terms I have outlined would enable the two organizations to merge honorably and with good grace. The AFT would be giving up only the illusory benefits of affiliation; the NEA would only be accepting a condition which will eventually be forced upon it in any case. Naturally, any merger should scrupulously respect the rights of all officers and paid staffs of the two organizations.

At the present time, the NEA is not making a strong effort either to support or to block collective bargaining by teachers. This indifference is bad enough, but it might change to active opposition if the Association is unable to change its membership structure so as to accommodate collective bargaining by teachers. For this reason, a strong case can be made for strengthening the AFT despite the futility of its affiliation with the AFL-CIO and despite the possibility that a substantial increase in its membership might make it more difficult to unite teachers later on. An increase in AFT membership might be necessary to jolt the NEA leadership into the realization that there is nothing unprofessional about collective bargaining and that employee organizations, whether of professionals or ditch-diggers, must be free from administrator domination.

In most national occupational organizations, the representation from the large urban centers in the North provides the liberal strength and leadership. Generally speaking, the teachers from these urban centers are more aggressive than those from other regions and from rural areas. The membership of the AFT is concentrated primarily in them—in Chicago, New York, San Francisco, Denver, St. Paul, and Detroit. For this reason, the existence of the AFT represents more than the mere absence of 55,000 teachers from the NEA. It represents the abandonment of the NEA by a group whose potential influence is much greater than is indicated by their numbers.

It is also a matter of some importance that the influence of the teachers now in the AFT is likely to be exerted on behalf of a more liberal policy on issues pertaining to the civil and professional rights of teachers. This is illustrated by the constitutional provisions of the two organizations concerning segregated locals. The NEA's constitution originally provided for only one state association in each state, but Negro teachers who were NEA members were excluded from these associations in the South. Because representation in the NEA is through affiliated state and local associations, Negro teachers were, therefore, unrepresented in the NEA. To afford them representation, the NEA finally authorized the affiliation of Negro state teachers' associations.

On the other hand, the AFT adopted the following amendment to its constitution in 1952:

> No charter of the American Federation of Teachers which defines or recognizes jurisdiction on a basis of race or color, or permits the practice of such jurisdiction, shall be recognized as valid, and the practice of any local in limiting its membership on account of race or color shall render its charter void.[18]

[18] Constitution of the American Federation of Teachers, art. IV, sec. 8, correct as of January 1, 1958. The 1958 Convention of the AFT turned down an appeal for reinstatement by Chattanooga Local 256. The charter of this local had been revoked for its failure to make any effort to enrol Negro teachers within its jurisdiction.

We thus have this striking contrast: the NEA amended its constitution to allow for segregated state associations, and the AFT amended its constitution to abolish racially segregated locals.

Although the existence of competing teachers' organizations is to be regretted, and although I see no hope that the AFT will become the majority organization of teachers as long as it adheres to affiliation with the labor movement, there is thus valid reason to encourage its existence. From an organizational point of view, it is much easier to change the basic policies of the AFT than those of the NEA. If certain changes were made in AFT policy and strategy, and if it were to show substantial increases in membership for a few years, the result might be to hasten these same changes in the NEA and also to speed a merger between the organizations.

TEACHER CONTROL OF ADMISSION TO TEACHING

With or without a merger of the AFT and NEA, teachers' organizations must give high priority to teacher control over admission to teaching. The strategic advantages of teacher control of entry would be tremendous. The professions typically exert their group strength at the point of entry. As a result, the employer, whether a public or private one, must pay well to get the services of the professional. On the other hand, non-professional control of teacher certification has made it easy for people to become teachers. After the flood gates are down, the teachers try to improve their status through negotiations with school boards or through state minimum salary laws. This is locking the barn door after the horse is stolen. It is precisely why the AFT emphasis upon collective bargaining, unaccompanied by teacher control over entry, is only half a program, and probably not the most important half at that. Collective bargaining is never very effective unless the employees have some degree of job control. The AFT apparently has yet to learn this principle, which is taken for granted in unions as it is in professional associations.

The current emphasis upon minimum salary laws and the failure of teachers to accord high priority to teacher control of entry illustrates the shortsighted strategy followed by teachers' organizations. Public opinion is easily aroused against legislation which provides adequate professional salaries. People do not like to support laws calling for specific and substantial salaries for public employees. Nevertheless, most persons who oppose high salary schedules would not get especially aroused over legislation calling for teacher control of admission to their own profession. I do not say that there would be no opposition, but this is not the kind of thing that stirs the man on the street to determined opposition. And because teacher control of entry is inherently reasonable, a determined effort by teachers to achieve it should be successful. The teachers might very well join with other groups seeking a similar objective and co-ordinate their efforts to achieve a sensible framework for state licensure.

EDUCATIONAL PUBLIC RELATIONS

At the present time, educational public relations are dominated by a policy of "educating the public." In the minds of most public school personnel, "educating the public" means not to make a move before getting public approval and to respond like a Geiger counter to every shift in public opinion.

At teachers meetings one often hears exhortations to teachers to win the respect of the public. It is generally assumed that the teachers will be paid better only as they gain a larger measure of public respect. Aside from the fact that respect usually follows rather than precedes high salaries, the exhortations are typically used to justify the very things that create disrespect for teachers. Thus teachers are persuaded to accept after-school assignments without pay in order to win respect. In the gushy ideology of cracker-barrel philosophers of education, teachers must be "professional" to gain respect; being "professional" is equated with contributing your services for nothing.

"Educating the public" has also led to an ineffectual buckshot approach to educational problems. The evaluation of strategy is concerned with how many times a movie was shown, how many brochures and pamphlets were mailed out, and how many people attended how many conferences. While there is something to be said for efforts to create a climate of opinion, this should not be a substitute for unremitting pressure on strategic individuals and agencies who have the power to take action ahead of, or even in opposition to, public opinion. A thousand PTA's convinced of the need for higher salaries for teachers are not as valuable as one congressman who knows that the organized teachers can mobilize enough votes to unseat him at the next election.

Thus far, teachers have miseducated the public very effectively, by their spineless abdication of professional autonomy, by their failure to enforce high standards for entry and performance, by their political impotence, and by their moral evasion. It is time for teachers to develop different concepts of how and for what they shall educate the public.

The teachers might begin by demonstrating to politicians that opposition to the sound professional recommendations of teachers is an invitation to political disaster. The best way to conduct this kind of demonstration is to deliver the votes. Teachers might try to educate the public to the importance of academic freedom by withholding their services where there are serious violations of it. These techniques have not been tried on a large scale, but they may be more effective than the techniques currently in use. The mass distribution of movies or literature cannot be effective while the everyday performance of teachers demonstrates that they are a weak and inconsequential group.

RELATIONSHIPS BETWEEN LOCAL, STATE, AND NATIONAL ORGANIZATIONS

There are local, state, and national organizations of teachers. Obviously, it is important that there be a functional distribution of work among these levels. If the national organization attempts to solve problems which should be handled locally, it will be less effective in advancing the objectives and interests of teachers at the national level. On the other hand, it is equally disastrous to leave national problems to local organizations, since the latter do not have the resources to grapple with them.

One important reason for the ineffectiveness of educators is their continuous failure to develop an organizational strategy within which local, state, and national organizations can operate with maximum effectiveness. For example, the NEA will ordinarily intervene in a local situation only if such action is requested by the local association and approved by the appropriate affiliated state education association. Obviously, approval is not forthcoming when, as often happens, the local and state associations are dominated by administrators whose policies and practices would likewise suffer from an objective investigation by an outside agency.

However, the most important weakness of NEA policy lies in the nature of its participation in state and local situations even when it does have the support of its affiliated state and local associations. For example, in tenure cases, its participation is almost always limited to making investigations and recommendations which seldom alter the course of events. Even when the recommendations are good ones, they are rarely supported by the mobilization and deployment of NEA resources in such a way as to strengthen materially the efforts of local associations to implement them.

Let me illustrate these points by analyzing the potential role of the NEA in tenure cases. Let us suppose that a school board has unjustly dismissed a teacher. Let us also suppose that the NEA adhered to the following policies:

1. If an investigation by the NEA itself indicated that a teacher was unjustly fired, the NEA would guarantee him an income until he was restored to his position or found suitable employment elsewhere.

2. Any educator who knowingly offered or accepted employment as a replacement for a teacher unjustly fired would be tried for unprofessional conduct. If found guilty, the NEA would so publicize the results that his professional career would be in serious jeopardy.

3. The school system involved would be designated as an unprofessional place to work. All employment agencies would be requested not to refer teachers to that system. Vigorous action would be taken to see that teachers did not register with any agency which continued to send applicants to the system. All school systems would be alerted not to accept applicants from any agency which knowingly referred applicants to positions created as a result of unjust dismissals.

4. The NEA would provide substantial assistance to those forces in the community which opposed the unjust dismissal. Such assistance might well include all-out support for new candidates for the school board.

5. The NEA would bring pressure to bear upon accreditation agencies to have the school system in question deprived of its accreditation.

6. Legal assistance at NEA expense would be provided the teacher unjustly dismissed.

If the NEA were to adopt such policies, the final agreements in this type of situation would still have to be worked out at a local level, but these agreements would be profoundly influenced by the policies of the NEA. A school board which knows that its actions are leading straight to an all-out contest with a national organization of teachers is not likely to invite such a contest unless it is sure of the merits of its case. Furthermore, it is one thing for a local board to carry public opinion when the teachers have neither the funds nor the facilities for making a sustained appeal; it is quite another matter when the resources available to the teachers far outweigh those available to the board.

Why should not the teachers follow this strategy? One might suppose that it would embroil the national organization in a multitude of local disputes and lead eventually to the dissipation of its energies and resources in matters which do not advance the interests of all teachers or of society as a whole. However, this point of view confuses cause and effect. We have many of these incidents now precisely because there is no powerful national organization of teachers, the very presence of which would serve to change the character of local solutions to educational problems.

A powerful national organization ready to step into local situations when a matter of principle is involved would serve a preventive function. The more determined it was to hurl its resources into local situations where the teacher's case was clearly justified, the less need there would be for it actually to do so. Of course, there would be such a need at the beginning so that everyone would know that the national organization meant business. But after that, local boards would think carefully before violating the basic professional and civic rights of teachers.

The probability that the proposed strategy would not result in endless intervention in local situations is borne out by the experience of the National Union of Teachers in England. The National Union of Teachers has long followed a policy such that if a teacher is dismissed for reasons found to be unwarranted by the organization, it pays the salary of the teacher until he resumes work, either in the system from which he was unjustly dismissed or in another system. The National Union guarantees this salary no matter how long it takes to secure employment for the teacher unjustly dismissed. Adherence to this policy has not led to its widespread involvement in disputes over individual teachers. The readiness of the Union to intervene if necessary has influenced local school boards to dismiss teachers only for good cause. The boards do not risk a test of strength when they have a weak case on the issues involved.

The relationships between local, state, and national organizations should facilitate and encourage the settlement of disputes at local and state levels. But the way to achieve this objective is not for the NEA, or for any national association of teachers, to turn its back on "local" disputes. This policy "facilitates" their settlement by insuring settlements which are at the expense of the teachers and the long-range interests of the public. "Local" problems are always settled in one context or another. A context which includes a powerful national organization, ready, willing, and able to intervene aggressively on matters of principle, will result in solutions at the local level which are much different from those reached in a context where the national organization is weak and where it hears no evil and sees no evil.

This suggested strategy is not at all invalidated by the fact that teachers are publicly employed. The strength of the national organization of employees is as crucial in public as it is in private employment. National organizations of publicly employed persons cannot always support their local associations in precisely the same way that national associations of privately employed persons support their local affiliates, but the similarities far outweigh the differences. For example, a national organization of publicly employed persons can work for federal legislation favorable to its members, just as the AMA and the AFL-CIO strive to achieve the same result for their members. Indeed, it is doubtful whether there is any major difference in the strategy and tactics which can and should be used by public, as distinct from private, employees.

It is also crucial to see that the strategy suggested is not limited to any particular type of problem which involves teachers as employees or as a professional group. If a local teachers' association refuses to accept a salary schedule, and if investigation by the national organization supports this refusal, the strategy of bringing the full power of the national association to bear upon the local board should be effectuated. This strategy is not limited to economic objectives; it is just as applicable to problems involving academic freedom or racial integration.

The NEA takes the position that integration is something to be worked out at state and local levels. Its resolutions on integration in the public schools from 1955 through 1959 have included the statement: "It is the conviction of the Association that all problems of integration are capable of solution at the state and local levels by citizens of intelligence, saneness, and reasonableness working together in the interests of national unity for the common good of all." In the light of this resolution and the almost complete absence of any active support for integration by the NEA, it is clear that the Association regards it as a problem which can be resolved without the active intervention of teachers at the national level.

It is unrealistic to think that integration can be carried out without face-to-face negotiations at local and state levels, and in this sense integration is indeed a state and local problem. But this is not to say that the actions of a national organization cannot influence the solutions reached and the rapidity with which they are carried out. This is why the NEA policies on integration are hypocritical. They sound vaguely like support for integration but actually leave intact the power structure which perpetuates segregation.

"Intelligence, saneness, and reasonableness" should prevail at the local level, but it is naïve to think that this is likely to happen without some outside assistance when dealing with integration. A school board would be in a much better position to eliminate segregated schools and a segregated profession if it could say to its community, "Look, regardless of what we believe on this issue, we have to treat our Negro teachers fairly or we'll lose many of the white teachers we have, we'll be unable to recruit new teachers, and our schools will lose accreditation."

It is true that there are some states and communities where teachers' organizations cannot influence the immediate course of integration. But there are many others all over the country where a trace of professional fortitude on this issue by national organizations of teachers would achieve tremendous results. NEA leaders who point to local opposition to integration as the excuse for their do-nothing policy ignore the fact that much of this opposition would never have arisen if teachers' associations, and especially the NEA, had lived up to their professional responsibilities in the first place. In and out of education, it is the people who do not wish to see integration come at all who sanctimoniously affirm that integration is a state and local problem.

Of course, if the NEA is to change the context within which issues are resolved at state and local levels, it must adopt concrete measures to achieve this end. For example, the Association would have to create a multimillion-dollar defense fund to back up its interventions. Again, I wish to emphasize that the very existence of such a fund, coupled with a firm determination to use it, would obviate the need to use it in most situations.

NEA leaders continually proclaim the virtues of negotiation and persuasion, apparently in complete ignorance of the fact that these are not substitutes for a position of strength. The teachers will be persuasive only when they have enough power to command the respect of school boards. Until that situation prevails, the power which other groups command will continue to frustrate the public interest in a better school system and the legitimate welfare objectives which the teachers have set for themselves.

Chapter XII

THE ROLE OF THE FOUNDATIONS

To bring about fundamental changes in American education, people must be brought together to plan and to implement such changes. Long and costly experiments must be carried out. Many different kinds of studies must be made, and their results disseminated to the public and the teaching profession. The things which must be done will cost money, and some will cost large amounts of money. Who will finance the activities needed to change the status quo in education?

One possible source is the philanthropic foundations. It is the business of the foundations to support activities likely to produce constructive change—the more far-reaching the change, the better. Of course, not all change is constructive. Nevertheless, it is an avowed purpose of some important foundations to support projects intended to shake the educational status quo. Since these foundations are currently the largest source of funds for this purpose, it is desirable to consider the role they might play in the years ahead. This will entail some consideration of what they have done in the past and of their current situation.

Foundations vary enormously in endowment and purposes, and generalizations about them have to be qualified. For example, they vary in size from the Ford Foundation, with assets of approximately $500,000,000, to those whose assets are practically nil or whose liabilities actually exceed their assets. According to a recent study, the assets of the seven largest foundations in 1954 were as follows:

Ford Foundation	$493,213,842
Rockefeller Foundation	447,686,573
The Carnegie Corporation	178,861,599
W. K. Kellogg Foundation	109,812,214
The Duke Endowment	109,522,000
The Commonwealth Fund	105,993,035
The Pew Memorial Fund	104,987,129 [1]

The larger foundations have typically been active in the field of education, broadly considered. However, until the establishment of the Fund for the Advancement of Education in 1951, there was not one whose resources were devoted primarily to strengthening elementary and secondary education.[2] The relative disinterest of the foundations in public education is a result of many factors, most of which need not detain us here. However, one possible reason which deserves more scrutiny than it has received thus far relates to the constituencies of their boards of trustees. A recent study revealed that of 202 trustees in the larger foundations, 46 per cent held degrees from Yale, Harvard, or Princeton, and only 20 per cent held degrees from state-supported institutions. According to the author of the study, "The typical trustee emerging from this composite picture is a man who graduated from one of the eastern Ivy League liberal arts colleges and went into business or law."[3]

Since education is not regarded as a worthy field of study in some Ivy League colleges, we should not expect their graduates to be especially concerned about it. We have also to consider the fact that liberal arts college presidents are frequently selected as members of foundation boards, whereas persons holding comparable positions in public education, such as superintendents

---

[1] Wilmer Shields Rich, *American Foundations and Their Fields* (7th ed.; (New York: American Foundations Information Service, 1955), p. xxii.

[2] The Fund has received all of its financial support from the Ford Foundation, but it is at present an independent organization with its own officers and board of trustees.

[3] F. Emerson Andrews, *Philanthropic Foundations* (New York: Russell Sage Foundation, 1956), p. 76. This book is probably the best general treatment of the foundations currently available.

of large city school systems, are practically never so selected. Without in any way advocating any particular geographical or occupational breakdown of these boards, I think it would be surprising if the heavy representation of foundation trustees with a private liberal arts college background were not a causal factor in their grant-making patterns.

To say that this is such a cause is not to condemn it. I happen to believe that public education is underrepresented in the larger foundations, in the sense that its needs and potentialities are not accorded the attention they deserve. No doubt many able and sincere individuals believe that the situation with regard to representation is as it should be. It must be conceded that there are good reasons to expect some concentration of trustees from, and of grants to, particular universities. Foundations should not distribute their funds to a wide range of institutions just to avoid the appearance of partiality. In fact, they are being criticized for being nice to everyone as well as for being over-generous to a few favored institutions. I think there is some justification for both criticisms, but the issue is not an easy one to resolve.

SOME REFLECTIONS ON GRANTMANSHIP

To avoid utopian expectations of the foundations, one must be aware of the difficulties confronting them. As tax-exempt organizations, they must be wary of the many legal limitations on their activities. They must make their grants to non-profit organizations or they run the risk of losing their own tax-exempt status. For the same reason, they must not become active in promoting legislation. They are frequently targets of irresponsible political abuse. They operate under subtle but heavy pressures to spread their grants geographically, religiously, and to different types of institutions. Their conservatism or alleged conservatism may be deplorable but under these circumstances it is understandable.[4]

---

[4] Most people in the foundations to whom I have talked agree that these pressures tend to make the foundations cautious. But why should founda-

In the field of public education, there is another important difficulty. The foundations do not receive a sufficient number of good proposals to support. I am referring now to proposals concerning teacher education, curriculum revision, teaching methods, teachers' organizations, the legal and administrative aspects of education, and the economics of public education. In the field of public education, broadly conceived, constructive ideas worth substantial foundation support are rare.

This point is never conceded, publicly at least, by the foundations. When requests are turned down, the reason given to the applicant is never that his ideas are poor. It is that the foundation is concentrating upon some other line of activity, or some other reason which casts no reflection upon the proposal is given. One cannot legitimately criticize the foundations for taking a public position that they receive many more worthwhile requests than they can possibly fulfil. This posture is a practical necessity. However, it should not mislead anyone into expecting more from the foundations than they can deliver.

Bear in mind that the foundations must spend their income or it will be taken by the tax collector. Furthermore, they cannot spend less during years when fewer good proposals come in; they have to spend their income on a regular basis. Thus the fact that unpromising proposals receive foundation support does not *ipso facto* justify the inference of poor judgment on their part—unless, of course, one expects them to turn their income over to the Collector of Internal Revenue rather than allocate it to less promising projects. One can imagine the howl that would be raised all over the country if one of the larger foundations should do this.

In education, the situation can be gauged in part from the weakness of the laboratory schools operated in conjunction with leading schools of education throughout the country. The physical facilities and staff for these schools have cost many millions of

---

tion trustees be cautious if their personal fortunes are not at stake? When I put this question to one foundation president, he replied that trustees don't care about money or power; they just want to be popular, and this calls for a policy of something for everybody.

dollars during the past few decades. Most of them have been unable to produce a single significant piece of research during their entire existence. With only a few exceptions, they have become schools where prospective teachers do student teaching or where graduate assistants can support themselves while working for a doctoral degree.

It is really surprising how few proposals of any kind are submitted to the foundations. Of course, they receive many more proposals than they can possibly support, but these come from only a small portion of the individuals who might reasonably be expected to submit them. There are many faculties of education which do not include one person who has submitted a serious proposal to a foundation. The foundations may themselves be partly to blame for this situation, since they have not done much to remove the atmosphere of mystery concerning their operating procedures. It would take very little effort on their part to eliminate the feeling at some institutions that they are remote and inscrutable institutions. Publications and a wide dissemination of information on the kinds of proposals they are interested in and on how to go about applying for grants would be helpful.

A useful technique of the Fund for the Advancement of Education is to send a field representative to various institutions. Anyone who wishes can discuss his ideas or problems of procedure with this representative. Listening to eight or ten professors a day explain how they can save the world—with the help of a few hundred thousand foundation dollars, of course— must be a punishing experience, but the practice has much to be said for it. For one thing, it clears away the red tape between the people who have proposals to make and the foundation. Some proposals which do not appear promising on paper actually have tremendous potential. Foundation personnel may lose interest in a written proposal because of objections which could be cleared up easily in face-to-face conversation.

Sometimes people have excellent ideas which they are unable or unwilling to implement themselves. They may be too busy, they may not be in an appropriate location, or their institution may be hostile to the idea. In these cases, the individuals may not care to devote a great deal of time to drafting a proposal but they might be willing to discuss their ideas on a conversational basis. Some of the best ideas for educational projects have come from individuals who were personally not in a position to implement them, even with a grant. For this reason, they did not bother to draft any proposals embodying these ideas. A simple visitation procedure might tap these ideas.

From the standpoint of the foundations, there is an understandable reluctance to establish a large staff which would reduce the funds available for grants. On the other hand, if their staffs are small for the volume of proposals that should be given careful consideration, there is the likelihood that propinquity and other fortuitous factors will determine which proposals receive support. In the larger foundations, these considerations lead to a policy of supporting large grants. If a foundation has $5 million to spend every year, it is administratively much easier to choose among fifty proposals, each asking for $200,000, than among two thousand proposals, each asking for $5,000.

Some foundation officials have condemned the "scatteration" of foundation funds in a host of small grants. I think, however, that it is a mistake for a foundation to begin with any preconceptions about the size of grants which are within its means. Such important discoveries as insulin and penicillin were made by individuals working on grants of less than $10,000. It is possible that discoveries of great importance in education could be made on the basis of relatively modest grants. For this reason, foundations should have great flexibility in this matter.

A LOOK AT SOME CRITICISMS

A common criticism of foundations is that they are dominated by people who have preconceptions about the kind of projects that should receive support.[5] This criticism is pointless. If a person came to a foundation job without any idea of what should be supported, he would be a poor choice indeed.

[5] In the following analysis, I have purposely omitted any discussion of whether the foundations are supporting subversive or "un-American" activities. This nonsense should not be dignified by a refutation.

Every person who has a genuine interest in research and experimentation has at any given time ideas which he believes to be worthy. He neither can nor should divest himself of these ideas.

This criticism really posits a kind of non-human entity which somehow chooses the "best" proposals quite apart from the preferences of the chooser. Instead of trying to find people without preconceptions, it is more realistic to find those who are realistic about their preconceptions. The fact that a proposal is the brainchild of the foundation gatekeepers is irrelevant to whether it deserves support. Some of the best as well as some of the worst proposals supported by foundations have originated with their own staff. It is, in any case, a fallacy to believe a person must have no ideas of his own about a topic to be objective about it.

In the case of the larger foundations, this criticism is pointless for still another reason: it is practically impossible to confine grants to the hobbyhorses of foundation personnel. The fact is that foundation officials do not always agree among themselves as to what is worthy of support. Foundations are human institutions much like others that we know, and their independence is not absolute. They are under strong pressures to support institutions of different denominations, regions, character, and approach to the same problems for which foundation support is requested. It is not unusual to find the same foundation supporting mutually exclusive approaches to the same problem.

The test of whether a foundation is doing a good job cannot lie in the source of the ideas and proposals it supports; it lies only in the quality of the proposals actually supported. Of course, if foundations automatically reject proposals because of their source, or automatically support others for the same reason, they would be subject to legitimate criticism. Such policies would inevitably be reflected in the lower quality of the results.

Another frequent criticism of the foundations also seems to me to be out of order. This is the charge that the foundations unjustifiably interfere with the internal operations of the institutions which apply for or receive grants. It is alleged that they attempt to dictate personnel policies and even specific appointments as a condition of making a grant. This criticism is often launched by academic personnel who believe that the foundations are using potential grants as a club to dictate all sorts of things which are properly the province of the universities themselves.

Such incidents may indeed occur. But what is in fact surprising is not how much the foundations throw their weight around but how much latitude they give grantees and how little regulation or supervision they undertake once a grant is made. For every incident in which a foundation has attempted to dictate a matter which was not its appropriate concern, there must be dozens wherein the grantees have substantially violated the letter and spirit of their grant and the foundations have looked the other way.

Actually, there is no clear-cut framework within which foundations and grantees act. A government grant for research ordinarily involves a much more highly regulated relationship than does a foundation grant. Institutions receiving grants often take advantage of the lack of a structured operating relationship between foundations and their grantees. This is partly intentional, but the results are frequently deplorable.

Here again, the problem involves the difficulty of applying principles which are sound in themselves. Foundations cannot administer their grants, nor do they wish to stand over anybody's shoulder or require so many detailed reports that projects bog down because of red tape. Nevertheless, their own laissez-faire attitude inevitably leads to a casual attitude on the part of the agencies requesting grants. "Say anything to get the grant and then do whatever you want"—this strategy is the predictable outcome of lack of regulation by the foundations once a grant is made.

The absence of supervision by the foundations during the life of a project would be a sounder policy if the foundations were to engage in critical and vigorous evaluation of the projects they support. I am referring now to evaluation of the results; there is already considerable evaluation of proposals as they come in. If there were critical study of the results of activities receiving support, there might be a different emphasis in the kinds of projects which foundations would support. Of course, there is always some evaluation by foundations of the enterprises they support. However, the resources devoted to this purpose are almost always much less than the resources devoted to evaluating the original proposals out of which the projects developed.

While most foundation grants of any size do provide for evaluation, such evaluation is usually controlled by the agencies receiving the grants. This is often a fatal weakness. An institution hiring some outside, "independent" evaluators is not likely to go out and employ complete strangers who might turn out to be severe critics of the entire project. Nor is a severe critic likely to receive many invitations to serve as an evaluator.

In any case, it is not easy to say publicly, even if one is so convinced, that a project costing hundreds of thousands, sometimes even millions of dollars, has been a waste of time and effort. Such a judgment reflects not only on the institution but also on the foundation supporting the project. For this reason, the evaluators are likely to render their judgments in more dulcet tones. And there are other obvious factors which tend to weaken the effectiveness of "independent evaluation" that is sponsored by the institution which has operated the project itself.

One reason we get so little evaluation of projects in education is that educators have a distorted sense of success in research and experimentation. "Success" has come to mean that the researcher has proved a hypothesis to be true, whereas it should mean either that the researcher has proved a hypothesis to be true *or else* that he has proved it to be false.

In other fields, such as medicine, the possibility that some promising hypotheses are false is taken for granted. In finding them false, the researcher has added to medical science and is satisfied. In education, however, every hypothesis has to be "true." Every experiment has "to work." The disease has even spread to the point where much educational "research" is devoted to proving the obvious.[6] Imagine what our medical

---

[6] For example, a recent U.S. Office of Education grant to Teachers College, Columbia University, was made to ascertain why male teachers leave the profession.

situation would be like if every piece of medical research had to be successful in the sense of finding a cure or else the researcher could not get additional funds for research.

We badly need to accept routinely the fact that some promising projects will not come up with anything better than what we have. When this happens, educators ought to be in a position to admit it without endangering their chances of getting another grant. If they must (or think they must) claim "success" for every foundation project in order to get subsequent grants, the whole level of research is debased.[7]

The answer to this problem lies largely in the hands of the foundations. If their staffs feel the same compulsive need for "success" in every grant, the people in the field will also. The whole process is a kind of chain reaction, whose terminals are the man in the field at one end and the foundation trustee at the other. The latter is the most important, since he has the money. The people in the field behave in whatever way is necessary (or they think is necessary) to get it.

WHAT FOUNDATIONS CAN DO TO STRENGTHEN PUBLIC EDUCATION

It is impossible to assess precisely the impact of foundation projects in the field of public education. No one can be certain what the situation would be like in their absence. Even when foundation projects are devoted to goals which are achieved, it is extremely difficult to assess the importance of foundation activity. Perhaps the goal might have been achieved a little later or with a heavier expenditure of non-foundation resources. However, conceding the difficulties of evaluation, I am convinced that the foundations active in public education are not emphasizing the kinds of proposals which, under present conditions, can result in widespread changes.

[7] Sometimes a willingness to face unpleasant facts has surprising results. The School of Education at the University of Wisconsin recently published a research study showing that a surprisingly low proportion of its graduates thought they had profited from their education courses. I am told that the reaction elsewhere in the university was not one of derision but of admiration for the honesty and courage displayed by the School of Education in making the results public.

To be specific, the foundations are not giving enough attention to proposals concerned with the power structure of education. Their current interests are in educational administration, teacher education, the curriculum, and teaching methods and techniques (and especially educational television). My reasons for thinking that these kinds of projects are not likely to result in fundamental changes at this time should be clear from the preceding chapters. No matter how worthwhile their results may be, it is practically impossible to get them accepted on a national basis under the present system. For this reason, the major emphasis of the foundations should not be upon the content and methodology of education or of teacher education. It should be upon the legal, administrative, and organizational structure of education. Unless basic changes are made in these areas, attempts to stimulate improvement in content and methods by pilot projects will be like trying to change the color of the ocean with an eyedropper.

Let me illustrate this point by a reference to the classic example of a foundation's impact upon a profession. In 1908, the Carnegie Foundation authorized Abraham Flexner to make a study of medical education in the United States and Canada. Flexner visited every medical school in the two countries. He then set forth his findings of fact, his criticisms, and his recommendations for future action in a historic report entitled *Medical Education in the United States and Canada*.[8]

In his study, Flexner went far beyond merely reporting on the physical, financial, and personnel resources of the medical schools then in existence. Nor did he confine himself to recommendations about what facilities should be required, or what changes should be made in the preprofessional and professional training of students. At the time of his report, many states excluded doctors from the state boards which licensed doctors, just as some states now exclude teachers from the boards which license teachers. Flexner recommended that the state boards be composed of doctors instead of laymen. He realized that it was useless to

[8] Abraham Flexner, *Medical Education in the United States and Canada* (New York: Carnegie Foundation for the Advancement of Teaching, 1910).

propose higher standards in medical education as long as there was no change in the structure of the boards which licensed doctors and accredited medical schools. He also realized that it was hopeless to expect the medical diploma mills to improve their facilities to the point where they should be permitted to exist. For this reason, he emphasized the need to create a new structure for medical education and licensure, a structure that would make it possible to establish and enforce high standards.

When the Flexner report was published, it immediately became a rallying point for overhauling medical education and licensure in the United States. Eventually, changes in these areas led to sweeping changes in medical practice. The elimination of substandard schools, the initiation of rigorous state board examinations, the removal of unwarranted non-professional interference with medical education, licensure, and practice—these were the direct results of the Flexner report. The indirect results were tremendous improvements in the actual practice of medicine. That is, the Flexner report led to a new framework of medical controls within which the science and art of medicine was able to make tremendous progress in the next few decades. The most fundamental changes in medical practice were thus brought about by a man who was neither a physician nor a scientist. Flexner was simply a keen and fearless observer whose contribution lay in getting the medical profession to eliminate the legal, administrative, and organizational weaknesses which hampered medical education, licensure, research, and practice.

The parallel between medicine in 1910 and education today is striking. There is the same chaotic variation in standards of professional training and practice from state to state and institution to institution, the same need for professional control over licensure, the same absence of high standards for admission to practice, the same widespread existence of substandard institutions providing professional training, and the same urgent need for an unimpeachable rallying point to serve as the basis for drastic changes.

My thesis here, however, is not merely the need for an educational Flexner report.[9] It is merely to emphasize the fact that one relatively inexpensive foundation project exposed the power structure which constituted the chief obstacle to advances in the actual practice of medicine. Anyone who reads the Flexner report will see at once that it really went far beyond medical education and actually proposed a new framework for the medical profession itself. Likewise, the crying need in education today is not for research on curriculum or teaching methods. It is for the elimination of the structural roadblocks that have retarded educational progress during the past half-century.

Studies of these roadblocks are important but they do not necessarily lead to their elimination. Herein lies a problem. We must remember that Flexner did not revolutionize the medical profession all by himself. Once his report was published, it was necessary for interested parties to implement it. Legislation had to be drafted and supported. Local, state, and national medical associations had to take appropriate action. In short, all sorts of things had to be done to implement his recommendations.

This raises a crucial question for the foundations. Assuming that they were to support comprehensive, no-holds-barred studies of the legal, administrative, organizational, and technological barriers to educational progress, what are the prospects for implementing the recommendations of such studies?

Candor compels the admission that implementation would be very difficult. On many issues, it would require vigorous action by educational organizations, and their record is certainly not one to inspire confidence in the outcome. Some worthwhile projects supported by the foundations have been greeted with outright hostility by teachers' organizations. The reactions of

[9] At least one foundation (the Fund for the Advancement of Education) has given some thought to such a report on teacher education. The Fund finally concluded, after getting the views of Flexner himself, that this would not be feasible. It is true that a critical and comprehensive survey of teacher education would be confronted by many difficulties which Flexner did not have to face in making his study of medical education. Nevertheless, I believe such a survey to be quite practicable. The major problems would not be in making the survey but in implementing its recommendations.

the NEA and the AFT to the teacher aide experiment at Bay City, Michigan (see page 100), are one example. To my knowledge, neither the NEA nor the AFT has ever made a proposal of their own to explore the possibilities of a different personnel structure in education. In fact, for all of its criticisms of foundation projects and its verbal support for experimentation and research, I doubt whether the AFT has ever made a proposal on any subject to any major foundation.

In the abstract, all teachers favor research and experimentation; in fact, many of them have a diffuse fear of any development that might justify drastic changes in their habitual ways of doing things. This fear frequently finds expression in overreacting to specific experiments while affirming a general interest in research. Few teachers are really prepared for the kinds of changes that would be necessary if there were important alterations in the personnel structure of education.

Some of the foundations have spent millions in exploring the potentialities of educational television. These foundations have been accused of making exaggerated claims about its results and potentialities. "Educational television will never replace the classroom teacher"—this cliché has become an article of faith for teachers' organizations. Whatever exaggerated claims for educational television may have been made by the foundations are insignificant compared to the dogmatic pronouncements of teachers' organizations concerning its limitations.

Some teachers are vaguely worried that educational television will make it possible to get by with fewer teachers. Instead of encouraging every effort to achieve this result, their organizations have concluded in the infancy of educational television that it must not reduce the number of teachers required for our schools. If their attitude had prevailed in other occupations, it would have been impossible to develop the high levels of productivity which characterize the American economy.

Educational television and efforts to change the personnel structure of education are significant for another reason. I have asserted that if we first make certain changes in the structure of American education, desirable changes in its content and methods will soon follow. It is also possible that desirable changes in the structure of American education will follow from changes in the content and methods. The Industrial Revolution was not simply an alteration in the way things were manufactured. This was first in point of time, but it also meant, or led to, the most profound changes in employer-employee relationships, employee organizations, and the social and economic status of various groups. It is possible that educational television or the development of a personnel hierarchy in education could lead to basic changes in other dimensions of education. This is why I ask for a different emphasis rather than for a complete about-face in foundation policy.

The foundations are currently supporting some proposals directly concerned with the structure of public education. They are supporting others which may alter the structure of American education, although this is not their primary purpose. The point is, however, that a comprehensive restructuring of educational controls is needed and that we are not likely to get it unless it becomes a focal area of foundation support.

I do not advocate that the foundations first decide what changes are needed and then spend their resources to get them accepted. It is only necessary that they recognize the crucial importance of changes in the power structure of American education. Clear recognition of this point would lead to ways and means by which they could help to remove the most important roadblocks to a better educational system.

A FOUNDATION APPROACH
TO MERIT PAY

To illustrate a number of points in this and preceding chapters, I would like to suggest a possible way for the foundations to help public education reach a better solution to the problem of merit pay. This problem is one of the old reliables of educational controversy, partly, I think, because people interested in the problem have always favored a community-by-community approach to resolving it. The foundations are in the best position to initiate a broader approach to the problem.

"Merit pay" (or "merit rating") is really a cluster of problems growing out of one major issue confronting public education. As pointed out earlier, most school systems pay all teachers strictly according to their level of training and years of experience. This policy is commonly referred to as "the single salary schedule." As a rule, the policy makes no allowance for the subject or grade level taught. An elementary teacher, a teacher of driver education, and a physics teacher, each with an M.A. degree and five years of teaching experience, receive the same salary in communities adhering to single salary schedules.

Single salary schedules vary from community to community. They may differ in their minimums, their maximums, the size of the increments from year to year, the number of steps on the schedule, the allowable credit for prior teaching experience, and other factors. Nevertheless, wherever they are used, teachers are not paid according to any judgment of their effectiveness as teachers. They are employed, retained, or fired on the basis of such judgments, but fewer and fewer are compensated on this basis. In 1956–57, less than 5 per cent of the public school teachers in cities of 2,500 or more population were employed under salary schedules which made any provision for merit pay. Less than half of the school systems which authorized or specified higher pay for superior service were actually paying any teachers for such service.[10]

Single salary schedules inevitably result in relatively low maximum salaries. Since all teachers are eligible to receive the maximum, and since teachers are a large occupational group, any schedule with high maximums encounters strong community opposition. Communities are, or may be, willing to pay outstanding teachers outstanding salaries, but they are not going to pay *every* teacher such a salary.

Teachers' organizations and probably most school adminis-

[10] This statement is based upon an estimate made in a letter to me from Hazel Davis, Associate Director, Research Division, NEA, dated August 25, 1958. The best recent summary of the extent and nature of merit pay may be found in NEA Research Division, *Superior-Service Maximums in Teachers Salary Schedules, 1956–57* (Washington, D.C.: National Education Association, 1957).

trators are opposed to salary differentials among teachers on the basis of merit or alleged merit. Merit rating is usually a divisive factor among teachers themselves, because there appears to be no commonly accepted procedure to implement it. If school administrators decide who gets the merit raises, teachers become unduly subservient to the administrators, and there is always the possibility if not the fact of favoritism in awarding merit increases. Many school administrators do not relish the task of singling out the "better" teachers for salary purposes, especially if they have to work with those who are turned down for merit increases. If teachers decide who get the merit raises, they end up wrangling among themselves.

A school system might conceivably employ consultants or an outside agency to evaluate its teachers. This procedure presents a dilemma. In order for the outside evaluators to make competent judgments, they would have to observe the teachers several times a year. However, if each teacher were visited only once a month by an evaluator, the costs would be enormous. As an illustration, consider the costs of evaluation in New York City, which has approximately 40,000 professional employees, of whom well over 30,000 are teachers. Sound personnel policy would require that the evaluators be at least as well qualified, and presumably as well paid, as the teachers they evaluate. The costs of visiting each of 30,000 teachers ten times per year would be prohibitively high under these circumstances.

It would be possible to reduce the over-all cost of merit rating by operating on a somewhat different plan. A school system might consider for merit raises only teachers who had been employed a certain number of years, and fewer than ten visits per teacher per year might be required. However, teaching is not an assembly-line operation. Even good teachers have their share of bad days. For this reason, few teachers would care to have important decisions about their future made on the basis of only a few visits a year. It is obvious that the fewer the visits, the more likelihood that non-merit factors will determine who gets the best ratings.

Earlier, I stated that merit rating was really a cluster of problems rather than one narrow and well-defined problem. A workable plan for merit rating must solve such issues as who shall do the rating, what shall be the criteria for rating, how often shall rating be carried out, who shall be rated, how much of the salary budget shall depend on merit rating, and what differentials are to be paid for what differences in rating. Practically all plans for paying teachers according to merit have eventually been rejected because one or another of these problems was not solved to the satisfaction of school boards or teachers or both.

Although there is no unanimity of opinion on any of these matters, the biggest stumbling block has probably been the question of who shall do the rating. Regular administrative personnel in a school system, such as department chairmen or principals, could do it without heavy additional expense, because their routine work usually requires them to evaluate teachers. Also, their daily presence in the school affords them many excellent opportunities to do so. However, reliance upon ratings by regular staff personnel is not likely to become widespread; too often severe tensions and poor morale are the outcomes of this solution. Administrator domination of teachers, even in their non-classroom activities, is also pronounced under this procedure. And since the employment of outside personnel is too costly, the situation appears to be hopeless. This stalemate has been a disaster to the teaching profession.

The opponents of merit rating have often contended that it is a device to reduce school budgets. High salaries for the few are allegedly used to justify low salaries for the many. This argument overlooks the historical fact that the economic position of teachers has been declining for several decades and that this decline has taken place during a pronounced shift away from merit rating to single salary schedules. Also, plans for paying teachers according to merit vary in so many ways that there is little point to blanket condemnations of merit rating. Nevertheless, such condemnations are the rule at teachers' conventions where the subject is considered. In taking this attitude, teachers have failed to realize the harm done to our educational system by the absence of high top salaries in teaching (I am referring to salaries in the $10,000–$25,000 range, not the $8,000–$10,000 range which seems to concern most teachers).

So far as I know, not a single public school teacher in the country receives $15,000 per year, which is a conservative estimate of the average income of the medical profession. There are well over 1,000,000 public school classroom teachers in the United States, but it is unlikely that more than 200 of them make $10,000 per year from their regular teaching salary. What is even more crucial is the fact that there are no income ceilings in medicine, law, engineering, and most other occupations which compete with education for personnel. Thus education fails to get its proper share of the most able, energetic, and aggressive persons. Since there are about 1,300,000 persons engaged in public education, it is obvious that many of them must have outstanding ability. Nonetheless, the tremendous disparity between top salaries in teaching and in other fields drives away from teaching many individuals who would pull up the entire group.

One cannot measure the loss to education merely in terms of the number of good teachers lost in this way. One must visualize it in terms of its impact upon the professional standing of teachers and upon the loss of able educational leadership. For these reasons, even those who criticize current proposals for merit rating should be exerting every effort to develop a feasible way of implementing it. Certainly, we should not waste any time on those who believe that good teachers are immune to economic considerations.

What, then, is the solution to the problem of merit pay? A partial solution may be found in the establishment of national specialty boards comparable to those in the medical profession. The latter provide special recognition in the form of a diplomate to physicians who achieve outstanding levels of skill and knowledge in a particular field, such as surgery or psychiatry. The procedure for acquiring the diplomate in a given field is handled by the national organization of specialists in that field, e.g., the American College of Surgeons sets the requirements and processes the examinations for the diplomate in surgery.

In education, such a plan might work in this way: The national organization of teachers in a given field, for example, the National Council of Teachers of Mathematics, could set up an examination procedure for the diplomate in their field. These examinations should be comprehensive and rigorous. They should test the applicant's knowledge of his subject and his ability to diagnose and prescribe for various kinds of teaching problems. They should include observation of the applicant in actual teaching situations and also evaluation of any instructional materials prepared by applicants. The entire procedure should be such that only outstanding teachers are "board certified."

The use of board certification would eliminate favoritism, bootlicking, horse-trading, and all the other evils inherent in merit rating procedures whereby teachers are rated by other personnel in their own school system. Since it would not be possible for anyone in the system to give or take away board certification from a teacher, the basis for the undesirable practices just mentioned would not exist. Furthermore, the fact that a teacher could carry his board certification with him to a new position would mean that his professional advancement would not be tied to the subjective judgment of particular administrators in particular school systems. The standards for board certification would have to be high and distinctive enough so that both the non-certified teachers and the public would regard board certification as a defensible basis for salary differentials. This would happen if there were a nationally recognized body which administered the board examinations under conditions scrupulously designed to achieve this purpose.

Notice also that a system of board certification should eliminate the opposition to merit rating by teachers' organizations. School administrators would not be in a position to coerce teachers' organizations by granting or withholding merit pay to particular teachers. There would be little occasion for squabbling within a teachers' organization over who should receive merit pay.

Opposition to merit pay based upon board certification might develop in the AFT if the organizations which administered the specialty board examinations were departments of the NEA. AFT members might fear that examinations under the control of organizations affiliated, albeit rather loosely, with the NEA might be prejudicial to AFT members.[11] I believe this organizational problem could be solved in several different ways. The examinations might be administered by an independent testing agency, such as the Educational Testing Service, or they might be administered by subject-matter organizations not affiliated with the NEA, such as the American Physical Society or the American Mathematical Association. Certainly, if any teachers' organization were to oppose such a plan merely out of its organizational fears, it would be rendering a great disservice to American education.

Specialty board certification should not become part of the state certification structure. It should be an extralegal process, so that the specialty boards could make necessary changes from time to time without going through legislative channels. It would also be essential that the specialty boards rigidly adhere to a single standard for teachers all over the country. In this way, any school system or college which employs a board certified teacher would be assured of getting a highly qualified professional employee.

A system of specialty boards would meet many of the objections to current proposals to pay salary differentials to superior teachers. The specialty boards would eliminate the morale problems inherent in having teachers and administrators evaluate their colleagues for salary purposes. Using board certification as the basis for merit pay would also eliminate the expense to school systems of evaluating teacher competence for purposes of salary differentiation. With a national specialty board, the cost of the examinations would be borne by the teachers, just as the cost of board certification in the medical profession is now borne by the doctors. The reason would be the same— the board certified teacher would receive substantial benefits from his new status. All that would be required of the school system is a policy decision to pay higher salaries to board certified

[11] At the 1958 Annual Convention of the AFT, I suggested the introduction of educational specialty boards to several AFT leaders. None objected to it *in principle* as a merit rating plan.

teachers. The salary differentials for such teachers would have to be large enough to make it worthwhile for them to strive for board certification at their own expense. I believe that many school boards would pay such differentials if they had confidence in the specialty board procedures.

The establishment of educational specialty boards might also help to solve some of the most pressing problems of teacher education. In chapter VI, I pointed out that teacher-training institutions have yet to solve the problem of providing adequate supervision for student teachers. The supervising teachers in the schools are usually persons who lack advanced training. They are often selected haphazardly, without any real inquiry into their ability to help beginning teachers. To supplement the supervision they give, the teacher-training institutions send out supervisors who go to a different school every day to catch a fleeting glimpse of prospective teachers in action. This is a costly and inefficient procedure; the colleges cannot stand the financial burden of providing effective daily supervision for every student teacher. As a result, student teachers are seldom observed more than once every three or four weeks by a college supervisor.

If educational specialty boards were established, student teachers could receive their practical training under the guidance of board certified teachers. As supervisors, the board certified teachers could be treated as adjunct professors of the teacher-training institutions. Indeed, the extent to which a school system employed board certified teachers would be an indication of the caliber of that system. This would also follow medical practice, where the extent to which a hospital or clinic employs board certified specialists is widely accepted as an indication of its caliber. Many other professions have established procedures to identify their most competent practitioners.

Let us turn next to the problem of how to transform the idea of educational specialty boards into an operating reality. The proposed solution will illustrate the role which the foundations might play in remaking the structure of American public education.

First of all, the foundations might bring together the leaders of a few national organizations of specialists in certain fields. The most effective procedure would be to bring together leaders of the national organizations of professors and public school teachers in the same field. Thus in the field of mathematics there should be representation from both the American Mathematical Association and the National Council of Teachers of Mathematics. If the leaders of these organizations were agreeable, as I am sure they would be, the foundation could make relatively modest grants, say of $75,000, to these organizations to draw up proposed plans for board certification in their fields.

In due course, these organizations should draw up fairly complete plans for the operation of a specialty board in their subject. The plans would include provisions for who would conduct the examinations, the nature of the examinations, where and how often they would be given, the budget for the specialty board, the fees to be charged, the qualifications required of applicants, and so on. The foundation grants would make it possible for the organizations to secure the very best advice on these matters from teachers, leading scholars in each subject, and others with ideas to contribute.

When the plans are completed, they should be disseminated to school administrators and school boards over the country. The participating foundations might then convene a large number of leading classroom teachers, school superintendents, and school boards to assess their reactions to the proposals, either in a series of regional meetings or in national conferences or both. At these meetings, educational personnel would become fully acquainted with the proposed boards. After everyone concerned had ample opportunity to study the proposals, and after they had been changed in whatever ways seemed desirable in the light of these reactions, the issue of participation should be put squarely up to teachers' organizations, superintendents, and school boards. Naturally, local, state, and national organizations would be expected to encourage lay and professional acceptance of the proposed specialty boards.

At this point, the attitude of the foundations should be something like this: Whenever a given number of school systems agree to pay at least a specified higher salary to board certified teachers, an additional grant would be made to cover the costs of specialty board operation for several years. After that time, the specialty boards would have to be self-supporting or supported by other sources. And if it were not possible to get a number of school boards to pay a substantial differential to board certified teachers, the foundation should indicate that it would abandon the enterprise.

This is only a skeletonized version of the strategy which might be employed to effectuate specialty boards, but it does illustrate some important points. One is that the foundations supporting such a project would not be trying to ram a particular change down anybody's throat. They would be making it possible to develop an idea, to discover whether it had widespread support, and to put it into effect if it did have such support. They would be foolish to push the idea of specialty boards past a certain point without support, but they would be fully justified in giving the idea an opportunity to catch on.

It would be easier to introduce board certification as a basis for merit pay on a national basis than on an isolated, local basis. It is always easier to get a school board to approve a change when many other boards have also approved it. Teachers are not likely to undertake the intensive study needed to pass their board examinations before they know how much more school systems will pay teachers who pass these examinations. School systems are not likely to pay an adequate differential to board certified teachers unless the boards are launched with unimpeachable professional and public support. All of this requires national planning and publicity.

The establishment of educational specialty boards would not be a complete answer to the problem of rewarding superior teachers. For one thing, the boards would not be geared directly to the teacher's actual performance on the job from year to year. A teacher who had passed his board examinations might nevertheless lie down on the job. Some outstanding teachers would never get around to securing board certification. Despite these and other potential weaknesses, the specialty boards could provide a reasonably objective way of distinguishing and rewarding outstanding teachers. The big danger would be the degeneration of board standards, such as would take place if board certification were based upon the accumulation of credits, travel, service to the community, and criteria of this nature. It might be feasible to begin with boards which examined only the teacher's knowledge of his subject. This seems to me to be unduly restrictive, but it would be better than no boards at all.

In evaluating the idea of educational specialty boards, one should not assume that the idea is not feasible unless the boards provide an unerring guide to teacher competence. Nor should it be thought necessary that the boards remove all need for evaluative judgment within a school system. Merit is not always rewarded in other occupations. Some persons receive more than their due in every occupation. It would, however, be a blunder to reject merit rating in principle because no current way of implementing it promises absolute accuracy. For that matter, even the supporters of the single salary schedule admit that it results in many inequities. We are urged to endure these inequities only because nothing better has been proposed. This may be, but the long-range harm resulting from single salary schedules should stimulate everyone to search for a better plan to compensate teachers.

My proposal for educational specialty boards has two objectives: first, to illustrate a possible answer to an important problem of professional compensation, and, second, to illustrate how the foundations might act to change the structure of American education. Let me conclude by discussing the latter objective briefly.

Like the people in the field, the foundations are characterized by an unwarranted faith in a community-by-community approach to educational reform. In their case, it is reflected in an emphasis upon "demonstrations" or "pilot projects." This faith is all the more plausible since, for some purposes, demonstrations or pilot projects are the only feasible way to get improvements. Nevertheless, reliance upon demonstrations and pilot projects has a tendency to narrow the scope of needed foundation activities.

At the national level, you cannot demonstrate the wisdom of certain changes by "pilot projects"; you either make the change or you don't.

The changes which the foundations must support will threaten vested interests of all kinds—professional, religious, political, racial, and economic. A great deal will depend upon the foundation trustees. They must provide the climate within which the permanent staff of the foundations can support the bold action that is needed. For this, the trustees must have a vision of what public education can be, and they must be persons not easily bluffed by legislatures, investigating committees, disgruntled applicants, or vested interests of any kind. Their difficulties and dangers will be great, but their opportunity is immeasurable.

Chapter XIII

BEYOND THE CLICHÉ BARRIER

In this concluding chapter, I should like to summarize the educational program set forth in previous chapters. Before doing so, a few words of caution and explanation seem appropriate.

Ordinarily, any educational improvement is cumulative. Raising the standards for a teaching certificate is likely to bring about improvements in classroom performance, in teachers' salaries, in the reduction of teacher turnover, and in other aspects of education. The reverse is also true; low standards anywhere along the line turn the interdependence of educational factors into a vicious circle. For this reason, we should be skeptical of single-factor explanations of, and solutions to, important educational problems. Such explanations and solutions raise expectations which cannot be fulfilled and which narrow our insight into the levers of educational improvement.

A realistic program must be specific; at the same time, such a program must not be a collection of itemized recipes incapable of general application. For instance, the development of collective bargaining between teachers and school boards will undoubtedly require vigorous campaigns by the state teachers' organizations. In some states, these organizations are so weak that it would be futile for them even to raise the issue at this time.

Where this is the case, the teachers might be better advised to concentrate upon organizational problems. In other states, the state organizations might be capable of conducting an effective campaign but may not be doing so because of the opposition of their leaders. Here, the task is to educate or to replace these leaders. In still other states, teachers' organizations may already be working for collective bargaining in public education but there may be opposition from various non-professional sources, which must be counteracted. In still other states, collective bargaining by teachers may be partly achieved, and the task is to extend it.

It is sometimes possible to list educational reforms in order of their strategic importance, but this order cannot fit the circumstances of each individual. The development of a strong national teachers' organization is much more important than the development of strong local citizens' committees for the public schools, but particular people will find themselves in a position to implement the latter but not the former objective. A person who has a position of authority in the United States Chamber of Commerce can do more to help public education by modifying some of the educational policies of this organization than thousands of citizens could accomplish by breathing down the necks of their school boards once a month.

In brief, regardless of the strategic importance of particular issues, the steps to be taken by each person can be decided only by reference to the concrete circumstances of his situation. These considerations do not mean that no priorities can be established. They mean only that priorities may be different from situation to situation. The basic educational goals will be the same for everyone, but people confronted by different obstacles and opportunities will have different things to do to help us reach our goals.

With these thoughts in mind, I have summarized in outline form the recommendations made in previous chapters. In some cases, recommendations not previously mentioned have been included, either to provide more specificity or simply as recommended proposals which could not be analyzed adequately in this book.

1. The leadership positions in teachers' organizations must be made attractive enough to compete with any other type of educational position, and with top-level positions in industry, the professions, government service, and other fields. The chief executive of such organizations as the NEA and the AAUP should be paid not less than $50,000 per year.

2. Teachers should pay at least $100 per year in dues, with perhaps $40.00 going to the national organization, $40.00 to the state organization, and $20.00 to their local organization.

3. There should be at least one full-time representative of the teachers wherever there are at least 2,000 teachers in a school system or combination of systems. The national and state organizations should set minimum professional and employment standards for these representatives and be ready to assist local organizations in employing them on a permanent basis.

4. There should be a merger of the NEA and the AFT on the basis of (*a*) an abandonment of affiliation with the labor movement and (*b*) adequate organizational safeguards to prevent administrator domination of the merged organization.

5. There may be a group of teachers' organizations differentiated according to their teaching fields of specialization, but there should be only one organization to represent the same kind of teachers in employer-employee affairs.

6. Organization dues should be collected by a check-off system at the source of payment.

7. Membership in the comprehensive teachers' organizations must be mandatory, though on an extralegal basis. One possible way to achieve this is for the organizations to be aggressive supporters of high administrative salaries; in return, administrative personnel must do everything they possibly can, such as instituting the check-off system, to strengthen the teachers' organizations. Such a *quid pro quo* would not mean administrator domina-

tion of the organizations but would be a natural alliance based upon mutual strength and respect. Every effort should be made to make membership attractive through cheap insurance, credit unions, and similar inducements.

8. The membership structure of teachers' organizations must reflect in part the certification regulations for different kinds of educational personnel; those persons with no training in common and with widely disparate levels of training should not be lumped together into one vast industrial union type organization.

9. Superintendents and other top-level managerial employees should not be allowed to join organizations which represent teachers in matters of employment.

10. Teachers' organizations should establish and enforce a code of professional ethics that would be nationwide in scope.

STRATEGY AND TACTICS

1. Long-range strategy must de-emphasize the community-by-community approach to educational improvements; there should be a correspondingly greater emphasis upon improvements at the state and national levels.

2. Teachers must rely more upon organizational pressure on school boards and other elected officials and less upon "educating the public" in the way typified by present-day PTA activities.

3. The power of national and state professional organizations must be utilized systematically to affect the outcome of negotiations between teachers and school boards at the local level.

4. Professional control over entry and collective bargaining must be given a high organizational priority; the present emphasis upon minimum salary laws should be abandoned.

5. Strategy which explicitly or implicitly weakens the professional autonomy of teachers should be avoided at virtually any cost.

6. Strategy should be based upon the premise that employee benefits are ordinarily not given freely by employers; they are *taken* by employees. Teachers should not be perturbed over anguished cries from the school boards or legislatures or private citizens when they take aggressive action to achieve their just

employment demands. Employers never jump for joy in these circumstances, no matter how justified the employee arguments may be.

TEACHERS AS EMPLOYEES

1. School boards should be required to recognize and negotiate with the majority organizations of teachers concerning conditions of employment; if it appears desirable to have different organizations representing different types of teachers, only the majority organization for each type should represent the teachers.

2. Teachers and school boards should sign master contracts which cover the following subjects:

Scope and purposes of the agreement

Definitions of terms used

Recognition of the bargaining unit

Regular schedule of meetings

Membership in the bargaining unit

Checkoff

Obligations of the various parties

Legislation limiting the agreement

Duration of the agreement

Provisions for termination and renegotiation

Salary schedule

Number of paydays

Travel pay and allowances

Pay for special duties (coaching, etc.)

Hours of work (normal school day)

Class schedules

Number of preparations

Sick leave

Absenteeism by teachers

Rest and lunch-hour periods

Vacations

Promotions

Transfers

Substitute teachers

Leaves of absence

Seniority

Decrease in personnel

Safety provisions

Pupil discipline

Military service credit

Suspension and discharge procedures

Grievance procedures

Supplies to be furnished

Time off for professional meetings

Procedures for handling parental complaints [1]

3. Procedures for changing the conditions of employment should be spelled out in the master contracts; it should be im-

[1] From Myron Lieberman, *Education as a Profession* (Englewood Cliffs, N.J.: Prentice-Hall, 1956), p. 357.

possible for school boards to make substantial changes by unilateral action.

4. Grievance procedures should protect the rights and dignity of teachers without providing unreasonable restrictions on the managerial discretion needed to run a school system efficiently.

5. Application forms for employment and promotion should omit references to race, religion, nationality, or lineage.

6. Unnecessary restrictions upon the mobility of educational personnel should be eliminated; for example, requirements that a state superintendent of schools be a resident of a given state for a certain number of years prior to election or appointment should be abolished. Ways must be found to overcome the immobilizing effects of forcing teachers to give up substantial pension or retirement benefits if they should move.

TEACHERS' SALARIES

1. Since teaching is essentially a cluster of different occupations, despite their common label, we should expect some salary differentiation according to the teaching field; this does not mean merely the elementary-secondary dichotomy, which is unrealistic as a basis for differentiation.

2. Top teachers must be paid $10,000–$15,000 a year as a minimum, through the use of educational specialty boards. Such boards may provide for more than one rank of superior teacher.

3. Teachers should not be required to teach full-time or not at all; older teachers should be allowed to decrease their load and salary, and we should utilize potential teachers who can teach only part-time.

4. Teachers should be given a direct economic stake in the efficiency and productivity of the school system. They should receive a fair share of the difference between the estimated and the actual costs of operating the schools at an agreed-upon level of educational achievement.

5. A school system should not be forced to give raises on a permanent basis or not at all; the salary structure should be sufficiently flexible so that systems can pay non-recurring raises.

6. The notion that the public will not pay high salaries is a

rationalization of teacher weakness and must not be accepted as the final state of the public mind on the subject. The businessman who knows it is to his business advantage to pay high salaries for good personnel can hardly deny the validity of this argument to the business of the public.

7. All salary data should be easily accessible to the public.

TEACHER EDUCATION AND CERTIFICATION

1. There must be national standards for teacher certification; the legal form of their implementation is important but not necessarily decisive.

2. Teacher education must be confined to institutions of higher education which are centers of research.

3. There must be day-to-day articulation of theoretical and practical training in teacher-education programs.

4. There must be unified control of teacher education and of the schools in which prospective teachers receive their practical training.

5. The academic course structure must recognize that not all education courses are professional and that some of the courses in the teaching field of specialization are of this non-professional nature.

6. There must be an examination system interposed between graduation from accredited teacher-preparing institutions and actual entry to teaching. This can be initiated with examinations in the teaching field of specialization, prepared by specialists in each field. All states should be encouraged to use the same examination, prepared and evaluated on a national basis.

7. Requirements for a teaching certificate must not be enacted into law by state legislatures but should be delegated to an agency responsible to organized professional opinion; the requirements of this agency should have the force of law.

8. The number of teacher-training institutions should be drastically reduced. This should be the natural consequence of raising the standards for admission, retention, and graduation along with a system of state board examinations for entry.

9. Certification requirements should be highly prescriptive and

allow relatively little room for electives in a total program of teacher education.

10. Teachers must learn to see their stake in high standards of entry and why this requires them to assume the control over teacher education which has passed by default to the colleges and universities.

11. The persons who teach methods courses and supervise the practical training of teachers of academic subjects should be members of the appropriate academic departments in their subject fields.

12. The practice of spelling out the requirements for a teaching certificate in terms of a given number of course credits must be replaced by a system which indicates the specific content which must be mastered, regardless of courses taken.

13. The most constructive step that liberal arts colleges can take for public education is to put their own house in order. This means eliminating course proliferation, curtailing emphasis upon non-educational activities, setting up a new framework of employer-employee relations, insisting upon high standards for admission, promotion, and graduation, stopping the intensive recruitment of high-school athletes, and otherwise setting a better example for education at lower levels.

14. The study of education as a social institution must be included in the general education program for all students.

THE FOUNDATIONS

1. Thorough studies must be undertaken of what will be required to eliminate the academic retardation of underprivileged socioeconomic groups.

2. A series of substantial awards should be given for outstanding theoretical contributions in such fields as educational psychology, elementary education, school finance, and so on. These awards should provide a substantial incentive for professors to publish something better than rehashes of previous textbooks in their fields.

3. An Institute for Educational Leadership could be estab-

lished to concentrate upon the re-education of organization leaders.

4. Preliminary studies of educational specialty boards should be initiated; if these studies indicate that such boards are feasible, the foundations should underwrite the necessary measures to effectuate them.

5. There should be a national program involving the National School Boards Association, the American Council To Improve Our Neighborhoods, the American Association of School Administrators, and other appropriate agencies, to insure that schools and school systems are given a respected place in the vast urban renewal movement which is going to remake the face of this country in the next few decades.

6. Studies should be made of the way in which students at various grade and ability levels spend their time—time and motion studies, if you will. We are undoubtedly operating with a very haphazard educational structure in terms of the number of courses and credits deemed feasible for students to carry. Similar studies are needed for teachers of different subjects and grade levels.

7. There should be a grant program, the ultimate objective of which is the establishment of national standards for doctoral degrees in fields which do not now have such standards. These programs should consider the feasibility of de-emphasizing the institution-by-institution approach to the improvement of doctoral programs.

8. Studies and action programs should be designed to bring about much heavier expenditures for educational research and experimentation. We need to develop a clear idea of how much ought to be spent on educational research on a nationwide basis and what sources should support this research and at what levels.

9. An Institute for Educational Theory could be set up which would concentrate upon studies of the institutional aspects of education. This institute might provide funds and facilities for a small number of persons to study such subjects as the economics of public education, the composition and operation of state

departments of education, the dynamics of educational legislation, how, why, and what news about education gets into the mass media, the influence of textbook publishers and of privately sponsored educational materials on the curriculum, and the internal operations of educational organizations. The institute might have only a few permanent members; others could be brought in on a rotating basis, as is done at the Center for Advanced Study in the Behavioral Sciences at Palo Alto and the Institute for Advanced Study at Princeton.[2]

10. An Institute for Educational Technology might be established which would be devoted to research and experimentation with the most advanced forms of technology for educational purposes.

11. Foundations must take the initiative to improve the quality of the proposals they receive. To this end, they should sponsor a series of conferences at least every few years to review their operations and evaluate their effectiveness. This should be done jointly with institutions of higher education, school systems, and teachers' organizations. The foundations should provide for systematic, independent evaluation of their activities, just as they urge others to undergo such evaluation. For example, they should find out what able individuals do not submit proposals (there are some!) and why they do not. If handled properly,

[2] This suggestion seems especially appropriate because the research centers just mentioned do not operate as if the problems of education are important. Thus in the first four years of its existence (1954–58), the Center for Advanced Study in the Behavioral Sciences invited persons from the following fields: Political science, psychology, history, anthropology, law, literature, sociology, biology, psychiatry, and others. Except for one professor holding a joint appointment in sociology and education at Harvard, no professor of education or person whose major field of study is educational theory was a fellow at the Center. It is difficult to see the justification for excluding persons interested in educational problems from a center for advanced study in the behavioral sciences. The Institute for Advanced Study has also invited professors from a wide range of the social sciences and the humanities, but it has never invited anyone to participate in the advantages of study at the Institute for the purpose of studying educational problems. There is a certain measure of irony in this situation also, since the Institute was founded upon the advice of Abraham Flexner, a man whose brilliant and deserved reputation as a scholar was built largely upon his studies of higher education. I do not think I am misstating the case when I say that Flexner himself would never have been invited to study at the Institute under present conditions and most certainly not if he were labeled a professor of education!

this suggestion would strengthen the foundations politically as well as increase their effectiveness.

1. Local control of education by laymen should be limited to peripheral and ceremonial functions of education. However, the rights of individual parents and students to make certain basic choices (for example, whether the student takes a college preparatory or a vocational program) must be carefully protected.

2. Laymen can ordinarily make their most valuable contribution to public education in their non-educational organizations. As members of organized groups, laymen can help to protect the integrity of the school program by opposing efforts to use the schools through special holidays, contests, activities, or subjects to advance organizational interests which are not necessary for the educational welfare of students.

3. In view of the fact that the people most active in educational affairs are usually from the upper classes and tend to favor policies which are unfair to less privileged groups, citizens should support school budgets which make all subjects and activities freely available to all students who have the capacity to profit from them. School-wide activities which are theoretically open to all students but which are usually not attended by poorer children, such as junior proms requiring formal dress, should be eliminated unless economic and social class factors in participation can be removed.

4. Laymen should support proposals to give teachers more authority over students and over parental behavior relating to school problems. A request from school authorities for a parent to discuss a school problem relating to his children should not be something the parent is free to ignore, as is almost everywhere the case at the present time.

5. Citizens should support school boards which are willing to negotiate conditions of employment with representatives of the majority organizations of teachers, provided such organizations have adequate safeguards against administrator domination.

6. School boards should provide contracts of perhaps five years' duration for superintendents. Superintendents hired for shorter periods are too busy building their political fences (to insure reappointment) to provide effective educational leadership; they frequently pass every controversy on to the public, regardless of the professional nature of the issues involved.

7. Citizen participation, like the work of the teachers, needs to be evaluated periodically and critically. It might be salutary for superintendents to reveal the record of citizen participation in their community for each past year. A great deal of this participation consists of pressure to fire an athletic coach after an unsuccessful season, protesting because one's child is not in an accelerated group, criticizing the school cafeteria for not providing home cooking, attempting to get the school bus to make a more convenient stop, and sundry other matters of this nature. Citizens tend to underestimate how ineffective the schools are; at the same time, their own participation and influence upon the school program is often the cause rather than the result of this ineffectiveness.

8. Citizens' committees on public education, PTA's, school boards, and other individuals and groups interested in improving public education should work with teachers through the systematic evaluation of student achievement, diagnoses of what must be done to improve performance, and support for the measures needed for improvement.

9. Respect for teachers should be reflected in support for adequate conditions of educational employment, rather than in annual "Teacher Recognition Days" (which often embarrass the teachers and certainly do not help them materially).

10. Citizens should make an inventory of what parents are doing to help or hinder the educational progress of their children. This inventory should be conducted with due regard for the economic status and living conditions of the families involved. School boards, perhaps in conjunction with PTA's and citizens' committees, should conduct this inventory. The sort of questions to be answered include the following: (*a*) Are pupils sent to school with an adequate breakfast? (*b*) Are pupils accorded a time and a place to do homework at home? (*c*)

How many children work after school and on weekends? At whose insistence do they work, how many hours do they put in, and how is school performance affected by this employment? (*d*) How many pupils have an automobile or the free use of an automobile? (*e*) How late do pupils stay up the night before a school day? (*f*) Are students readily provided with funds for school supplies and equipment? (*g*) How many pupils are absent on school days before and after holidays? (*h*) How often are children absent or tardy for trivial reasons with parental knowledge? (*i*) Do parents have a reasonably adequate understanding of their children's academic aptitude and progress in school? (*j*) Are the educational policies of citizens groups formulated with due regard for the less powerful and less articulate groups in the community?

11. Citizens should recognize that the concept of "participation" is one of the vaguest of the many vague terms that make communication difficult in education. Laymen "participate" in helping to solve the medical problems of their children, but the nature and limits of this participation are well understood. Everyone has a stake in a clear-cut delineation of parental, public, and professional authority in public education. It is probably more important that the delineation be clear to everyone than that it be a perfect division of labor between professionals and non-professionals.

12. Insofar as elective officials are concerned, the rule is clear: for short-run, relatively minor, but more immediate improvements, concentrate upon local school board elections; for long-range major improvements, concentrate upon the state and national election of education-minded legislators and executives who have the power to shape the context and limits of local action.

13. Laymen who become active in the field of public education should bear in mind the fact that the worst evils of public education are more often due to teacher acquiescence in public opinion than teacher resistance to it.

Past experience in discussing these proposals leads me to anticipate certain reactions. One is that these proposals would take education away from the people who pay for it and would destroy public interest in it. This reaction is usually based on the premise that local control has been responsible for a strong grass-roots concern with public education. "The schools are close to the people"—this is now part of the folklore of American education.

This folklore persists in the face of the strongest kinds of evidence to refute it. Elections to school boards usually have a smaller turnout than elections to any other public office, local, state or federal. Statistics on the subject are not available, but my guess would be that as a rule less than 5 per cent of the eligible voters turn out in a school board election.

The reality is that public education is not in the mainstream of American life. For example, one cannot think of a person working in the field of public education who is a nationally known personality. The field of labor brings to mind names like John L. Lewis, Walter Reuther, or George Meany. In medicine, one thinks of Dr. Jonas Salk, of Dr. Paul Dudley White. Similarly, in the arts, government, law, theology, industry, and many other major fields, one can quickly name several persons whose names are known all over the country. Not all are known for desirable reasons, but they are people who make national and even international news. It is a measure of the public indifference to our schools that there are no such names in the field of public education. Even in the segregation crisis, educators are secondary figures. Politicians, journalists, NAACP leaders, and some students are more important personalities than the professional school people, who are more or less puppets in the whole situation.

Newspapers have daily interpretive columnists who write on politics, economics, fashion, family life, the arts, literature, and many other fields. To my knowledge, not a single newspaper has a daily column devoted to education. There are columnists on home and family life, but none of them is capable of serious interpretive writing about education even if he wished to do so.

It must be conceded that professional educators are not ahead of the public on this problem. For example, current education textbooks are seldom critical of local control. These textbooks tell us that the schools are "close to the people," an example of "grass-roots democracy" at its best, a thrilling example of the virtues of good old-fashioned town-hall Americanism. Turn the pages and you read a seemingly endless list of techniques to overcome public apathy toward school needs. Educators have really become enfeebled by their own propaganda; many of them think that it is flirting with totalitarianism to regard local control as a dangerous anachronism.

The centralization of public education, in whatever form it comes, will bring public education into the mainstream of American life. Centralization means that some people are going to make educational decisions that will be important in every community. When this happens, education will be news and educational leaders will be nationally known, for good or evil as the case may be. When this happens, public education may become close to the people, but in a new and more fruitful sense than it is now.

At the present time, public education presents a paradox: the work of teachers is dominated by political considerations but the teachers themselves are political nonentities. The need is to transform teachers into political animals so that their work can be based on professional instead of political considerations. Without political power, teachers will never be able to protect the integrity of their work.

Along with political power, what teachers need as much as anything is a spirit of adventure. For all their talk of change, teachers have changed their occupation less than virtually any other major occupational group. It is almost frightening to notice how much teachers take for granted in their approach to education. Over and over again, they try to solve problems within a framework that is the root cause of the problems themselves. Their perpetual frustration in trying to improve their conditions of employment through minimum salary laws is only one such example.

Educational leaders seem resigned to the fact that the salaries of public employees usually lag behind salaries in private employment during periods of inflation. Instead of regarding this lag as a practical problem, to be solved by a diagnosis and an action program, their approach has been to cite the lag as a reason for not expecting very much. However, the reasons why the salaries of teachers lag behind those in industry are not immutable laws engraved in stone. They are causes which can and should be eliminated by intelligent group action.

Many teachers have one final crushing answer to a proposed change: it is against the law, or it will require some changes in the law. To teachers, this often seems an impenetrable barrier which relieves them of the necessity to think any further. Proposals to change the legal structure of public education are dreamy utopian stuff to many teachers. Most of them are too busy running on the treadmill of community-by-community improvement to realize that there is no local solution to the basic problems of public education.

This will appear to be a message of despair to many people who work for better schools. They cannot even influence local school board elections, and now they are told that these are not as crucial as they have always supposed. The really important elections are at state and national levels, where their influence will be even more attenuated than it is on the local scene. But this thesis is a message of despair only if we assume that the present political impotence of teachers and citizens interested in public education is an unchangeable fact of life. The latter assumption would indeed be a message of despair, but I, for one, do not accept it.

The tendency to take for granted the present structure of public education weakens teachers at one important point after another. For example, to hear teachers ask in puzzled tones how they are to get control over entry or collective bargaining, one might suppose that no occupational group had achieved these objectives. Granted, the changes needed will involve some difficult problems of strategy and tactics. Nevertheless, the difficulties are not primarily strategic; they lie mainly in the failure of teachers to realize what changes are in fact needed. The strategy to be used to secure these changes is basically no different from that utilized in scores of other occupations, professional and non-professional, public and private, to achieve the same objectives.

The fact is that the essentials of the forthcoming revolution in education are already evident in other fields. For this reason, sweeping changes in education are not a remote prospect. If, for example, teachers were the only group of public employees interested in collective bargaining, there would be strong reason to doubt its eventual acceptance in public education. But this is not the case. Collective bargaining by public employees will soon be so common that its widespread introduction into public education will appear to be a reasonable development to persons who reject it now.

Apart from the merits of any proposals made in this book, their chances of gaining acceptance should not be judged according to the attitudes which people currently may have toward them. People have vowed that they would close down their public schools rather than support integrated ones, but when confronted by the realities of this policy, they have accepted integration, albeit under protest. Later, their acceptance of integration became so matter of fact that they would have been surprised to learn that they had vowed last-ditch resistance to it only a short time ago. Utopianism is, of course, to be avoided, but so is the error of assessing future attitudes in the light of present instead of future realities. This error leads to a kind of conservatism that is as unrealistic as utopianism.

From this perspective, it would be surprising if we were to continue to have a national policy for industry, finance, labor relations, transportation, communications, and other areas of contemporary life, while public education remained primarily a matter for local control. The pressures generated by the life we lead and the kind of world in which we live will not permit this inconsistency to endure indefinitely. This conclusion in no way presupposes that we are headed for a totalitarian state or one in which all the decisions are made in Washington. It presupposes only that our interdependence will be reflected in our educational as well as our political and economic policies.

The problem in education, as in so many other areas, is to maintain the substance of democracy and a high level of efficiency while modifying an important social institution so that it takes into account the conditions of modern life.

My final comment relates to the convictions set forth in the first chapter of this book. Public education constitutes one of the important occupational frontiers in American life. This frontier requires pioneers, every bit as resourceful as those who conquered geographical frontiers in an earlier day. It is a frontier on which many roles are wandering in search of leaders who understand the problems and the potentialities of public education. My firm conviction is that a handful of such leaders can bring about a revolution in education, a revolution such that the practice of free public education in the United States will stand as its major contribution to the human community of the future.

INDEX

Academic freedom, 42, 53–55, 141, 204

Adler, Irving, 61

Administration: and professional autonomy, 60–61, 67; as separate profession, 91; training for, 91. *See also* Administrators; Lay-professional relations; Local control of education; School boards; Teachers' organizations

Administrators: and authority, 222, 224; certification and preparation of, 91; and collective bargaining, 171–77, 273–74; membership of, in teachers' organizations, 182, 232–34; and merit rating, 262, 264–65; and professional autonomy, 60, 67; relationships of, with teachers, 171–77, 232–34; specialized training of, 91. *See also* Administration

Affiliation. *See* American Federation of Teachers; National Education Association

American Association of School Administrators, 180, 222, 223, 233, 279

American Association of University Professors: and academic freedom, 204–5; and collective bargaining, 152; effectiveness of, 213–14; local and state chapters of, 200–201; membership in, 173, 209–11; prejudices in, 149; as a professional organization, 199–206; program of, 202–3, 214; strategy followed by, 203–4, 206–8; and tenure, 205

American Federation of Teachers: administrator exclusion from, 173;

affiliation with labor, 193–96, 231–32; and collective bargaining, 234; Constitution of, 232, 235; future of, 198; history of, 192–93; membership in, 197, 232–35; merger of, with NEA, 230–36; and merit rating, 264–65; no-strike policy of, 193, 196; professional inadequacies of, 197–98, 236–37; and racial segregation, 235–36; and teacher aides, 258; teacher attitudes toward, 197–98; and teachers' salaries, 265

American College of Surgeons, 263

American Council To Improve Our Neighborhoods, 279

American Federation of Labor–Congress of Industrial Organizations, 182, 194–95, 216. *See also* American Federation of Teachers

American Historical Association, 210–11

American Legion, 64

American Mathematical Association, 265–66

American Medical Association, 51, 106, 189, 209

American Physical Society, 265

Anderson, Archibald W., 16

Andrews, F. Emerson, 246

Armstrong, W. Earl, 103, 142

Athletics, 136–40

Authority, 34–38. *See also* Education, at state level; Federal government and education; Local control of education

Baltzell, E. Digby, 146

Benne, Kenneth D., 16

Bent, Rudyard K., 223

PRINTED IN U.S.A.

PHOENIX BOOKS

PHOENIX BOOKS

 PHOENIX SCIENCE SERIES

Join me on the line and Play to Win.

In the New Testament the great apostle Paul was a man who "played to win," and wanted others to do the same: " . . . run in such a way that you will win," he urged the Corinthians. He pictures a runner going hard for the tape, eyes on the goal, hands outstretched, body bent forward, every muscle strained as he gives his all to win the race. The image in hockey would be of a player driving the net, coming back hard, digging in the corners, controlling the puck, taking the hit and leaving everything on the ice.

The hockey players and coaches featured in this volume of the *Play to Win Hockey New Testament* embrace discipline and determination in their training and preparation. For them, winning is performing at their highest level. Recognizing that their talents and abilities are gifts from God they are highly motivated to train and compete to express their thankfulness for all that He has given to them. They want to live for God and they compete to fulfill God's purpose for their lives. In this pursuit they are unstoppable because of Him.

The spiritual dimension of these highly motivated athletes is evident not only in their on-ice performance but also in their daily relationship with God. They hold firmly to Paul's words to Timothy, "Physical exercise has some value but spiritual exercise is much more important, for it promises a reward in both this life and the next"(1 Timothy 4:8). Reading the Bible, praying, meeting with other Christians and caring for others are significant parts of their life. These disciplines enable them to "fight the good fight of faith" as they wrestle with the challenges of their life and the game. They have tasted victory and failure, yet hold to an inner faith in Jesus Christ, with whom they share a relationship. Many players and fans are seeking real meaning and purpose in their lives that will point them to Christ. Their faith is based on their belief in the Word of God, the New Testament, you hold in your hands. As you read it you will grow in understanding of who He is and how much He loves you.

As a player in the NHL myself and as a fellow team... ...ho lay claim to eternal life in Jesus Christ, all I ask of each of you is that you, ...mmate, join me on the line and "Play to Win."

Looking forward,

Eric Staal

Eric Staal

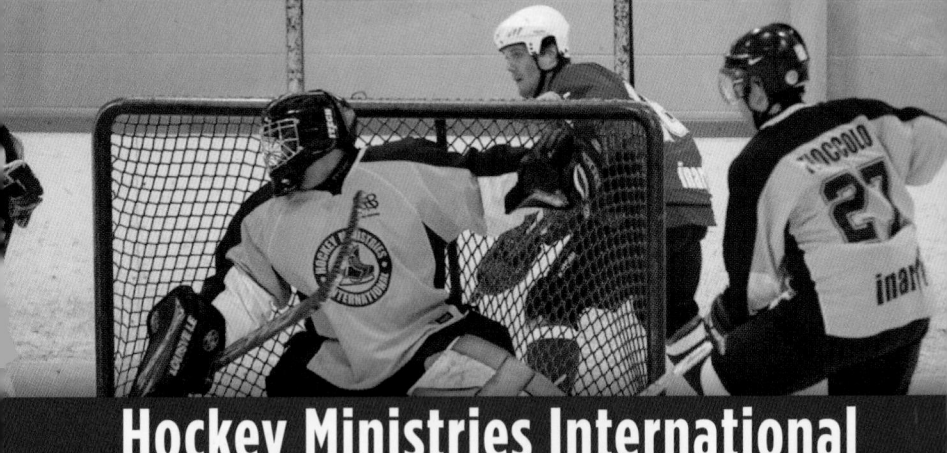

Hockey Ministries International
Inspiring players to Win

Winning in hockey demands much of a player but grants little in the way of emotional or spiritual support enabling players to win in life. Hockey's demanding schedules—practices, games and travel—make it almost impossible for players to attend a familiar community church on a regular basis. HMI's answer to this problem was a simple one—why not bring the church to the rink?

Chico Resch, Former NHL All Star Goaltender, Stanley Cup Winner and current Color Analyst for the New Jersey Devils, experienced the impact during his successful NHL career and makes the following analysis:

"Today church is not restricted to a dwelling or a building; it's much more fluid than that. At *Hockey Ministries International ("HMI")*, church is sometimes a rink, a locker room, a hotel lobby or a personal encounter on the ice.

From Humble Beginnings

Forty years ago a young junior and then professional hockey player felt quite alone in his Christian faith in the game. Keenly aware of the demands hockey imposes on players and their families, he recognized too the absence of any meaningful moral or spiritual support systems.

He felt the need for a dimension of hope and faith among his teammates and opponents, their families, friends and fans. What could be done? How could this hockey culture be introduced to the answers found in the Christian faith? How could the Hope that he knew be brought to the rink?

Inspiring players to win

In 1977 first seeds were sown in the form of a Christian hockey camp for youth in Montreal. That first year Christian NHL and CFL players provided instruction on ice and in dry land sports. They also explained how their faith helped them in their careers and personal lives and how what you believe can change the way you live your life. Campers learned that being a Christian gives you help for your problems each day and hope for your future. It's about courage, perseverance, teamwork and trophies that last forever.

HMI's first camp was a small one, but big enough to form the foundation of everything that *HMI* is today. Since the 1970's a Christian movement has been growing throughout hockey communities in North America and in other countries around the world as players and fans have taken up the cause together.

The Spirit of HMI . . .

Perhaps our core programs, camps and chapels, best exemplify the spirit of *HMI*. Every summer HMI hosts 34 week-long Christian Hockey Camps in 6 different countries: Canada, USA, Sweden, Switzerland, Slovakia and the Czech Republic. Over 600 volunteers, including NHL players and coaches, give their time each summer to make these camps happen. Training programs blend physical, mental and spiritual conditioning, preparing players for challenges on and off the ice and helping them to win in the game of life. Morning and evening chapels feature youth-oriented music programs, inspirational testimony and opportunities to get to know the pros. Humor, practical jokes and fun are an important part of the mix. Professional players, coaches and counselors provide positive role models that remain with the young players long after camp ends. Noah Welch of the Swedish Elite League said this about his experience at the HMI camp in Calgary: " I got to coach these kids teaching them to be better hockey players but most importantly, I shared the Lord with them. I came here to serve but have been served by the kids and the staff. It really has been a true blessing." At the camps a profound impact is made in the lives of youth hockey players. Heather Cruz, a Minnesota camper's mom, writes about her son's experience at an HMI camp in 2012:

"My son, Delfin, had a devastating head injury while playing hockey in a tournament in Marshfield, WI. He has had many symptoms we have had to overcome, including dizziness, nausea, vision problems, 30 days of school missed, emotional challenges, in-patient hospital care, etc. We were told by the doctors yesterday that he is out of hockey for at least a year and they are not sure when or if ever he will get to play again. I just wanted you to know that he gave his life to Christ at your camp last year and he has truly followed it. His faith has carried him through this devastating time. He has endured more than most adults could handle and he is only 10. If he would have gone to just any old hockey camp he would not have had the strength to carry him through this recovery process. He kept talking about going back to HMI this year. He will never give up the love of hockey, but his love for the Lord will be the love that carries him through his life. I pray that hockey will still be a channel for him to share his faith with others, but if God has another plan for him we will let God be our guide. **I just hope all of your campers know that hockey is a temporary win, but faith in God is the eternal championship! Thank you for helping to instill that faith in my son.**"

HMI's chapel programs are another way of bringing our message of hope to the arena. Active in 30 different North American and European hockey

Inspiring players to win

leagues at the college, junior and professional levels, *HMI's* chapels engage 250 chaplains who meet with players and coaches on a regular basis to help them develop their own support network and to facilitate a consistent worship time. Meetings include a brief message and a prayer time and provide an opportunity for players to talk about what is going on in their own lives, things that matter to them, things they struggle with and how to take hold of biblical principles that can point their lives and careers in the right direction. HMI chaplain, Eric Lubbert, makes this observation:

"This is my 7th season serving as chaplain for the Sound Tigers. Recently it hit me how amazing it is to be sitting in a room surrounded by young men from around the world in the prime of their lives who are in the room because they want to hear something about God. And I have the green light to pour out the gospel to these guys. Many who have never heard the clear message are expecting and want to hear it. It doesn't get any better than that!"

... and more ...

> Each year *HMI* hosts a Breakfast during the NHL All-Star weekend, and occasionally at other major hockey events and tournaments. Fans hear players talk about their ups and downs, dreams and hopes and Jesus Christ, who they trust for their future.

> *HMI* also organizes special conferences, hockey and golf tournaments for players, and Faith Nights for fans at professional and junior games.

> In association with other Christian organizations, *HMI* produces videos and literature of faith stories of hockey players.

> *HMI* is developing new on-line resources to assist families in hockey with the day-to-day challenges of the game and to inspire them to reach out to teammates and their families.

> *HMI* works with the NHL Players' Association "Goals and Dreams" program to provide hockey equipment for young hockey players in places like the Czech Republic, Slovakia and Kazakhstan.

How You Can Be Involved

Since the 1970's HMI has used the game as a starting point to affect the lives of thousands of players, their families, friends and fans. Further expansion hinges on the passion of interested people who recognize the importance of a Christian influence in the hockey world and want to get involved.

Please see HMI's web site at www.hockeyministries.org for opportunities or for more details on our ministry programs.

And if you are going to be at the rink anyway, why not consider meeting someone from *Hockey Ministries International*.

HOLY BIBLE
New Living Translation

HOLY BIBLE

New Living Translation®

SECOND EDITION

Tyndale House Publishers, Inc.
Carol Stream, Illinois

Play to Win Hockey New Testament

© 2013 by Hockey Ministries International
Windsor Station PO Box 7, Suite 265
1100 Ave. Des Canadiens-de-Montreal
Montreal, QC H3B 2S2 CANADA

ISBN 978-1-61970-143-4

Editor, Cathy Ellis
Cover design, Maria Poulopoulos
Production, John LeBrun

Photos: Getty Images, Michigan State Spartans Hockey Team, United States National Team Hockey Development Program, Vaxjo Lakers Hockey Team, Connecticut Whale Hockey Team, Toronto Marlies Hockey Team, Boston Blades (CWHL), Anne Schleper, Laura Halldorson, Kevin Compton, Glen Wesley, Jeff Jackson.

Hockey Ministries International thanks the players featured in the HMI pages of the *Play to Win Hockey New Testament* for their willingness to share their personal stories of faith in Jesus Christ. The athletes themselves are the subject of much public scrutiny—tests which like all of us they may pass or they may fail. But at Hockey Ministries we know that our God is a loving and forgiving God and we trust in Him to lead us in ways that will strengthen us to serve Him and humanity to His eternal glory.

HMI expresses appreciation as well to: Paul Hendrickson and his associates at Hendrickson Publishers for their teamwork on this project; Tim Burke, Laurie Boschman, Brad Henderson, Rodd Swatzky, and Paul Hendrickson for coordinating player participation; Rob Dessouroux for securing photo images and proofreading and Phil Frank, Lois Gamble, and Jean Liesemer for proofreading.

Printed in the United States of America

Second Printing — March 2014

A NOTE TO READERS

The *Holy Bible,* New Living Translation, was first published in 1996. It quickly became one of the most popular Bible translations in the English-speaking world. While the NLT's influence was rapidly growing, the Bible Translation Committee determined that an additional investment in scholarly review and text refinement could make it even better. So shortly after its initial publication, the committee began an eight-year process with the purpose of increasing the level of the NLT's precision without sacrificing its easy-to-understand quality. This second-generation text was completed in 2004, with minor changes subsequently introduced in 2007.

The goal of any Bible translation is to convey the meaning and content of the ancient Hebrew, Aramaic, and Greek texts as accurately as possible to contemporary readers. The challenge for our translators was to create a text that would communicate as clearly and powerfully to today's readers as the original texts did to readers and listeners in the ancient biblical world. The resulting translation is easy to read and understand, while also accurately communicating the meaning and content of the original biblical texts. The NLT is a general-purpose text especially good for study, devotional reading, and reading aloud in worship services.

We believe that the New Living Translation—which combines the latest biblical scholarship with a clear, dynamic writing style—will communicate God's word powerfully to all who read it. We publish it with the prayer that God will use it to speak his timeless truth to the church and the world in a fresh, new way.

The Publishers
October 2007

INTRODUCTION TO THE
New Living Translation

Translation Philosophy and Methodology

English Bible translations tend to be governed by one of two general translation theories. The first theory has been called "formal-equivalence," "literal," or "word-for-word" translation. According to this theory, the translator attempts to render each word of the original language into English and seeks to preserve the original syntax and sentence structure as much as possible in translation. The second theory has been called "dynamic-equivalence," "functional-equivalence," or "thought-for-thought" translation. The goal of this translation theory is to produce in English the closest natural equivalent of the message expressed by the original-language text, both in meaning and in style.

Both of these translation theories have their strengths. A formal-equivalence translation preserves aspects of the original text—including ancient idioms, term consistency, and original-language syntax—that are valuable for scholars and professional study. It allows a reader to trace formal elements of the original-language text through the English translation. A dynamic-equivalence translation, on the other hand, focuses on translating the message of the original-language text. It ensures that the meaning of the text is readily apparent to the contemporary reader. This allows the message to come through with immediacy, without requiring the reader to struggle with foreign idioms and awkward syntax. It also facilitates serious study of the text's message and clarity in both devotional and public reading.

The pure application of either of these translation philosophies would create translations at opposite ends of the translation spectrum. But in reality, all translations contain a mixture of these two philosophies. A purely formal-equivalence translation would be unintelligible in English, and a purely dynamic-equivalence translation would risk being unfaithful to the original. That is why translations shaped by dynamic-equivalence theory are usually quite literal when the original text is relatively clear, and the translations shaped by formal-equivalence theory are sometimes quite dynamic when the original text is obscure.

The translators of the New Living Translation set out to render the message of the original texts of Scripture into clear, contemporary English. As they did so, they kept the concerns of both formal-equivalence and dynamic-equivalence in mind. On the one hand, they translated as simply and literally as possible when that approach yielded an accurate, clear, and natural English text. Many words and phrases were rendered literally and consistently into English, preserving essential literary and rhetorical devices, ancient metaphors, and word choices that give structure to the text and provide echoes of meaning from one passage to the next.

On the other hand, the translators rendered the message more dynamically when the literal rendering was hard to understand, was misleading, or yielded archaic or foreign wording. They clarified difficult metaphors and terms to aid in the reader's understanding. The translators first struggled with the meaning of the words and phrases in the ancient context; then they rendered the message into clear, natural English. Their goal was to be both faithful to the ancient texts and eminently readable. The result is a translation that is both exegetically accurate and idiomatically powerful.

Translation Process and Team

To produce an accurate translation of the Bible into contemporary English, the translation team needed the skills necessary to enter into the thought patterns of the ancient authors and then to render their ideas, connotations, and effects into clear, contemporary English. To begin this process, qualified biblical scholars were needed to interpret the meaning of the original text and to check it against our base English translation. In order to guard against personal and theological biases, the scholars needed to represent a diverse group of Evangelicals who would employ the best exegetical tools. Then to work alongside the scholars, skilled English stylists were needed to shape the text into clear, contemporary English.

With these concerns in mind, the Bible Translation Committee recruited teams of scholars that represented a broad spectrum of denominations, theological perspectives, and backgrounds within the worldwide Evangelical community. (These scholars are listed at the end of this introduction.) Each book of the Bible was assigned to three different scholars with proven expertise in the book or group of books to be reviewed. Each of these scholars made a thorough review of a base translation and submitted suggested revisions to the appropriate Senior Translator. The Senior Translator then reviewed and summarized these suggestions and proposed a first-draft revision of the base text. This draft served as the basis for several additional phases of exegetical and stylistic committee review. Then the Bible Translation Committee jointly reviewed and approved every verse of the final translation.

Throughout the translation and editing process, the Senior Translators and their scholar teams were given a chance to review the editing done by the team of stylists. This ensured that exegetical errors would not be introduced late in the process and that the entire Bible Translation Committee was happy with the final result. By choosing a team of qualified scholars and skilled stylists and by setting up a process that allowed their interaction throughout the process, the New Living Translation has been refined to preserve the essential formal elements of the original biblical texts, while also creating a clear, understandable English text.

The New Living Translation was first published in 1996. Shortly after its initial publication, the Bible Translation Committee began a process of further committee review and translation refinement. The purpose of this continued revision was to increase the level of precision without sacrificing the text's easy-to-understand quality. This second-edition text was completed in 2004, and an additional update with minor changes was subsequently introduced in 2007. This printing of the New Living Translation reflects the updated 2007 text.

Written to Be Read Aloud

It is evident in Scripture that the biblical documents were written to be read aloud, often in public worship (see Nehemiah 8; Luke 4:16-20; 1 Timothy 4:13; Revelation 1:3). It is still the case today that more people will hear the Bible read aloud in church than are likely to read it for themselves. Therefore, a new translation must communicate with clarity and power when it is read publicly. Clarity was a primary goal for the NLT translators, not only to facilitate private reading and understanding, but also to ensure that it would be excellent for public reading and make an immediate and powerful impact on any listener.

The Texts behind the New Living Translation

The Old Testament translators used the Masoretic Text of the Hebrew Bible as represented in *Biblia Hebraica Stuttgartensia* (1977), with its extensive system of textual notes; this is an update of Rudolf Kittel's *Biblia Hebraica* (Stuttgart, 1937). The translators also further compared the Dead Sea Scrolls, the Septuagint and other Greek manuscripts, the Samaritan Pentateuch, the Syriac Peshitta, the Latin Vulgate, and any other versions or manuscripts that shed light on the meaning of difficult passages.

The New Testament translators used the two standard editions of the Greek New Testament: the *Greek New Testament,* published by the United Bible Societies (UBS, fourth revised edition, 1993), and *Novum Testamentum Graece,* edited by Nestle and Aland (NA, twenty-seventh edition, 1993). These two editions, which have the same text but differ in punctuation and textual notes, represent, for the most part, the best in modern textual scholarship. However, in cases where strong textual or other scholarly evidence supported the decision, the translators sometimes chose to differ from the UBS and NA Greek texts and followed variant readings found in other ancient witnesses. Significant textual variants of this sort are always noted in the textual notes of the New Living Translation.

Translation Issues
The translators have made a conscious effort to provide a text that can be easily understood by the typical reader of modern English. To this end, we sought to use only vocabulary and language structures in common use today. We avoided using language likely to become quickly dated or that reflects only a narrow subdialect of English, with the goal of making the New Living Translation as broadly useful and timeless as possible.

But our concern for readability goes beyond the concerns of vocabulary and sentence structure. We are also concerned about historical and cultural barriers to understanding the Bible, and we have sought to translate terms shrouded in history and culture in ways that can be immediately understood. To this end:

♦ We have converted ancient weights and measures (for example, "ephah" [a unit of dry volume] or "cubit" [a unit of length]) to modern English (American) equivalents, since the ancient measures are not generally meaningful to today's readers. Then in the textual footnotes we offer the literal Hebrew, Aramaic, or Greek measures, along with modern metric equivalents.

♦ Instead of translating ancient currency values literally, we have expressed them in common terms that communicate the message. For example, in the Old Testament, "ten shekels of silver" becomes "ten pieces of silver" to convey the intended message. In the New Testament, we have often translated the "denarius" as "the normal daily wage" to facilitate understanding. Then a footnote offers: "Greek *a denarius,* the payment for a full day's wage." In general, we give a clear English rendering and then state the literal Hebrew, Aramaic, or Greek in a textual footnote.

♦ Since the names of Hebrew months are unknown to most contemporary readers, and since the Hebrew lunar calendar fluctuates from year to year in relation to the solar calendar used today, we have looked for clear ways to communicate the time of year the Hebrew months (such as Abib) refer to. When an expanded or interpretive rendering is given in the text, a textual note gives the literal rendering. Where it is possible to define a specific ancient date in terms of our modern calendar, we use modern dates in the text. A textual footnote then gives the literal Hebrew date and states the rationale for our rendering. For example, Ezra 6:15 pinpoints the date when the postexilic Temple was completed in Jerusalem: "the third day of the month Adar." This was during the sixth year of King Darius's reign (that is, 515 B.C.). We have translated that date as March 12, with a footnote giving the Hebrew and identifying the year as 515 B.C.

♦ Since ancient references to the time of day differ from our modern methods of denoting time, we have used renderings that are instantly understandable to the modern reader. Accordingly, we have rendered specific times of day by using approximate equivalents in terms of our common "o'clock" system. On occasion, translations such as "at dawn the next morning" or "as the sun was setting" have been used when the biblical reference is more general.

◆ When the meaning of a proper name (or a wordplay inherent in a proper name) is relevant to the message of the text, its meaning is often illuminated with a textual footnote. For example, in Exodus 2:10 the text reads: "The princess named him Moses, for she explained, 'I lifted him out of the water.' " The accompanying footnote reads: "*Moses* sounds like a Hebrew term that means 'to lift out.' "

◆ Sometimes, when the actual meaning of a name is clear, that meaning is included in parentheses within the text itself. For example, the text at Genesis 16:11 reads: "You are to name him Ishmael *(which means 'God hears'),* for the Lord has heard your cry of distress." Since the original hearers and readers would have instantly understood the meaning of the name "Ishmael," we have provided modern readers with the same information so they can experience the text in a similar way.

◆ Many words and phrases carry a great deal of cultural meaning that was obvious to the original readers but needs explanation in our own culture. For example, the phrase "they beat their breasts" (Luke 23:48) in ancient times meant that people were very upset, often in mourning. In our translation we chose to translate this phrase dynamically for clarity: "They went home *in deep sorrow.*" Then we included a footnote with the literal Greek, which reads: "Greek *went home beating their breasts.*" In other similar cases, however, we have sometimes chosen to illuminate the existing literal expression to make it immediately understandable. For example, here we might have expanded the literal phrase to read: "They went home beating their breasts *in sorrow.*" If we had done this, we would not have included a textual footnote, since the literal Greek clearly appears in translation.

◆ Metaphorical language is sometimes difficult for contemporary readers to understand, so at times we have chosen to translate or illuminate the meaning of a metaphor. For example, the ancient poet writes, "Your neck is *like* the tower of David" (Song of Songs 4:4). We have rendered it "Your neck is *as beautiful as* the tower of David" to clarify the intended positive meaning of the simile. Another example comes in Ecclesiastes 12:3, which can be literally rendered: "Remember him . . . when the grinding women cease because they are few, and the women who look through the windows see dimly." We have rendered it: "Remember him before your teeth—your few remaining servants—stop grinding; and before your eyes—the women looking through the windows—see dimly." We clarified such metaphors only when we believed a typical reader might be confused by the literal text.

◆ When the content of the original language text is poetic in character, we have rendered it in English poetic form. We sought to break lines in ways that clarify and highlight the relationships between phrases of the text. Hebrew poetry often uses parallelism, a literary form where a second phrase (or in some instances a third or fourth) echoes the initial phrase in some way. In Hebrew parallelism, the subsequent parallel phrases continue, while also furthering and sharpening the thought expressed in the initial line or phrase. Whenever possible, we sought to represent these parallel phrases in natural poetic English.

◆ The Greek term *hoi Ioudaioi* is literally translated "the Jews" in many English translations. In the Gospel of John, however, this term doesn't always refer to the Jewish people generally. In some contexts, it refers more particularly to the Jewish religious leaders. We have attempted to capture the meaning in these different contexts by using terms such as "the people" (with a footnote: Greek *the Jewish people*) or "the religious leaders," where appropriate.

◆ One challenge we faced was how to translate accurately the ancient biblical text that was originally written in a context where male-oriented terms were used to refer to humanity generally. We needed to respect the nature of the ancient context while also trying to make the translation clear to a modern audience that tends to read male-oriented language as applying only to males. Often the original text, though using masculine nouns and pronouns, clearly intends that the message be applied to both men and women. A typical example is found in the New Testament letters, where the believers are called "brothers" (*adelphoi*). Yet it is clear from the content of these letters that they were addressed to all the believers—male and female. Thus, we have usually translated this Greek word as "brothers and sisters" in order to represent the historical situation more accurately.

We have also been sensitive to passages where the text applies generally to human beings or to the human condition. In some instances we have used plural pronouns (they, them) in place of the masculine singular (he, him). For example, a traditional rendering of Proverbs 22:6 is: "Train up a child in the way he should go, and when he is old he will not turn from it." We have rendered it: "Direct your children onto the right path, and when they are older, they will not leave it." At times, we have also replaced third person pronouns with the second person to ensure clarity. A traditional rendering of Proverbs 26:27 is: "He who digs a pit will fall into it, and he who rolls a stone, it will come back on him." We have rendered it: "If you set a trap for others, you will get caught in it yourself. If you roll a boulder down on others, it will crush you instead."

We should emphasize, however, that all masculine nouns and pronouns used to represent God (for example, "Father") have been maintained without exception. All decisions of this kind have been driven by the concern to reflect accurately the intended meaning of the original texts of Scripture.

Lexical Consistency in Terminology
For the sake of clarity, we have translated certain original-language terms consistently, especially within synoptic passages and for commonly repeated rhetorical phrases, and within certain word categories such as divine names and non-theological technical terminology (e.g., liturgical, legal, cultural, zoological, and botanical terms). For theological terms, we have allowed a greater semantic range of acceptable English words or phrases for a single Hebrew or Greek word. We have avoided some theological terms that are not readily understood by many modern readers. For example, we avoided using words such as "justification" and "sanctification," which are carryovers from Latin translations. In place of these words, we have provided renderings such as "made right with God" and "made holy."

The Spelling of Proper Names
Many individuals in the Bible, especially the Old Testament, are known by more than one name (e.g., Uzziah/Azariah). For the sake of clarity, we have tried to use a single spelling for any one individual, footnoting the literal spelling whenever we differ from it. This is especially helpful in delineating the kings of Israel and Judah. King Joash/Jehoash of Israel has been consistently called Jehoash, while King Joash/Jehoash of Judah is called Joash. A similar distinction has been used to distinguish between Joram/Jehoram of Israel and Joram/Jehoram of Judah. All such decisions were made with the goal of clarifying the text for the reader. When the ancient biblical writers clearly had a theological purpose in their choice of a variant name (e.g., Esh-baal/Ishbosheth), the different names have been maintained with an explanatory footnote.

For the names Jacob and Israel, which are used interchangeably for both the individual patriarch and the nation, we generally render it "Israel" when it refers to the nation and "Jacob" when it refers to the individual. When our rendering of the name differs from the underlying Hebrew text, we provide a textual footnote, which includes this explanation: "The names 'Jacob' and 'Israel' are often interchanged throughout the Old Testament, referring sometimes to the individual patriarch and sometimes to the nation."

The Rendering of Divine Names

All appearances of *'el, 'elohim,* or *'eloah* have been translated "God," except where the context demands the translation "god(s)." We have generally rendered the tetragrammaton (*YHWH*) consistently as "the LORD," utilizing a form with small capitals that is common among English translations. This will distinguish it from the name *'adonai,* which we render "Lord." When *'adonai* and *YHWH* appear together, we have rendered it "Sovereign LORD." This also distinguishes *'adonai YHWH* from cases where *YHWH* appears with *'elohim,* which is rendered "LORD God." When *YH* (the short form of *YHWH*) and *YHWH* appear together, we have rendered it "LORD GOD." When *YHWH* appears with the term *tseba'oth,* we have rendered it "LORD of Heaven's Armies" to translate the meaning of the name. In a few cases, we have utilized the transliteration, *Yahweh,* when the personal character of the name is being invoked in contrast to another divine name or the name of some other god (for example, see Exodus 3:15; 6:2-3).

In the New Testament, the Greek word *christos* has been translated as "Messiah" when the context assumes a Jewish audience. When a Gentile audience can be assumed, *christos* has been translated as "Christ." The Greek word *kurios* is consistently translated "Lord," except that it is translated "LORD" wherever the New Testament text explicitly quotes from the Old Testament, and the text there has it in small capitals.

Textual Footnotes

The New Living Translation provides several kinds of textual footnotes, all designated in the text with an asterisk:

- When for the sake of clarity the NLT renders a difficult or potentially confusing phrase dynamically, we generally give the literal rendering in a textual footnote. This allows the reader to see the literal source of our dynamic rendering and how our translation relates to other more literal translations. These notes are prefaced with "Hebrew," "Aramaic," or "Greek," identifying the language of the underlying source text. For example, in Acts 2:42 we translated the literal "breaking of bread" (from the Greek) as "the Lord's Supper" to clarify that this verse refers to the ceremonial practice of the church rather than just an ordinary meal. Then we attached a footnote to "the Lord's Supper," which reads: "Greek *the breaking of bread.*"

- Textual footnotes are also used to show alternative renderings, prefaced with the word "Or." These normally occur for passages where an aspect of the meaning is debated. On occasion, we also provide notes on words or phrases that represent a departure from long-standing tradition. These notes are prefaced with "Traditionally rendered." For example, the footnote to the translation "serious skin disease" at Leviticus 13:2 says: "Traditionally rendered *leprosy.* The Hebrew word used throughout this passage is used to describe various skin diseases."

- When our translators follow a textual variant that differs significantly from our standard Hebrew or Greek texts (listed earlier), we document that difference with a footnote. We also footnote cases when the NLT excludes a passage that is included in the Greek text known as the *Textus Receptus* (and familiar to readers through its translation in the King

James Version). In such cases, we offer a translation of the excluded text in a footnote, even though it is generally recognized as a later addition to the Greek text and not part of the original Greek New Testament.

◆ All Old Testament passages that are quoted in the New Testament are identified by a textual footnote at the New Testament location. When the New Testament clearly quotes from the Greek translation of the Old Testament, and when it differs significantly in wording from the Hebrew text, we also place a textual footnote at the Old Testament location. This note includes a rendering of the Greek version, along with a cross-reference to the New Testament passage(s) where it is cited (for example, see notes on Psalms 8:2; 53:3; Proverbs 3:12).

◆ Some textual footnotes provide cultural and historical information on places, things, and people in the Bible that are probably obscure to modern readers. Such notes should aid the reader in understanding the message of the text. For example, in Acts 12:1, "King Herod" is named in this translation as "King Herod Agrippa" and is identified in a footnote as being "the nephew of Herod Antipas and a grandson of Herod the Great."

◆ When the meaning of a proper name (or a wordplay inherent in a proper name) is relevant to the meaning of the text, it is either illuminated with a textual footnote or included within parentheses in the text itself. For example, the footnote concerning the name "Eve" at Genesis 3:20 reads: "*Eve* sounds like a Hebrew term that means 'to give life.' " This wordplay in the Hebrew illuminates the meaning of the text, which goes on to say that Eve "would be the mother of all who live."

AS WE SUBMIT this translation for publication, we recognize that any translation of the Scriptures is subject to limitations and imperfections. Anyone who has attempted to communicate the richness of God's Word into another language will realize it is impossible to make a perfect translation. Recognizing these limitations, we sought God's guidance and wisdom throughout this project. Now we pray that he will accept our efforts and use this translation for the benefit of the church and of all people.

We pray that the New Living Translation will overcome some of the barriers of history, culture, and language that have kept people from reading and understanding God's Word. We hope that readers unfamiliar with the Bible will find the words clear and easy to understand and that readers well versed in the Scriptures will gain a fresh perspective. We pray that readers will gain insight and wisdom for living, but most of all that they will meet the God of the Bible and be forever changed by knowing him.

The Bible Translation Committee

October 2007

BIBLE TRANSLATION TEAM
Holy Bible, New Living Translation

PENTATEUCH
Daniel I. Block, Senior Translator
  Wheaton College

GENESIS
Allen Ross, *Beeson Divinity School, Samford University*
Gordon Wenham, *Trinity College, Bristol*

EXODUS
Robert Bergen, *Hannibal-LaGrange College*
Daniel I. Block, *Wheaton College*
Eugene Carpenter, *Bethel College, Mishawaka, Indiana*

LEVITICUS
David Baker, *Ashland Theological Seminary*
Victor Hamilton, *Asbury College*
Kenneth Mathews, *Beeson Divinity School, Samford University*

NUMBERS
Dale A. Brueggemann, *Assemblies of God Division of Foreign Missions*
R. K. Harrison (deceased), *Wycliffe College*
Paul R. House, *Beeson Divinity School, Samford University*
Gerald L. Mattingly, *Johnson Bible College*

DEUTERONOMY
J. Gordon McConville, *University of Gloucester*
Eugene H. Merrill, *Dallas Theological Seminary*
John A. Thompson (deceased), *University of Melbourne*

HISTORICAL BOOKS
Barry J. Beitzel, Senior Translator
  Trinity Evangelical Divinity School

JOSHUA, JUDGES
Carl E. Armerding, *Schloss Mittersill Study Centre*
Barry J. Beitzel, *Trinity Evangelical Divinity School*
Lawson Stone, *Asbury Theological Seminary*

1 & 2 SAMUEL
Robert Gordon, *Cambridge University*
V. Philips Long, *Regent College*
J. Robert Vannoy, *Biblical Theological Seminary*

1 & 2 KINGS
Bill T. Arnold, *Asbury Theological Seminary*
William H. Barnes, *North Central University*
Frederic W. Bush, *Fuller Theological Seminary*

1 & 2 CHRONICLES
Raymond B. Dillard (deceased), *Westminster Theological Seminary*
David A. Dorsey, *Evangelical School of Theology*
Terry Eves, *Erskine College*

RUTH, EZRA—ESTHER
William C. Williams, *Vanguard University*
H. G. M. Williamson, *Oxford University*

WISDOM BOOKS
Tremper Longman III, Senior Translator
  Westmont College

JOB
August Konkel, *Providence Theological Seminary*
Tremper Longman III, *Westmont College*
Al Wolters, *Redeemer College*

PSALMS 1–75
Mark D. Futato, *Reformed Theological Seminary*
Douglas Green, *Westminster Theological Seminary*
Richard Pratt, *Reformed Theological Seminary*

PSALMS 76–150
David M. Howard Jr., *Bethel Theological Seminary*
Raymond C. Ortlund Jr., *Immanuel Church, Nashville, Tennessee*
Willem VanGemeren, *Trinity Evangelical Divinity School*

PROVERBS
Ted Hildebrandt, *Gordon College*
Richard Schultz, *Wheaton College*
Raymond C. Van Leeuwen, *Eastern College*

ECCLESIASTES, SONG OF SONGS
Daniel C. Fredericks, *Belhaven College*
David Hubbard (deceased), *Fuller Theological Seminary*
Tremper Longman III, *Westmont College*

PROPHETS
John N. Oswalt, Senior Translator
  Asbury Theological Seminary

ISAIAH
John N. Oswalt, *Asbury Theological Seminary*
Gary Smith, *Union University*
John Walton, *Wheaton College*

Matthew

The Ancestors of Jesus the Messiah

1 This is a record of the ancestors of Jesus the Messiah, a descendant of David* and of Abraham:

² Abraham was the father of Isaac.
Isaac was the father of Jacob.
Jacob was the father of Judah and his brothers.
³ Judah was the father of Perez and Zerah (whose mother was Tamar).
Perez was the father of Hezron.
Hezron was the father of Ram.*
⁴ Ram was the father of Amminadab.
Amminadab was the father of Nahshon.
Nahshon was the father of Salmon.
⁵ Salmon was the father of Boaz (whose mother was Rahab).
Boaz was the father of Obed (whose mother was Ruth).
Obed was the father of Jesse.
⁶ Jesse was the father of King David.
David was the father of Solomon (whose mother was Bathsheba, the widow of Uriah).
⁷ Solomon was the father of Rehoboam.
Rehoboam was the father of Abijah.
Abijah was the father of Asa.*
⁸ Asa was the father of Jehoshaphat.
Jehoshaphat was the father of Jehoram.*
Jehoram was the father* of Uzziah.
⁹ Uzziah was the father of Jotham.
Jotham was the father of Ahaz.
Ahaz was the father of Hezekiah.
¹⁰ Hezekiah was the father of Manasseh.
Manasseh was the father of Amon.*
Amon was the father of Josiah.
¹¹ Josiah was the father of Jehoiachin* and his brothers (born at the time of the exile to Babylon).
¹² After the Babylonian exile:
Jehoiachin was the father of Shealtiel.
Shealtiel was the father of Zerubbabel.
¹³ Zerubbabel was the father of Abiud.
Abiud was the father of Eliakim.
Eliakim was the father of Azor.
¹⁴ Azor was the father of Zadok.
Zadok was the father of Akim.
Akim was the father of Eliud.
¹⁵ Eliud was the father of Eleazar.
Eleazar was the father of Matthan.
Matthan was the father of Jacob.
¹⁶ Jacob was the father of Joseph, the husband of Mary.
Mary gave birth to Jesus, who is called the Messiah.

¹⁷All those listed above include fourteen generations from Abraham to David, fourteen from David to the Babylonian exile, and fourteen from the Babylonian exile to the Messiah.

The Birth of Jesus the Messiah

¹⁸This is how Jesus the Messiah was born. His mother, Mary, was engaged to be married to Joseph. But before the marriage took place, while she was still a virgin, she became pregnant through the power of the Holy Spirit. ¹⁹Joseph, her fiancé, was a good man and did not want to disgrace her publicly, so he decided to break the engagement* quietly.

²⁰As he considered this, an angel of the Lord appeared to him in a dream. "Joseph, son of David," the angel said, "do not be afraid to take Mary as your wife. For the child within her was conceived by the Holy Spirit. ²¹And she will have a son, and you are to name him Jesus,* for he will save his people from their sins."

²²All of this occurred to fulfill the Lord's message through his prophet:

²³ "Look! The virgin will conceive a child!
She will give birth to a son,
and they will call him Immanuel,*
which means 'God is with us.'"

²⁴When Joseph woke up, he did as the angel of the Lord commanded and took Mary as his wife. ²⁵But he did not have sexual relations with her until her son was born. And Joseph named him Jesus.

1:1 Greek *Jesus the Messiah, son of David.* **1:3** Greek *Aram,* a variant spelling of Ram; also in 1:4. See 1 Chr 2:9-10. **1:7** Greek *Asaph,* a variant spelling of Asa; also in 1:8. See 1 Chr 3:10. **1:8a** Greek *Joram,* a variant spelling of Jehoram; also in 1:8b. See 1 Kgs 22:50 and note at 1 Chr 3:11. **1:8b** Or *ancestor;* also in 1:11. **1:10** Greek *Amos,* a variant spelling of Amon; also in 1:10b. See 1 Chr 3:14. **1:11** Greek *Jeconiah,* a variant spelling of Jehoiachin; also in 1:12. See 2 Kgs 24:6 and note at 1 Chr 3:16. **1:19** Greek *to divorce her.* **1:21** *Jesus* means "The LORD saves." **1:23** Isa 7:14; 8:8, 10 (Greek version).

Visitors from the East

2 Jesus was born in Bethlehem in Judea, during the reign of King Herod. About that time some wise men* from eastern lands arrived in Jerusalem, asking, 2"Where is the newborn king of the Jews? We saw his star as it rose,* and we have come to worship him."

3King Herod was deeply disturbed when he heard this, as was everyone in Jerusalem. 4He called a meeting of the leading priests and teachers of religious law and asked, "Where is the Messiah supposed to be born?"

5"In Bethlehem in Judea," they said, "for this is what the prophet wrote:

6 'And you, O Bethlehem in the land of Judah,
   are not least among the ruling cities* of Judah,
for a ruler will come from you
   who will be the shepherd for my people Israel.'*"

7Then Herod called for a private meeting with the wise men, and he learned from them the time when the star first appeared. 8Then he told them, "Go to Bethlehem and search carefully for the child. And when you find him, come back and tell me so that I can go and worship him, too!"

9After this interview the wise men went their way. And the star they had seen in the east guided them to Bethlehem. It went ahead of them and stopped over the place where the child was. 10When they saw the star, they were filled with joy! 11They entered the house and saw the child with his mother, Mary, and they bowed down and worshiped him. Then they opened their treasure chests and gave him gifts of gold, frankincense, and myrrh.

12When it was time to leave, they returned to their own country by another route, for God had warned them in a dream not to return to Herod.

The Escape to Egypt

13After the wise men were gone, an angel of the Lord appeared to Joseph in a dream. "Get up! Flee to Egypt with the child and his mother," the angel said. "Stay there until I tell you to return, because Herod is going to search for the child to kill him."

14That night Joseph left for Egypt with the child and Mary, his mother, 15and they stayed there until Herod's death. This fulfilled what the Lord had spoken through the prophet: "I called my Son out of Egypt."*

16Herod was furious when he realized that the wise men had outwitted him. He sent soldiers to kill all the boys in and around Bethlehem who were two years old and under, based on the wise men's report of the star's first appearance. 17Herod's brutal action fulfilled what God had spoken through the prophet Jeremiah:

18 "A cry was heard in Ramah—
   weeping and great mourning.
Rachel weeps for her children,
   refusing to be comforted,
   for they are dead."*

The Return to Nazareth

19When Herod died, an angel of the Lord appeared in a dream to Joseph in Egypt. 20"Get up!" the angel said. "Take the child and his mother back to the land of Israel, because those who were trying to kill the child are dead."

21So Joseph got up and returned to the land of Israel with Jesus and his mother. 22But when he learned that the new ruler of Judea was Herod's son Archelaus, he was afraid to go there. Then, after being warned in a dream, he left for the region of Galilee. 23So the family went and lived in a town called Nazareth. This fulfilled what the prophets had said: "He will be called a Nazarene."

John the Baptist Prepares the Way

3 In those days John the Baptist came to the Judean wilderness and began preaching. His message was, 2"Repent of your sins and turn to God, for the Kingdom of Heaven is near.*" 3The prophet Isaiah was speaking about John when he said,

"He is a voice shouting in the wilderness,
'Prepare the way for the LORD's coming!
   Clear the road for him!'"*

4John's clothes were woven from coarse camel hair, and he wore a leather belt around his waist. For food he ate locusts and wild honey. 5People from Jerusalem and from all of Judea and all over the Jordan Valley went out to see and hear John. 6And when they confessed their sins, he baptized them in the Jordan River.

7But when he saw many Pharisees and Sadducees coming to watch him baptize,* he denounced them. "You brood of snakes!" he exclaimed. "Who warned you to flee God's coming wrath? 8Prove by the way you live that you have repented of your sins and turned to God. 9Don't just say to each other, 'We're safe, for we are descendants of Abraham.' That means nothing, for I tell you, God can create children of Abraham from these very stones. 10Even now the ax of God's judgment is poised, ready to sever the roots of the trees. Yes, every tree that does not produce good fruit will be chopped down and thrown into the fire.

11"I baptize with* water those who repent of their sins and turn to God. But someone is com-

2:1 Or *royal astrologers;* Greek reads *magi;* also in 2:7, 16. **2:2** Or *star in the east.* **2:6a** Greek *the rulers.* **2:6b** Mic 5:2; 2 Sam 5:2. **2:15** Hos 11:1. **2:18** Jer 31:15. **3:2** Or *has come,* or *is coming soon.* **3:3** Isa 40:3 (Greek version). **3:7** Or *coming to be baptized.* **3:11a** Or *in.*

ing soon who is greater than I am—so much greater that I'm not worthy even to be his slave and carry his sandals. He will baptize you with the Holy Spirit and with fire.* ¹²He is ready to separate the chaff from the wheat with his winnowing fork. Then he will clean up the threshing area, gathering the wheat into his barn but burning the chaff with never-ending fire."

The Baptism of Jesus

¹³Then Jesus went from Galilee to the Jordan River to be baptized by John. ¹⁴But John tried to talk him out of it. "I am the one who needs to be baptized by you," he said, "so why are you coming to me?"

¹⁵But Jesus said, "It should be done, for we must carry out all that God requires.*" So John agreed to baptize him.

¹⁶After his baptism, as Jesus came up out of the water, the heavens were opened* and he saw the Spirit of God descending like a dove and settling on him. ¹⁷And a voice from heaven said, "This is my dearly loved Son, who brings me great joy."

The Temptation of Jesus

4 Then Jesus was led by the Spirit into the wilderness to be tempted there by the devil. ²For forty days and forty nights he fasted and became very hungry.

³During that time the devil* came and said to him, "If you are the Son of God, tell these stones to become loaves of bread."

⁴But Jesus told him, "No! The Scriptures say,

'People do not live by bread alone,
 but by every word that comes from the
 mouth of God.'*"

⁵Then the devil took him to the holy city, Jerusalem, to the highest point of the Temple, ⁶and said, "If you are the Son of God, jump off! For the Scriptures say,

'He will order his angels to protect you.
And they will hold you up with their hands
 so you won't even hurt your foot on a
 stone.'*"

⁷Jesus responded, "The Scriptures also say, 'You must not test the LORD your God.'*"

⁸Next the devil took him to the peak of a very high mountain and showed him all the kingdoms of the world and their glory. ⁹"I will give it all to you," he said, "if you will kneel down and worship me."

¹⁰"Get out of here, Satan," Jesus told him. "For the Scriptures say,

'You must worship the LORD your God
 and serve only him.'*"

¹¹Then the devil went away, and angels came and took care of Jesus.

The Ministry of Jesus Begins

¹²When Jesus heard that John had been arrested, he left Judea and returned to Galilee. ¹³He went first to Nazareth, then left there and moved to Capernaum, beside the Sea of Galilee, in the region of Zebulun and Naphtali. ¹⁴This fulfilled what God said through the prophet Isaiah:

¹⁵ "In the land of Zebulun and of Naphtali,
 beside the sea, beyond the Jordan River,
 in Galilee where so many Gentiles live,
¹⁶ the people who sat in darkness
 have seen a great light.
And for those who lived in the land where
 death casts its shadow,
 a light has shined."*

¹⁷From then on Jesus began to preach, "Repent of your sins and turn to God, for the Kingdom of Heaven is near.*"

The First Disciples

¹⁸One day as Jesus was walking along the shore of the Sea of Galilee, he saw two brothers—Simon, also called Peter, and Andrew—throwing a net into the water, for they fished for a living. ¹⁹Jesus called out to them, "Come, follow me, and I will show you how to fish for people!" ²⁰And they left their nets at once and followed him.

²¹A little farther up the shore he saw two other brothers, James and John, sitting in a boat with their father, Zebedee, repairing their nets. And he called them to come, too. ²²They immediately followed him, leaving the boat and their father behind.

Crowds Follow Jesus

²³Jesus traveled throughout the region of Galilee, teaching in the synagogues and announcing the Good News about the Kingdom. And he healed every kind of disease and illness. ²⁴News about him spread as far as Syria, and people soon began bringing to him all who were sick. And whatever their sickness or disease, or if they were demon possessed or epileptic or paralyzed—he healed them all. ²⁵Large crowds followed him wherever he went—people from Galilee, the Ten Towns,* Jerusalem, from all over Judea, and from east of the Jordan River.

The Sermon on the Mount

5 One day as he saw the crowds gathering, Jesus went up on the mountainside and sat down. His disciples gathered around him, ²and he began to teach them.

3:11b Or *in the Holy Spirit and in fire.*   **3:15** Or *for we must fulfill all righteousness.*   **3:16** Some manuscripts read *opened to him.*
4:3 Greek *the tempter.*   **4:4** Deut 8:3.   **4:6** Ps 91:11-12.   **4:7** Deut 6:16.   **4:10** Deut 6:13.   **4:15-16** Isa 9:1-2 (Greek version).
4:17 Or *has come,* or *is coming soon.*   **4:25** Greek *Decapolis.*

The Beatitudes

³ "God blesses those who are poor and realize
their need for him,*
  for the Kingdom of Heaven is theirs.
⁴ God blesses those who mourn,
  for they will be comforted.
⁵ God blesses those who are humble,
  for they will inherit the whole earth.
⁶ God blesses those who hunger and thirst
    for justice,*
  for they will be satisfied.
⁷ God blesses those who are merciful,
  for they will be shown mercy.
⁸ God blesses those whose hearts are pure,
  for they will see God.
⁹ God blesses those who work for peace,
  for they will be called the children of God.
¹⁰ God blesses those who are persecuted for
    doing right,
  for the Kingdom of Heaven is theirs.

¹¹"God blesses you when people mock you
and persecute you and lie about you* and say all
sorts of evil things against you because you are
my followers. ¹²Be happy about it! Be very glad!
For a great reward awaits you in heaven. And remember, the ancient prophets were persecuted
in the same way.

Teaching about Salt and Light

¹³"You are the salt of the earth. But what good is
salt if it has lost its flavor? Can you make it salty
again? It will be thrown out and trampled under-
foot as worthless.

¹⁴"You are the light of the world—like a city on
a hilltop that cannot be hidden. ¹⁵No one lights a
lamp and then puts it under a basket. Instead, a
lamp is placed on a stand, where it gives light to
everyone in the house. ¹⁶In the same way, let your
good deeds shine out for all to see, so that everyone will praise your heavenly Father.

Teaching about the Law

¹⁷"Don't misunderstand why I have come. I did
not come to abolish the law of Moses or the writings of the prophets. No, I came to accomplish
their purpose. ¹⁸I tell you the truth, until heaven
and earth disappear, not even the smallest detail
of God's law will disappear until its purpose is
achieved. ¹⁹So if you ignore the least commandment and teach others to do the same, you will be
called the least in the Kingdom of Heaven. But
anyone who obeys God's laws and teaches them
will be called great in the Kingdom of Heaven.

²⁰"But I warn you—unless your righteousness
is better than the righteousness of the teachers
of religious law and the Pharisees, you will never
enter the Kingdom of Heaven!

Teaching about Anger

²¹"You have heard that our ancestors were told,
'You must not murder. If you commit murder,
you are subject to judgment.'* ²²But I say, if you
are even angry with someone,* you are subject to
judgment! If you call someone an idiot,* you are
in danger of being brought before the court. And
if you curse someone,* you are in danger of the
fires of hell.*

²³"So if you are presenting a sacrifice* at the
altar in the Temple and you suddenly remember
that someone has something against you, ²⁴leave
your sacrifice there at the altar. Go and be reconciled to that person. Then come and offer your
sacrifice to God.

²⁵"When you are on the way to court with your
adversary, settle your differences quickly. Otherwise, your accuser may hand you over to the
judge, who will hand you over to an officer, and
you will be thrown into prison. ²⁶And if that happens, you surely won't be free again until you
have paid the last penny.*

Teaching about Adultery

²⁷"You have heard the commandment that says,
'You must not commit adultery.'* ²⁸But I say, anyone who even looks at a woman with lust has already committed adultery with her in his heart.
²⁹So if your eye—even your good eye*—causes
you to lust, gouge it out and throw it away. It is
better for you to lose one part of your body than
for your whole body to be thrown into hell. ³⁰And
if your hand—even your stronger hand*—causes
you to sin, cut it off and throw it away. It is better
for you to lose one part of your body than for
your whole body to be thrown into hell.

Teaching about Divorce

³¹"You have heard the law that says, 'A man can
divorce his wife by merely giving her a written
notice of divorce.'* ³²But I say that a man who divorces his wife, unless she has been unfaithful,
causes her to commit adultery. And anyone who
marries a divorced woman also commits adultery.

Teaching about Vows

³³"You have also heard that our ancestors were
told, 'You must not break your vows; you must
carry out the vows you make to the LORD.'* ³⁴But
I say, do not make any vows! Do not say, 'By
heaven!' because heaven is God's throne. ³⁵And
do not say, 'By the earth!' because the earth is his
footstool. And do not say, 'By Jerusalem!' for Jerusalem is the city of the great King. ³⁶Do not
even say, 'By my head!' for you can't turn one
hair white or black. ³⁷Just say a simple, 'Yes, I
will,' or 'No, I won't.' Anything beyond this is
from the evil one.

5:3 Greek *poor in spirit.* **5:6** Or *for righteousness.* **5:11** Some manuscripts do not include *and lie about you.* **5:21** Exod 20:13;
Deut 5:17. **5:22a** Some manuscripts add *without cause.* **5:22b** Greek uses an Aramaic term of contempt: *If you say to your
brother, 'Raca.'* **5:22c** Greek *if you say, 'You fool.'* **5:22d** Greek *Gehenna;* also in 5:29, 30. **5:23** Greek *gift;* also in 5:24.
5:26 Greek *the last kodrantes* [i.e., quadrans]. **5:27** Exod 20:14; Deut 5:18. **5:29** Greek *your right eye.* **5:30** Greek *your right
hand.* **5:31** Deut 24:1. **5:33** Num 30:2.

Teaching about Revenge

38"You have heard the law that says the punishment must match the injury: 'An eye for an eye, and a tooth for a tooth.'* 39But I say, do not resist an evil person! If someone slaps you on the right cheek, offer the other cheek also. 40If you are sued in court and your shirt is taken from you, give your coat, too. 41If a soldier demands that you carry his gear for a mile,* carry it two miles. 42Give to those who ask, and don't turn away from those who want to borrow.

Teaching about Love for Enemies

43"You have heard the law that says, 'Love your neighbor'* and hate your enemy. 44But I say, love your enemies!* Pray for those who persecute you! 45In that way, you will be acting as true children of your Father in heaven. For he gives his sunlight to both the evil and the good, and he sends rain on the just and the unjust alike. 46If you love only those who love you, what reward is there for that? Even corrupt tax collectors do that much. 47If you are kind only to your friends,* how are you different from anyone else? Even pagans do that. 48But you are to be perfect, even as your Father in heaven is perfect.

Teaching about Giving to the Needy

6 "Watch out! Don't do your good deeds publicly, to be admired by others, for you will lose the reward from your Father in heaven. 2When you give to someone in need, don't do as the hypocrites do—blowing trumpets in the synagogues and streets to call attention to their acts of charity! I tell you the truth, they have received all the reward they will ever get. 3But when you give to someone in need, don't let your left hand know what your right hand is doing. 4Give your gifts in private, and your Father, who sees everything, will reward you.

Teaching about Prayer and Fasting

5"When you pray, don't be like the hypocrites who love to pray publicly on street corners and in the synagogues where everyone can see them. I tell you the truth, that is all the reward they will ever get. 6But when you pray, go away by yourself, shut the door behind you, and pray to your Father in private. Then your Father, who sees everything, will reward you.

7"When you pray, don't babble on and on as people of other religions do. They think their prayers are answered merely by repeating their words again and again. 8Don't be like them, for your Father knows exactly what you need even before you ask him! 9Pray like this:

Our Father in heaven,
   may your name be kept holy.
10 May your Kingdom come soon.
May your will be done on earth,
   as it is in heaven.
11 Give us today the food we need,*
12 and forgive us our sins,
   as we have forgiven those who sin
   against us.
13 And don't let us yield to temptation,*
   but rescue us from the evil one.*

14"If you forgive those who sin against you, your heavenly Father will forgive you. 15But if you refuse to forgive others, your Father will not forgive your sins.

16"And when you fast, don't make it obvious, as the hypocrites do, for they try to look miserable and disheveled so people will admire them for their fasting. I tell you the truth, that is the only reward they will ever get. 17But when you fast, comb your hair and wash your face. 18Then no one will notice that you are fasting, except your Father, who knows what you do in private. And your Father, who sees everything, will reward you.

Teaching about Money and Possessions

19"Don't store up treasures here on earth, where moths eat them and rust destroys them, and where thieves break in and steal. 20Store your treasures in heaven, where moths and rust cannot destroy, and thieves do not break in and steal. 21Wherever your treasure is, there the desires of your heart will also be.

22"Your eye is a lamp that provides light for your body. When your eye is good, your whole body is filled with light. 23But when your eye is bad, your whole body is filled with darkness. And if the light you think you have is actually darkness, how deep that darkness is!

24"No one can serve two masters. For you will hate one and love the other; you will be devoted to one and despise the other. You cannot serve both God and money.

25"That is why I tell you not to worry about everyday life—whether you have enough food and drink, or enough clothes to wear. Isn't life more than food, and your body more than clothing? 26Look at the birds. They don't plant or harvest or store food in barns, for your heavenly Father feeds them. And aren't you far more valuable to him than they are? 27Can all your worries add a single moment to your life?

28"And why worry about your clothing? Look at the lilies of the field and how they grow. They don't work or make their clothing, 29yet Solomon in all his glory was not dressed as beautifully as

---

5:38 Greek *the law that says: 'An eye for an eye and a tooth for a tooth.'* Exod 21:24; Lev 24:20; Deut 19:21. **5:41** Greek *milion* [4,854 feet or 1,478 meters]. **5:43** Lev 19:18. **5:44** Some manuscripts add *Bless those who curse you. Do good to those who hate you.* Compare Luke 6:27-28. **5:47** Greek *your brothers.* **6:11** Or *Give us today our food for the day;* or *Give us today our food for tomorrow.* **6:13a** Or *And keep us from being tested.* **6:13b** Or *from evil.* Some manuscripts add *For yours is the kingdom and the power and the glory forever. Amen.*

they are. ³⁰And if God cares so wonderfully for wildflowers that are here today and thrown into the fire tomorrow, he will certainly care for you. Why do you have so little faith? ³¹"So don't worry about these things, saying, 'What will we eat? What will we drink? What will we wear?' ³²These things dominate the thoughts of unbelievers, but your heavenly Father already knows all your needs. ³³Seek the Kingdom of God* above all else, and live righteously, and he will give you everything you need.

³⁴"So don't worry about tomorrow, for tomorrow will bring its own worries. Today's trouble is enough for today.

Do Not Judge Others

7 "Do not judge others, and you will not be judged. ²For you will be treated as you treat others.* The standard you use in judging is the standard by which you will be judged.*

³"And why worry about a speck in your friend's eye* when you have a log in your own? ⁴How can you think of saying to your friend,* 'Let me help you get rid of that speck in your eye,' when you can't see past the log in your own eye? ⁵Hypocrite! First get rid of the log in your own eye; then you will see well enough to deal with the speck in your friend's eye.

⁶"Don't waste what is holy on people who are unholy.* Don't throw your pearls to pigs! They will trample the pearls, then turn and attack you.

Effective Prayer

⁷"Keep on asking, and you will receive what you ask for. Keep on seeking, and you will find. Keep on knocking, and the door will be opened to you. ⁸For everyone who asks, receives. Everyone who seeks, finds. And to everyone who knocks, the door will be opened.

⁹"You parents—if your children ask for a loaf of bread, do you give them a stone instead? ¹⁰Or if they ask for a fish, do you give them a snake? Of course not! ¹¹So if you sinful people know how to give good gifts to your children, how much more will your heavenly Father give good gifts to those who ask him.

The Golden Rule

¹²"Do to others whatever you would like them to do to you. This is the essence of all that is taught in the law and the prophets.

The Narrow Gate

¹³"You can enter God's Kingdom only through the narrow gate. The highway to hell* is broad, and its gate is wide for the many who choose that way. ¹⁴But the gateway to life is very narrow and the road is difficult, and only a few ever find it.

The Tree and Its Fruit

¹⁵"Beware of false prophets who come disguised as harmless sheep but are really vicious wolves. ¹⁶You can identify them by their fruit, that is, by the way they act. Can you pick grapes from thornbushes, or figs from thistles? ¹⁷A good tree produces good fruit, and a bad tree produces bad fruit. ¹⁸A good tree can't produce bad fruit, and a bad tree can't produce good fruit. ¹⁹So every tree that does not produce good fruit is chopped down and thrown into the fire. ²⁰Yes, just as you can identify a tree by its fruit, so you can identify people by their actions.

True Disciples

²¹"Not everyone who calls out to me, 'Lord! Lord!' will enter the Kingdom of Heaven. Only those who actually do the will of my Father in heaven will enter. ²²On judgment day many will say to me, 'Lord! Lord! We prophesied in your name and cast out demons in your name and performed many miracles in your name.' ²³But I will reply, 'I never knew you. Get away from me, you who break God's laws.'

Building on a Solid Foundation

²⁴"Anyone who listens to my teaching and follows it is wise, like a person who builds a house on solid rock. ²⁵Though the rain comes in torrents and the floodwaters rise and the winds beat against that house, it won't collapse because it is built on bedrock. ²⁶But anyone who hears my teaching and doesn't obey it is foolish, like a person who builds a house on sand. ²⁷When the rains and floods come and the winds beat against that house, it will collapse with a mighty crash."

²⁸When Jesus had finished saying these things, the crowds were amazed at his teaching, ²⁹for he taught with real authority—quite unlike their teachers of religious law.

Jesus Heals a Man with Leprosy

8 Large crowds followed Jesus as he came down the mountainside. ²Suddenly, a man with leprosy approached him and knelt before him. "Lord," the man said, "if you are willing, you can heal me and make me clean."

³Jesus reached out and touched him. "I am willing," he said. "Be healed!" And instantly the leprosy disappeared. ⁴Then Jesus said to him, "Don't tell anyone about this. Instead, go to the priest and let him examine you. Take along the offering required in the law of Moses for those who have been healed of leprosy.* This will be a public testimony that you have been cleansed."

The Faith of a Roman Officer

⁵When Jesus returned to Capernaum, a Roman officer* came and pleaded with him, ⁶"Lord, my

young servant* lies in bed, paralyzed and in terrible pain."

⁷Jesus said, "I will come and heal him."

⁸But the officer said, "Lord, I am not worthy to have you come into my home. Just say the word from where you are, and my servant will be healed. ⁹I know this because I am under the authority of my superior officers, and I have authority over my soldiers. I only need to say, 'Go,' and they go, or 'Come,' and they come. And if I say to my slaves, 'Do this,' they do it."

¹⁰When Jesus heard this, he was amazed. Turning to those who were following him, he said, "I tell you the truth, I haven't seen faith like this in all Israel! ¹¹And I tell you this, that many Gentiles will come from all over the world—from east and west—and sit down with Abraham, Isaac, and Jacob at the feast in the Kingdom of Heaven. ¹²But many Israelites—those for whom the Kingdom was prepared—will be thrown into outer darkness, where there will be weeping and gnashing of teeth."

¹³Then Jesus said to the Roman officer, "Go back home. Because you believed, it has happened." And the young servant was healed that same hour.

Jesus Heals Many People

¹⁴When Jesus arrived at Peter's house, Peter's mother-in-law was sick in bed with a high fever. ¹⁵But when Jesus touched her hand, the fever left her. Then she got up and prepared a meal for him.

¹⁶That evening many demon-possessed people were brought to Jesus. He cast out the evil spirits with a simple command, and he healed all the sick. ¹⁷This fulfilled the word of the Lord through the prophet Isaiah, who said,

> "He took our sicknesses
> and removed our diseases."*

The Cost of Following Jesus

¹⁸When Jesus saw the crowd around him, he instructed his disciples to cross to the other side of the lake.

¹⁹Then one of the teachers of religious law said to him, "Teacher, I will follow you wherever you go."

²⁰But Jesus replied, "Foxes have dens to live in, and birds have nests, but the Son of Man* has no place even to lay his head."

²¹Another of his disciples said, "Lord, first let me return home and bury my father."

²²But Jesus told him, "Follow me now. Let the spiritually dead bury their own dead.*"

Jesus Calms the Storm

²³Then Jesus got into the boat and started across the lake with his disciples. ²⁴Suddenly, a fierce storm struck the lake, with waves breaking into the boat. But Jesus was sleeping. ²⁵The disciples went and woke him up, shouting, "Lord, save us! We're going to drown!"

²⁶Jesus responded, "Why are you afraid? You have so little faith!" Then he got up and rebuked the wind and waves, and suddenly there was a great calm.

²⁷The disciples were amazed. "Who is this man?" they asked. "Even the winds and waves obey him!"

Jesus Heals Two Demon-Possessed Men

²⁸When Jesus arrived on the other side of the lake, in the region of the Gadarenes,* two men who were possessed by demons met him. They lived in a cemetery and were so violent that no one could go through that area.

²⁹They began screaming at him, "Why are you interfering with us, Son of God? Have you come here to torture us before God's appointed time?"

³⁰There happened to be a large herd of pigs feeding in the distance. ³¹So the demons begged, "If you cast us out, send us into that herd of pigs."

³²"All right, go!" Jesus commanded them. So the demons came out of the men and entered the pigs, and the whole herd plunged down the steep hillside into the lake and drowned in the water.

³³The herdsmen fled to the nearby town, telling everyone what happened to the demon-possessed men. ³⁴Then the entire town came out to meet Jesus, but they begged him to go away and leave them alone.

Jesus Heals a Paralyzed Man

9 Jesus climbed into a boat and went back across the lake to his own town. ²Some people brought to him a paralyzed man on a mat. Seeing their faith, Jesus said to the paralyzed man, "Be encouraged, my child! Your sins are forgiven."

³But some of the teachers of religious law said to themselves, "That's blasphemy! Does he think he's God?"

⁴Jesus knew* what they were thinking, so he asked them, "Why do you have such evil thoughts in your hearts? ⁵Is it easier to say 'Your sins are forgiven,' or 'Stand up and walk'? ⁶So I will prove to you that the Son of Man* has the authority on earth to forgive sins." Then Jesus turned to the paralyzed man and said, "Stand up, pick up your mat, and go home!"

⁷And the man jumped up and went home! ⁸Fear swept through the crowd as they saw this happen. And they praised God for sending a man with such great authority.*

Jesus Calls Matthew

⁹As Jesus was walking along, he saw a man named Matthew sitting at his tax collector's

---

8:6 Or *child;* also in 8:13. **8:17** Isa 53:4. **8:20** "Son of Man" is a title Jesus used for himself. **8:22** Greek *Let the dead bury their own dead.* **8:28** Other manuscripts read *Gerasenes;* still others read *Gergesenes.* Compare Mark 5:1; Luke 8:26. **9:4** Some manuscripts read *saw.* **9:6** "Son of Man" is a title Jesus used for himself. **9:8** Greek *for giving such authority to human beings.*

booth. "Follow me and be my disciple," Jesus said to him. So Matthew got up and followed him.

¹⁰Later, Matthew invited Jesus and his disciples to his home as dinner guests, along with many tax collectors and other disreputable sinners. ¹¹But when the Pharisees saw this, they asked his disciples, "Why does your teacher eat with such scum?*"

¹²When Jesus heard this, he said, "Healthy people don't need a doctor—sick people do." ¹³Then he added, "Now go and learn the meaning of this Scripture: 'I want you to show mercy, not offer sacrifices.'* For I have come to call not those who think they are righteous, but those who know they are sinners."

A Discussion about Fasting

¹⁴One day the disciples of John the Baptist came to Jesus and asked him, "Why don't your disciples fast* like we do and the Pharisees do?"

¹⁵Jesus replied, "Do wedding guests mourn while celebrating with the groom? Of course not. But someday the groom will be taken away from them, and then they will fast.

¹⁶"Besides, who would patch old clothing with new cloth? For the new patch would shrink and rip away from the old cloth, leaving an even bigger tear than before.

¹⁷"And no one puts new wine into old wineskins. For the old skins would burst from the pressure, spilling the wine and ruining the skins. New wine is stored in new wineskins so that both are preserved."

Jesus Heals in Response to Faith

¹⁸As Jesus was saying this, the leader of a synagogue came and knelt before him. "My daughter has just died," he said, "but you can bring her back to life again if you just come and lay your hand on her."

¹⁹So Jesus and his disciples got up and went with him. ²⁰Just then a woman who had suffered for twelve years with constant bleeding came up behind him. She touched the fringe of his robe, ²¹for she thought, "If I can just touch his robe, I will be healed."

²²Jesus turned around, and when he saw her he said, "Daughter, be encouraged! Your faith has made you well." And the woman was healed at that moment.

²³When Jesus arrived at the official's home, he saw the noisy crowd and heard the funeral music. ²⁴"Get out!" he told them. "The girl isn't dead; she's only asleep." But the crowd laughed at him. ²⁵After the crowd was put outside, however, Jesus went in and took the girl by the hand, and she stood up! ²⁶The report of this miracle swept through the entire countryside.

Jesus Heals the Blind

²⁷After Jesus left the girl's home, two blind men followed along behind him, shouting, "Son of David, have mercy on us!"

²⁸They went right into the house where he was staying, and Jesus asked them, "Do you believe I can make you see?"

"Yes, Lord," they told him, "we do."

²⁹Then he touched their eyes and said, "Because of your faith, it will happen." ³⁰Then their eyes were opened, and they could see! Jesus sternly warned them, "Don't tell anyone about this." ³¹But instead, they went out and spread his fame all over the region.

³²When they left, a demon-possessed man who couldn't speak was brought to Jesus. ³³So Jesus cast out the demon, and then the man began to speak. The crowds were amazed. "Nothing like this has ever happened in Israel!" they exclaimed.

³⁴But the Pharisees said, "He can cast out demons because he is empowered by the prince of demons."

The Need for Workers

³⁵Jesus traveled through all the towns and villages of that area, teaching in the synagogues and announcing the Good News about the Kingdom. And he healed every kind of disease and illness. ³⁶When he saw the crowds, he had compassion on them because they were confused and helpless, like sheep without a shepherd. ³⁷He said to his disciples, "The harvest is great, but the workers are few. ³⁸So pray to the Lord who is in charge of the harvest; ask him to send more workers into his fields."

Jesus Sends Out the Twelve Apostles

10 Jesus called his twelve disciples together and gave them authority to cast out evil* spirits and to heal every kind of disease and illness. ²Here are the names of the twelve apostles:

first, Simon (also called Peter),
then Andrew (Peter's brother),
James (son of Zebedee),
John (James's brother),
³ Philip,
Bartholomew,
Thomas,
Matthew (the tax collector),
James (son of Alphaeus),
Thaddaeus,*
⁴ Simon (the zealot*),
Judas Iscariot (who later betrayed him).

⁵Jesus sent out the twelve apostles with these instructions: "Don't go to the Gentiles or the Samaritans, ⁶but only to the people of Israel—God's lost sheep. ⁷Go and announce to them

9:11 Greek *with tax collectors and sinners?* **9:13** Hos 6:6 (Greek version). **9:14** Some manuscripts read *fast often.* **10:1** Greek *unclean.* **10:3** Other manuscripts read *Lebbaeus;* still others read *Lebbaeus who is called Thaddaeus.* **10:4** Greek *the Cananean,* an Aramaic term for Jewish nationalists.

that the Kingdom of Heaven is near.* ⁸Heal the sick, raise the dead, cure those with leprosy, and cast out demons. Give as freely as you have received!

⁹"Don't take any money in your money belts— no gold, silver, or even copper coins. ¹⁰Don't carry a traveler's bag with a change of clothes and sandals or even a walking stick. Don't hesitate to accept hospitality, because those who work deserve to be fed.

¹¹"Whenever you enter a city or village, search for a worthy person and stay in his home until you leave town. ¹²When you enter the home, give it your blessing. ¹³If it turns out to be a worthy home, let your blessing stand; if it is not, take back the blessing. ¹⁴If any household or town refuses to welcome you or listen to your message, shake its dust from your feet as you leave. ¹⁵I tell you the truth, the wicked cities of Sodom and Gomorrah will be better off than such a town on the judgment day.

¹⁶"Look, I am sending you out as sheep among wolves. So be as shrewd as snakes and harmless as doves. ¹⁷But beware! For you will be handed over to the courts and will be flogged with whips in the synagogues. ¹⁸You will stand trial before governors and kings because you are my followers. But this will be your opportunity to tell the rulers and other unbelievers about me.* ¹⁹When you are arrested, don't worry about how to respond or what to say. God will give you the right words at the right time. ²⁰For it is not you who will be speaking—it will be the Spirit of your Father speaking through you.

²¹"A brother will betray his brother to death, a father will betray his own child, and children will rebel against their parents and cause them to be killed. ²²And all nations will hate you because you are my followers.* But everyone who endures to the end will be saved. ²³When you are persecuted in one town, flee to the next. I tell you the truth, the Son of Man* will return before you have reached all the towns of Israel.

²⁴"Students* are not greater than their teacher, and slaves are not greater than their master. ²⁵Students are to be like their teacher, and slaves are to be like their master. And since I, the master of the household, have been called the prince of demons,* the members of my household will be called by even worse names!

²⁶"But don't be afraid of those who threaten you. For the time is coming when everything that is covered will be revealed, and all that is secret will be made known to all. ²⁷What I tell you now in the darkness, shout abroad when daybreak comes. What I whisper in your ear, shout from the housetops for all to hear! ²⁸"Don't be afraid of those who want to kill your body; they cannot touch your soul. Fear only God, who can destroy both soul and body in hell.* ²⁹What is the price of two sparrows—one copper coin*? But not a single sparrow can fall to the ground without your Father knowing it. ³⁰And the very hairs on your head are all numbered. ³¹So don't be afraid; you are more valuable to God than a whole flock of sparrows.

³²"Everyone who acknowledges me publicly here on earth, I will also acknowledge before my Father in heaven. ³³But everyone who denies me here on earth, I will also deny before my Father in heaven.

³⁴"Don't imagine that I came to bring peace to the earth! I came not to bring peace, but a sword.

³⁵ 'I have come to set a man against his father,
 a daughter against her mother,
and a daughter-in-law against her
 mother-in-law.
³⁶ Your enemies will be right in your own
 household!'*

³⁷"If you love your father or mother more than you love me, you are not worthy of being mine; or if you love your son or daughter more than me, you are not worthy of being mine. ³⁸If you refuse to take up your cross and follow me, you are not worthy of being mine. ³⁹If you cling to your life, you will lose it; but if you give up your life for me, you will find it.

⁴⁰"Anyone who receives you receives me, and anyone who receives me receives the Father who sent me. ⁴¹If you receive a prophet as one who speaks for God,* you will be given the same reward as a prophet. And if you receive righteous people because of their righteousness, you will be given a reward like theirs. ⁴²And if you give even a cup of cold water to one of the least of my followers, you will surely be rewarded."

Jesus and John the Baptist

11 When Jesus had finished giving these instructions to his twelve disciples, he went out to teach and preach in towns throughout the region.

²John the Baptist, who was in prison, heard about all the things the Messiah was doing. So he sent his disciples to ask Jesus, ³"Are you the Messiah we've been expecting,* or should we keep looking for someone else?"

⁴Jesus told them, "Go back to John and tell him what you have heard and seen—⁵the blind see, the lame walk, the lepers are cured, the deaf hear, the dead are raised to life, and the Good News is being preached to the poor. ⁶And tell him, 'God blesses those who do not turn away because of me.*' "

10:7 Or *has come,* or *is coming soon.*   10:18 Or *But this will be your testimony against the rulers and other unbelievers.*
10:22 Greek *on account of my name.*   10:23 "Son of Man" is a title Jesus used for himself.   10:24 Or *Disciples.*   10:25 Greek *Beelzeboul;* other manuscripts read *Beezeboul;* Latin version reads *Beelzebub.*   10:28 Greek *Gehenna.*   10:29 Greek *one assarion* [i.e., one "as," a Roman coin equal to ¹⁄₁₆ of a denarius].   10:35-36 Mic 7:6.   10:41 Greek *receive a prophet in the name of a prophet.*
11:3 Greek *Are you the one who is coming?*   11:6 Or *who are not offended by me.*

[7]As John's disciples were leaving, Jesus began talking about him to the crowds. "What kind of man did you go into the wilderness to see? Was he a weak reed, swayed by every breath of wind? [8]Or were you expecting to see a man dressed in expensive clothes? No, people with expensive clothes live in palaces. [9]Were you looking for a prophet? Yes, and he is more than a prophet. [10]John is the man to whom the Scriptures refer when they say,

'Look, I am sending my messenger ahead
　of you,
and he will prepare your way before you.'*

[11]"I tell you the truth, of all who have ever lived, none is greater than John the Baptist. Yet even the least person in the Kingdom of Heaven is greater than he is! [12]And from the time John the Baptist began preaching until now, the Kingdom of Heaven has been forcefully advancing,* and violent people are attacking it. [13]For before John came, all the prophets and the law of Moses looked forward to this present time. [14]And if you are willing to accept what I say, he is Elijah, the one the prophets said would come.* [15]Anyone with ears to hear should listen and understand!

[16]"To what can I compare this generation? It is like children playing a game in the public square. They complain to their friends,

[17] 'We played wedding songs,
　and you didn't dance,
so we played funeral songs,
　and you didn't mourn.'

[18]For John didn't spend his time eating and drinking, and you say, 'He's possessed by a demon.' [19]The Son of Man,* on the other hand, feasts and drinks, and you say, 'He's a glutton and a drunkard, and a friend of tax collectors and other sinners!' But wisdom is shown to be right by its results."

Judgment for the Unbelievers

[20]Then Jesus began to denounce the towns where he had done so many of his miracles, because they hadn't repented of their sins and turned to God. [21]"What sorrow awaits you, Korazin and Bethsaida! For if the miracles I did in you had been done in wicked Tyre and Sidon, their people would have repented of their sins long ago, clothing themselves in burlap and throwing ashes on their heads to show their remorse. [22]I tell you, Tyre and Sidon will be better off on judgment day than you.

[23]"And you people of Capernaum, will you be honored in heaven? No, you will go down to the place of the dead.* For if the miracles I did for you had been done in wicked Sodom, it would still be here today. [24]I tell you, even Sodom will be better off on judgment day than you."

Jesus' Prayer of Thanksgiving

[25]At that time Jesus prayed this prayer: "O Father, Lord of heaven and earth, thank you for hiding these things from those who think themselves wise and clever, and for revealing them to the childlike. [26]Yes, Father, it pleased you to do it this way!

[27]"My Father has entrusted everything to me. No one truly knows the Son except the Father, and no one truly knows the Father except the Son and those to whom the Son chooses to reveal him."

[28]Then Jesus said, "Come to me, all of you who are weary and carry heavy burdens, and I will give you rest. [29]Take my yoke upon you. Let me teach you, because I am humble and gentle at heart, and you will find rest for your souls. [30]For my yoke is easy to bear, and the burden I give you is light."

A Discussion about the Sabbath

12 At about that time Jesus was walking through some grainfields on the Sabbath. His disciples were hungry, so they began breaking off some heads of grain and eating them. [2]But some Pharisees saw them do it and protested, "Look, your disciples are breaking the law by harvesting grain on the Sabbath."

[3]Jesus said to them, "Haven't you read in the Scriptures what David did when he and his companions were hungry? [4]He went into the house of God, and he and his companions broke the law by eating the sacred loaves of bread that only the priests are allowed to eat. [5]And haven't you read in the law of Moses that the priests on duty in the Temple may work on the Sabbath? [6]I tell you, there is one here who is even greater than the Temple! [7]But you would not have condemned my innocent disciples if you knew the meaning of this Scripture: 'I want you to show mercy, not offer sacrifices.'* [8]For the Son of Man* is Lord, even over the Sabbath!"

Jesus Heals on the Sabbath

[9]Then Jesus went over to their synagogue, [10]where he noticed a man with a deformed hand. The Pharisees asked Jesus, "Does the law permit a person to work by healing on the Sabbath?" (They were hoping he would say yes, so they could bring charges against him.)

[11]And he answered, "If you had a sheep that fell into a well on the Sabbath, wouldn't you work to pull it out? Of course you would. [12]And how much more valuable is a person than a sheep! Yes, the law permits a person to do good on the Sabbath."

[13]Then he said to the man, "Hold out your

11:10 Mal 3:1.　**11:12** Or *the Kingdom of Heaven has suffered from violence.*　**11:14** See Mal 4:5.　**11:19** "Son of Man" is a title Jesus used for himself.　**11:23** Greek *to Hades.*　**12:7** Hos 6:6 (Greek version).　**12:8** "Son of Man" is a title Jesus used for himself.

hand." So the man held out his hand, and it was restored, just like the other one! ¹⁴Then the Pharisees called a meeting to plot how to kill Jesus.

Jesus, God's Chosen Servant

¹⁵But Jesus knew what they were planning. So he left that area, and many people followed him. He healed all the sick among them, ¹⁶but he warned them not to reveal who he was. ¹⁷This fulfilled the prophecy of Isaiah concerning him:

¹⁸ "Look at my Servant, whom I have chosen.
He is my Beloved, who pleases me.
I will put my Spirit upon him,
and he will proclaim justice to the nations.
¹⁹ He will not fight or shout
or raise his voice in public.
²⁰ He will not crush the weakest reed
or put out a flickering candle.
Finally he will cause justice to be
victorious.
²¹ And his name will be the hope
of all the world."*

Jesus and the Prince of Demons

²²Then a demon-possessed man, who was blind and couldn't speak, was brought to Jesus. He healed the man so that he could both speak and see. ²³The crowd was amazed and asked, "Could it be that Jesus is the Son of David, the Messiah?"

²⁴But when the Pharisees heard about the miracle, they said, "No wonder he can cast out demons. He gets his power from Satan,* the prince of demons."

²⁵Jesus knew their thoughts and replied, "Any kingdom divided by civil war is doomed. A town or family splintered by feuding will fall apart. ²⁶And if Satan is casting out Satan, he is divided and fighting against himself. His own kingdom will not survive. ²⁷And if I am empowered by Satan, what about your own exorcists? They cast out demons, too, so they will condemn you for what you have said. ²⁸But if I am casting out demons by the Spirit of God, then the Kingdom of God has arrived among you. ²⁹For who is powerful enough to enter the house of a strong man like Satan and plunder his goods? Only someone even stronger—someone who could tie him up and then plunder his house.

³⁰"Anyone who isn't with me opposes me, and anyone who isn't working with me is actually working against me.

³¹"So I tell you, every sin and blasphemy can be forgiven—except blasphemy against the Holy Spirit, which will never be forgiven. ³²Anyone who speaks against the Son of Man can be forgiven, but anyone who speaks against the Holy Spirit will never be forgiven, either in this world or in the world to come.

³³"A tree is identified by its fruit. If a tree is good, its fruit will be good. If a tree is bad, its fruit will be bad. ³⁴You brood of snakes! How could evil men like you speak what is good and right? For whatever is in your heart determines what you say. ³⁵A good person produces good things from the treasury of a good heart, and an evil person produces evil things from the treasury of an evil heart. ³⁶And I tell you this, you must give an account on judgment day for every idle word you speak. ³⁷The words you say will either acquit you or condemn you."

The Sign of Jonah

³⁸One day some teachers of religious law and Pharisees came to Jesus and said, "Teacher, we want you to show us a miraculous sign to prove your authority."

³⁹But Jesus replied, "Only an evil, adulterous generation would demand a miraculous sign; but the only sign I will give them is the sign of the prophet Jonah. ⁴⁰For as Jonah was in the belly of the great fish for three days and three nights, so will the Son of Man be in the heart of the earth for three days and three nights.

⁴¹"The people of Nineveh will stand up against this generation on judgment day and condemn it, for they repented of their sins at the preaching of Jonah. Now someone greater than Jonah is here—but you refuse to repent. ⁴²The queen of Sheba* will also stand up against this generation on judgment day and condemn it, for she came from a distant land to hear the wisdom of Solomon. Now someone greater than Solomon is here—but you refuse to listen.

⁴³"When an evil* spirit leaves a person, it goes into the desert, seeking rest but finding none. ⁴⁴Then it says, 'I will return to the person I came from.' So it returns and finds its former home empty, swept, and in order. ⁴⁵Then the spirit finds seven other spirits more evil than itself, and they all enter the person and live there. And so that person is worse off than before. That will be the experience of this evil generation."

The True Family of Jesus

⁴⁶As Jesus was speaking to the crowd, his mother and brothers stood outside, asking to speak to him. ⁴⁷Someone told Jesus, "Your mother and your brothers are outside, and they want to speak to you."*

⁴⁸Jesus asked, "Who is my mother? Who are my brothers?" ⁴⁹Then he pointed to his disciples and said, "Look, these are my mother and brothers. ⁵⁰Anyone who does the will of my Father in heaven is my brother and sister and mother!"

12:18-21 Isa 42:1-4 (Greek version for 42:4).   **12:24** Greek *Beelzeboul*; also in 12:27. Other manuscripts read *Beezeboul*; Latin version reads *Beelzebub*.   **12:42** Greek *The queen of the south*.   **12:43** Greek *unclean*.   **12:47** Some manuscripts do not include verse 47. Compare Mark 3:32 and Luke 8:20.

Parable of the Farmer Scattering Seed

13 Later that same day Jesus left the house and sat beside the lake. [2]A large crowd soon gathered around him, so he got into a boat. Then he sat there and taught as the people stood on the shore. [3]He told many stories in the form of parables, such as this one:

"Listen! A farmer went out to plant some seeds. [4]As he scattered them across his field, some seeds fell on a footpath, and the birds came and ate them. [5]Other seeds fell on shallow soil with underlying rock. The seeds sprouted quickly because the soil was shallow. [6]But the plants soon wilted under the hot sun, and since they didn't have deep roots, they died. [7]Other seeds fell among thorns that grew up and choked out the tender plants. [8]Still other seeds fell on fertile soil, and they produced a crop that was thirty, sixty, and even a hundred times as much as had been planted! [9]Anyone with ears to hear should listen and understand."

[10]His disciples came and asked him, "Why do you use parables when you talk to the people?"

[11]He replied, "You are permitted to understand the secrets* of the Kingdom of Heaven, but others are not. [12]To those who listen to my teaching, more understanding will be given, and they will have an abundance of knowledge. But for those who are not listening, even what little understanding they have will be taken away from them. [13]That is why I use these parables,

For they look, but they don't really see.
They hear, but they don't really listen or
understand.

[14]This fulfills the prophecy of Isaiah that says,

'When you hear what I say,
you will not understand.
When you see what I do,
you will not comprehend.
[15] For the hearts of these people are hardened,
and their ears cannot hear,
and they have closed their eyes—
so their eyes cannot see,
and their ears cannot hear,
and their hearts cannot understand,
and they cannot turn to me
and let me heal them.'*

[16]"But blessed are your eyes, because they see; and your ears, because they hear. [17]I tell you the truth, many prophets and righteous people longed to see what you see, but they didn't see it. And they longed to hear what you hear, but they didn't hear it.

[18]"Now listen to the explanation of the parable about the farmer planting seeds: [19]The seed that fell on the footpath represents those who hear the message about the Kingdom and don't understand it. Then the evil one comes and snatches away the seed that was planted in their hearts. [20]The seed on the rocky soil represents those who hear the message and immediately receive it with joy. [21]But since they don't have deep roots, they don't last long. They fall away as soon as they have problems or are persecuted for believing God's word. [22]The seed that fell among the thorns represents those who hear God's word, but all too quickly the message is crowded out by the worries of this life and the lure of wealth, so no fruit is produced. [23]The seed that fell on good soil represents those who truly hear and understand God's word and produce a harvest of thirty, sixty, or even a hundred times as much as had been planted!"

Parable of the Wheat and Weeds

[24]Here is another story Jesus told: "The Kingdom of Heaven is like a farmer who planted good seed in his field. [25]But that night as the workers slept, his enemy came and planted weeds among the wheat, then slipped away. [26]When the crop began to grow and produce grain, the weeds also grew.

[27]"The farmer's workers went to him and said, 'Sir, the field where you planted that good seed is full of weeds! Where did they come from?'

[28]"'An enemy has done this!' the farmer exclaimed.

"'Should we pull out the weeds?' they asked.

[29]"'No,' he replied, 'you'll uproot the wheat if you do. [30]Let both grow together until the harvest. Then I will tell the harvesters to sort out the weeds, tie them into bundles, and burn them, and to put the wheat in the barn.'"

Parable of the Mustard Seed

[31]Here is another illustration Jesus used: "The Kingdom of Heaven is like a mustard seed planted in a field. [32]It is the smallest of all seeds, but it becomes the largest of garden plants; it grows into a tree, and birds come and make nests in its branches."

Parable of the Yeast

[33]Jesus also used this illustration: "The Kingdom of Heaven is like the yeast a woman used in making bread. Even though she put only a little yeast in three measures of flour, it permeated every part of the dough."

[34]Jesus always used stories and illustrations like these when speaking to the crowds. In fact, he never spoke to them without using such parables. [35]This fulfilled what God had spoken through the prophet:

"I will speak to you in parables.
I will explain things hidden since the
creation of the world.*"

13:11 Greek *the mysteries.*   **13:14-15** Isa 6:9-10 (Greek version).   **13:35** Some manuscripts do not include *of the world.* Ps 78:2.

Parable of the Wheat and Weeds Explained

36Then, leaving the crowds outside, Jesus went into the house. His disciples said, "Please explain to us the story of the weeds in the field."

37Jesus replied, "The Son of Man* is the farmer who plants the good seed. 38The field is the world, and the good seed represents the people of the Kingdom. The weeds are the people who belong to the evil one. 39The enemy who planted the weeds among the wheat is the devil. The harvest is the end of the world,* and the harvesters are the angels.

40"Just as the weeds are sorted out and burned in the fire, so it will be at the end of the world. 41The Son of Man will send his angels, and they will remove from his Kingdom everything that causes sin and all who do evil. 42And the angels will throw them into the fiery furnace, where there will be weeping and gnashing of teeth. 43Then the righteous will shine like the sun in their Father's Kingdom. Anyone with ears to hear should listen and understand!

Parables of the Hidden Treasure and the Pearl

44"The Kingdom of Heaven is like a treasure that a man discovered hidden in a field. In his excitement, he hid it again and sold everything he owned to get enough money to buy the field.

45"Again, the Kingdom of Heaven is like a merchant on the lookout for choice pearls. 46When he discovered a pearl of great value, he sold everything he owned and bought it!

Parable of the Fishing Net

47"Again, the Kingdom of Heaven is like a fishing net that was thrown into the water and caught fish of every kind. 48When the net was full, they dragged it up onto the shore, sat down, and sorted the good fish into crates, but threw the bad ones away. 49That is the way it will be at the end of the world. The angels will come and separate the wicked people from the righteous, 50throwing the wicked into the fiery furnace, where there will be weeping and gnashing of teeth. 51Do you understand all these things?"

"Yes," they said, "we do."

52Then he added, "Every teacher of religious law who becomes a disciple in the Kingdom of Heaven is like a homeowner who brings from his storeroom new gems of truth as well as old."

Jesus Rejected at Nazareth

53When Jesus had finished telling these stories and illustrations, he left that part of the country. 54He returned to Nazareth, his hometown. When he taught there in the synagogue, everyone was amazed and said, "Where does he get this wisdom and the power to do miracles?" 55Then they scoffed, "He's just the carpenter's son, and we know Mary, his mother, and his brothers—James, Joseph,* Simon, and Judas. 56All his sisters live right here among us. Where did he learn all these things?" 57And they were deeply offended and refused to believe in him.

Then Jesus told them, "A prophet is honored everywhere except in his own hometown and among his own family." 58And so he did only a few miracles there because of their unbelief.

The Death of John the Baptist

14 When Herod Antipas, the ruler of Galilee,* heard about Jesus, 2he said to his advisers, "This must be John the Baptist raised from the dead! That is why he can do such miracles."

3For Herod had arrested and imprisoned John as a favor to his wife Herodias (the former wife of Herod's brother Philip). 4John had been telling Herod, "It is against God's law for you to marry her." 5Herod wanted to kill John, but he was afraid of a riot, because all the people believed John was a prophet.

6But at a birthday party for Herod, Herodias's daughter performed a dance that greatly pleased him, 7so he promised with a vow to give her anything she wanted. 8At her mother's urging, the girl said, "I want the head of John the Baptist on a tray!" 9Then the king regretted what he had said; but because of the vow he had made in front of his guests, he issued the necessary orders. 10So John was beheaded in the prison, 11and his head was brought on a tray and given to the girl, who took it to her mother. 12Later, John's disciples came for his body and buried it. Then they went and told Jesus what had happened.

Jesus Feeds Five Thousand

13As soon as Jesus heard the news, he left in a boat to a remote area to be alone. But the crowds heard where he was headed and followed on foot from many towns. 14Jesus saw the huge crowd as he stepped from the boat, and he had compassion on them and healed their sick.

15That evening the disciples came to him and said, "This is a remote place, and it's already getting late. Send the crowds away so they can go to the villages and buy food for themselves."

16But Jesus said, "That isn't necessary—you feed them."

17"But we have only five loaves of bread and two fish!" they answered.

18"Bring them here," he said. 19Then he told the people to sit down on the grass. Jesus took the five loaves and two fish, looked up toward heaven, and blessed them. Then, breaking the loaves into pieces, he gave the bread to the disciples, who distributed it to the people. 20They all ate as much as they wanted, and afterward, the disciples picked up twelve baskets of leftovers.

13:37 "Son of Man" is a title Jesus used for himself. **13:39** Or *the age;* also in 13:40, 49. **13:55** Other manuscripts read *Joses;* still others read *John.* **14:1** Greek *Herod the tetrarch.* Herod Antipas was a son of King Herod and was ruler over Galilee.

²¹About 5,000 men were fed that day, in addition to all the women and children!

Jesus Walks on Water

²²Immediately after this, Jesus insisted that his disciples get back into the boat and cross to the other side of the lake, while he sent the people home. ²³After sending them home, he went up into the hills by himself to pray. Night fell while he was there alone.

²⁴Meanwhile, the disciples were in trouble far away from land, for a strong wind had risen, and they were fighting heavy waves. ²⁵About three o'clock in the morning* Jesus came toward them, walking on the water. ²⁶When the disciples saw him walking on the water, they were terrified. In their fear, they cried out, "It's a ghost!" ²⁷But Jesus spoke to them at once. "Don't be afraid," he said. "Take courage. I am here!*"

²⁸Then Peter called to him, "Lord, if it's really you, tell me to come to you, walking on the water." ²⁹"Yes, come," Jesus said.

So Peter went over the side of the boat and walked on the water toward Jesus. ³⁰But when he saw the strong* wind and the waves, he was terrified and began to sink. "Save me, Lord!" he shouted.

³¹Jesus immediately reached out and grabbed him. "You have so little faith," Jesus said. "Why did you doubt me?"

³²When they climbed back into the boat, the wind stopped. ³³Then the disciples worshiped him. "You really are the Son of God!" they exclaimed.

³⁴After they had crossed the lake, they landed at Gennesaret. ³⁵When the people recognized Jesus, the news of his arrival spread quickly throughout the whole area, and soon people were bringing all their sick to be healed. ³⁶They begged him to let the sick touch at least the fringe of his robe, and all who touched him were healed.

Jesus Teaches about Inner Purity

15 Some Pharisees and teachers of religious law now arrived from Jerusalem to see Jesus. They asked him, ²"Why do your disciples disobey our age-old tradition? For they ignore our tradition of ceremonial hand washing before they eat."

³Jesus replied, "And why do you, by your traditions, violate the direct commandments of God? ⁴For instance, God says, 'Honor your father and mother,'* and 'Anyone who speaks disrespectfully of father or mother must be put to death.'* ⁵But you say it is all right for people to say to their parents, 'Sorry, I can't help you. For I have vowed to give to God what I would have given to you.' ⁶In this way, you say they don't need to

honor their parents.* And so you cancel the word of God for the sake of your own tradition. ⁷You hypocrites! Isaiah was right when he prophesied about you, for he wrote,

⁸ 'These people honor me with their lips,
  but their hearts are far from me.
⁹ Their worship is a farce,
  for they teach man-made ideas as
  commands from God.'*"

¹⁰Then Jesus called to the crowd to come and hear. "Listen," he said, "and try to understand. ¹¹It's not what goes into your mouth that defiles you; you are defiled by the words that come out of your mouth."

¹²Then the disciples came to him and asked, "Do you realize you offended the Pharisees by what you just said?"

¹³Jesus replied, "Every plant not planted by my heavenly Father will be uprooted, ¹⁴so ignore them. They are blind guides leading the blind, and if one blind person guides another, they will both fall into a ditch."

¹⁵Then Peter said to Jesus, "Explain to us the parable that says people aren't defiled by what they eat."

¹⁶"Don't you understand yet?" Jesus asked. ¹⁷"Anything you eat passes through the stomach and then goes into the sewer. ¹⁸But the words you speak come from the heart—that's what defiles you. ¹⁹For from the heart come evil thoughts, murder, adultery, all sexual immorality, theft, lying, and slander. ²⁰These are what defile you. Eating with unwashed hands will never defile you."

The Faith of a Gentile Woman

²¹Then Jesus left Galilee and went north to the region of Tyre and Sidon. ²²A Gentile* woman who lived there came to him, pleading, "Have mercy on me, O Lord, Son of David! For my daughter is possessed by a demon that torments her severely."

²³But Jesus gave her no reply, not even a word. Then his disciples urged him to send her away. "Tell her to go away," they said. "She is bothering us with all her begging."

²⁴Then Jesus said to the woman, "I was sent only to help God's lost sheep—the people of Israel."

²⁵But she came and worshiped him, pleading again, "Lord, help me!"

²⁶Jesus responded, "It isn't right to take food from the children and throw it to the dogs."

²⁷She replied, "That's true, Lord, but even dogs are allowed to eat the scraps that fall beneath their masters' table."

²⁸"Dear woman," Jesus said to her, "your faith is great. Your request is granted." And her daughter was instantly healed.

14:25 Greek *In the fourth watch of the night.* **14:27** Or *The 'I AM' is here;* Greek reads *I am.* See Exod 3:14. **14:30** Some manuscripts do not include *strong.* **15:4a** Exod 20:12; Deut 5:16. **15:4b** Exod 21:17 (Greek version); Lev 20:9 (Greek version). **15:6** Greek *their father;* other manuscripts read *their father or their mother.* **15:8-9** Isa 29:13 (Greek version). **15:22** Greek *Canaanite.*

Jesus Heals Many People

²⁹Jesus returned to the Sea of Galilee and climbed a hill and sat down. ³⁰A vast crowd brought to him people who were lame, blind, crippled, those who couldn't speak, and many others. They laid them before Jesus, and he healed them all. ³¹The crowd was amazed! Those who hadn't been able to speak were talking, the crippled were made well, the lame were walking, and the blind could see again! And they praised the God of Israel.

Jesus Feeds Four Thousand

³²Then Jesus called his disciples and told them, "I feel sorry for these people. They have been here with me for three days, and they have nothing left to eat. I don't want to send them away hungry, or they will faint along the way."

³³The disciples replied, "Where would we get enough food here in the wilderness for such a huge crowd?"

³⁴Jesus asked, "How much bread do you have?"

They replied, "Seven loaves, and a few small fish."

³⁵So Jesus told all the people to sit down on the ground. ³⁶Then he took the seven loaves and the fish, thanked God for them, and broke them into pieces. He gave them to the disciples, who distributed the food to the crowd.

³⁷They all ate as much as they wanted. Afterward, the disciples picked up seven large baskets of leftover food. ³⁸There were 4,000 men who were fed that day, in addition to all the women and children. ³⁹Then Jesus sent the people home, and he got into a boat and crossed over to the region of Magadan.

Leaders Demand a Miraculous Sign

16 One day the Pharisees and Sadducees came to test Jesus, demanding that he show them a miraculous sign from heaven to prove his authority.

²He replied, "You know the saying, 'Red sky at night means fair weather tomorrow; ³red sky in the morning means foul weather all day.' You know how to interpret the weather signs in the sky, but you don't know how to interpret the signs of the times!* ⁴Only an evil, adulterous generation would demand a miraculous sign, but the only sign I will give them is the sign of the prophet Jonah.*" Then Jesus left them and went away.

Yeast of the Pharisees and Sadducees

⁵Later, after they crossed to the other side of the lake, the disciples discovered they had forgotten to bring any bread. ⁶"Watch out!" Jesus warned them. "Beware of the yeast of the Pharisees and Sadducees."

⁷At this they began to argue with each other because they hadn't brought any bread. ⁸Jesus knew what they were saying, so he said, "You have so little faith! Why are you arguing with each other about having no bread? ⁹Don't you understand even yet? Don't you remember the 5,000 I fed with five loaves, and the baskets of leftovers you picked up? ¹⁰Or the 4,000 I fed with seven loaves, and the large baskets of leftovers you picked up? ¹¹Why can't you understand that I'm not talking about bread? So again I say, 'Beware of the yeast of the Pharisees and Sadducees.'"

¹²Then at last they understood that he wasn't speaking about the yeast in bread, but about the deceptive teaching of the Pharisees and Sadducees.

Peter's Declaration about Jesus

¹³When Jesus came to the region of Caesarea Philippi, he asked his disciples, "Who do people say that the Son of Man is?"*

¹⁴"Well," they replied, "some say John the Baptist, some say Elijah, and others say Jeremiah or one of the other prophets."

¹⁵Then he asked them, "But who do you say I am?"

¹⁶Simon Peter answered, "You are the Messiah,* the Son of the living God."

¹⁷Jesus replied, "You are blessed, Simon son of John,* because my Father in heaven has revealed this to you. You did not learn this from any human being. ¹⁸Now I say to you that you are Peter (which means 'rock'),* and upon this rock I will build my church, and all the powers of hell* will not conquer it. ¹⁹And I will give you the keys of the Kingdom of Heaven. Whatever you forbid* on earth will be forbidden in heaven, and whatever you permit* on earth will be permitted in heaven."

²⁰Then he sternly warned the disciples not to tell anyone that he was the Messiah.

Jesus Predicts His Death

²¹From then on Jesus* began to tell his disciples plainly that it was necessary for him to go to Jerusalem, and that he would suffer many terrible things at the hands of the elders, the leading priests, and the teachers of religious law. He would be killed, but on the third day he would be raised from the dead.

²²But Peter took him aside and began to reprimand him* for saying such things. "Heaven forbid, Lord," he said. "This will never happen to you!"

²³Jesus turned to Peter and said, "Get away from me, Satan! You are a dangerous trap to me.

16:2-3 Several manuscripts do not include any of the words in 16:2-3 after *He replied.* **16:4** Greek *the sign of Jonah.* **16:13** "Son of Man" is a title Jesus used for himself. **16:16** Or *the Christ. Messiah* (a Hebrew term) and *Christ* (a Greek term) both mean "the anointed one." **16:17** Greek *Simon bar-Jonah;* see John 1:42; 21:15-17. **16:18a** Greek *that you are Peter.* **16:18b** Greek *and the gates of Hades.* **16:19a** Or *bind,* or *lock.* **16:19b** Or *loose,* or *open.* **16:21** Some manuscripts read *Jesus the Messiah.* **16:22** Or *began to correct him.*

You are seeing things merely from a human point of view, not from God's."

²⁴Then Jesus said to his disciples, "If any of you wants to be my follower, you must turn from your selfish ways, take up your cross, and follow me. ²⁵If you try to hang on to your life, you will lose it. But if you give up your life for my sake, you will save it. ²⁶And what do you benefit if you gain the whole world but lose your own soul?* Is anything worth more than your soul? ²⁷For the Son of Man will come with his angels in the glory of his Father and will judge all people according to their deeds. ²⁸And I tell you the truth, some standing here right now will not die before they see the Son of Man coming in his Kingdom."

The Transfiguration

17 Six days later Jesus took Peter and the two brothers, James and John, and led them up a high mountain to be alone. ²As the men watched, Jesus' appearance was transformed so that his face shone like the sun, and his clothes became as white as light. ³Suddenly, Moses and Elijah appeared and began talking with Jesus.

⁴Peter exclaimed, "Lord, it's wonderful for us to be here! If you want, I'll make three shelters as memorials*—one for you, one for Moses, and one for Elijah."

⁵But even as he spoke, a bright cloud overshadowed them, and a voice from the cloud said, "This is my dearly loved Son, who brings me great joy. Listen to him." ⁶The disciples were terrified and fell face down on the ground.

⁷Then Jesus came over and touched them. "Get up," he said. "Don't be afraid." ⁸And when they looked up, Moses and Elijah were gone, and they saw only Jesus.

⁹As they went back down the mountain, Jesus commanded them, "Don't tell anyone what you have seen until the Son of Man* has been raised from the dead."

¹⁰Then his disciples asked him, "Why do the teachers of religious law insist that Elijah must return before the Messiah comes?*"

¹¹Jesus replied, "Elijah is indeed coming first to get everything ready. ¹²But I tell you, Elijah has already come, but he wasn't recognized, and they chose to abuse him. And in the same way they will also make the Son of Man suffer." ¹³Then the disciples realized he was talking about John the Baptist.

Jesus Heals a Demon-Possessed Boy

¹⁴At the foot of the mountain, a large crowd was waiting for them. A man came and knelt before Jesus and said, ¹⁵"Lord, have mercy on my son. He has seizures and suffers terribly. He often falls into the fire or into the water. ¹⁶So I brought him to your disciples, but they couldn't heal him."

¹⁷Jesus said, "You faithless and corrupt people! How long must I be with you? How long must I put up with you? Bring the boy here to me." ¹⁸Then Jesus rebuked the demon in the boy, and it left him. From that moment the boy was well.

¹⁹Afterward the disciples asked Jesus privately, "Why couldn't we cast out that demon?"

²⁰"You don't have enough faith," Jesus told them. "I tell you the truth, if you had faith even as small as a mustard seed, you could say to this mountain, 'Move from here to there,' and it would move. Nothing would be impossible.*"

Jesus Again Predicts His Death

²²After they gathered again in Galilee, Jesus told them, "The Son of Man is going to be betrayed into the hands of his enemies. ²³He will be killed, but on the third day he will be raised from the dead." And the disciples were filled with grief.

Payment of the Temple Tax

²⁴On their arrival in Capernaum, the collectors of the Temple tax* came to Peter and asked him, "Doesn't your teacher pay the Temple tax?"

²⁵"Yes, he does," Peter replied. Then he went into the house.

But before he had a chance to speak, Jesus asked him, "What do you think, Peter?* Do kings tax their own people or the people they have conquered?*"

²⁶"They tax the people they have conquered," Peter replied.

"Well, then," Jesus said, "the citizens are free! ²⁷However, we don't want to offend them, so go down to the lake and throw in a line. Open the mouth of the first fish you catch, and you will find a large silver coin.* Take it and pay the tax for both of us."

The Greatest in the Kingdom

18 About that time the disciples came to Jesus and asked, "Who is greatest in the Kingdom of Heaven?"

²Jesus called a little child to him and put the child among them. ³Then he said, "I tell you the truth, unless you turn from your sins and become like little children, you will never get into the Kingdom of Heaven. ⁴So anyone who becomes as humble as this little child is the greatest in the Kingdom of Heaven.

⁵"And anyone who welcomes a little child like this on my behalf* is welcoming me. ⁶But if you cause one of these little ones who trusts in me to fall into sin, it would be better for you to have a large millstone tied around your neck and be drowned in the depths of the sea.

16:26 Or *your self?* also in 16:26b. **17:4** Greek *three tabernacles.* **17:9** "Son of Man" is a title Jesus used for himself.
17:10 Greek *that Elijah must come first?* **17:20** Some manuscripts add verse 21, *But this kind of demon won't leave except by prayer and fasting.* Compare Mark 9:29. **17:24** Greek *the two-drachma [tax];* also in 17:24b. See Exod 30:13-16; Neh 10:32-33.
17:25a Greek *Simon?* **17:25b** Greek *their sons or others?* **17:27** Greek *a stater* [a Greek coin equivalent to four drachmas].
18:5 Greek *in my name.*

7"What sorrow awaits the world, because it tempts people to sin. Temptations are inevitable, but what sorrow awaits the person who does the tempting. 8So if your hand or foot causes you to sin, cut it off and throw it away. It's better to enter eternal life with only one hand or one foot than to be thrown into eternal fire with both of your hands and feet. 9And if your eye causes you to sin, gouge it out and throw it away. It's better to enter eternal life with only one eye than to have two eyes and be thrown into the fire of hell.*

10"Beware that you don't look down on any of these little ones. For I tell you that in heaven their angels are always in the presence of my heavenly Father.*

Parable of the Lost Sheep

12"If a man has a hundred sheep and one of them wanders away, what will he do? Won't he leave the ninety-nine others on the hills and go out to search for the one that is lost? 13And if he finds it, I tell you the truth, he will rejoice over it more than over the ninety-nine that didn't wander away! 14In the same way, it is not my heavenly Father's will that even one of these little ones should perish.

Correcting Another Believer

15"If another believer* sins against you,* go privately and point out the offense. If the other person listens and confesses it, you have won that person back. 16But if you are unsuccessful, take one or two others with you and go back again, so that everything you say may be confirmed by two or three witnesses. 17If the person still refuses to listen, take your case to the church. Then if he or she won't accept the church's decision, treat that person as a pagan or a corrupt tax collector.

18"I tell you the truth, whatever you forbid* on earth will be forbidden in heaven, and whatever you permit* on earth will be permitted in heaven.

19"I also tell you this: If two of you agree here on earth concerning anything you ask, my Father in heaven will do it for you. 20For where two or three gather together as my followers,* I am there among them."

Parable of the Unforgiving Debtor

21Then Peter came to him and asked, "Lord, how often should I forgive someone* who sins against me? Seven times?"

22"No, not seven times," Jesus replied, "but seventy times seven!*

23"Therefore, the Kingdom of Heaven can be compared to a king who decided to bring his accounts up to date with servants who had bor-

rowed money from him. 24In the process, one of his debtors was brought in who owed him millions of dollars.* 25He couldn't pay, so his master ordered that he be sold—along with his wife, his children, and everything he owned—to pay the debt.

26"But the man fell down before his master and begged him, 'Please, be patient with me, and I will pay it all.' 27Then his master was filled with pity for him, and he released him and forgave his debt.

28"But when the man left the king, he went to a fellow servant who owed him a few thousand dollars.* He grabbed him by the throat and demanded instant payment.

29"His fellow servant fell down before him and begged for a little more time. 'Be patient with me, and I will pay it,' he pleaded. 30But his creditor wouldn't wait. He had the man arrested and put in prison until the debt could be paid in full.

31"When some of the other servants saw this, they were very upset. They went to the king and told him everything that had happened. 32Then the king called in the man he had forgiven and said, 'You evil servant! I forgave you that tremendous debt because you pleaded with me. 33Shouldn't you have mercy on your fellow servant, just as I had mercy on you?' 34Then the angry king sent the man to prison to be tortured until he had paid his entire debt.

35"That's what my heavenly Father will do to you if you refuse to forgive your brothers and sisters* from your heart."

Discussion about Divorce and Marriage

19 When Jesus had finished saying these things, he left Galilee and went down to the region of Judea east of the Jordan River. 2Large crowds followed him there, and he healed their sick.

3Some Pharisees came and tried to trap him with this question: "Should a man be allowed to divorce his wife for just any reason?"

4"Haven't you read the Scriptures?" Jesus replied. "They record that from the beginning 'God made them male and female.'*" 5And he said, "'This explains why a man leaves his father and mother and is joined to his wife, and the two are united into one.'* 6Since they are no longer two but one, let no one split apart what God has joined together."

7"Then why did Moses say in the law that a man could give his wife a written notice of divorce and send her away?"* they asked.

8Jesus replied, "Moses permitted divorce only as a concession to your hard hearts, but it was not what God had originally intended. 9And I tell you this, whoever divorces his wife and marries

18:9 Greek *the Gehenna of fire.* **18:10** Some manuscripts add verse 11, *And the Son of Man came to save those who are lost.* Compare Luke 19:10. **18:15a** Greek *If your brother.* **18:15b** Some manuscripts do not include *against you.* **18:18a** Or *bind,* or *lock.* **18:18b** Or *loose,* or *open.* **18:20** Greek *gather together in my name.* **18:21** Greek *my brother.* **18:22** Or *seventy-seven times.* **18:24** Greek *10,000 talents* [375 tons or 340 metric tons of silver]. **18:28** Greek *100 denarii.* A denarius was equivalent to a laborer's full day's wage. **18:35** Greek *your brother.* **19:4** Gen 1:27; 5:2. **19:5** Gen 2:24. **19:7** See Deut 24:1.

someone else commits adultery—unless his wife has been unfaithful.*"

¹⁰Jesus' disciples then said to him, "If this is the case, it is better not to marry!"

¹¹"Not everyone can accept this statement," Jesus said. "Only those whom God helps. ¹²Some are born as eunuchs, some have been made eunuchs by others, and some choose not to marry* for the sake of the Kingdom of Heaven. Let anyone accept this who can."

Jesus Blesses the Children

¹³One day some parents brought their children to Jesus so he could lay his hands on them and pray for them. But the disciples scolded the parents for bothering him.

¹⁴But Jesus said, "Let the children come to me. Don't stop them! For the Kingdom of Heaven belongs to those who are like these children." ¹⁵And he placed his hands on their heads and blessed them before he left.

The Rich Man

¹⁶Someone came to Jesus with this question: "Teacher,* what good deed must I do to have eternal life?"

¹⁷"Why ask me about what is good?" Jesus replied. "There is only One who is good. But to answer your question—if you want to receive eternal life, keep* the commandments."

¹⁸"Which ones?" the man asked.

And Jesus replied: " 'You must not murder. You must not commit adultery. You must not steal. You must not testify falsely. ¹⁹Honor your father and mother. Love your neighbor as yourself.'*"

²⁰"I've obeyed all these commandments," the young man replied. "What else must I do?"

²¹Jesus told him, "If you want to be perfect, go and sell all your possessions and give the money to the poor, and you will have treasure in heaven. Then come, follow me."

²²But when the young man heard this, he went away sad, for he had many possessions.

²³Then Jesus said to his disciples, "I tell you the truth, it is very hard for a rich person to enter the Kingdom of Heaven. ²⁴I'll say it again—it is easier for a camel to go through the eye of a needle than for a rich person to enter the Kingdom of God!"

²⁵The disciples were astounded. "Then who in the world can be saved?" they asked.

²⁶Jesus looked at them intently and said, "Humanly speaking, it is impossible. But with God everything is possible."

²⁷Then Peter said to him, "We've given up everything to follow you. What will we get?"

²⁸Jesus replied, "I assure you that when the world is made new* and the Son of Man* sits upon his glorious throne, you who have been my followers will also sit on twelve thrones, judging the twelve tribes of Israel. ²⁹And everyone who has given up houses or brothers or sisters or father or mother or children or property, for my sake, will receive a hundred times as much in return and will inherit eternal life. ³⁰But many who are the greatest now will be least important then, and those who seem least important now will be the greatest then.*

Parable of the Vineyard Workers

20 "For the Kingdom of Heaven is like the landowner who went out early one morning to hire workers for his vineyard. ²He agreed to pay the normal daily wage* and sent them out to work.

³"At nine o'clock in the morning he was passing through the marketplace and saw some people standing around doing nothing. ⁴So he hired them, telling them he would pay them whatever was right at the end of the day. ⁵So they went to work in the vineyard. At noon and again at three o'clock he did the same thing.

⁶"At five o'clock that afternoon he was in town again and saw some more people standing around. He asked them, 'Why haven't you been working today?'

⁷"They replied, 'Because no one hired us.'

"The landowner told them, 'Then go out and join the others in my vineyard.'

⁸"That evening he told the foreman to call the workers in and pay them, beginning with the last workers first. ⁹When those hired at five o'clock were paid, each received a full day's wage. ¹⁰When those hired first came to get their pay, they assumed they would receive more. But they, too, were paid a day's wage. ¹¹When they received their pay, they protested to the owner, ¹²'Those people worked only one hour, and yet you've paid them just as much as you paid us who worked all day in the scorching heat.'

¹³"He answered one of them, 'Friend, I haven't been unfair! Didn't you agree to work all day for the usual wage? ¹⁴Take your money and go. I wanted to pay this last worker the same as you. ¹⁵Is it against the law for me to do what I want with my money? Should you be jealous because I am kind to others?'

¹⁶"So those who are last now will be first then, and those who are first will be last."

Jesus Again Predicts His Death

¹⁷As Jesus was going up to Jerusalem, he took the twelve disciples aside privately and told them what was going to happen to him. ¹⁸"Listen," he said, "we're going up to Jerusalem, where the

---

19:9 Some manuscripts add *And anyone who marries a divorced woman commits adultery.* Compare Matt 5:32. **19:12** Greek *and some make themselves eunuchs.* **19:16** Some manuscripts read *Good Teacher.* **19:17** Some manuscripts read *continue to keep.* **19:18-19** Exod 20:12-16; Deut 5:16-20; Lev 19:18. **19:28a** Or *in the regeneration.* **19:28b** "Son of Man" is a title Jesus used for himself. **19:30** Greek *But many who are first will be last; and the last, first.* **20:2** Greek *a denarius,* the payment for a full day's labor; similarly in 20:9, 10, 13.

Son of Man* will be betrayed to the leading priests and the teachers of religious law. They will sentence him to die. ¹⁹Then they will hand him over to the Romans* to be mocked, flogged with a whip, and crucified. But on the third day he will be raised from the dead."

Jesus Teaches about Serving Others

²⁰Then the mother of James and John, the sons of Zebedee, came to Jesus with her sons. She knelt respectfully to ask a favor. ²¹"What is your request?" he asked.

She replied, "In your Kingdom, please let my two sons sit in places of honor next to you, one on your right and the other on your left."

²²But Jesus answered by saying to them, "You don't know what you are asking! Are you able to drink from the bitter cup of suffering I am about to drink?"

"Oh yes," they replied, "we are able!"

²³Jesus told them, "You will indeed drink from my bitter cup. But I have no right to say who will sit on my right or my left. My Father has prepared those places for the ones he has chosen."

²⁴When the ten other disciples heard what James and John had asked, they were indignant. ²⁵But Jesus called them together and said, "You know that the rulers in this world lord it over their people, and officials flaunt their authority over those under them. ²⁶But among you it will be different. Whoever wants to be a leader among you must be your servant, ²⁷and whoever wants to be first among you must become your slave. ²⁸For even the Son of Man came not to be served but to serve others and to give his life as a ransom for many."

Jesus Heals Two Blind Men

²⁹As Jesus and the disciples left the town of Jericho, a large crowd followed behind. ³⁰Two blind men were sitting beside the road. When they heard that Jesus was coming that way, they began shouting, "Lord, Son of David, have mercy on us!"

³¹"Be quiet!" the crowd yelled at them.

But they only shouted louder, "Lord, Son of David, have mercy on us!"

³²When Jesus heard them, he stopped and called, "What do you want me to do for you?"

³³"Lord," they said, "we want to see!" ³⁴Jesus felt sorry for them and touched their eyes. Instantly they could see! Then they followed him.

Jesus' Triumphant Entry

21 As Jesus and the disciples approached Jerusalem, they came to the town of Bethphage on the Mount of Olives. Jesus sent two of them on ahead. ²"Go into the village over there," he said. "As soon as you enter it, you will see a donkey tied there, with its colt beside it. Untie them and bring them to me. ³If anyone asks what you are doing, just say, 'The Lord needs them,' and he will immediately let you take them."

⁴This took place to fulfill the prophecy that said,

⁵ "Tell the people of Jerusalem,*
    'Look, your King is coming to you.
He is humble, riding on a donkey—
    riding on a donkey's colt.'"*

⁶The two disciples did as Jesus commanded. ⁷They brought the donkey and the colt to him and threw their garments over the colt, and he sat on it.*

⁸Most of the crowd spread their garments on the road ahead of him, and others cut branches from the trees and spread them on the road. ⁹Jesus was in the center of the procession, and the people all around him were shouting,

"Praise God* for the Son of David!
    Blessings on the one who comes in the
        name of the Lord!
    Praise God in highest heaven!"*

¹⁰The entire city of Jerusalem was in an uproar as he entered. "Who is this?" they asked.

¹¹And the crowds replied, "It's Jesus, the prophet from Nazareth in Galilee."

Jesus Clears the Temple

¹²Jesus entered the Temple and began to drive out all the people buying and selling animals for sacrifice. He knocked over the tables of the money changers and the chairs of those selling doves. ¹³He said to them, "The Scriptures declare, 'My Temple will be called a house of prayer,' but you have turned it into a den of thieves!"*

¹⁴The blind and the lame came to him in the Temple, and he healed them. ¹⁵The leading priests and the teachers of religious law saw these wonderful miracles and heard even the children in the Temple shouting, "Praise God for the Son of David."

But the leaders were indignant. ¹⁶They asked Jesus, "Do you hear what these children are saying?"

"Yes," Jesus replied. "Haven't you ever read the Scriptures? For they say, 'You have taught children and infants to give you praise.'*"

¹⁷Then he returned to Bethany, where he stayed overnight.

Jesus Curses the Fig Tree

¹⁸In the morning, as Jesus was returning to Jerusalem, he was hungry, ¹⁹and he noticed a fig tree beside the road. He went over to see if there

20:18 "Son of Man" is a title Jesus used for himself.　**20:19** Greek *the Gentiles.*　**21:5a** Greek *Tell the daughter of Zion.* Isa 62:11.
21:5b Zech 9:9.　**21:7** Greek *over them, and he sat on them.*　**21:9a** Greek *Hosanna,* an exclamation of praise that literally means
"save now"; also in 21:9b, 15.　**21:9b** Pss 118:25-26; 148:1.　**21:13** Isa 56:7; Jer 7:11.　**21:16** Ps 8:2.

were any figs, but there were only leaves. Then he said to it, "May you never bear fruit again!" And immediately the fig tree withered up.

²⁰The disciples were amazed when they saw this and asked, "How did the fig tree wither so quickly?"

²¹Then Jesus told them, "I tell you the truth, if you have faith and don't doubt, you can do things like this and much more. You can even say to this mountain, 'May you be lifted up and thrown into the sea,' and it will happen. ²²You can pray for anything, and if you have faith, you will receive it."

The Authority of Jesus Challenged

²³When Jesus returned to the Temple and began teaching, the leading priests and elders came up to him. They demanded, "By what authority are you doing all these things? Who gave you the right?"

²⁴"I'll tell you by what authority I do these things if you answer one question," Jesus replied. ²⁵"Did John's authority to baptize come from heaven, or was it merely human?"

They talked it over among themselves. "If we say it was from heaven, he will ask us why we didn't believe John. ²⁶But if we say it was merely human, we'll be mobbed because the people believe John was a prophet." ²⁷So they finally replied, "We don't know."

And Jesus responded, "Then I won't tell you by what authority I do these things.

Parable of the Two Sons

²⁸"But what do you think about this? A man with two sons told the older boy, 'Son, go out and work in the vineyard today.' ²⁹The son answered, 'No, I won't go,' but later he changed his mind and went anyway. ³⁰Then the father told the other son, 'You go,' and he said, 'Yes, sir, I will.' But he didn't go.

³¹"Which of the two obeyed his father?"

They replied, "The first."*

Then Jesus explained his meaning: "I tell you the truth, corrupt tax collectors and prostitutes will get into the Kingdom of God before you do. ³²For John the Baptist came and showed you the right way to live, but you didn't believe him, while tax collectors and prostitutes did. And even when you saw this happening, you refused to believe him and repent of your sins.

Parable of the Evil Farmers

³³"Now listen to another story. A certain landowner planted a vineyard, built a wall around it, dug a pit for pressing out the grape juice, and built a lookout tower. Then he leased the vineyard to tenant farmers and moved to another country. ³⁴At the time of the grape harvest, he

sent his servants to collect his share of the crop. ³⁵But the farmers grabbed his servants, beat one, killed one, and stoned another. ³⁶So the landowner sent a larger group of his servants to collect for him, but the results were the same.

³⁷"Finally, the owner sent his son, thinking, 'Surely they will respect my son.'

³⁸"But when the tenant farmers saw his son coming, they said to one another, 'Here comes the heir to this estate. Come on, let's kill him and get the estate for ourselves!' ³⁹So they grabbed him, dragged him out of the vineyard, and murdered him.

⁴⁰"When the owner of the vineyard returns," Jesus asked, "what do you think he will do to those farmers?"

⁴¹The religious leaders replied, "He will put the wicked men to a horrible death and lease the vineyard to others who will give him his share of the crop after each harvest."

⁴²Then Jesus asked them, "Didn't you ever read this in the Scriptures?

'The stone that the builders rejected
   has now become the cornerstone.
This is the LORD's doing,
   and it is wonderful to see.'*

⁴³I tell you, the Kingdom of God will be taken away from you and given to a nation that will produce the proper fruit. ⁴⁴Anyone who stumbles over that stone will be broken to pieces, and it will crush anyone it falls on.*"

⁴⁵When the leading priests and Pharisees heard this parable, they realized he was telling the story against them—they were the wicked farmers. ⁴⁶They wanted to arrest him, but they were afraid of the crowds, who considered Jesus to be a prophet.

Parable of the Great Feast

22 Jesus also told them other parables. He said, ²"The Kingdom of Heaven can be illustrated by the story of a king who prepared a great wedding feast for his son. ³When the banquet was ready, he sent his servants to notify those who were invited. But they all refused to come!

⁴"So he sent other servants to tell them, 'The feast has been prepared. The bulls and fattened cattle have been killed, and everything is ready. Come to the banquet!' ⁵But the guests he had invited ignored them and went their own way, one to his farm, another to his business. ⁶Others seized his messengers and insulted them and killed them.

⁷"The king was furious, and he sent out his army to destroy the murderers and burn their town. ⁸And he said to his servants, 'The wedding feast is ready, and the guests I invited aren't wor-

21:29-31 Other manuscripts read *"The second."* In still other manuscripts the first son says "Yes" but does nothing, the second son says "No" but then repents and goes, and the answer to Jesus' question is that the second son obeyed his father.   **21:42** Ps 118:22-23.
21:44 This verse is not included in some early manuscripts. Compare Luke 20:18.

thy of the honor. [9]Now go out to the street corners and invite everyone you see.' [10]So the servants brought in everyone they could find, good and bad alike, and the banquet hall was filled with guests.

[11]"But when the king came in to meet the guests, he noticed a man who wasn't wearing the proper clothes for a wedding. [12]'Friend,' he asked, 'how is it that you are here without wedding clothes?' But the man had no reply. [13]Then the king said to his aides, 'Bind his hands and feet and throw him into the outer darkness, where there will be weeping and gnashing of teeth.'

[14]"For many are called, but few are chosen."

Taxes for Caesar

[15]Then the Pharisees met together to plot how to trap Jesus into saying something for which he could be arrested. [16]They sent some of their disciples, along with the supporters of Herod, to meet with him. "Teacher," they said, "we know how honest you are. You teach the way of God truthfully. You are impartial and don't play favorites. [17]Now tell us what you think about this: Is it right to pay taxes to Caesar or not?"

[18]But Jesus knew their evil motives. "You hypocrites!" he said. "Why are you trying to trap me? [19]Here, show me the coin used for the tax." When they handed him a Roman coin,* [20]he asked, "Whose picture and title are stamped on it?"

[21]"Caesar's," they replied.

"Well, then," he said, "give to Caesar what belongs to Caesar, and give to God what belongs to God."

[22]His reply amazed them, and they went away.

Discussion about Resurrection

[23]That same day Jesus was approached by some Sadducees—religious leaders who say there is no resurrection from the dead. They posed this question: [24]"Teacher, Moses said, 'If a man dies without children, his brother should marry the widow and have a child who will carry on the brother's name.'* [25]Well, suppose there were seven brothers. The oldest one married and then died without children, so his brother married the widow. [26]But the second brother also died, and the third brother married her. This continued with all seven of them. [27]Last of all, the woman also died. [28]So tell us, whose wife will she be in the resurrection? For all seven were married to her."

[29]Jesus replied, "Your mistake is that you don't know the Scriptures, and you don't know the power of God. [30]For when the dead rise, they will neither marry nor be given in marriage. In this respect they will be like the angels in heaven. [31]"But now, as to whether there will be a resurrection of the dead—haven't you ever read about this in the Scriptures? Long after Abraham, Isaac, and Jacob had died, God said,* [32]'I am the God of Abraham, the God of Isaac, and the God of Jacob.'* So he is the God of the living, not the dead."

[33]When the crowds heard him, they were astounded at his teaching.

The Most Important Commandment

[34]But when the Pharisees heard that he had silenced the Sadducees with his reply, they met together to question him again. [35]One of them, an expert in religious law, tried to trap him with this question: [36]"Teacher, which is the most important commandment in the law of Moses?"

[37]Jesus replied, "'You must love the LORD your God with all your heart, all your soul, and all your mind.'* [38]This is the first and greatest commandment. [39]A second is equally important: 'Love your neighbor as yourself.'* [40]The entire law and all the demands of the prophets are based on these two commandments."

Whose Son Is the Messiah?

[41]Then, surrounded by the Pharisees, Jesus asked them a question: [42]"What do you think about the Messiah? Whose son is he?"

They replied, "He is the son of David."

[43]Jesus responded, "Then why does David, speaking under the inspiration of the Spirit, call the Messiah 'my Lord'? For David said,

[44] 'The LORD said to my Lord,
Sit in the place of honor at my right hand
until I humble your enemies beneath your feet.'*

[45]Since David called the Messiah 'my Lord,' how can the Messiah be his son?"

[46]No one could answer him. And after that, no one dared to ask him any more questions.

Jesus Criticizes the Religious Leaders

23 Then Jesus said to the crowds and to his disciples, [2]"The teachers of religious law and the Pharisees are the official interpreters of the law of Moses.* [3]So practice and obey whatever they tell you, but don't follow their example. For they don't practice what they teach. [4]They crush people with unbearable religious demands and never lift a finger to ease the burden.

[5]"Everything they do is for show. On their arms they wear extra wide prayer boxes with Scripture verses inside, and they wear robes with extra long tassels.* [6]And they love to sit at the head table at banquets and in the seats of honor in the synagogues. [7]They love to receive respectful greetings as they walk in the marketplaces, and to be called 'Rabbi.'*

[8]"Don't let anyone call you 'Rabbi,' for you

have only one teacher, and all of you are equal as brothers and sisters.* 9And don't address anyone here on earth as 'Father,' for only God in heaven is your spiritual Father. 10And don't let anyone call you 'Teacher,' for you have only one teacher, the Messiah. 11The greatest among you must be a servant. 12But those who exalt themselves will be humbled, and those who humble themselves will be exalted.

13"What sorrow awaits you teachers of religious law and you Pharisees. Hypocrites! For you shut the door of the Kingdom of Heaven in people's faces. You won't go in yourselves, and you don't let others enter either.*

15"What sorrow awaits you teachers of religious law and you Pharisees. Hypocrites! For you cross land and sea to make one convert, and then you turn that person into twice the child of hell* you yourselves are!

16"Blind guides! What sorrow awaits you! For you say that it means nothing to swear 'by God's Temple,' but that it is binding to swear 'by the gold in the Temple.' 17Blind fools! Which is more important—the gold or the Temple that makes the gold sacred? 18And you say that to swear 'by the altar' is not binding, but to swear 'by the gifts on the altar' is binding. 19How blind! For which is more important—the gift on the altar or the altar that makes the gift sacred? 20When you swear 'by the altar,' you are swearing by it and by everything on it. 21And when you swear 'by the Temple,' you are swearing by it and by God, who lives in it. 22And when you swear 'by heaven,' you are swearing by the throne of God and by God, who sits on the throne.

23"What sorrow awaits you teachers of religious law and you Pharisees. Hypocrites! For you are careful to tithe even the tiniest income from your herb gardens,* but you ignore the more important aspects of the law—justice, mercy, and faith. You should tithe, yes, but do not neglect the more important things. 24Blind guides! You strain your water so you won't accidentally swallow a gnat, but you swallow a camel!*

25"What sorrow awaits you teachers of religious law and you Pharisees. Hypocrites! For you are so careful to clean the outside of the cup and the dish, but inside you are filthy—full of greed and self-indulgence! 26You blind Pharisee! First wash the inside of the cup and the dish,* and then the outside will become clean, too.

27"What sorrow awaits you teachers of religious law and you Pharisees. Hypocrites! For you are like whitewashed tombs—beautiful on the outside but filled on the inside with dead people's bones and all sorts of impurity. 28Outwardly you look like righteous people, but

inwardly your hearts are filled with hypocrisy and lawlessness.

29"What sorrow awaits you teachers of religious law and you Pharisees. Hypocrites! For you build tombs for the prophets your ancestors killed, and you decorate the monuments of the godly people your ancestors destroyed. 30Then you say, 'If we had lived in the days of our ancestors, we would never have joined them in killing the prophets.'

31"But in saying that, you testify against yourselves that you are indeed the descendants of those who murdered the prophets. 32Go ahead and finish what your ancestors started. 33Snakes! Sons of vipers! How will you escape the judgment of hell?

34"Therefore, I am sending you prophets and wise men and teachers of religious law. But you will kill some by crucifixion, and you will flog others with whips in your synagogues, chasing them from city to city. 35As a result, you will be held responsible for the murder of all godly people of all time—from the murder of righteous Abel to the murder of Zechariah son of Berekiah, whom you killed in the Temple between the sanctuary and the altar. 36I tell you the truth, this judgment will fall on this very generation.

Jesus Grieves over Jerusalem

37"O Jerusalem, Jerusalem, the city that kills the prophets and stones God's messengers! How often I have wanted to gather your children together as a hen protects her chicks beneath her wings, but you wouldn't let me. 38And now, look, your house is abandoned and desolate.* 39For I tell you this, you will never see me again until you say, 'Blessings on the one who comes in the name of the LORD!'* "

Jesus Foretells the Future

24 As Jesus was leaving the Temple grounds, his disciples pointed out to him the various Temple buildings. 2But he responded, "Do you see all these buildings? I tell you the truth, they will be completely demolished. Not one stone will be left on top of another!"

3Later, Jesus sat on the Mount of Olives. His disciples came to him privately and said, "Tell us, when will all this happen? What sign will signal your return and the end of the world?*"

4Jesus told them, "Don't let anyone mislead you, 5for many will come in my name, claiming, 'I am the Messiah.' They will deceive many. 6And you will hear of wars and threats of wars, but don't panic. Yes, these things must take place, but the end won't follow immediately. 7Nation will go to war against nation, and kingdom

23:8 Greek *brothers.* 23:13 Some manuscripts add verse 14, *What sorrow awaits you teachers of religious law and you Pharisees. Hypocrites! You shamelessly cheat widows out of their property and then pretend to be pious by making long prayers in public. Because of this, you will be severely punished.* Compare Mark 12:40 and Luke 20:47. 23:15 Greek *of Gehenna;* also in 23:33. 23:23 Greek *tithe the mint, the dill, and the cumin.* 23:24 See Lev 11:4, 23, where gnats and camels are both forbidden as food. 23:26 Some manuscripts do not include *and the dish.* 23:38 Some manuscripts do not include *and desolate.* 23:39 Ps 118:26. 24:3 Or *the age?*

against kingdom. There will be famines and earthquakes in many parts of the world. [8]But all this is only the first of the birth pains, with more to come.

[9]"Then you will be arrested, persecuted, and killed. You will be hated all over the world because you are my followers.* [10]And many will turn away from me and betray and hate each other. [11]And many false prophets will appear and will deceive many people. [12]Sin will be rampant everywhere, and the love of many will grow cold. [13]But the one who endures to the end will be saved. [14]And the Good News about the Kingdom will be preached throughout the whole world, so that all nations* will hear it; and then the end will come.

[15]"The day is coming when you will see what Daniel the prophet spoke about—the sacrilegious object that causes desecration* standing in the Holy Place." (Reader, pay attention!) [16]"Then those in Judea must flee to the hills. [17]A person out on the deck of a roof must not go down into the house to pack. [18]A person out in the field must not return even to get a coat. [19]How terrible it will be for pregnant women and for nursing mothers in those days. [20]And pray that your flight will not be in winter or on the Sabbath. [21]For there will be greater anguish than at any time since the world began. And it will never be so great again. [22]In fact, unless that time of calamity is shortened, not a single person will survive. But it will be shortened for the sake of God's chosen ones.

[23]"Then if anyone tells you, 'Look, here is the Messiah,' or 'There he is,' don't believe it. [24]For false messiahs and false prophets will rise up and perform great signs and wonders so as to deceive, if possible, even God's chosen ones. [25]See, I have warned you about this ahead of time.

[26]"So if someone tells you, 'Look, the Messiah is out in the desert,' don't bother to go and look. Or, 'Look, he is hiding here,' don't believe it! [27]For as the lightning flashes in the east and shines to the west, so it will be when the Son of Man* comes. [28]Just as the gathering of vultures shows there is a carcass nearby, so these signs indicate that the end is near.*

[29]"Immediately after the anguish of those days,

the sun will be darkened,
　the moon will give no light,
the stars will fall from the sky,
　and the powers in the heavens will be
　　shaken.*

[30]And then at last, the sign that the Son of Man is coming will appear in the heavens, and there will be deep mourning among all the peoples of the earth. And they will see the Son of Man coming on the clouds of heaven with power and great glory.* [31]And he will send out his angels with the mighty blast of a trumpet, and they will gather his chosen ones from all over the world*—from the farthest ends of the earth and heaven.

[32]"Now learn a lesson from the fig tree. When its branches bud and its leaves begin to sprout, you know that summer is near. [33]In the same way, when you see all these things, you can know his return is very near, right at the door. [34]I tell you the truth, this generation* will not pass from the scene until all these things take place. [35]Heaven and earth will disappear, but my words will never disappear.

[36]"However, no one knows the day or hour when these things will happen, not even the angels in heaven or the Son himself.* Only the Father knows.

[37]"When the Son of Man returns, it will be like it was in Noah's day. [38]In those days before the flood, the people were enjoying banquets and parties and weddings right up to the time Noah entered his boat. [39]People didn't realize what was going to happen until the flood came and swept them all away. That is the way it will be when the Son of Man comes.

[40]"Two men will be working together in the field; one will be taken, the other left. [41]Two women will be grinding flour at the mill; one will be taken, the other left.

[42]"So you, too, must keep watch! For you don't know what day your Lord is coming. [43]Understand this: If a homeowner knew exactly when a burglar was coming, he would keep watch and not permit his house to be broken into. [44]You also must be ready all the time, for the Son of Man will come when least expected.

[45]"A faithful, sensible servant is one to whom the master can give the responsibility of managing his other household servants and feeding them. [46]If the master returns and finds that the servant has done a good job, there will be a reward. [47]I tell you the truth, the master will put that servant in charge of all he owns. [48]But what if the servant is evil and thinks, 'My master won't be back for a while,' [49]and he begins beating the other servants, partying, and getting drunk? [50]The master will return unannounced and unexpected, [51]and he will cut the servant to pieces and assign him a place with the hypocrites. In that place there will be weeping and gnashing of teeth.

Parable of the Ten Bridesmaids

25 "Then the Kingdom of Heaven will be like ten bridesmaids* who took their lamps and went to meet the bridegroom. [2]Five of them were foolish, and five were wise. [3]The five who were foolish didn't take enough olive

24:9 Greek *on account of my name.*　**24:14** Or *all peoples.* 12:11.　**24:27** "Son of Man" is a title Jesus used for himself. **24:29** See Isa 13:10; 34:4; Joel 2:10.　**24:30** See Dan 7:13. **24:36** Some manuscripts do not include *or the Son himself.* **24:15** Greek *the abomination of desolation.* See Dan 9:27; 11:31; **24:28** Greek *Wherever the carcass is, the vultures gather.* **24:31** Greek *from the four winds.*　**24:34** Or *this age,* or *this nation.* **25:1** Or *virgins;* also in 25:7, 11.

oil for their lamps, [4]but the other five were wise enough to take along extra oil. [5]When the bridegroom was delayed, they all became drowsy and fell asleep.

[6]"At midnight they were roused by the shout, 'Look, the bridegroom is coming! Come out and meet him!'

[7]"All the bridesmaids got up and prepared their lamps. [8]Then the five foolish ones asked the others, 'Please give us some of your oil because our lamps are going out.'

[9]"But the others replied, 'We don't have enough for all of us. Go to a shop and buy some for yourselves.'

[10]"But while they were gone to buy oil, the bridegroom came. Then those who were ready went in with him to the marriage feast, and the door was locked. [11]Later, when the other five bridesmaids returned, they stood outside, calling, 'Lord! Lord! Open the door for us!'

[12]"But he called back, 'Believe me, I don't know you!'

[13]"So you, too, must keep watch! For you do not know the day or hour of my return.

Parable of the Three Servants

[14]"Again, the Kingdom of Heaven can be illustrated by the story of a man going on a long trip. He called together his servants and entrusted his money to them while he was gone. [15]He gave five bags of silver* to one, two bags of silver to another, and one bag of silver to the last—dividing it in proportion to their abilities. He then left on his trip.

[16]"The servant who received the five bags of silver began to invest the money and earned five more. [17]The servant with two bags of silver also went to work and earned two more. [18]But the servant who received the one bag of silver dug a hole in the ground and hid the master's money.

[19]"After a long time their master returned from his trip and called them to give an account of how they had used his money. [20]The servant to whom he had entrusted the five bags of silver came forward with five more and said, 'Master, you gave me five bags of silver to invest, and I have earned five more.'

[21]"The master was full of praise. 'Well done, my good and faithful servant. You have been faithful in handling this small amount, so now I will give you many more responsibilities. Let's celebrate together!*'

[22]"The servant who had received the two bags of silver came forward and said, 'Master, you gave me two bags of silver to invest, and I have earned two more.'

[23]"The master said, 'Well done, my good and faithful servant. You have been faithful in handling this small amount, so now I will give you

many more responsibilities. Let's celebrate together!'

[24]"Then the servant with the one bag of silver came and said, 'Master, I knew you were a harsh man, harvesting crops you didn't plant and gathering crops you didn't cultivate. [25]I was afraid I would lose your money, so I hid it in the earth. Look, here is your money back.'

[26]"But the master replied, 'You wicked and lazy servant! If you knew I harvested crops I didn't plant and gathered crops I didn't cultivate, [27]why didn't you deposit my money in the bank? At least I could have gotten some interest on it.'

[28]"Then he ordered, 'Take the money from this servant, and give it to the one with the ten bags of silver. [29]To those who use well what they are given, even more will be given, and they will have an abundance. But from those who do nothing, even what little they have will be taken away. [30]Now throw this useless servant into outer darkness, where there will be weeping and gnashing of teeth.'

The Final Judgment

[31]"But when the Son of Man* comes in his glory, and all the angels with him, then he will sit upon his glorious throne. [32]All the nations* will be gathered in his presence, and he will separate the people as a shepherd separates the sheep from the goats. [33]He will place the sheep at his right hand and the goats at his left.

[34]"Then the King will say to those on his right, 'Come, you who are blessed by my Father, inherit the Kingdom prepared for you from the creation of the world. [35]For I was hungry, and you fed me. I was thirsty, and you gave me a drink. I was a stranger, and you invited me into your home. [36]I was naked, and you gave me clothing. I was sick, and you cared for me. I was in prison, and you visited me.'

[37]"Then these righteous ones will reply, 'Lord, when did we ever see you hungry and feed you? Or thirsty and give you something to drink? [38]Or a stranger and show you hospitality? Or naked and give you clothing? [39]When did we ever see you sick or in prison and visit you?'

[40]"And the King will say, 'I tell you the truth, when you did it to one of the least of these my brothers and sisters,* you were doing it to me!'

[41]"Then the King will turn to those on the left and say, 'Away with you, you cursed ones, into the eternal fire prepared for the devil and his demons.* [42]For I was hungry, and you didn't feed me. I was thirsty, and you didn't give me a drink. [43]I was a stranger, and you didn't invite me into your home. I was naked, and you didn't give me clothing. I was sick and in prison, and you didn't visit me.'

[44]"Then they will reply, 'Lord, when did we

25:15 Greek *talents;* also throughout the story. A talent is equal to 75 pounds or 34 kilograms. **25:21** Greek *Enter into the joy of your master* (or *your Lord*); also in 25:23. **25:31** "Son of Man" is a title Jesus used for himself. **25:32** Or *peoples.* **25:40** Greek *my brothers.* **25:41** Greek *his angels.*

ever see you hungry or thirsty or a stranger or naked or sick or in prison, and not help you?'

⁴⁵"And he will answer, 'I tell you the truth, when you refused to help the least of these my brothers and sisters, you were refusing to help me.'

⁴⁶"And they will go away into eternal punishment, but the righteous will go into eternal life."

The Plot to Kill Jesus

26 When Jesus had finished saying all these things, he said to his disciples, ²"As you know, Passover begins in two days, and the Son of Man* will be handed over to be crucified."

³At that same time the leading priests and elders were meeting at the residence of Caiaphas, the high priest, ⁴plotting how to capture Jesus secretly and kill him. ⁵"But not during the Passover celebration," they agreed, "or the people may riot."

Jesus Anointed at Bethany

⁶Meanwhile, Jesus was in Bethany at the home of Simon, a man who had previously had leprosy. ⁷While he was eating,* a woman came in with a beautiful alabaster jar of expensive perfume and poured it over his head.

⁸The disciples were indignant when they saw this. "What a waste!" they said. ⁹"It could have been sold for a high price and the money given to the poor."

¹⁰But Jesus, aware of this, replied, "Why criticize this woman for doing such a good thing to me? ¹¹You will always have the poor among you, but you will not always have me. ¹²She has poured this perfume on me to prepare my body for burial. ¹³I tell you the truth, wherever the Good News is preached throughout the world, this woman's deed will be remembered and discussed."

Judas Agrees to Betray Jesus

¹⁴Then Judas Iscariot, one of the twelve disciples, went to the leading priests ¹⁵and asked, "How much will you pay me to betray Jesus to you?" And they gave him thirty pieces of silver. ¹⁶From that time on, Judas began looking for an opportunity to betray Jesus.

The Last Supper

¹⁷On the first day of the Festival of Unleavened Bread, the disciples came to Jesus and asked, "Where do you want us to prepare the Passover meal for you?"

¹⁸"As you go into the city," he told them, "you will see a certain man. Tell him, 'The Teacher says: My time has come, and I will eat the Passover meal with my disciples at your house.'" ¹⁹So the disciples did as Jesus told them and prepared the Passover meal there.

²⁰When it was evening, Jesus sat down at the table* with the twelve disciples.* ²¹While they were eating, he said, "I tell you the truth, one of you will betray me."

²²Greatly distressed, each one asked in turn, "Am I the one, Lord?"

²³He replied, "One of you who has just eaten from this bowl with me will betray me. ²⁴For the Son of Man must die, as the Scriptures declared long ago. But how terrible it will be for the one who betrays him. It would be far better for that man if he had never been born!"

²⁵Judas, the one who would betray him, also asked, "Rabbi, am I the one?"

And Jesus told him, "You have said it."

²⁶As they were eating, Jesus took some bread and blessed it. Then he broke it in pieces and gave it to the disciples, saying, "Take this and eat it, for this is my body."

²⁷And he took a cup of wine and gave thanks to God for it. He gave it to them and said, "Each of you drink from it, ²⁸for this is my blood, which confirms the covenant* between God and his people. It is poured out as a sacrifice to forgive the sins of many. ²⁹Mark my words—I will not drink wine again until the day I drink it new with you in my Father's Kingdom."

³⁰Then they sang a hymn and went out to the Mount of Olives.

Jesus Predicts Peter's Denial

³¹On the way, Jesus told them, "Tonight all of you will desert me. For the Scriptures say,

'God will strike* the Shepherd,
    and the sheep of the flock will be
        scattered.'

³²But after I have been raised from the dead, I will go ahead of you to Galilee and meet you there."

³³Peter declared, "Even if everyone else deserts you, I will never desert you."

³⁴Jesus replied, "I tell you the truth, Peter—this very night, before the rooster crows, you will deny three times that you even know me."

³⁵"No!" Peter insisted. "Even if I have to die with you, I will never deny you!" And all the other disciples vowed the same.

Jesus Prays in Gethsemane

³⁶Then Jesus went with them to the olive grove called Gethsemane, and he said, "Sit here while I go over there to pray." ³⁷He took Peter and Zebedee's two sons, James and John, and he became anguished and distressed. ³⁸He told them, "My soul is crushed with grief to the point of death. Stay here and keep watch with me."

³⁹He went on a little farther and bowed with his face to the ground, praying, "My Father! If it is possible, let this cup of suffering be taken

26:2 "Son of Man" is a title Jesus used for himself. **26:7** Or *reclining.* **26:20a** Or *Jesus reclined.* **26:20b** Some manuscripts read *the Twelve.* **26:28** Some manuscripts read *the new covenant.* **26:31** Greek *I will strike.* Zech 13:7.

away from me. Yet I want your will to be done, not mine."

⁴⁰Then he returned to the disciples and found them asleep. He said to Peter, "Couldn't you watch with me even one hour? ⁴¹Keep watch and pray, so that you will not give in to temptation. For the spirit is willing, but the body is weak!"

⁴²Then Jesus left them a second time and prayed, "My Father! If this cup cannot be taken away* unless I drink it, your will be done." ⁴³When he returned to them again, he found them sleeping, for they couldn't keep their eyes open.

⁴⁴So he went to pray a third time, saying the same things again. ⁴⁵Then he came to the disciples and said, "Go ahead and sleep. Have your rest. But look—the time has come. The Son of Man is betrayed into the hands of sinners. ⁴⁶Up, let's be going. Look, my betrayer is here!"

Jesus Is Betrayed and Arrested

⁴⁷And even as Jesus said this, Judas, one of the twelve disciples, arrived with a crowd of men armed with swords and clubs. They had been sent by the leading priests and elders of the people. ⁴⁸The traitor, Judas, had given them a prearranged signal: "You will know which one to arrest when I greet him with a kiss." ⁴⁹So Judas came straight to Jesus. "Greetings, Rabbi!" he exclaimed and gave him the kiss.

⁵⁰Jesus said, "My friend, go ahead and do what you have come for."

Then the others grabbed Jesus and arrested him. ⁵¹But one of the men with Jesus pulled out his sword and struck the high priest's slave, slashing off his ear.

⁵²"Put away your sword," Jesus told him. "Those who use the sword will die by the sword. ⁵³Don't you realize that I could ask my Father for thousands* of angels to protect us, and he would send them instantly? ⁵⁴But if I did, how would the Scriptures be fulfilled that describe what must happen now?"

⁵⁵Then Jesus said to the crowd, "Am I some dangerous revolutionary, that you come with swords and clubs to arrest me? Why didn't you arrest me in the Temple? I was there teaching every day. ⁵⁶But this is all happening to fulfill the words of the prophets as recorded in the Scriptures." At that point, all the disciples deserted him and fled.

Jesus before the Council

⁵⁷Then the people who had arrested Jesus led him to the home of Caiaphas, the high priest, where the teachers of religious law and the elders had gathered. ⁵⁸Meanwhile, Peter followed him at a distance and came to the high priest's courtyard. He went in and sat with the guards and waited to see how it would all end.

⁵⁹Inside, the leading priests and the entire high council* were trying to find witnesses who would lie about Jesus, so they could put him to death. ⁶⁰But even though they found many who agreed to give false witness, they could not use anyone's testimony. Finally, two men came forward ⁶¹who declared, "This man said, 'I am able to destroy the Temple of God and rebuild it in three days.'"

⁶²Then the high priest stood up and said to Jesus, "Well, aren't you going to answer these charges? What do you have to say for yourself?" ⁶³But Jesus remained silent. Then the high priest said to him, "I demand in the name of the living God—tell us if you are the Messiah, the Son of God."

⁶⁴Jesus replied, "You have said it. And in the future you will see the Son of Man seated in the place of power at God's right hand* and coming on the clouds of heaven."*

⁶⁵Then the high priest tore his clothing to show his horror and said, "Blasphemy! Why do we need other witnesses? You have all heard his blasphemy. ⁶⁶What is your verdict?"

"Guilty!" they shouted. "He deserves to die!"

⁶⁷Then they began to spit in Jesus' face and beat him with their fists. And some slapped him, ⁶⁸jeering, "Prophesy to us, you Messiah! Who hit you that time?"

Peter Denies Jesus

⁶⁹Meanwhile, Peter was sitting outside in the courtyard. A servant girl came over and said to him, "You were one of those with Jesus the Galilean."

⁷⁰But Peter denied it in front of everyone. "I don't know what you're talking about," he said.

⁷¹Later, out by the gate, another servant girl noticed him and said to those standing around, "This man was with Jesus of Nazareth.*"

⁷²Again Peter denied it, this time with an oath. "I don't even know the man," he said.

⁷³A little later some of the other bystanders came over to Peter and said, "You must be one of them; we can tell by your Galilean accent."

⁷⁴Peter swore, "A curse on me if I'm lying—I don't know the man!" And immediately the rooster crowed.

⁷⁵Suddenly, Jesus' words flashed through Peter's mind: "Before the rooster crows, you will deny three times that you even know me." And he went away, weeping bitterly.

Judas Hangs Himself

27 Very early in the morning the leading priests and the elders of the people met again to lay plans for putting Jesus to death. ²Then they bound him, led him away, and took him to Pilate, the Roman governor.

³When Judas, who had betrayed him, realized that Jesus had been condemned to die, he was filled with remorse. So he took the thirty pieces

---

26:42 Greek *If this cannot pass.*   **26:53** Greek *twelve legions.*   **26:59** Greek *the Sanhedrin.*   **26:64a** Greek *seated at the right hand of the power.* See Ps 110:1.   **26:64b** See Dan 7:13.   **26:71** Or *Jesus the Nazarene.*

of silver back to the leading priests and the elders. ⁴"I have sinned," he declared, "for I have betrayed an innocent man."

"What do we care?" they retorted. "That's your problem."

⁵Then Judas threw the silver coins down in the Temple and went out and hanged himself.

⁶The leading priests picked up the coins. "It wouldn't be right to put this money in the Temple treasury," they said, "since it was payment for murder."* ⁷After some discussion they finally decided to buy the potter's field, and they made it into a cemetery for foreigners. ⁸That is why the field is still called the Field of Blood. ⁹This fulfilled the prophecy of Jeremiah that says,

"They took* the thirty pieces of silver—
    the price at which he was valued by the
        people of Israel,
¹⁰ and purchased the potter's field,
    as the Lᴏʀᴅ directed.*"

Jesus' Trial before Pilate

¹¹Now Jesus was standing before Pilate, the Roman governor. "Are you the king of the Jews?" the governor asked him.

Jesus replied, "You have said it."

¹²But when the leading priests and the elders made their accusations against him, Jesus remained silent. ¹³"Don't you hear all these charges they are bringing against you?" Pilate demanded. ¹⁴But Jesus made no response to any of the charges, much to the governor's surprise.

¹⁵Now it was the governor's custom each year during the Passover celebration to release one prisoner to the crowd—anyone they wanted. ¹⁶This year there was a notorious prisoner, a man named Barabbas.* ¹⁷As the crowds gathered before Pilate's house that morning, he asked them, "Which one do you want me to release to you—Barabbas, or Jesus who is called the Messiah?" ¹⁸(He knew very well that the religious leaders had arrested Jesus out of envy.)

¹⁹Just then, as Pilate was sitting on the judgment seat, his wife sent him this message: "Leave that innocent man alone. I suffered through a terrible nightmare about him last night."

²⁰Meanwhile, the leading priests and the elders persuaded the crowd to ask for Barabbas to be released and for Jesus to be put to death. ²¹So the governor asked again, "Which of these two do you want me to release to you?"

The crowd shouted back, "Barabbas!"

²²Pilate responded, "Then what should I do with Jesus who is called the Messiah?"

They shouted back, "Crucify him!"

²³"Why?" Pilate demanded. "What crime has he committed?"

But the mob roared even louder, "Crucify him!"

²⁴Pilate saw that he wasn't getting anywhere and that a riot was developing. So he sent for a bowl of water and washed his hands before the crowd, saying, "I am innocent of this man's blood. The responsibility is yours!"

²⁵And all the people yelled back, "We will take responsibility for his death—we and our children!"*

²⁶So Pilate released Barabbas to them. He ordered Jesus flogged with a lead-tipped whip, then turned him over to the Roman soldiers to be crucified.

The Soldiers Mock Jesus

²⁷Some of the governor's soldiers took Jesus into their headquarters* and called out the entire regiment. ²⁸They stripped him and put a scarlet robe on him. ²⁹They wove thorn branches into a crown and put it on his head, and they placed a reed stick in his right hand as a scepter. Then they knelt before him in mockery and taunted, "Hail! King of the Jews!" ³⁰And they spit on him and grabbed the stick and struck him on the head with it. ³¹When they were finally tired of mocking him, they took off the robe and put his own clothes on him again. Then they led him away to be crucified.

The Crucifixion

³²Along the way, they came across a man named Simon, who was from Cyrene,* and the soldiers forced him to carry Jesus' cross. ³³And they went out to a place called Golgotha (which means "Place of the Skull"). ³⁴The soldiers gave him wine mixed with bitter gall, but when he had tasted it, he refused to drink it.

³⁵After they had nailed him to the cross, the soldiers gambled for his clothes by throwing dice.* ³⁶Then they sat around and kept guard as he hung there. ³⁷A sign was fastened above Jesus' head, announcing the charge against him. It read: "This is Jesus, the King of the Jews." ³⁸Two revolutionaries* were crucified with him, one on his right and one on his left.

³⁹The people passing by shouted abuse, shaking their heads in mockery. ⁴⁰"Look at you now!" they yelled at him. "You said you were going to destroy the Temple and rebuild it in three days. Well then, if you are the Son of God, save yourself and come down from the cross!"

⁴¹The leading priests, the teachers of religious law, and the elders also mocked Jesus. ⁴²"He saved others," they scoffed, "but he can't save himself! So he is the King of Israel, is he? Let him come down from the cross right now, and we will believe in him! ⁴³He trusted God, so let God rescue him now if he wants him! For he

27:6 Greek *since it is the price for blood.*   **27:9** Or *I took.*   **27:9-10** Greek *as the Lᴏʀᴅ directed me.* Zech 11:12-13; Jer 32:6-9. **27:16** Some manuscripts read *Jesus Barabbas;* also in 27:17.   **27:25** Greek *"His blood be on us and on our children."*   **27:27** Or *into the Praetorium.*   **27:32** *Cyrene* was a city in northern Africa.   **27:35** Greek *by casting lots.* A few late manuscripts add *This fulfilled the word of the prophet: "They divided my garments among themselves and cast lots for my robe."* See Ps 22:18.   **27:38** Or *criminals;* also in 27:44.

said, 'I am the Son of God.'" [44]Even the revolutionaries who were crucified with him ridiculed him in the same way.

The Death of Jesus

[45]At noon, darkness fell across the whole land until three o'clock. [46]At about three o'clock, Jesus called out with a loud voice, *"Eli, Eli,* lema sabachthani?" which means "My God, my God, why have you abandoned me?"*

[47]Some of the bystanders misunderstood and thought he was calling for the prophet Elijah. [48]One of them ran and filled a sponge with sour wine, holding it up to him on a reed stick so he could drink. [49]But the rest said, "Wait! Let's see whether Elijah comes to save him."*

[50]Then Jesus shouted out again, and he released his spirit. [51]At that moment the curtain in the sanctuary of the Temple was torn in two, from top to bottom. The earth shook, rocks split apart, [52]and tombs opened. The bodies of many godly men and women who had died were raised from the dead. [53]They left the cemetery after Jesus' resurrection, went into the holy city of Jerusalem, and appeared to many people.

[54]The Roman officer* and the other soldiers at the crucifixion were terrified by the earthquake and all that had happened. They said, "This man truly was the Son of God!"

[55]And many women who had come from Galilee with Jesus to care for him were watching from a distance. [56]Among them were Mary Magdalene, Mary (the mother of James and Joseph), and the mother of James and John, the sons of Zebedee.

The Burial of Jesus

[57]As evening approached, Joseph, a rich man from Arimathea who had become a follower of Jesus, [58]went to Pilate and asked for Jesus' body. And Pilate issued an order to release it to him. [59]Joseph took the body and wrapped it in a long sheet of clean linen cloth. [60]He placed it in his own new tomb, which had been carved out of the rock. Then he rolled a great stone across the entrance and left. [61]Both Mary Magdalene and the other Mary were sitting across from the tomb and watching.

The Guard at the Tomb

[62]The next day, on the Sabbath,* the leading priests and Pharisees went to see Pilate. [63]They told him, "Sir, we remember what that deceiver once said while he was still alive: 'After three days I will rise from the dead.' [64]So we request that you seal the tomb until the third day. This will prevent his disciples from coming and stealing his body and then telling everyone he was raised from the dead! If that happens, we'll be worse off than we were at first."

[65]Pilate replied, "Take guards and secure it the best you can." [66]So they sealed the tomb and posted guards to protect it.

The Resurrection

28 Early on Sunday morning,* as the new day was dawning, Mary Magdalene and the other Mary went out to visit the tomb.

[2]Suddenly there was a great earthquake! For an angel of the Lord came down from heaven, rolled aside the stone, and sat on it. [3]His face shone like lightning, and his clothing was as white as snow. [4]The guards shook with fear when they saw him, and they fell into a dead faint.

[5]Then the angel spoke to the women. "Don't be afraid!" he said. "I know you are looking for Jesus, who was crucified. [6]He isn't here! He is risen from the dead, just as he said would happen. Come, see where his body was lying. [7]And now, go quickly and tell his disciples that he has risen from the dead, and he is going ahead of you to Galilee. You will see him there. Remember what I have told you."

[8]The women ran quickly from the tomb. They were very frightened but also filled with great joy, and they rushed to give the disciples the angel's message. [9]And as they went, Jesus met them and greeted them. And they ran to him, grasped his feet, and worshiped him. [10]Then Jesus said to them, "Don't be afraid! Go tell my brothers to leave for Galilee, and they will see me there."

The Report of the Guard

[11]As the women were on their way, some of the guards went into the city and told the leading priests what had happened. [12]A meeting with the elders was called, and they decided to give the soldiers a large bribe. [13]They told the soldiers, "You must say, 'Jesus' disciples came during the night while we were sleeping, and they stole his body.' [14]If the governor hears about it, we'll stand up for you so you won't get in trouble." [15]So the guards accepted the bribe and said what they were told to say. Their story spread widely among the Jews, and they still tell it today.

The Great Commission

[16]Then the eleven disciples left for Galilee, going to the mountain where Jesus had told them to go. [17]When they saw him, they worshiped him—but some of them doubted!

[18]Jesus came and told his disciples, "I have been given all authority in heaven and on earth. [19]Therefore, go and make disciples of all the nations,* baptizing them in the name of the Father and the Son and the Holy Spirit. [20]Teach these new disciples to obey all the commands I have given you. And be sure of this: I am with you always, even to the end of the age."

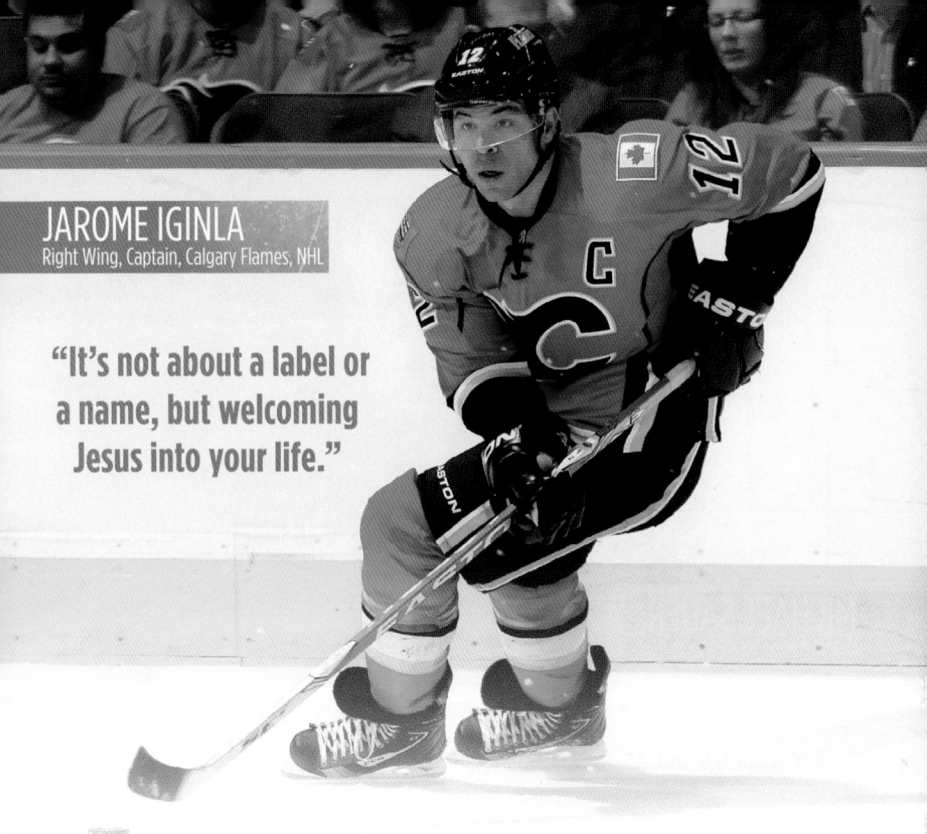

JAROME IGINLA
Right Wing, Captain, Calgary Flames, NHL

"It's not about a label or a name, but welcoming Jesus into your life."

Being known as a believer in Jesus and having a personal relationship with Him is the most important thing to me. It's not about a label or a name but just welcoming Jesus into your life.

My dad has mentored me. We talk about different questions of faith all the time. I was also very close to my grandparents. We went to church together. I remember my grandma reading Bible stories to me. I always believed in God but did not really understand my relationship with Jesus. When I was 15 I had an experience that changed all that. My best friend asked, "what if when you die, there's nothing?" That really unsettled and unnerved me. I tried not to think about it. I started wondering, if that's the case, what's the point? I wrestled with this for about a year before I confided in my dad. He said, "why don't you pray and ask Jesus to come into your life and give you peace?" So I prayed and invited Him into my life and I found the peace I was looking for. That peace has continued throughout my life.

Sometimes it's tough to keep going in the direction of growing closer to God, but His peace keeps me close to Him and always allows me to appreciate what I have. I've been blessed in my life: not just in my career, but also with family, friends, and health.

As a believer in Jesus I try to live by His example the best I can. We all make mistakes, but my personal relationship with Jesus gives me direction and helps me to be a better person. I'm not always a great dad, husband, or teammate, but I try to learn and get better. It's important to ask for forgiveness from others and also from God.

Life has gone so fast. I hope to live to be one hundred and after that I look forward to going to heaven.

I have been encouraged by Psalm 27:1, *"The Lord is my light and my salvation—whom shall I fear? The Lord is the stronghold of my life—of whom shall I be afraid?"* I would say that Deuteronomy 31:6 and Philippians 4:13 are favorite passages.

MICHAEL SAUER
Defense, New York Rangers, NHL

"When I was at my lowest point I opened my Bible."

When I was 20 years old I hit an all time low with hockey and life. I was in the AHL at the time and was tired of feeling guilty and shameful for my bad decisions. I grew up in a Christian home and I knew of Jesus, and this time I really experienced His showing up when I needed Him most. When I was at my lowest point I opened up my Bible to Hebrews 13:5-6. It changed my life. *"For God has said, 'I will never fail you. I will never abandon you.' So we can say with confidence, 'The LORD is my helper, so I will have no fear. What can mere people do to me?'"*

Even today, the hockey season can get long and there are many ups and downs. I find the Bible helps me keep a level head and stay positive, even amidst the trials I face. Two passages in the New Testament encourage me. 1 Thessalonians 5:16 says, "Always be joyful," and Romans 5:3 reads, *"We can rejoice, too, when we run into problems and trials, for we know that they help us develop endurance."*

Sometimes I can feel alone because I choose not to do things others may be doing. However, I've come to realize that what Jesus wants for me is best and as long as He is with me and protecting me, I will never be alone. Being a Christian helps me stay out of situations that can hurt my career and keeps me focused on my goals instead of all the other distractions.

Surrendering myself to Jesus has changed my life because it's made doing the right things easier and confirmed that He has great things in store for me, both on and off the ice.

NOAH WELCH
Defense, Vaxjo Lakers,
Swedish Elite League

Who is Jesus? This is the most important question there is, and we cannot ignore it; the claims Jesus made are too magnificent to ignore.

"I love the game, but it no longer defines who I am."

Jesus claimed to be God (John 10:30). He forgave people for their sins (Luke 5:18-20). He said He is the way, the truth, and the life and through Him is the only way to the Father (John 14:6). He promised salvation to people (Luke 23:42-43).

For 25 years I ignored these claims. I thought I knew what was best for my life. I followed the world's advice: success brings joy and happiness. In my early twenties I made it to the NHL and I was making a lot of money. I already had a degree from Harvard. In the world's eyes I was doing all right. Looking back, I was so lost. I was on a road that led to destruction.

Jesus said that he came to save the sick. Despite some worldly success, by God's grace I realized I was sick. I suffered from a disease that all men and women have called sin. Because of our sin we all deserve God's wrath and judgment. However, by God's grace, those who believe Jesus died for their sins and on the third day rose from the dead receive mercy, grace, love, forgiveness, and salvation. This is the greatest news in the history of mankind. Jesus died for our sins, He served our penalty, and now we can spend eternity with our Creator and Father.

I'm still playing hockey and some people identify me as a hockey player. I love the game, but it no longer defines who I am. By God's sovereign grace, I'm an adopted son into His kingdom through Christ's death and resurrection. My new identity is found in Christ. Knowing that my sins of the past, present, and future have been forgiven on the Cross with Jesus brings true eternal joy and peace. My primary job now is to get to know my King, to learn about Him, to worship, glorify, and follow Him—not because He needs it, but because He deserves it and this is what I was created to do.

JEFF PETRY
Defense, Edmonton Oilers, NHL

Early in my career I doubted myself a lot and compared myself to others, but I always tried to remind myself that God made me the way I am to play the way I play. That constant reminder to just be myself and play the way He designed me to play always reassured me and gave me the confidence I needed. Also, knowing that He has a plan and His plan is the best comforted me and got me through the hard times of being sent down to the minors and other adversities that hockey can throw at you.

When I was playing in college I was so hard on myself in trying to make the next level and in not letting down the fans and my teammates. My relationship with Jesus grew much closer during this time and made me realize that I am playing for Him because He is the one who gave me my talents. Using them to the best of my ability is a way I can glorify Him.

Knowing He is always there with me and goes with me through everything is one of the most freeing and strengthening feelings ever.

> ## "Knowing He is always there with me . . . is one of the most freeing and strengthening feelings ever."

My favorite Bible verse is Proverbs 3:5: *"Trust in the LORD with all your heart, and lean not on your own understanding."* This verse stands out to me because it reminds me that God has a specific plan for me and sometimes it is different than what I envisioned or planned for myself. Whenever things aren't going the way I would like them to go, somehow this verse always pops into my head and reminds me to keep believing and not to doubt myself, because the future will be bright.

Mark

John the Baptist Prepares the Way

1 This is the Good News about Jesus the Messiah, the Son of God.* It began ²just as the prophet Isaiah had written:

> "Look, I am sending my messenger ahead
>   of you,
>   and he will prepare your way.*
> ³ He is a voice shouting in the wilderness,
>   'Prepare the way for the LORD's coming!
>   Clear the road for him!'*"

⁴This messenger was John the Baptist. He was in the wilderness and preached that people should be baptized to show that they had repented of their sins and turned to God to be forgiven. ⁵All of Judea, including all the people of Jerusalem, went out to see and hear John. And when they confessed their sins, he baptized them in the Jordan River. ⁶His clothes were woven from coarse camel hair, and he wore a leather belt around his waist. For food he ate locusts and wild honey.

⁷John announced: "Someone is coming soon who is greater than I am—so much greater that I'm not even worthy to stoop down like a slave and untie the straps of his sandals. ⁸I baptize you with* water, but he will baptize you with the Holy Spirit!"

The Baptism and Temptation of Jesus

⁹One day Jesus came from Nazareth in Galilee, and John baptized him in the Jordan River. ¹⁰As Jesus came up out of the water, he saw the heavens splitting apart and the Holy Spirit descending on him* like a dove. ¹¹And a voice from heaven said, "You are my dearly loved Son, and you bring me great joy."

¹²The Spirit then compelled Jesus to go into the wilderness, ¹³where he was tempted by Satan for forty days. He was out among the wild animals, and angels took care of him.

¹⁴Later on, after John was arrested, Jesus went into Galilee, where he preached God's Good News.* ¹⁵"The time promised by God has come at last!" he announced. "The Kingdom of God is near! Repent of your sins and believe the Good News!"

The First Disciples

¹⁶One day as Jesus was walking along the shore of the Sea of Galilee, he saw Simon* and his brother Andrew throwing a net into the water, for they fished for a living. ¹⁷Jesus called out to them, "Come, follow me, and I will show you how to fish for people!" ¹⁸And they left their nets at once and followed him.

¹⁹A little farther up the shore Jesus saw Zebedee's sons, James and John, in a boat repairing their nets. ²⁰He called them at once, and they also followed him, leaving their father, Zebedee, in the boat with the hired men.

Jesus Casts Out an Evil Spirit

²¹Jesus and his companions went to the town of Capernaum. When the Sabbath day came, he went into the synagogue and began to teach. ²²The people were amazed at his teaching, for he taught with real authority—quite unlike the teachers of religious law.

²³Suddenly, a man in the synagogue who was possessed by an evil* spirit began shouting, ²⁴"Why are you interfering with us, Jesus of Nazareth? Have you come to destroy us? I know who you are—the Holy One of God!"

²⁵Jesus cut him short. "Be quiet! Come out of the man," he ordered. ²⁶At that, the evil spirit screamed, threw the man into a convulsion, and then came out of him.

²⁷Amazement gripped the audience, and they began to discuss what had happened. "What sort of new teaching is this?" they asked excitedly. "It has such authority! Even evil spirits obey his orders!" ²⁸The news about Jesus spread quickly throughout the entire region of Galilee.

Jesus Heals Many People

²⁹After Jesus left the synagogue with James and John, they went to Simon and Andrew's home. ³⁰Now Simon's mother-in-law was sick in bed with a high fever. They told Jesus about her right away. ³¹So he went to her bedside, took her by the hand, and helped her sit up. Then the fever left her, and she prepared a meal for them.

³²That evening after sunset, many sick and demon-possessed people were brought to Jesus.

1:1 Some manuscripts do not include *the Son of God.*   **1:2** Mal 3:1.   **1:3** Isa 40:3 (Greek version).   **1:8** Or *in;* also in 1:8b.   **1:10** Or *toward him,* or *into him.*   **1:14** Some manuscripts read *the Good News of the Kingdom of God.*   **1:16** *Simon* is called "Peter" in 3:16 and thereafter.   **1:23** Greek *unclean;* also in 1:26, 27.

[33]The whole town gathered at the door to watch. [34]So Jesus healed many people who were sick with various diseases, and he cast out many demons. But because the demons knew who he was, he did not allow them to speak.

Jesus Preaches in Galilee

[35]Before daybreak the next morning, Jesus got up and went out to an isolated place to pray. [36]Later Simon and the others went out to find him. [37]When they found him, they said, "Everyone is looking for you."

[38]But Jesus replied, "We must go on to other towns as well, and I will preach to them, too. That is why I came." [39]So he traveled throughout the region of Galilee, preaching in the synagogues and casting out demons.

Jesus Heals a Man with Leprosy

[40]A man with leprosy came and knelt in front of Jesus, begging to be healed. "If you are willing, you can heal me and make me clean," he said.

[41]Moved with compassion,* Jesus reached out and touched him. "I am willing," he said. "Be healed!" [42]Instantly the leprosy disappeared, and the man was healed. [43]Then Jesus sent him on his way with a stern warning: [44]"Don't tell anyone about this. Instead, go to the priest and let him examine you. Take along the offering required in the law of Moses for those who have been healed of leprosy.* This will be a public testimony that you have been cleansed."

[45]But the man went and spread the word, proclaiming to everyone what had happened. As a result, large crowds soon surrounded Jesus, and he couldn't publicly enter a town anywhere. He had to stay out in the secluded places, but people from everywhere kept coming to him.

Jesus Heals a Paralyzed Man

2 When Jesus returned to Capernaum several days later, the news spread quickly that he was back home. [2]Soon the house where he was staying was so packed with visitors that there was no more room, even outside the door. While he was preaching God's word to them, [3]four men arrived carrying a paralyzed man on a mat. [4]They couldn't bring him to Jesus because of the crowd, so they dug a hole through the roof above his head. Then they lowered the man on his mat, right down in front of Jesus. [5]Seeing their faith, Jesus said to the paralyzed man, "My child, your sins are forgiven."

[6]But some of the teachers of religious law who were sitting there thought to themselves, [7]"What is he saying? This is blasphemy! Only God can forgive sins!"

[8]Jesus knew immediately what they were thinking, so he asked them, "Why do you question this in your hearts? [9]Is it easier to say to the paralyzed man 'Your sins are forgiven,' or 'Stand up, pick up your mat, and walk'? [10]So I will prove to you that the Son of Man* has the authority on earth to forgive sins." Then Jesus turned to the paralyzed man and said, [11]"Stand up, pick up your mat, and go home!"

[12]And the man jumped up, grabbed his mat, and walked out through the stunned onlookers. They were all amazed and praised God, exclaiming, "We've never seen anything like this before!"

Jesus Calls Levi (Matthew)

[13]Then Jesus went out to the lakeshore again and taught the crowds that were coming to him. [14]As he walked along, he saw Levi son of Alphaeus sitting at his tax collector's booth. "Follow me and be my disciple," Jesus said to him. So Levi got up and followed him.

[15]Later, Levi invited Jesus and his disciples to his home as dinner guests, along with many tax collectors and other disreputable sinners. (There were many people of this kind among Jesus' followers.) [16]But when the teachers of religious law who were Pharisees* saw him eating with tax collectors and other sinners, they asked his disciples, "Why does he eat with such scum?*"

[17]When Jesus heard this, he told them, "Healthy people don't need a doctor—sick people do. I have come to call not those who think they are righteous, but those who know they are sinners."

A Discussion about Fasting

[18]Once when John's disciples and the Pharisees were fasting, some people came to Jesus and asked, "Why don't your disciples fast like John's disciples and the Pharisees do?"

[19]Jesus replied, "Do wedding guests fast while celebrating with the groom? Of course not. They can't fast while the groom is with them. [20]But someday the groom will be taken away from them, and then they will fast.

[21]"Besides, who would patch old clothing with new cloth? For the new patch would shrink and rip away from the old cloth, leaving an even bigger tear than before.

[22]"And no one puts new wine into old wineskins. For the wine would burst the wineskins, and the wine and the skins would both be lost. New wine calls for new wineskins."

A Discussion about the Sabbath

[23]One Sabbath day as Jesus was walking through some grainfields, his disciples began breaking off heads of grain to eat. [24]But the Pharisees said to Jesus, "Look, why are they breaking the law by harvesting grain on the Sabbath?"

[25]Jesus said to them, "Haven't you ever read in the Scriptures what David did when he and his companions were hungry? [26]He went into the

1:41 Some manuscripts read *Moved with anger.*   **1:44** See Lev 14:2-32.   **2:10** "Son of Man" is a title Jesus used for himself.
2:16a Greek *the scribes of the Pharisees.*   **2:16b** Greek *with tax collectors and sinners?*

house of God (during the days when Abiathar was high priest) and broke the law by eating the sacred loaves of bread that only the priests are allowed to eat. He also gave some to his companions."

²⁷Then Jesus said to them, "The Sabbath was made to meet the needs of people, and not people to meet the requirements of the Sabbath. ²⁸So the Son of Man is Lord, even over the Sabbath!"

Jesus Heals on the Sabbath

3 Jesus went into the synagogue again and noticed a man with a deformed hand. ²Since it was the Sabbath, Jesus' enemies watched him closely. If he healed the man's hand, they planned to accuse him of working on the Sabbath.

³Jesus said to the man with the deformed hand, "Come and stand in front of everyone." ⁴Then he turned to his critics and asked, "Does the law permit good deeds on the Sabbath, or is it a day for doing evil? Is this a day to save life or to destroy it?" But they wouldn't answer him.

⁵He looked around at them angrily and was deeply saddened by their hard hearts. Then he said to the man, "Hold out your hand." So the man held out his hand, and it was restored! ⁶At once the Pharisees went away and met with the supporters of Herod to plot how to kill Jesus.

Crowds Follow Jesus

⁷Jesus went out to the lake with his disciples, and a large crowd followed him. They came from all over Galilee, Judea, ⁸Jerusalem, Idumea, from east of the Jordan River, and even from as far north as Tyre and Sidon. The news about his miracles had spread far and wide, and vast numbers of people came to see him.

⁹Jesus instructed his disciples to have a boat ready so the crowd would not crush him. ¹⁰He had healed many people that day, so all the sick people eagerly pushed forward to touch him. ¹¹And whenever those possessed by evil* spirits caught sight of him, the spirits would throw them to the ground in front of him shrieking, "You are the Son of God!" ¹²But Jesus sternly commanded the spirits not to reveal who he was.

Jesus Chooses the Twelve Apostles

¹³Afterward Jesus went up on a mountain and called out the ones he wanted to go with him. And they came to him. ¹⁴Then he appointed twelve of them and called them his apostles.* They were to accompany him, and he would send them out to preach, ¹⁵giving them authority to cast out demons. ¹⁶These are the twelve he chose:

Simon (whom he named Peter),

¹⁷ James and John (the sons of Zebedee, but Jesus nicknamed "Sons of Thunder"*),

¹⁸ Andrew,
Philip,
Bartholomew,
Matthew,
Thomas,
James (son of Alphaeus),
Thaddaeus,
Simon (the zealot*),

¹⁹ Judas Iscariot (who later betrayed him).

Jesus and the Prince of Demons

²⁰One time Jesus entered a house, and the crowds began to gather again. Soon he and his disciples couldn't even find time to eat. ²¹When his family heard what was happening, they tried to take him away. "He's out of his mind," they said.

²²But the teachers of religious law who had arrived from Jerusalem said, "He's possessed by Satan,* the prince of demons. That's where he gets the power to cast out demons."

²³Jesus called them over and responded with an illustration. "How can Satan cast out Satan?" he asked. ²⁴"A kingdom divided by civil war will collapse. ²⁵Similarly, a family splintered by feuding will fall apart. ²⁶And if Satan is divided and fights against himself, how can he stand? He would never survive. ²⁷Let me illustrate this further. Who is powerful enough to enter the house of a strong man like Satan and plunder his goods? Only someone even stronger—someone who could tie him up and then plunder his house.

²⁸"I tell you the truth, all sin and blasphemy can be forgiven, ²⁹but anyone who blasphemes the Holy Spirit will never be forgiven. This is a sin with eternal consequences." ³⁰He told them this because they were saying, "He's possessed by an evil spirit."

The True Family of Jesus

³¹Then Jesus' mother and brothers came to see him. They stood outside and sent word for him to come out and talk with them. ³²There was a crowd sitting around Jesus, and someone said, "Your mother and your brothers* are outside asking for you."

³³Jesus replied, "Who is my mother? Who are my brothers?" ³⁴Then he looked at those around him and said, "Look, these are my mother and brothers. ³⁵Anyone who does God's will is my brother and sister and mother."

Parable of the Farmer Scattering Seed

4 Once again Jesus began teaching by the lakeshore. A very large crowd soon gathered around him, so he got into a boat. Then he sat in the boat while all the people remained on the shore. ²He taught them by telling many stories in the form of parables, such as this one:

3:11 Greek *unclean;* also in 3:30.   **3:14** Some manuscripts do not include *and called them his apostles.*   **3:17** Greek *whom he named Boanerges, which means Sons of Thunder.*   **3:18** Greek *the Cananean,* an Aramaic term for Jewish nationalists.   **3:22** Greek *Beelzeboul;* other manuscripts read *Beezeboul;* Latin version reads *Beelzebub.*   **3:32** Some manuscripts add *and sisters.*

³"Listen! A farmer went out to plant some seed. ⁴As he scattered it across his field, some of the seed fell on a footpath, and the birds came and ate it. ⁵Other seed fell on shallow soil with underlying rock. The seed sprouted quickly because the soil was shallow. ⁶But the plant soon wilted under the hot sun, and since it didn't have deep roots, it died. ⁷Other seed fell among thorns that grew up and choked out the tender plants so they produced no grain. ⁸Still other seeds fell on fertile soil, and they sprouted, grew, and produced a crop that was thirty, sixty, and even a hundred times as much as had been planted!" ⁹Then he said, "Anyone with ears to hear should listen and understand."

¹⁰Later, when Jesus was alone with the twelve disciples and with the others who were gathered around, they asked him what the parables meant.

¹¹He replied, "You are permitted to understand the secret* of the Kingdom of God. But I use parables for everything I say to outsiders, ¹²so that the Scriptures might be fulfilled:

'When they see what I do,
   they will learn nothing.
When they hear what I say,
   they will not understand.
Otherwise, they will turn to me
   and be forgiven.'*"

¹³Then Jesus said to them, "If you can't understand the meaning of this parable, how will you understand all the other parables? ¹⁴The farmer plants seed by taking God's word to others. ¹⁵The seed that fell on the footpath represents those who hear the message, only to have Satan come at once and take it away. ¹⁶The seed on the rocky soil represents those who hear the message and immediately receive it with joy. ¹⁷But since they don't have deep roots, they don't last long. They fall away as soon as they have problems or are persecuted for believing God's word. ¹⁸The seed that fell among the thorns represents others who hear God's word, ¹⁹but all too quickly the message is crowded out by the worries of this life, the lure of wealth, and the desire for other things, so no fruit is produced. ²⁰And the seed that fell on good soil represents those who hear and accept God's word and produce a harvest of thirty, sixty, or even a hundred times as much as had been planted!"

Parable of the Lamp

²¹Then Jesus asked them, "Would anyone light a lamp and then put it under a basket or under a bed? Of course not! A lamp is placed on a stand, where its light will shine. ²²For everything that is hidden will eventually be brought into the open, and every secret will be brought to light. ²³Anyone with ears to hear should listen and understand."

²⁴Then he added, "Pay close attention to what you hear. The closer you listen, the more understanding you will be given*—and you will receive even more. ²⁵To those who listen to my teaching, more understanding will be given. But for those who are not listening, even what little understanding they have will be taken away from them."

Parable of the Growing Seed

²⁶Jesus also said, "The Kingdom of God is like a farmer who scatters seed on the ground. ²⁷Night and day, while he's asleep or awake, the seed sprouts and grows, but he does not understand how it happens. ²⁸The earth produces the crops on its own. First a leaf blade pushes through, then the heads of wheat are formed, and finally the grain ripens. ²⁹And as soon as the grain is ready, the farmer comes and harvests it with a sickle, for the harvest time has come."

Parable of the Mustard Seed

³⁰Jesus said, "How can I describe the Kingdom of God? What story should I use to illustrate it? ³¹It is like a mustard seed planted in the ground. It is the smallest of all seeds, ³²but it becomes the largest of all garden plants; it grows long branches, and birds can make nests in its shade."

³³Jesus used many similar stories and illustrations to teach the people as much as they could understand. ³⁴In fact, in his public ministry he never taught without using parables; but afterward, when he was alone with his disciples, he explained everything to them.

Jesus Calms the Storm

³⁵As evening came, Jesus said to his disciples, "Let's cross to the other side of the lake." ³⁶So they took Jesus in the boat and started out, leaving the crowds behind (although other boats followed). ³⁷But soon a fierce storm came up. High waves were breaking into the boat, and it began to fill with water.

³⁸Jesus was sleeping at the back of the boat with his head on a cushion. The disciples woke him up, shouting, "Teacher, don't you care that we're going to drown?"

³⁹When Jesus woke up, he rebuked the wind and said to the waves, "Silence! Be still!" Suddenly the wind stopped, and there was a great calm. ⁴⁰Then he asked them, "Why are you afraid? Do you still have no faith?"

⁴¹The disciples were absolutely terrified. "Who is this man?" they asked each other. "Even the wind and waves obey him!"

Jesus Heals a Demon-Possessed Man

5 So they arrived at the other side of the lake, in the region of the Gerasenes.* ²When Jesus climbed out of the boat, a man possessed

4:11 Greek *mystery*.   **4:12** Isa 6:9-10 (Greek version).   **4:24** Or *The measure you give will be the measure you get back*.   **5:1** Other manuscripts read *Gadarenes;* still others read *Gergesenes*. See Matt 8:28; Luke 8:26.

by an evil* spirit came out from a cemetery to meet him. ³This man lived among the burial caves and could no longer be restrained, even with a chain. ⁴Whenever he was put into chains and shackles—as he often was—he snapped the chains from his wrists and smashed the shackles. No one was strong enough to subdue him. ⁵Day and night he wandered among the burial caves and in the hills, howling and cutting himself with sharp stones.

⁶When Jesus was still some distance away, the man saw him, ran to meet him, and bowed low before him. ⁷With a shriek, he screamed, "Why are you interfering with me, Jesus, Son of the Most High God? In the name of God, I beg you, don't torture me!" ⁸For Jesus had already said to the spirit, "Come out of the man, you evil spirit."

⁹Then Jesus demanded, "What is your name?"

And he replied, "My name is Legion, because there are many of us inside this man." ¹⁰Then the evil spirits begged him again and again not to send them to some distant place.

¹¹There happened to be a large herd of pigs feeding on the hillside nearby. ¹²"Send us into those pigs," the spirits begged. "Let us enter them."

¹³So Jesus gave them permission. The evil spirits came out of the man and entered the pigs, and the entire herd of about 2,000 pigs plunged down the steep hillside into the lake and drowned in the water.

¹⁴The herdsmen fled to the nearby town and the surrounding countryside, spreading the news as they ran. People rushed out to see what had happened. ¹⁵A crowd soon gathered around Jesus, and they saw the man who had been possessed by the legion of demons. He was sitting there fully clothed and perfectly sane, and they were all afraid. ¹⁶Then those who had seen what happened told the others about the demon-possessed man and the pigs. ¹⁷And the crowd began pleading with Jesus to go away and leave them alone.

¹⁸As Jesus was getting into the boat, the man who had been demon possessed begged to go with him. ¹⁹But Jesus said, "No, go home to your family, and tell them everything the Lord has done for you and how merciful he has been." ²⁰So the man started off to visit the Ten Towns* of that region and began to proclaim the great things Jesus had done for him; and everyone was amazed at what he told them.

Jesus Heals in Response to Faith

²¹Jesus got into the boat again and went back to the other side of the lake, where a large crowd gathered around him on the shore. ²²Then a leader of the local synagogue, whose name was Jairus, arrived. When he saw Jesus, he fell at his feet, ²³pleading fervently with him. "My little daughter is dying," he said.

"Please come and lay your hands on her; heal her so she can live."

²⁴Jesus went with him, and all the people followed, crowding around him. ²⁵A woman in the crowd had suffered for twelve years with constant bleeding. ²⁶She had suffered a great deal from many doctors, and over the years she had spent everything she had to pay them, but she had gotten no better. In fact, she had gotten worse. ²⁷She had heard about Jesus, so she came up behind him through the crowd and touched his robe. ²⁸For she thought to herself, "If I can just touch his robe, I will be healed." ²⁹Immediately the bleeding stopped, and she could feel in her body that she had been healed of her terrible condition.

³⁰Jesus realized at once that healing power had gone out from him, so he turned around in the crowd and asked, "Who touched my robe?"

³¹His disciples said to him, "Look at this crowd pressing around you. How can you ask, 'Who touched me?'"

³²But he kept on looking around to see who had done it. ³³Then the frightened woman, trembling at the realization of what had happened to her, came and fell to her knees in front of him and told him what she had done. ³⁴And he said to her, "Daughter, your faith has made you well. Go in peace. Your suffering is over."

³⁵While he was still speaking to her, messengers arrived from the home of Jairus, the leader of the synagogue. They told him, "Your daughter is dead. There's no use troubling the Teacher now."

³⁶But Jesus overheard* them and said to Jairus, "Don't be afraid. Just have faith."

³⁷Then Jesus stopped the crowd and wouldn't let anyone go with him except Peter, James, and John (the brother of James). ³⁸When they came to the home of the synagogue leader, Jesus saw much commotion and weeping and wailing. ³⁹He went inside and asked, "Why all this commotion and weeping? The child isn't dead; she's only asleep."

⁴⁰The crowd laughed at him. But he made them all leave, and he took the girl's father and mother and his three disciples into the room where the girl was lying. ⁴¹Holding her hand, he said to her, *"Talitha koum,"* which means "Little girl, get up!" ⁴²And the girl, who was twelve years old, immediately stood up and walked around! They were overwhelmed and totally amazed. ⁴³Jesus gave them strict orders not to tell anyone what had happened, and then he told them to give her something to eat.

Jesus Rejected at Nazareth

6 Jesus left that part of the country and returned with his disciples to Nazareth, his hometown. ²The next Sabbath he began teaching in the synagogue, and many who heard him were amazed. They asked, "Where did he get all this wisdom and the power to perform such

---

5:2 Greek *unclean;* also in 5:8, 13.   **5:20** Greek *Decapolis.*   **5:36** Or *ignored.*

miracles?" ³Then they scoffed, "He's just a carpenter, the son of Mary* and the brother of James, Joseph,* Judas, and Simon. And his sisters live right here among us." They were deeply offended and refused to believe in him.

⁴Then Jesus told them, "A prophet is honored everywhere except in his own hometown and among his relatives and his own family." ⁵And because of their unbelief, he couldn't do any miracles among them except to place his hands on a few sick people and heal them. ⁶And he was amazed at their unbelief.

Jesus Sends Out the Twelve Disciples

Then Jesus went from village to village, teaching the people. ⁷And he called his twelve disciples together and began sending them out two by two, giving them authority to cast out evil* spirits. ⁸He told them to take nothing for their journey except a walking stick—no food, no traveler's bag, no money.* ⁹He allowed them to wear sandals but not to take a change of clothes.

¹⁰"Wherever you go," he said, "stay in the same house until you leave town. ¹¹But if any place refuses to welcome you or listen to you, shake its dust from your feet as you leave to show that you have abandoned those people to their fate."

¹²So the disciples went out, telling everyone they met to repent of their sins and turn to God. ¹³And they cast out many demons and healed many sick people, anointing them with olive oil.

The Death of John the Baptist

¹⁴Herod Antipas, the king, soon heard about Jesus, because everyone was talking about him. Some were saying,* "This must be John the Baptist raised from the dead. That is why he can do such miracles." ¹⁵Others said, "He's the prophet Elijah." Still others said, "He's a prophet like the other great prophets of the past."

¹⁶When Herod heard about Jesus, he said, "John, the man I beheaded, has come back from the dead."

¹⁷For Herod had sent soldiers to arrest and imprison John as a favor to Herodias. She had been his brother Philip's wife, but Herod had married her. ¹⁸John had been telling Herod, "It is against God's law for you to marry your brother's wife." ¹⁹So Herodias bore a grudge against John and wanted to kill him. But without Herod's approval she was powerless, ²⁰for Herod respected John; and knowing that he was a good and holy man, he protected him. Herod was greatly disturbed whenever he talked with John, but even so, he liked to listen to him.

²¹Herodias's chance finally came on Herod's birthday. He gave a party for his high government officials, army officers, and the leading citizens of Galilee. ²²Then his daughter, also named Herodias,* came in and performed a dance that greatly pleased Herod and his guests. "Ask me for anything you like," the king said to the girl, "and I will give it to you." ²³He even vowed, "I will give you whatever you ask, up to half my kingdom!"

²⁴She went out and asked her mother, "What should I ask for?"

Her mother told her, "Ask for the head of John the Baptist!"

²⁵So the girl hurried back to the king and told him, "I want the head of John the Baptist, right now, on a tray!"

²⁶Then the king deeply regretted what he had said; but because of the vows he had made in front of his guests, he couldn't refuse her. ²⁷So he immediately sent an executioner to the prison to cut off John's head and bring it to him. The soldier beheaded John in the prison, ²⁸brought his head on a tray, and gave it to the girl, who took it to her mother. ²⁹When John's disciples heard what had happened, they came to get his body and buried it in a tomb.

Jesus Feeds Five Thousand

³⁰The apostles returned to Jesus from their ministry tour and told him all they had done and taught. ³¹Then Jesus said, "Let's go off by ourselves to a quiet place and rest awhile." He said this because there were so many people coming and going that Jesus and his apostles didn't even have time to eat.

³²So they left by boat for a quiet place, where they could be alone. ³³But many people recognized them and saw them leaving, and people from many towns ran ahead along the shore and got there ahead of them. ³⁴Jesus saw the huge crowd as he stepped from the boat, and he had compassion on them because they were like sheep without a shepherd. So he began teaching them many things.

³⁵Late in the afternoon his disciples came to him and said, "This is a remote place, and it's already getting late. ³⁶Send the crowds away so they can go to the nearby farms and villages and buy something to eat."

³⁷But Jesus said, "You feed them."

"With what?" they asked. "We'd have to work for months to earn enough money* to buy food for all these people!"

³⁸"How much bread do you have?" he asked. "Go and find out."

They came back and reported, "We have five loaves of bread and two fish."

³⁹Then Jesus told the disciples to have the people sit down in groups on the green grass. ⁴⁰So they sat down in groups of fifty or a hundred.

6:3a Some manuscripts read *He's just the son of the carpenter and of Mary.* **6:3b** Most manuscripts read *Joses;* see Matt 13:55. **6:7** Greek *unclean.* **6:8** Greek *no copper coins in their money belts.* **6:14** Some manuscripts read *He was saying.* **6:22** Some manuscripts read *the daughter of Herodias herself.* **6:37** Greek *It would take 200 denarii.* A denarius was equivalent to a laborer's full day's wage.

⁴¹Jesus took the five loaves and two fish, looked up toward heaven, and blessed them. Then, breaking the loaves into pieces, he kept giving the bread to the disciples so they could distribute it to the people. He also divided the fish for everyone to share. ⁴²They all ate as much as they wanted, ⁴³and afterward, the disciples picked up twelve baskets of leftover bread and fish. ⁴⁴A total of 5,000 men and their families were fed from those loaves!

Jesus Walks on Water

⁴⁵Immediately after this, Jesus insisted that his disciples get back into the boat and head across the lake to Bethsaida, while he sent the people home. ⁴⁶After telling everyone good-bye, he went up into the hills by himself to pray.

⁴⁷Late that night, the disciples were in their boat in the middle of the lake, and Jesus was alone on land. ⁴⁸He saw that they were in serious trouble, rowing hard and struggling against the wind and waves. About three o'clock in the morning* Jesus came toward them, walking on the water. He intended to go past them, ⁴⁹but when they saw him walking on the water, they cried out in terror, thinking he was a ghost. ⁵⁰They were all terrified when they saw him.

But Jesus spoke to them at once. "Don't be afraid," he said. "Take courage! I am here!*" ⁵¹Then he climbed into the boat, and the wind stopped. They were totally amazed, ⁵²for they still didn't understand the significance of the miracle of the loaves. Their hearts were too hard to take it in.

⁵³After they had crossed the lake, they landed at Gennesaret. They brought the boat to shore ⁵⁴and climbed out. The people recognized Jesus at once, ⁵⁵and they ran throughout the whole area, carrying sick people on mats to wherever they heard he was. ⁵⁶Wherever he went—in villages, cities, or the countryside—they brought the sick out to the marketplaces. They begged him to let the sick touch at least the fringe of his robe, and all who touched him were healed.

Jesus Teaches about Inner Purity

7 One day some Pharisees and teachers of religious law arrived from Jerusalem to see Jesus. ²They noticed that some of his disciples failed to follow the Jewish ritual of hand washing before eating. ³(The Jews, especially the Pharisees, do not eat until they have poured water over their cupped hands,* as required by their ancient traditions. ⁴Similarly, they don't eat anything from the market until they immerse their hands* in water. This is but one of many traditions they have clung to—such as their ceremonial washing of cups, pitchers, and kettles.*)

⁵So the Pharisees and teachers of religious law asked him, "Why don't your disciples follow our age-old tradition? They eat without first performing the hand-washing ceremony."

⁶Jesus replied, "You hypocrites! Isaiah was right when he prophesied about you, for he wrote,

'These people honor me with their lips,
    but their hearts are far from me.
⁷ Their worship is a farce,
    for they teach man-made ideas as
        commands from God.'*

⁸For you ignore God's law and substitute your own tradition."

⁹Then he said, "You skillfully sidestep God's law in order to hold on to your own tradition. ¹⁰For instance, Moses gave you this law from God: 'Honor your father and mother,'* and 'Anyone who speaks disrespectfully of father or mother must be put to death.'* ¹¹But you say it is all right for people to say to their parents, 'Sorry, I can't help you. For I have vowed to give to God what I would have given to you.'* ¹²In this way, you let them disregard their needy parents. ¹³And so you cancel the word of God in order to hand down your own tradition. And this is only one example among many others."

¹⁴Then Jesus called to the crowd to come and hear. "All of you listen," he said, "and try to understand. ¹⁵It's not what goes into your body that defiles you; you are defiled by what comes from your heart.*"

¹⁷Then Jesus went into a house to get away from the crowd, and his disciples asked him what he meant by the parable he had just used. ¹⁸"Don't you understand either?" he asked. "Can't you see that the food you put into your body cannot defile you? ¹⁹Food doesn't go into your heart, but only passes through the stomach and then goes into the sewer." (By saying this, he declared that every kind of food is acceptable in God's eyes.)

²⁰And then he added, "It is what comes from inside that defiles you. ²¹For from within, out of a person's heart, come evil thoughts, sexual immorality, theft, murder, ²²adultery, greed, wickedness, deceit, lustful desires, envy, slander, pride, and foolishness. ²³All these vile things come from within; they are what defile you."

The Faith of a Gentile Woman

²⁴Then Jesus left Galilee and went north to the region of Tyre.* He didn't want anyone to know which house he was staying in, but he couldn't keep it a secret. ²⁵Right away a woman who had heard about him came and fell at his feet. Her

6:48 Greek *About the fourth watch of the night.*   **6:50** Or *The 'I Am' is here;* Greek reads *I am.* See Exod 3:14.   **7:3** Greek *have washed with the fist.*   **7:4a** Some manuscripts read *sprinkle themselves.*   **7:4b** Some manuscripts add *and dining couches.*   **7:7** Isa 29:13 (Greek version).   **7:10a** Exod 20:12; Deut 5:16.   **7:10b** Exod 21:17 (Greek version); Lev 20:9 (Greek version).   **7:11** Greek *'What I would have given to you is Corban' (that is, a gift).*   **7:15** Some manuscripts add verse 16, *Anyone with ears to hear should listen and understand.* Compare 4:9, 23.   **7:24** Some manuscripts add *and Sidon.*

little girl was possessed by an evil* spirit, ²⁶and she begged him to cast out the demon from her daughter.

Since she was a Gentile, born in Syrian Phoenicia, ²⁷Jesus told her, "First I should feed the children—my own family, the Jews.* It isn't right to take food from the children and throw it to the dogs."

²⁸She replied, "That's true, Lord, but even the dogs under the table are allowed to eat the scraps from the children's plates."

²⁹"Good answer!" he said. "Now go home, for the demon has left your daughter." ³⁰And when she arrived home, she found her little girl lying quietly in bed, and the demon was gone.

Jesus Heals a Deaf Man

³¹Jesus left Tyre and went up to Sidon before going back to the Sea of Galilee and the region of the Ten Towns.* ³²A deaf man with a speech impediment was brought to him, and the people begged Jesus to lay his hands on the man to heal him.

³³Jesus led him away from the crowd so they could be alone. He put his fingers into the man's ears. Then, spitting on his own fingers, he touched the man's tongue. ³⁴Looking up to heaven, he sighed and said, *"Ephphatha,"* which means, "Be opened!" ³⁵Instantly the man could hear perfectly, and his tongue was freed so he could speak plainly!

³⁶Jesus told the crowd not to tell anyone, but the more he told them not to, the more they spread the news. ³⁷They were completely amazed and said again and again, "Everything he does is wonderful. He even makes the deaf to hear and gives speech to those who cannot speak."

Jesus Feeds Four Thousand

8 About this time another large crowd had gathered, and the people ran out of food again. Jesus called his disciples and told them, ²"I feel sorry for these people. They have been here with me for three days, and they have nothing left to eat. ³If I send them home hungry, they will faint along the way. For some of them have come a long distance."

⁴His disciples replied, "How are we supposed to find enough food to feed them out here in the wilderness?"

⁵Jesus asked, "How much bread do you have?"

"Seven loaves," they replied.

⁶So Jesus told all the people to sit down on the ground. Then he took the seven loaves, thanked God for them, and broke them into pieces. He gave them to his disciples, who distributed the bread to the crowd. ⁷A few small fish were found, too, so Jesus also blessed these and told the disciples to distribute them.

⁸They ate as much as they wanted. Afterward, the disciples picked up seven large baskets of leftover food. ⁹There were about 4,000 people in the crowd that day, and Jesus sent them home after they had eaten. ¹⁰Immediately after this, he got into a boat with his disciples and crossed over to the region of Dalmanutha.

Pharisees Demand a Miraculous Sign

¹¹When the Pharisees heard that Jesus had arrived, they came and started to argue with him. Testing him, they demanded that he show them a miraculous sign from heaven to prove his authority.

¹²When he heard this, he sighed deeply in his spirit and said, "Why do these people keep demanding a miraculous sign? I tell you the truth, I will not give this generation any such sign." ¹³So he got back into the boat and left them, and he crossed to the other side of the lake.

Yeast of the Pharisees and Herod

¹⁴But the disciples had forgotten to bring any food. They had only one loaf of bread with them in the boat. ¹⁵As they were crossing the lake, Jesus warned them, "Watch out! Beware of the yeast of the Pharisees and of Herod."

¹⁶At this they began to argue with each other because they hadn't brought any bread. ¹⁷Jesus knew what they were saying, so he said, "Why are you arguing about having no bread? Don't you know or understand even yet? Are your hearts too hard to take it in? ¹⁸You have eyes—can't you see? You have ears—can't you hear?* Don't you remember anything at all? ¹⁹When I fed the 5,000 with five loaves of bread, how many baskets of leftovers did you pick up afterward?"

"Twelve," they said.

²⁰"And when I fed the 4,000 with seven loaves, how many large baskets of leftovers did you pick up?"

"Seven," they said.

²¹"Don't you understand yet?" he asked them.

Jesus Heals a Blind Man

²²When they arrived at Bethsaida, some people brought a blind man to Jesus, and they begged him to touch the man and heal him. ²³Jesus took the blind man by the hand and led him out of the village. Then, spitting on the man's eyes, he laid his hands on him and asked, "Can you see anything now?"

²⁴The man looked around. "Yes," he said, "I see people, but I can't see them very clearly. They look like trees walking around."

²⁵Then Jesus placed his hands on the man's eyes again, and his eyes were opened. His sight was completely restored, and he could see everything clearly. ²⁶Jesus sent him away, saying, "Don't go back into the village on your way home."

7:25 Greek *unclean.*   **7:27** Greek *Let the children eat first.*   **7:31** Greek *Decapolis.*   **8:18** Jer 5:21.

Peter's Declaration about Jesus

²⁷Jesus and his disciples left Galilee and went up to the villages near Caesarea Philippi. As they were walking along, he asked them, "Who do people say I am?"

²⁸"Well," they replied, "some say John the Baptist, some say Elijah, and others say you are one of the other prophets."

²⁹Then he asked them, "But who do you say I am?"

Peter replied, "You are the Messiah.*"

³⁰But Jesus warned them not to tell anyone about him.

Jesus Predicts His Death

³¹Then Jesus began to tell them that the Son of Man* must suffer many terrible things and be rejected by the elders, the leading priests, and the teachers of religious law. He would be killed, but three days later he would rise from the dead. ³²As he talked about this openly with his disciples, Peter took him aside and began to reprimand him for saying such things.*

³³Jesus turned around and looked at his disciples, then reprimanded Peter. "Get away from me, Satan!" he said. "You are seeing things merely from a human point of view, not from God's."

³⁴Then, calling the crowd to join his disciples, he said, "If any of you wants to be my follower, you must turn from your selfish ways, take up your cross, and follow me. ³⁵If you try to hang on to your life, you will lose it. But if you give up your life for my sake and for the sake of the Good News, you will save it. ³⁶And what do you benefit if you gain the whole world but lose your own soul?* ³⁷Is anything worth more than your soul? ³⁸If anyone is ashamed of me and my message in these adulterous and sinful days, the Son of Man will be ashamed of that person when he returns in the glory of his Father with the holy angels."

9 Jesus went on to say, "I tell you the truth, some standing here right now will not die before they see the Kingdom of God arrive in great power!"

The Transfiguration

²Six days later Jesus took Peter, James, and John, and led them up a high mountain to be alone. As the men watched, Jesus' appearance was transformed, ³and his clothes became dazzling white, far whiter than any earthly bleach could ever make them. ⁴Then Elijah and Moses appeared and began talking with Jesus.

⁵Peter exclaimed, "Rabbi, it's wonderful for us to be here! Let's make three shelters as memorials*—one for you, one for Moses, and one

for Elijah." ⁶He said this because he didn't really know what else to say, for they were all terrified.

⁷Then a cloud overshadowed them, and a voice from the cloud said, "This is my dearly loved Son. Listen to him." ⁸Suddenly, when they looked around, Moses and Elijah were gone, and they saw only Jesus with them.

⁹As they went back down the mountain, he told them not to tell anyone what they had seen until the Son of Man* had risen from the dead. ¹⁰So they kept it to themselves, but they often asked each other what he meant by "rising from the dead."

¹¹Then they asked him, "Why do the teachers of religious law insist that Elijah must return before the Messiah comes?*"

¹²Jesus responded, "Elijah is indeed coming first to get everything ready. Yet why do the Scriptures say that the Son of Man must suffer greatly and be treated with utter contempt? ¹³But I tell you, Elijah has already come, and they chose to abuse him, just as the Scriptures predicted."

Jesus Heals a Demon-Possessed Boy

¹⁴When they returned to the other disciples, they saw a large crowd surrounding them, and some teachers of religious law were arguing with them. ¹⁵When the crowd saw Jesus, they were overwhelmed with awe, and they ran to greet him.

¹⁶"What is all this arguing about?" Jesus asked.

¹⁷One of the men in the crowd spoke up and said, "Teacher, I brought my son so you could heal him. He is possessed by an evil spirit that won't let him talk. ¹⁸And whenever this spirit seizes him, it throws him violently to the ground. Then he foams at the mouth and grinds his teeth and becomes rigid.* So I asked your disciples to cast out the evil spirit, but they couldn't do it."

¹⁹Jesus said to them,* "You faithless people! How long must I be with you? How long must I put up with you? Bring the boy to me."

²⁰So they brought the boy. But when the evil spirit saw Jesus, it threw the child into a violent convulsion, and he fell to the ground, writhing and foaming at the mouth.

²¹"How long has this been happening?" Jesus asked the boy's father.

He replied, "Since he was a little boy. ²²The spirit often throws him into the fire or into water, trying to kill him. Have mercy on us and help us, if you can."

²³"What do you mean, 'If I can'?" Jesus asked. "Anything is possible if a person believes."

²⁴The father instantly cried out, "I do believe, but help me overcome my unbelief!"

8:29 Or *the Christ. Messiah* (a Hebrew term) and *Christ* (a Greek term) both mean "the anointed one." **8:31** "Son of Man" is a title Jesus used for himself. **8:32** Or *began to correct him.* **8:36** Or *your self?* also in 8:37. **9:5** Greek *three tabernacles.* **9:9** "Son of Man" is a title Jesus used for himself. **9:11** Greek *that Elijah must come first?* **9:18** Or *becomes weak.* **9:19** Or *said to his disciples.*

²⁵When Jesus saw that the crowd of onlookers was growing, he rebuked the evil* spirit. "Listen, you spirit that makes this boy unable to hear and speak," he said. "I command you to come out of this child and never enter him again!"

²⁶Then the spirit screamed and threw the boy into another violent convulsion and left him. The boy appeared to be dead. A murmur ran through the crowd as people said, "He's dead." ²⁷But Jesus took him by the hand and helped him to his feet, and he stood up.

²⁸Afterward, when Jesus was alone in the house with his disciples, they asked him, "Why couldn't we cast out that evil spirit?"

²⁹Jesus replied, "This kind can be cast out only by prayer.*"

Jesus Again Predicts His Death

³⁰Leaving that region, they traveled through Galilee. Jesus didn't want anyone to know he was there, ³¹for he wanted to spend more time with his disciples and teach them. He said to them, "The Son of Man is going to be betrayed into the hands of his enemies. He will be killed, but three days later he will rise from the dead." ³²They didn't understand what he was saying, however, and they were afraid to ask him what he meant.

The Greatest in the Kingdom

³³After they arrived at Capernaum and settled in a house, Jesus asked his disciples, "What were you discussing out on the road?" ³⁴But they didn't answer, because they had been arguing about which of them was the greatest. ³⁵He sat down, called the twelve disciples over to him, and said, "Whoever wants to be first must take last place and be the servant of everyone else."

³⁶Then he put a little child among them. Taking the child in his arms, he said to them, ³⁷"Anyone who welcomes a little child like this on my behalf* welcomes me, and anyone who welcomes me welcomes not only me but also my Father who sent me."

Using the Name of Jesus

³⁸John said to Jesus, "Teacher, we saw someone using your name to cast out demons, but we told him to stop because he wasn't in our group."

³⁹"Don't stop him!" Jesus said. "No one who performs a miracle in my name will soon be able to speak evil of me. ⁴⁰Anyone who is not against us is for us. ⁴¹If anyone gives you even a cup of water because you belong to the Messiah, I tell you the truth, that person will surely be rewarded.

⁴²"But if you cause one of these little ones who trusts in me to fall into sin, it would be better for you to be thrown into the sea with a large millstone hung around your neck. ⁴³If your hand causes you to sin, cut it off. It's better to enter eternal life with only one hand than to go into the unquenchable fires of hell* with two hands.* ⁴⁵If your foot causes you to sin, cut it off. It's better to enter eternal life with only one foot than to be thrown into hell with two feet.* ⁴⁷And if your eye causes you to sin, gouge it out. It's better to enter the Kingdom of God with only one eye than to have two eyes and be thrown into hell, ⁴⁸"where the maggots never die and the fire never goes out.'*

⁴⁹"For everyone will be tested with fire.* ⁵⁰Salt is good for seasoning. But if it loses its flavor, how do you make it salty again? You must have the qualities of salt among yourselves and live in peace with each other."

Discussion about Divorce and Marriage

10 Then Jesus left Capernaum and went down to the region of Judea and into the area east of the Jordan River. Once again crowds gathered around him, and as usual he was teaching them.

²Some Pharisees came and tried to trap him with this question: "Should a man be allowed to divorce his wife?"

³Jesus answered them with a question: "What did Moses say in the law about divorce?"

⁴"Well, he permitted it," they replied. "He said a man can give his wife a written notice of divorce and send her away."*

⁵But Jesus responded, "He wrote this commandment only as a concession to your hard hearts. ⁶But 'God made them male and female'* from the beginning of creation. ⁷'This explains why a man leaves his father and mother and is joined to his wife,* ⁸and the two are united into one.'* Since they are no longer two but one, ⁹let no one split apart what God has joined together."

¹⁰Later, when he was alone with his disciples in the house, they brought up the subject again. ¹¹He told them, "Whoever divorces his wife and marries someone else commits adultery against her. ¹²And if a woman divorces her husband and marries someone else, she commits adultery."

Jesus Blesses the Children

¹³One day some parents brought their children to Jesus so he could touch and bless them. But the disciples scolded the parents for bothering him.

¹⁴When Jesus saw what was happening, he was angry with his disciples. He said to them, "Let the children come to me. Don't stop them! For the Kingdom of God belongs to those who are like these children. ¹⁵I tell you the truth, anyone who doesn't receive the Kingdom of God

9:25 Greek *unclean.* 9:29 Some manuscripts read *by prayer and fasting.* 9:37 Greek *in my name.* 9:43a Greek *Gehenna;* also in 9:45, 47. 9:43b Some manuscripts add verse 44, '*where the maggots never die and the fire never goes out.*' See 9:48. 9:45 Some manuscripts add verse 46, '*where the maggots never die and the fire never goes out.*' See 9:48. 9:48 Isa 66:24. 9:49 Greek *salted with fire;* other manuscripts add *and every sacrifice will be salted with salt.* 10:4 See Deut 24:1. 10:6 Gen 1:27; 5:2. 10:7 Some manuscripts do not include *and is joined to his wife.* 10:7-8 Gen 2:24.

like a child will never enter it." ¹⁶Then he took the children in his arms and placed his hands on their heads and blessed them.

The Rich Man

¹⁷As Jesus was starting out on his way to Jerusalem, a man came running up to him, knelt down, and asked, "Good Teacher, what must I do to inherit eternal life?"

¹⁸"Why do you call me good?" Jesus asked. "Only God is truly good. ¹⁹But to answer your question, you know the commandments: 'You must not murder. You must not commit adultery. You must not steal. You must not testify falsely. You must not cheat anyone. Honor your father and mother.'*"

²⁰"Teacher," the man replied, "I've obeyed all these commandments since I was young."

²¹Looking at the man, Jesus felt genuine love for him. "There is still one thing you haven't done," he told him. "Go and sell all your possessions and give the money to the poor, and you will have treasure in heaven. Then come, follow me."

²²At this the man's face fell, and he went away sad, for he had many possessions.

²³Jesus looked around and said to his disciples, "How hard it is for the rich to enter the Kingdom of God!" ²⁴This amazed them. But Jesus said again, "Dear children, it is very hard* to enter the Kingdom of God. ²⁵In fact, it is easier for a camel to go through the eye of a needle than for a rich person to enter the Kingdom of God!"

²⁶The disciples were astounded. "Then who in the world can be saved?" they asked.

²⁷Jesus looked at them intently and said, "Humanly speaking, it is impossible. But not with God. Everything is possible with God."

²⁸Then Peter began to speak up. "We've given up everything to follow you," he said.

²⁹"Yes," Jesus replied, "and I assure you that everyone who has given up house or brothers or sisters or mother or father or children or property, for my sake and for the Good News, ³⁰will receive now in return a hundred times as many houses, brothers, sisters, mothers, children, and property—along with persecution. And in the world to come that person will have eternal life. ³¹But many who are the greatest now will be least important then, and those who seem least important now will be the greatest then.*"

Jesus Again Predicts His Death

³²They were now on the way up to Jerusalem, and Jesus was walking ahead of them. The disciples were filled with awe, and the people following behind were overwhelmed with fear. Taking the twelve disciples aside, Jesus once more be-

gan to describe everything that was about to happen to him. ³³"Listen," he said, "we're going up to Jerusalem, where the Son of Man* will be betrayed to the leading priests and the teachers of religious law. They will sentence him to die and hand him over to the Romans.* ³⁴They will mock him, spit on him, flog him with a whip, and kill him, but after three days he will rise again."

Jesus Teaches about Serving Others

³⁵Then James and John, the sons of Zebedee, came over and spoke to him. "Teacher," they said, "we want you to do us a favor."

³⁶"What is your request?" he asked.

³⁷They replied, "When you sit on your glorious throne, we want to sit in places of honor next to you, one on your right and the other on your left."

³⁸But Jesus said to them, "You don't know what you are asking! Are you able to drink from the bitter cup of suffering I am about to drink? Are you able to be baptized with the baptism of suffering I must be baptized with?"

³⁹"Oh yes," they replied, "we are able!"

Then Jesus told them, "You will indeed drink from my bitter cup and be baptized with my baptism of suffering. ⁴⁰But I have no right to say who will sit on my right or my left. God has prepared those places for the ones he has chosen."

⁴¹When the ten other disciples heard what James and John had asked, they were indignant. ⁴²So Jesus called them together and said, "You know that the rulers in this world lord it over their people, and officials flaunt their authority over those under them. ⁴³But among you it will be different. Whoever wants to be a leader among you must be your servant, ⁴⁴and whoever wants to be first among you must be the slave of everyone else. ⁴⁵For even the Son of Man came not to be served but to serve others and to give his life as a ransom for many."

Jesus Heals Blind Bartimaeus

⁴⁶Then they reached Jericho, and as Jesus and his disciples left town, a large crowd followed him. A blind beggar named Bartimaeus (son of Timaeus) was sitting beside the road. ⁴⁷When Bartimaeus heard that Jesus of Nazareth was nearby, he began to shout, "Jesus, Son of David, have mercy on me!"

⁴⁸"Be quiet!" many of the people yelled at him.

But he only shouted louder, "Son of David, have mercy on me!"

⁴⁹When Jesus heard him, he stopped and said, "Tell him to come here."

So they called the blind man. "Cheer up," they said. "Come on, he's calling you!" ⁵⁰Bartimaeus threw aside his coat, jumped up, and came to Jesus.

10:19 Exod 20:12-16; Deut 5:16-20.   **10:24** Some manuscripts read *very hard for those who trust in riches.*   **10:31** Greek *But many who are first will be last; and the last, first.*   **10:33a** "Son of Man" is a title Jesus used for himself.   **10:33b** Greek *the Gentiles.*

⁵¹"What do you want me to do for you?" Jesus asked.

"My rabbi,*" the blind man said, "I want to see!"

⁵²And Jesus said to him, "Go, for your faith has healed you." Instantly the man could see, and he followed Jesus down the road.*

Jesus' Triumphant Entry

11 As Jesus and his disciples approached Jerusalem, they came to the towns of Bethphage and Bethany on the Mount of Olives. Jesus sent two of them on ahead. ²"Go into that village over there," he told them. "As soon as you enter it, you will see a young donkey tied there that no one has ever ridden. Untie it and bring it here. ³If anyone asks, 'What are you doing?' just say, 'The Lord needs it and will return it soon.'"

⁴The two disciples left and found the colt standing in the street, tied outside the front door. ⁵As they were untying it, some bystanders demanded, "What are you doing, untying that colt?" ⁶They said what Jesus had told them to say, and they were permitted to take it. ⁷Then they brought the colt to Jesus and threw their garments over it, and he sat on it.

⁸Many in the crowd spread their garments on the road ahead of him, and others spread leafy branches they had cut in the fields. ⁹Jesus was in the center of the procession, and the people all around him were shouting,

"Praise God!*
Blessings on the one who comes in the
name of the LORD!
¹⁰ Blessings on the coming Kingdom of our
ancestor David!
Praise God in highest heaven!"*

¹¹So Jesus came to Jerusalem and went into the Temple. After looking around carefully at everything, he left because it was late in the afternoon. Then he returned to Bethany with the twelve disciples.

Jesus Curses the Fig Tree

¹²The next morning as they were leaving Bethany, Jesus was hungry. ¹³He noticed a fig tree in full leaf a little way off, so he went over to see if he could find any figs. But there were only leaves because it was too early in the season for fruit. ¹⁴Then Jesus said to the tree, "May no one ever eat your fruit again!" And the disciples heard him say it.

Jesus Clears the Temple

¹⁵When they arrived back in Jerusalem, Jesus entered the Temple and began to drive out the people buying and selling animals for sacrifices.

He knocked over the tables of the money changers and the chairs of those selling doves, ¹⁶and he stopped everyone from using the Temple as a marketplace.* ¹⁷He said to them, "The Scriptures declare, 'My Temple will be called a house of prayer for all nations,' but you have turned it into a den of thieves.'"*

¹⁸When the leading priests and teachers of religious law heard what Jesus had done, they began planning how to kill him. But they were afraid of him because the people were so amazed at his teaching.

¹⁹That evening Jesus and the disciples left* the city.

²⁰The next morning as they passed by the fig tree he had cursed, the disciples noticed it had withered from the roots up. ²¹Peter remembered what Jesus had said to the tree on the previous day and exclaimed, "Look, Rabbi! The fig tree you cursed has withered and died!"

²²Then Jesus said to the disciples, "Have faith in God. ²³I tell you the truth, you can say to this mountain, 'May you be lifted up and thrown into the sea,' and it will happen. But you must really believe it will happen and have no doubt in your heart. ²⁴I tell you, you can pray for anything, and if you believe that you've received it, it will be yours. ²⁵But when you are praying, first forgive anyone you are holding a grudge against, so that your Father in heaven will forgive your sins, too.*"

The Authority of Jesus Challenged

²⁷Again they entered Jerusalem. As Jesus was walking through the Temple area, the leading priests, the teachers of religious law, and the elders came up to him. ²⁸They demanded, "By what authority are you doing all these things? Who gave you the right to do them?"

²⁹"I'll tell you by what authority I do these things if you answer one question," Jesus replied. ³⁰"Did John's authority to baptize come from heaven, or was it merely human? Answer me!"

³¹They talked it over among themselves. "If we say it was from heaven, he will ask why we didn't believe John. ³²But do we dare say it was merely human?" For they were afraid of what the people would do, because everyone believed that John was a prophet. ³³So they finally replied, "We don't know."

And Jesus responded, "Then I won't tell you by what authority I do these things."

Parable of the Evil Farmers

12 Then Jesus began teaching them with stories: "A man planted a vineyard. He built a wall around it, dug a pit for pressing out the grape juice, and built a lookout tower. Then he leased the vineyard to tenant farmers and

---

10:51 Greek uses the Hebrew term *Rabboni.*   **10:52** Or *on the way.*   **11:9** Greek *Hosanna,* an exclamation of praise that literally means "save now"; also in 11:10.   **11:9-10** Pss 118:25-26; 148:1.   **11:16** Or *from carrying merchandise through the Temple.* **11:17** Isa 56:7; Jer 7:11.   **11:19** Greek *they left;* other manuscripts read *he left.*   **11:25** Some manuscripts add verse 26, *But if you refuse to forgive, your Father in heaven will not forgive your sins.* Compare Matt 6:15.

moved to another country. ²At the time of the grape harvest, he sent one of his servants to collect his share of the crop. ³But the farmers grabbed the servant, beat him up, and sent him back empty-handed. ⁴The owner then sent another servant, but they insulted him and beat him over the head. ⁵The next servant he sent was killed. Others he sent were either beaten or killed, ⁶until there was only one left—his son whom he loved dearly. The owner finally sent him, thinking, 'Surely they will respect my son.'

⁷"But the tenant farmers said to one another, 'Here comes the heir to this estate. Let's kill him and get the estate for ourselves!' ⁸So they grabbed him and murdered him and threw his body out of the vineyard.

⁹"What do you suppose the owner of the vineyard will do?" Jesus asked. "I'll tell you—he will come and kill those farmers and lease the vineyard to others. ¹⁰Didn't you ever read this in the Scriptures?

'The stone that the builders rejected
    has now become the cornerstone.
¹¹ This is the LORD's doing,
    and it is wonderful to see.'*"

¹²The religious leaders* wanted to arrest Jesus because they realized he was telling the story against them—they were the wicked farmers. But they were afraid of the crowd, so they left him and went away.

Taxes for Caesar

¹³Later the leaders sent some Pharisees and supporters of Herod to trap Jesus into saying something for which he could be arrested. ¹⁴"Teacher," they said, "we know how honest you are. You are impartial and don't play favorites. You teach the way of God truthfully. Now tell us—is it right to pay taxes to Caesar or not? ¹⁵Should we pay them, or shouldn't we?"

Jesus saw through their hypocrisy and said, "Why are you trying to trap me? Show me a Roman coin,* and I'll tell you." ¹⁶When they handed it to him, he asked, "Whose picture and title are stamped on it?"

"Caesar's," they replied.

¹⁷"Well, then," Jesus said, "give to Caesar what belongs to Caesar, and give to God what belongs to God."

His reply completely amazed them.

Discussion about Resurrection

¹⁸Then Jesus was approached by some Sadducees—religious leaders who say there is no resurrection from the dead. They posed this question: ¹⁹"Teacher, Moses gave us a law that if a man dies, leaving a wife without children, his brother should marry the widow and have a child who will carry on the brother's name.*

²⁰Well, suppose there were seven brothers. The oldest one married and then died without children. ²¹So the second brother married the widow, but he also died without children. Then the third brother married her. ²²This continued with all seven of them, and still there were no children. Last of all, the woman also died. ²³So tell us, whose wife will she be in the resurrection? For all seven were married to her."

²⁴Jesus replied, "Your mistake is that you don't know the Scriptures, and you don't know the power of God. ²⁵For when the dead rise, they will neither marry nor be given in marriage. In this respect they will be like the angels in heaven.

²⁶"But now, as to whether the dead will be raised—haven't you ever read about this in the writings of Moses, in the story of the burning bush? Long after Abraham, Isaac, and Jacob had died, God said to Moses,* 'I am the God of Abraham, the God of Isaac, and the God of Jacob.'* ²⁷So he is the God of the living, not the dead. You have made a serious error."

The Most Important Commandment

²⁸One of the teachers of religious law was standing there listening to the debate. He realized that Jesus had answered well, so he asked, "Of all the commandments, which is the most important?"

²⁹Jesus replied, "The most important commandment is this: 'Listen, O Israel! The LORD our God is the one and only LORD. ³⁰And you must love the LORD your God with all your heart, all your soul, all your mind, and all your strength.'* ³¹The second is equally important: 'Love your neighbor as yourself.'* No other commandment is greater than these."

³²The teacher of religious law replied, "Well said, Teacher. You have spoken the truth by saying that there is only one God and no other. ³³And I know it is important to love him with all my heart and all my understanding and all my strength, and to love my neighbor as myself. This is more important than to offer all of the burnt offerings and sacrifices required in the law."

³⁴Realizing how much the man understood, Jesus said to him, "You are not far from the Kingdom of God." And after that, no one dared to ask him any more questions.

Whose Son Is the Messiah?

³⁵Later, as Jesus was teaching the people in the Temple, he asked, "Why do the teachers of religious law claim that the Messiah is the son of David? ³⁶For David himself, speaking under the inspiration of the Holy Spirit, said,

'The LORD said to my Lord,
    Sit in the place of honor at my right hand
    until I humble your enemies beneath
        your feet.'*

12:10-11 Ps 118:22-23. **12:12** Greek *They.* **12:15** Greek *a denarius.* **12:19** See Deut 25:5-6. **12:26a** Greek *in the story of the bush? God said to him.* **12:26b** Exod 3:6. **12:29-30** Deut 6:4-5. **12:31** Lev 19:18. **12:36** Ps 110:1.

37Since David himself called the Messiah 'my Lord,' how can the Messiah be his son?" The large crowd listened to him with great delight.

38Jesus also taught: "Beware of these teachers of religious law! For they like to parade around in flowing robes and receive respectful greetings as they walk in the marketplaces. 39And how they love the seats of honor in the synagogues and the head table at banquets. 40Yet they shamelessly cheat widows out of their property and then pretend to be pious by making long prayers in public. Because of this, they will be more severely punished."

The Widow's Offering

41Jesus sat down near the collection box in the Temple and watched as the crowds dropped in their money. Many rich people put in large amounts. 42Then a poor widow came and dropped in two small coins.*

43Jesus called his disciples to him and said, "I tell you the truth, this poor widow has given more than all the others who are making contributions. 44For they gave a tiny part of their surplus, but she, poor as she is, has given everything she had to live on."

Jesus Foretells the Future

13 As Jesus was leaving the Temple that day, one of his disciples said, "Teacher, look at these magnificent buildings! Look at the impressive stones in the walls."

2Jesus replied, "Yes, look at these great buildings. But they will be completely demolished. Not one stone will be left on top of another!"

3Later, Jesus sat on the Mount of Olives across the valley from the Temple. Peter, James, John, and Andrew came to him privately and asked him, 4"Tell us, when will all this happen? What sign will show us that these things are about to be fulfilled?"

5Jesus replied, "Don't let anyone mislead you, 6for many will come in my name, claiming, 'I am the Messiah.'* They will deceive many. 7And you will hear of wars and threats of wars, but don't panic. Yes, these things must take place, but the end won't follow immediately. 8Nation will go to war against nation, and kingdom against kingdom. There will be earthquakes in many parts of the world, as well as famines. But this is only the first of the birth pains, with more to come.

9"When these things begin to happen, watch out! You will be handed over to the local councils and beaten in the synagogues. You will stand trial before governors and kings because you are my followers. But this will be your opportunity to tell them about me.* 10For the Good News must first be preached to all nations.* 11But when you are arrested and stand trial, don't worry in advance about what to say. Just say what God tells you at that time, for it is not you who will be speaking, but the Holy Spirit.

12"A brother will betray his brother to death, a father will betray his own child, and children will rebel against their parents and cause them to be killed. 13And everyone will hate you because you are my followers.* But the one who endures to the end will be saved.

14"The day is coming when you will see the sacrilegious object that causes desecration* standing where he* should not be." (Reader, pay attention!) "Then those in Judea must flee to the hills. 15A person out on the deck of a roof must not go down into the house to pack. 16A person out in the field must not return even to get a coat. 17How terrible it will be for pregnant women and for nursing mothers in those days. 18And pray that your flight will not be in winter. 19For there will be greater anguish in those days than at any time since God created the world. And it will never be so great again. 20In fact, unless the Lord shortens that time of calamity, not a single person will survive. But for the sake of his chosen ones he has shortened those days.

21"Then if anyone tells you, 'Look, here is the Messiah,' or 'There he is,' don't believe it. 22For false messiahs and false prophets will rise up and perform signs and wonders so as to deceive, if possible, even God's chosen ones. 23Watch out! I have warned you about this ahead of time!

24"At that time, after the anguish of those days,

the sun will be darkened,
the moon will give no light,
25 the stars will fall from the sky,
and the powers in the heavens will be shaken.*

26Then everyone will see the Son of Man* coming on the clouds with great power and glory.* 27And he will send out his angels to gather his chosen ones from all over the world*—from the farthest ends of the earth and heaven.

28"Now learn a lesson from the fig tree. When its branches bud and its leaves begin to sprout, you know that summer is near. 29In the same way, when you see all these things taking place, you can know that his return is very near, right at the door. 30I tell you the truth, this generation* will not pass from the scene before all these things take place. 31Heaven and earth will disappear, but my words will never disappear.

32"However, no one knows the day or hour when these things will happen, not even the angels in heaven or the Son himself. Only the Fa-

---

12:42 Greek *two lepta, which is a kodrantes* [i.e., a quadrans]. **13:6** Greek *claiming, 'I am.'* **13:9** Or *But this will be your testimony against them.* **13:10** Or *all peoples.* **13:13** Greek *on account of my name.* **13:14a** Greek *the abomination of desolation.* See Dan 9:27; 11:31; 12:11. **13:14b** Or *it.* **13:24-25** See Isa 13:10; 34:4; Joel 2:10. **13:26a** "Son of Man" is a title Jesus used for himself. **13:26b** See Dan 7:13. **13:27** Greek *from the four winds.* **13:30** Or *this age,* or *this nation.*

ther knows. ³³And since you don't know when that time will come, be on guard! Stay alert*!

³⁴"The coming of the Son of Man can be illustrated by the story of a man going on a long trip. When he left home, he gave each of his slaves instructions about the work they were to do, and he told the gatekeeper to watch for his return. ³⁵You, too, must keep watch! For you don't know when the master of the household will return—in the evening, at midnight, before dawn, or at daybreak. ³⁶Don't let him find you sleeping when he arrives without warning. ³⁷I say to you what I say to everyone: Watch for him!"

Jesus Anointed at Bethany

14 It was now two days before Passover and the Festival of Unleavened Bread. The leading priests and the teachers of religious law were still looking for an opportunity to capture Jesus secretly and kill him. ²"But not during the Passover celebration," they agreed, "or the people may riot."

³Meanwhile, Jesus was in Bethany at the home of Simon, a man who had previously had leprosy. While he was eating,* a woman came in with a beautiful alabaster jar of expensive perfume made from essence of nard. She broke open the jar and poured the perfume over his head.

⁴Some of those at the table were indignant. "Why waste such expensive perfume?" they asked. ⁵"It could have been sold for a year's wages* and the money given to the poor!" So they scolded her harshly.

⁶But Jesus replied, "Leave her alone. Why criticize her for doing such a good thing to me? ⁷You will always have the poor among you, and you can help them whenever you want to. But you will not always have me. ⁸She has done what she could and has anointed my body for burial ahead of time. ⁹I tell you the truth, wherever the Good News is preached throughout the world, this woman's deed will be remembered and discussed."

Judas Agrees to Betray Jesus

¹⁰Then Judas Iscariot, one of the twelve disciples, went to the leading priests to arrange to betray Jesus to them. ¹¹They were delighted when they heard why he had come, and they promised to give him money. So he began looking for an opportunity to betray Jesus.

The Last Supper

¹²On the first day of the Festival of Unleavened Bread, when the Passover lamb is sacrificed, Jesus' disciples asked him, "Where do you want us to go to prepare the Passover meal for you?"

¹³So Jesus sent two of them into Jerusalem with these instructions: "As you go into the city, a man carrying a pitcher of water will meet you. Follow him. ¹⁴At the house he enters, say to the owner, 'The Teacher asks: Where is the guest room where I can eat the Passover meal with my disciples?' ¹⁵He will take you upstairs to a large room that is already set up. That is where you should prepare our meal." ¹⁶So the two disciples went into the city and found everything just as Jesus had said, and they prepared the Passover meal there.

¹⁷In the evening Jesus arrived with the twelve disciples.* ¹⁸As they were at the table* eating, Jesus said, "I tell you the truth, one of you eating with me here will betray me."

¹⁹Greatly distressed, each one asked in turn, "Am I the one?"

²⁰He replied, "It is one of you twelve who is eating from this bowl with me. ²¹For the Son of Man* must die, as the Scriptures declared long ago. But how terrible it will be for the one who betrays him. It would be far better for that man if he had never been born!"

²²As they were eating, Jesus took some bread and blessed it. Then he broke it in pieces and gave it to the disciples, saying, "Take it, for this is my body."

²³And he took a cup of wine and gave thanks to God for it. He gave it to them, and they all drank from it. ²⁴And he said to them, "This is my blood, which confirms the covenant* between God and his people. It is poured out as a sacrifice for many. ²⁵I tell you the truth, I will not drink wine again until the day I drink it new in the Kingdom of God."

²⁶Then they sang a hymn and went out to the Mount of Olives.

Jesus Predicts Peter's Denial

²⁷On the way, Jesus told them, "All of you will desert me. For the Scriptures say,

'God will strike* the Shepherd,
    and the sheep will be scattered.'

²⁸But after I am raised from the dead, I will go ahead of you to Galilee and meet you there."

²⁹Peter said to him, "Even if everyone else deserts you, I never will."

³⁰Jesus replied, "I tell you the truth, Peter—this very night, before the rooster crows twice, you will deny three times that you even know me."

³¹"No!" Peter declared emphatically. "Even if I have to die with you, I will never deny you!" And all the others vowed the same.

Jesus Prays in Gethsemane

³²They went to the olive grove called Gethsemane, and Jesus said, "Sit here while I go and pray." ³³He took Peter, James, and John with him, and he became deeply troubled and distressed. ³⁴He told

13:33 Some manuscripts add *and pray.* **14:3** Or *reclining.* **14:5** Greek *for 300 denarii.* A denarius was equivalent to a laborer's full day's wage. **14:17** Greek *the Twelve.* **14:18** Or *As they reclined.* **14:21** "Son of Man" is a title Jesus used for himself. **14:24** Some manuscripts read *the new covenant.* **14:27** Greek *I will strike.* Zech 13:7.

them, "My soul is crushed with grief to the point of death. Stay here and keep watch with me."

³⁵He went on a little farther and fell to the ground. He prayed that, if it were possible, the awful hour awaiting him might pass him by. ³⁶"Abba, Father,"* he cried out, "everything is possible for you. Please take this cup of suffering away from me. Yet I want your will to be done, not mine."

³⁷Then he returned and found the disciples asleep. He said to Peter, "Simon, are you asleep? Couldn't you watch with me even one hour? ³⁸Keep watch and pray, so that you will not give in to temptation. For the spirit is willing, but the body is weak."

³⁹Then Jesus left them again and prayed the same prayer as before. ⁴⁰When he returned to them again, he found them sleeping, for they couldn't keep their eyes open. And they didn't know what to say.

⁴¹When he returned to them the third time, he said, "Go ahead and sleep. Have your rest. But no—the time has come. The Son of Man is betrayed into the hands of sinners. ⁴²Up, let's be going. Look, my betrayer is here!"

Jesus Is Betrayed and Arrested

⁴³And immediately, even as Jesus said this, Judas, one of the twelve disciples, arrived with a crowd of men armed with swords and clubs. They had been sent by the leading priests, the teachers of religious law, and the elders. ⁴⁴The traitor, Judas, had given them a prearranged signal: "You will know which one to arrest when I greet him with a kiss. Then you can take him away under guard." ⁴⁵As soon as they arrived, Judas walked up to Jesus. "Rabbi!" he exclaimed, and gave him the kiss.

⁴⁶Then the others grabbed Jesus and arrested him. ⁴⁷But one of the men with Jesus pulled out his sword and struck the high priest's slave, slashing off his ear.

⁴⁸Jesus asked them, "Am I some dangerous revolutionary, that you come with swords and clubs to arrest me? ⁴⁹Why didn't you arrest me in the Temple? I was there among you teaching every day. But these things are happening to fulfill what the Scriptures say about me."

⁵⁰Then all his disciples deserted him and ran away. ⁵¹One young man following behind was clothed only in a long linen shirt. When the mob tried to grab him, ⁵²he slipped out of his shirt and ran away naked.

Jesus before the Council

⁵³They took Jesus to the high priest's home where the leading priests, the elders, and the teachers of religious law had gathered. ⁵⁴Meanwhile, Peter followed him at a distance and went right into the high priest's courtyard. There he sat with the guards, warming himself by the fire.

⁵⁵Inside, the leading priests and the entire high council* were trying to find evidence against Jesus, so they could put him to death. But they couldn't find any. ⁵⁶Many false witnesses spoke against him, but they contradicted each other. ⁵⁷Finally, some men stood up and gave this false testimony: ⁵⁸"We heard him say, 'I will destroy this Temple made with human hands, and in three days I will build another, made without human hands.'" ⁵⁹But even then they didn't get their stories straight!

⁶⁰Then the high priest stood up before the others and asked Jesus, "Well, aren't you going to answer these charges? What do you have to say for yourself?" ⁶¹But Jesus was silent and made no reply. Then the high priest asked him, "Are you the Messiah, the Son of the Blessed One?"

⁶²Jesus said, "I Am.* And you will see the Son of Man seated in the place of power at God's right hand* and coming on the clouds of heaven.*"

⁶³Then the high priest tore his clothing to show his horror and said, "Why do we need other witnesses? ⁶⁴You have all heard his blasphemy. What is your verdict?"

"Guilty!" they all cried. "He deserves to die!"

⁶⁵Then some of them began to spit at him, and they blindfolded him and beat him with their fists. "Prophesy to us," they jeered. And the guards slapped him as they took him away.

Peter Denies Jesus

⁶⁶Meanwhile, Peter was in the courtyard below. One of the servant girls who worked for the high priest came by ⁶⁷and noticed Peter warming himself at the fire. She looked at him closely and said, "You were one of those with Jesus of Nazareth.*"

⁶⁸But Peter denied it. "I don't know what you're talking about," he said, and he went out into the entryway. Just then, a rooster crowed.*

⁶⁹When the servant girl saw him standing there, she began telling the others, "This man is definitely one of them!" ⁷⁰But Peter denied it again.

A little later some of the other bystanders confronted Peter and said, "You must be one of them, because you are a Galilean."

⁷¹Peter swore, "A curse on me if I'm lying—I don't know this man you're talking about!" ⁷²And immediately the rooster crowed the second time.

Suddenly, Jesus' words flashed through Peter's mind: "Before the rooster crows twice, you will deny three times that you even know me." And he broke down and wept.

14:36 *Abba* is an Aramaic term for "father." **14:55** Greek *the Sanhedrin.* **14:62a** Or *The 'I Am' is here;* or *I am the Lord.* See Exod 3:14. **14:62b** Greek *at the right hand of the power.* See Ps 110:1. **14:62c** See Dan 7:13. **14:67** Or *Jesus the Nazarene.* **14:68** Some manuscripts do not include *Just then, a rooster crowed.*

Jesus' Trial before Pilate

15 Very early in the morning the leading priests, the elders, and the teachers of religious law—the entire high council*—met to discuss their next step. They bound Jesus, led him away, and took him to Pilate, the Roman governor.

[2] Pilate asked Jesus, "Are you the king of the Jews?"

Jesus replied, "You have said it."

[3] Then the leading priests kept accusing him of many crimes, [4] and Pilate asked him, "Aren't you going to answer them? What about all these charges they are bringing against you?" [5] But Jesus said nothing, much to Pilate's surprise.

[6] Now it was the governor's custom each year during the Passover celebration to release one prisoner—anyone the people requested. [7] One of the prisoners at that time was Barabbas, a revolutionary who had committed murder in an uprising. [8] The crowd went to Pilate and asked him to release a prisoner as usual.

[9] "Would you like me to release to you this 'King of the Jews'?" Pilate asked. [10] (For he realized by now that the leading priests had arrested Jesus out of envy.) [11] But at this point the leading priests stirred up the crowd to demand the release of Barabbas instead of Jesus. [12] Pilate asked them, "Then what should I do with this man you call the king of the Jews?"

[13] They shouted back, "Crucify him!"

[14] "Why?" Pilate demanded. "What crime has he committed?"

But the mob roared even louder, "Crucify him!"

[15] So to pacify the crowd, Pilate released Barabbas to them. He ordered Jesus flogged with a lead-tipped whip, then turned him over to the Roman soldiers to be crucified.

The Soldiers Mock Jesus

[16] The soldiers took Jesus into the courtyard of the governor's headquarters (called the Praetorium) and called out the entire regiment. [17] They dressed him in a purple robe, and they wove thorn branches into a crown and put it on his head. [18] Then they saluted him and taunted, "Hail! King of the Jews!" [19] And they struck him on the head with a reed stick, spit on him, and dropped to their knees in mock worship. [20] When they were finally tired of mocking him, they took off the purple robe and put his own clothes on him again. Then they led him away to be crucified.

The Crucifixion

[21] A passerby named Simon, who was from Cyrene,* was coming in from the countryside just then, and the soldiers forced him to carry Jesus' cross. (Simon was the father of Alexander and Rufus.) [22] And they brought Jesus to a place called Golgotha (which means "Place of the Skull"). [23] They offered him wine drugged with myrrh, but he refused it.

[24] Then the soldiers nailed him to the cross. They divided his clothes and threw dice* to decide who would get each piece. [25] It was nine o'clock in the morning when they crucified him. [26] A sign announced the charge against him. It read, "The King of the Jews." [27] Two revolutionaries* were crucified with him, one on his right and one on his left.*

[29] The people passing by shouted abuse, shaking their heads in mockery. "Ha! Look at you now!" they yelled at him. "You said you were going to destroy the Temple and rebuild it in three days. [30] Well then, save yourself and come down from the cross!"

[31] The leading priests and teachers of religious law also mocked Jesus. "He saved others," they scoffed, "but he can't save himself! [32] Let this Messiah, this King of Israel, come down from the cross so we can see it and believe him!" Even the men who were crucified with Jesus ridiculed him.

The Death of Jesus

[33] At noon, darkness fell across the whole land until three o'clock. [34] Then at three o'clock Jesus called out with a loud voice, *"Eloi, Eloi, lema sabachthani?"* which means "My God, my God, why have you abandoned me?"*

[35] Some of the bystanders misunderstood and thought he was calling for the prophet Elijah. [36] One of them ran and filled a sponge with sour wine, holding it up to him on a reed stick so he could drink. "Wait!" he said. "Let's see whether Elijah comes to take him down!"

[37] Then Jesus uttered another loud cry and breathed his last. [38] And the curtain in the sanctuary of the Temple was torn in two, from top to bottom.

[39] When the Roman officer* who stood facing him* saw how he had died, he exclaimed, "This man truly was the Son of God!"

[40] Some women were there, watching from a distance, including Mary Magdalene, Mary (the mother of James the younger and of Joseph*), and Salome. [41] They had been followers of Jesus and had cared for him while he was in Galilee. Many other women who had come with him to Jerusalem were also there.

The Burial of Jesus

[42] This all happened on Friday, the day of preparation,* the day before the Sabbath. As evening

---

15:1 Greek *the Sanhedrin;* also in 15:43.   **15:21** *Cyrene* was a city in northern Africa.   **15:24** Greek *cast lots.* See Ps 22:18.
15:27a Or *Two criminals.*   **15:27b** Some manuscripts add verse 28, *And the Scripture was fulfilled that said, "He was counted among those who were rebels."* See Isa 53:12; also compare Luke 22:37.   **15:34** Ps 22:1.   **15:39a** Greek *the centurion;* similarly in 15:44, 45.   **15:39b** Some manuscripts add *heard his cry and.*   **15:40** Greek *Joses;* also in 15:47. See Matt 27:56.   **15:42** Greek *It was the day of preparation.*

approached, ⁴³Joseph of Arimathea took a risk and went to Pilate and asked for Jesus' body. (Joseph was an honored member of the high council, and he was waiting for the Kingdom of God to come.) ⁴⁴Pilate couldn't believe that Jesus was already dead, so he called for the Roman officer and asked if he had died yet. ⁴⁵The officer confirmed that Jesus was dead, so Pilate told Joseph he could have the body. ⁴⁶Joseph bought a long sheet of linen cloth. Then he took Jesus' body down from the cross, wrapped it in the cloth, and laid it in a tomb that had been carved out of the rock. Then he rolled a stone in front of the entrance. ⁴⁷Mary Magdalene and Mary the mother of Joseph saw where Jesus' body was laid.

The Resurrection

16 Saturday evening, when the Sabbath ended, Mary Magdalene, Mary the mother of James, and Salome went out and purchased burial spices so they could anoint Jesus' body. ²Very early on Sunday morning,* just at sunrise, they went to the tomb. ³On the way they were asking each other, "Who will roll away the stone for us from the entrance to the tomb?" ⁴But as they arrived, they looked up and saw that the stone, which was very large, had already been rolled aside.

⁵When they entered the tomb, they saw a young man clothed in a white robe sitting on the right side. The women were shocked, ⁶but the angel said, "Don't be alarmed. You are looking for Jesus of Nazareth,* who was crucified. He isn't here! He is risen from the dead! Look, this is where they laid his body. ⁷Now go and tell his disciples, including Peter, that Jesus is going ahead of you to Galilee. You will see him there, just as he told you before he died."

⁸The women fled from the tomb, trembling and bewildered, and they said nothing to anyone because they were too frightened.*

[*Shorter Ending of Mark*]

Then they briefly reported all this to Peter and his companions. Afterward Jesus himself sent them out from east to west with the sacred and unfailing message of salvation that gives eternal life. Amen.

[*Longer Ending of Mark*]

⁹After Jesus rose from the dead early on Sunday morning, the first person who saw him was Mary Magdalene, the woman from whom he had cast out seven demons. ¹⁰She went to the disciples, who were grieving and weeping, and told them what had happened. ¹¹But when she told them that Jesus was alive and she had seen him, they didn't believe her.

¹²Afterward he appeared in a different form to two of his followers who were walking from Jerusalem into the country. ¹³They rushed back to tell the others, but no one believed them.

¹⁴Still later he appeared to the eleven disciples as they were eating together. He rebuked them for their stubborn unbelief because they refused to believe those who had seen him after he had been raised from the dead.*

¹⁵And then he told them, "Go into all the world and preach the Good News to everyone. ¹⁶Anyone who believes and is baptized will be saved. But anyone who refuses to believe will be condemned. ¹⁷These miraculous signs will accompany those who believe: They will cast out demons in my name, and they will speak in new languages.* ¹⁸They will be able to handle snakes with safety, and if they drink anything poisonous, it won't hurt them. They will be able to place their hands on the sick, and they will be healed."

¹⁹When the Lord Jesus had finished talking with them, he was taken up into heaven and sat down in the place of honor at God's right hand. ²⁰And the disciples went everywhere and preached, and the Lord worked through them, confirming what they said by many miraculous signs.

16:2 Greek *on the first day of the week;* also in 16:9.   **16:6** Or *Jesus the Nazarene.*   **16:8** The most reliable early manuscripts of the Gospel of Mark end at verse 8. Other manuscripts include various endings to the Gospel. A few include both the "shorter ending" and the "longer ending." The majority of manuscripts include the "longer ending" immediately after verse 8.   **16:14** Some early manuscripts add: *And they excused themselves, saying, "This age of lawlessness and unbelief is under Satan, who does not permit God's truth and power to conquer the evil [unclean] spirits. Therefore, reveal your justice now." This is what they said to Christ. And Christ replied to them, "The period of years of Satan's power has been fulfilled, but other dreadful things will happen soon. And I was handed over to death for those who have sinned, so that they may return to the truth and sin no more, and so they may inherit the spiritual, incorruptible, and righteous glory in heaven."*   **16:17** Or *new tongues;* some manuscripts do not include *new.*

Luke

Introduction

1 Many people have set out to write accounts about the events that have been fulfilled among us. [2]They used the eyewitness reports circulating among us from the early disciples.* [3]Having carefully investigated everything from the beginning, I also have decided to write a careful account for you, most honorable Theophilus, [4]so you can be certain of the truth of everything you were taught.

The Birth of John the Baptist Foretold

[5]When Herod was king of Judea, there was a Jewish priest named Zechariah. He was a member of the priestly order of Abijah, and his wife, Elizabeth, was also from the priestly line of Aaron. [6]Zechariah and Elizabeth were righteous in God's eyes, careful to obey all of the Lord's commandments and regulations. [7]They had no children because Elizabeth was unable to conceive, and they were both very old.

[8]One day Zechariah was serving God in the Temple, for his order was on duty that week. [9]As was the custom of the priests, he was chosen by lot to enter the sanctuary of the Lord and burn incense. [10]While the incense was being burned, a great crowd stood outside, praying.

[11]While Zechariah was in the sanctuary, an angel of the Lord appeared to him, standing to the right of the incense altar. [12]Zechariah was shaken and overwhelmed with fear when he saw him. [13]But the angel said, "Don't be afraid, Zechariah! God has heard your prayer. Your wife, Elizabeth, will give you a son, and you are to name him John. [14]You will have great joy and gladness, and many will rejoice at his birth, [15]for he will be great in the eyes of the Lord. He must never touch wine or other alcoholic drinks. He will be filled with the Holy Spirit, even before his birth.* [16]And he will turn many Israelites to the Lord their God. [17]He will be a man with the spirit and power of Elijah. He will prepare the people for the coming of the Lord. He will turn the hearts of the fathers to their children,* and he will cause those who are rebellious to accept the wisdom of the godly."

[18]Zechariah said to the angel, "How can I be sure this will happen? I'm an old man now, and my wife is also well along in years."

[19]Then the angel said, "I am Gabriel! I stand in the very presence of God. It was he who sent me to bring you this good news! [20]But now, since you didn't believe what I said, you will be silent and unable to speak until the child is born. For my words will certainly be fulfilled at the proper time."

[21]Meanwhile, the people were waiting for Zechariah to come out of the sanctuary, wondering why he was taking so long. [22]When he finally did come out, he couldn't speak to them. Then they realized from his gestures and his silence that he must have seen a vision in the sanctuary.

[23]When Zechariah's week of service in the Temple was over, he returned home. [24]Soon afterward his wife, Elizabeth, became pregnant and went into seclusion for five months. [25]"How kind the Lord is!" she exclaimed. "He has taken away my disgrace of having no children."

The Birth of Jesus Foretold

[26]In the sixth month of Elizabeth's pregnancy, God sent the angel Gabriel to Nazareth, a village in Galilee, [27]to a virgin named Mary. She was engaged to be married to a man named Joseph, a descendant of King David. [28]Gabriel appeared to her and said, "Greetings, favored woman! The Lord is with you!*"

[29]Confused and disturbed, Mary tried to think what the angel could mean. [30]"Don't be afraid, Mary," the angel told her, "for you have found favor with God! [31]You will conceive and give birth to a son, and you will name him Jesus. [32]He will be very great and will be called the Son of the Most High. The Lord God will give him the throne of his ancestor David. [33]And he will reign over Israel* forever; his Kingdom will never end!"

[34]Mary asked the angel, "But how can this happen? I am a virgin."

[35]The angel replied, "The Holy Spirit will come upon you, and the power of the Most High will overshadow you. So the baby to be born will

---

1:2 Greek *from those who from the beginning were servants of the word.*   **1:15** Or *even from birth.*   **1:17** See Mal 4:5-6.
1:28 Some manuscripts add *Blessed are you among women.*   **1:33** Greek *over the house of Jacob.*

be holy, and he will be called the Son of God. ³⁶What's more, your relative Elizabeth has become pregnant in her old age! People used to say she was barren, but she has conceived a son and is now in her sixth month. ³⁷For nothing is impossible with God.*"

³⁸Mary responded, "I am the Lord's servant. May everything you have said about me come true." And then the angel left her.

Mary Visits Elizabeth

³⁹A few days later Mary hurried to the hill country of Judea, to the town ⁴⁰where Zechariah lived. She entered the house and greeted Elizabeth. ⁴¹At the sound of Mary's greeting, Elizabeth's child leaped within her, and Elizabeth was filled with the Holy Spirit.

⁴²Elizabeth gave a glad cry and exclaimed to Mary, "God has blessed you above all women, and your child is blessed. ⁴³Why am I so honored, that the mother of my Lord should visit me? ⁴⁴When I heard your greeting, the baby in my womb jumped for joy. ⁴⁵You are blessed because you believed that the Lord would do what he said."

The Magnificat: Mary's Song of Praise

⁴⁶Mary responded,

"Oh, how my soul praises the Lord.
⁴⁷   How my spirit rejoices in God my Savior!
⁴⁸ For he took notice of his lowly servant girl,
    and from now on all generations will call me blessed.
⁴⁹ For the Mighty One is holy,
    and he has done great things for me.
⁵⁰ He shows mercy from generation to generation
    to all who fear him.
⁵¹ His mighty arm has done tremendous things!
    He has scattered the proud and haughty ones.
⁵² He has brought down princes from their thrones
    and exalted the humble.
⁵³ He has filled the hungry with good things
    and sent the rich away with empty hands.
⁵⁴ He has helped his servant Israel
    and remembered to be merciful.
⁵⁵ For he made this promise to our ancestors,
    to Abraham and his children forever."

⁵⁶Mary stayed with Elizabeth about three months and then went back to her own home.

The Birth of John the Baptist

⁵⁷When it was time for Elizabeth's baby to be born, she gave birth to a son. ⁵⁸And when her neighbors and relatives heard that the Lord had been very merciful to her, everyone rejoiced with her.

⁵⁹When the baby was eight days old, they all came for the circumcision ceremony. They wanted to name him Zechariah, after his father. ⁶⁰But Elizabeth said, "No! His name is John!"

⁶¹"What?" they exclaimed. "There is no one in all your family by that name." ⁶²So they used gestures to ask the baby's father what he wanted to name him. ⁶³He motioned for a writing tablet, and to everyone's surprise he wrote, "His name is John." ⁶⁴Instantly Zechariah could speak again, and he began praising God.

⁶⁵Awe fell upon the whole neighborhood, and the news of what had happened spread throughout the Judean hills. ⁶⁶Everyone who heard about it reflected on these events and asked, "What will this child turn out to be?" For the hand of the Lord was surely upon him in a special way.

Zechariah's Prophecy

⁶⁷Then his father, Zechariah, was filled with the Holy Spirit and gave this prophecy:

⁶⁸ "Praise the Lord, the God of Israel,
    because he has visited and redeemed his people.
⁶⁹ He has sent us a mighty Savior*
    from the royal line of his servant David,
⁷⁰ just as he promised
    through his holy prophets long ago.
⁷¹ Now we will be saved from our enemies
    and from all who hate us.
⁷² He has been merciful to our ancestors
    by remembering his sacred covenant—
⁷³ the covenant he swore with an oath
    to our ancestor Abraham.
⁷⁴ We have been rescued from our enemies
    so we can serve God without fear,
⁷⁵ in holiness and righteousness
    for as long as we live.

⁷⁶ "And you, my little son,
    will be called the prophet of the Most High,
    because you will prepare the way for the Lord.
⁷⁷ You will tell his people how to find salvation
    through forgiveness of their sins.
⁷⁸ Because of God's tender mercy,
    the morning light from heaven is about to break upon us,*
⁷⁹ to give light to those who sit in darkness and in the shadow of death,
    and to guide us to the path of peace."

⁸⁰John grew up and became strong in spirit. And he lived in the wilderness until he began his public ministry to Israel.

1:37 Some manuscripts read *For the word of God will never fail.* **1:69** Greek *has raised up a horn of salvation for us.* **1:78** Or *the Morning Light from Heaven is about to visit us.*

The Birth of Jesus

2 At that time the Roman emperor, Augustus, decreed that a census should be taken throughout the Roman Empire. 2(This was the first census taken when Quirinius was governor of Syria.) 3All returned to their own ancestral towns to register for this census. 4And because Joseph was a descendant of King David, he had to go to Bethlehem in Judea, David's ancient home. He traveled there from the village of Nazareth in Galilee. 5He took with him Mary, his fiancée, who was now obviously pregnant.

6And while they were there, the time came for her baby to be born. 7She gave birth to her first child, a son. She wrapped him snugly in strips of cloth and laid him in a manger, because there was no lodging available for them.

The Shepherds and Angels

8That night there were shepherds staying in the fields nearby, guarding their flocks of sheep. 9Suddenly, an angel of the Lord appeared among them, and the radiance of the Lord's glory surrounded them. They were terrified, 10but the angel reassured them. "Don't be afraid!" he said. "I bring you good news that will bring great joy to all people. 11The Savior—yes, the Messiah, the Lord—has been born today in Bethlehem, the city of David! 12And you will recognize him by this sign: You will find a baby wrapped snugly in strips of cloth, lying in a manger."

13Suddenly, the angel was joined by a vast host of others—the armies of heaven—praising God and saying,

14 "Glory to God in highest heaven,
and peace on earth to those with whom
God is pleased."

15When the angels had returned to heaven, the shepherds said to each other, "Let's go to Bethlehem! Let's see this thing that has happened, which the Lord has told us about."

16They hurried to the village and found Mary and Joseph. And there was the baby, lying in the manger. 17After seeing him, the shepherds told everyone what had happened and what the angel had said to them about this child. 18All who heard the shepherds' story were astonished, 19but Mary kept all these things in her heart and thought about them often. 20The shepherds went back to their flocks, glorifying and praising God for all they had heard and seen. It was just as the angel had told them.

Jesus Is Presented in the Temple

21Eight days later, when the baby was circumcised, he was named Jesus, the name given him by the angel even before he was conceived.

22Then it was time for their purification offering, as required by the law of Moses after the birth of a child; so his parents took him to Jerusalem to present him to the Lord. 23The law of the Lord says, "If a woman's first child is a boy, he must be dedicated to the LORD."* 24So they offered the sacrifice required in the law of the Lord—"either a pair of turtledoves or two young pigeons."*

The Prophecy of Simeon

25At that time there was a man in Jerusalem named Simeon. He was righteous and devout and was eagerly waiting for the Messiah to come and rescue Israel. The Holy Spirit was upon him 26and had revealed to him that he would not die until he had seen the Lord's Messiah. 27That day the Spirit led him to the Temple. So when Mary and Joseph came to present the baby Jesus to the Lord as the law required, 28Simeon was there. He took the child in his arms and praised God, saying,

29 "Sovereign Lord, now let your servant die
in peace,
as you have promised.
30 I have seen your salvation,
31 which you have prepared for all people.
32 He is a light to reveal God to the nations,
and he is the glory of your people Israel!"

33Jesus' parents were amazed at what was being said about him. 34Then Simeon blessed them, and he said to Mary, the baby's mother, "This child is destined to cause many in Israel to fall, but he will be a joy to many others. He has been sent as a sign from God, but many will oppose him. 35As a result, the deepest thoughts of many hearts will be revealed. And a sword will pierce your very soul."

The Prophecy of Anna

36Anna, a prophet, was also there in the Temple. She was the daughter of Phanuel from the tribe of Asher, and she was very old. Her husband died when they had been married only seven years. 37Then she lived as a widow to the age of eighty-four.* She never left the Temple but stayed there day and night, worshiping God with fasting and prayer. 38She came along just as Simeon was talking with Mary and Joseph, and she began praising God. She talked about the child to everyone who had been waiting expectantly for God to rescue Jerusalem.

39When Jesus' parents had fulfilled all the requirements of the law of the Lord, they returned home to Nazareth in Galilee. 40There the child grew up healthy and strong. He was filled with wisdom, and God's favor was on him.

Jesus Speaks with the Teachers

41Every year Jesus' parents went to Jerusalem for the Passover festival. 42When Jesus was twelve

2:23 Exod 13:2. **2:24** Lev 12:8. **2:37** Or *She had been a widow for eighty-four years.*

years old, they attended the festival as usual.
⁴³After the celebration was over, they started home to Nazareth, but Jesus stayed behind in Jerusalem. His parents didn't miss him at first, ⁴⁴because they assumed he was among the other travelers. But when he didn't show up that evening, they started looking for him among their relatives and friends.

⁴⁵When they couldn't find him, they went back to Jerusalem to search for him there. ⁴⁶Three days later they finally discovered him in the Temple, sitting among the religious teachers, listening to them and asking questions. ⁴⁷All who heard him were amazed at his understanding and his answers.

⁴⁸His parents didn't know what to think. "Son," his mother said to him, "why have you done this to us? Your father and I have been frantic, searching for you everywhere."

⁴⁹"But why did you need to search?" he asked. "Didn't you know that I must be in my Father's house?"* ⁵⁰But they didn't understand what he meant.

⁵¹Then he returned to Nazareth with them and was obedient to them. And his mother stored all these things in her heart.

⁵²Jesus grew in wisdom and in stature and in favor with God and all the people.

John the Baptist Prepares the Way

3 It was now the fifteenth year of the reign of Tiberius, the Roman emperor. Pontius Pilate was governor over Judea; Herod Antipas was ruler* over Galilee; his brother Philip was ruler* over Iturea and Traconitis; Lysanias was ruler over Abilene. ²Annas and Caiaphas were the high priests. At this time a message from God came to John son of Zechariah, who was living in the wilderness. ³Then John went from place to place on both sides of the Jordan River, preaching that people should be baptized to show that they had repented of their sins and turned to God to be forgiven. ⁴Isaiah had spoken of John when he said,

"He is a voice shouting in the wilderness,
'Prepare the way for the LORD's coming!
Clear the road for him!
⁵ The valleys will be filled,
and the mountains and hills made level.
The curves will be straightened,
and the rough places made smooth.
⁶ And then all people will see
the salvation sent from God.'"*

⁷When the crowds came to John for baptism, he said, "You brood of snakes! Who warned you to flee God's coming wrath? ⁸Prove by the way you live that you have repented of your sins and turned to God. Don't just say to each other,

'We're safe, for we are descendants of Abraham.' That means nothing, for I tell you, God can create children of Abraham from these very stones. ⁹Even now the ax of God's judgment is poised, ready to sever the roots of the trees. Yes, every tree that does not produce good fruit will be chopped down and thrown into the fire."

¹⁰The crowds asked, "What should we do?"

¹¹John replied, "If you have two shirts, give one to the poor. If you have food, share it with those who are hungry."

¹²Even corrupt tax collectors came to be baptized and asked, "Teacher, what should we do?"

¹³He replied, "Collect no more taxes than the government requires."

¹⁴"What should we do?" asked some soldiers.

John replied, "Don't extort money or make false accusations. And be content with your pay."

¹⁵Everyone was expecting the Messiah to come soon, and they were eager to know whether John might be the Messiah. ¹⁶John answered their questions by saying, "I baptize you with* water; but someone is coming soon who is greater than I am—so much greater that I'm not even worthy to be his slave and untie the straps of his sandals. He will baptize you with the Holy Spirit and with fire.* ¹⁷He is ready to separate the chaff from the wheat with his winnowing fork. Then he will clean up the threshing area, gathering the wheat into his barn but burning the chaff with never-ending fire." ¹⁸John used many such warnings as he announced the Good News to the people.

¹⁹John also publicly criticized Herod Antipas, the ruler of Galilee,* for marrying Herodias, his brother's wife, and for many other wrongs he had done. ²⁰So Herod put John in prison, adding this sin to his many others.

The Baptism of Jesus

²¹One day when the crowds were being baptized, Jesus himself was baptized. As he was praying, the heavens opened, ²²and the Holy Spirit, in bodily form, descended on him like a dove. And a voice from heaven said, "You are my dearly loved Son, and you bring me great joy.*"

The Ancestors of Jesus

²³Jesus was about thirty years old when he began his public ministry.

Jesus was known as the son of Joseph.
Joseph was the son of Heli.
²⁴ Heli was the son of Matthat.
Matthat was the son of Levi.
Levi was the son of Melki.
Melki was the son of Jannai.
Jannai was the son of Joseph.

2:49 Or *"Didn't you realize that I should be involved with my Father's affairs?"*   **3:1a** Greek *Herod was tetrarch.* Herod Antipas was a son of King Herod.   **3:1b** Greek *tetrarch;* also in 3:1c.   **3:4-6** Isa 40:3-5 (Greek version).   **3:16a** Or *in.*   **3:16b** Or *in the Holy Spirit and in fire.*   **3:19** Greek *Herod the tetrarch.*   **3:22** Some manuscripts read *my Son, and today I have become your Father.*

25 Joseph was the son of Mattathias.
Mattathias was the son of Amos.
Amos was the son of Nahum.
Nahum was the son of Esli.
Esli was the son of Naggai.
26 Naggai was the son of Maath.
Maath was the son of Mattathias.
Mattathias was the son of Semein.
Semein was the son of Josech.
Josech was the son of Joda.
27 Joda was the son of Joanan.
Joanan was the son of Rhesa.
Rhesa was the son of Zerubbabel.
Zerubbabel was the son of Shealtiel.
Shealtiel was the son of Neri.
28 Neri was the son of Melki.
Melki was the son of Addi.
Addi was the son of Cosam.
Cosam was the son of Elmadam.
Elmadam was the son of Er.
29 Er was the son of Joshua.
Joshua was the son of Eliezer.
Eliezer was the son of Jorim.
Jorim was the son of Matthat.
Matthat was the son of Levi.
30 Levi was the son of Simeon.
Simeon was the son of Judah.
Judah was the son of Joseph.
Joseph was the son of Jonam.
Jonam was the son of Eliakim.
31 Eliakim was the son of Melea.
Melea was the son of Menna.
Menna was the son of Mattatha.
Mattatha was the son of Nathan.
Nathan was the son of David.
32 David was the son of Jesse.
Jesse was the son of Obed.
Obed was the son of Boaz.
Boaz was the son of Salmon.*
Salmon was the son of Nahshon.
33 Nahshon was the son of Amminadab.
Amminadab was the son of Admin.
Admin was the son of Arni.*
Arni was the son of Hezron.
Hezron was the son of Perez.
Perez was the son of Judah.
34 Judah was the son of Jacob.
Jacob was the son of Isaac.
Isaac was the son of Abraham.
Abraham was the son of Terah.
Terah was the son of Nahor.
35 Nahor was the son of Serug.
Serug was the son of Reu.
Reu was the son of Peleg.
Peleg was the son of Eber.
Eber was the son of Shelah.
36 Shelah was the son of Cainan.
Cainan was the son of Arphaxad.

Arphaxad was the son of Shem.
Shem was the son of Noah.
Noah was the son of Lamech.
37 Lamech was the son of Methuselah.
Methuselah was the son of Enoch.
Enoch was the son of Jared.
Jared was the son of Mahalalel.
Mahalalel was the son of Kenan.
38 Kenan was the son of Enosh.*
Enosh was the son of Seth.
Seth was the son of Adam.
Adam was the son of God.

The Temptation of Jesus

4 Then Jesus, full of the Holy Spirit, returned from the Jordan River. He was led by the Spirit in the wilderness,* ²where he was tempted by the devil for forty days. Jesus ate nothing all that time and became very hungry.

³Then the devil said to him, "If you are the Son of God, tell this stone to become a loaf of bread."

⁴But Jesus told him, "No! The Scriptures say, 'People do not live by bread alone.'*"

⁵Then the devil took him up and revealed to him all the kingdoms of the world in a moment of time. ⁶"I will give you the glory of these kingdoms and authority over them," the devil said, "because they are mine to give to anyone I please. ⁷I will give it all to you if you will worship me."

⁸Jesus replied, "The Scriptures say,

'You must worship the LORD your God
and serve only him.'*"

⁹Then the devil took him to Jerusalem, to the highest point of the Temple, and said, "If you are the Son of God, jump off! ¹⁰For the Scriptures say,

'He will order his angels to protect and guard you.
¹¹ And they will hold you up with their hands
so you won't even hurt your foot on a stone.'*"

¹²Jesus responded, "The Scriptures also say, 'You must not test the LORD your God.'*"

¹³When the devil had finished tempting Jesus, he left him until the next opportunity came.

Jesus Rejected at Nazareth

¹⁴Then Jesus returned to Galilee, filled with the Holy Spirit's power. Reports about him spread quickly through the whole region. ¹⁵He taught regularly in their synagogues and was praised by everyone.

¹⁶When he came to the village of Nazareth, his boyhood home, he went as usual to the synagogue on the Sabbath and stood up to read the

---

3:32 Greek *Sala,* a variant spelling of Salmon; also in 3:32b. See Ruth 4:20.   3:33 Some manuscripts read *Amminadab was the son of Aram. Arni* and *Aram* are alternate spellings of Ram. See 1 Chr 2:9-10.   3:38 Greek *Enos,* a variant spelling of Enosh; also in 3:38b. See Gen 5:6.   4:1 Some manuscripts read *into the wilderness.*   4:4 Deut 8:3.   4:8 Deut 6:13.   4:10-11 Ps 91:11-12. 4:12 Deut 6:16.

Scriptures. [17]The scroll of Isaiah the prophet was handed to him. He unrolled the scroll and found the place where this was written:

[18] "The Spirit of the LORD is upon me,
  for he has anointed me to bring Good
    News to the poor.
  He has sent me to proclaim that captives
    will be released,
    that the blind will see,
  that the oppressed will be set free,
[19]   and that the time of the LORD's favor
    has come.*"

[20]He rolled up the scroll, handed it back to the attendant, and sat down. All eyes in the synagogue looked at him intently. [21]Then he began to speak to them. "The Scripture you've just heard has been fulfilled this very day!"

[22]Everyone spoke well of him and was amazed by the gracious words that came from his lips. "How can this be?" they asked. "Isn't this Joseph's son?"

[23]Then he said, "You will undoubtedly quote me this proverb: 'Physician, heal yourself'—meaning, 'Do miracles here in your hometown like those you did in Capernaum.' [24]But I tell you the truth, no prophet is accepted in his own hometown.

[25]"Certainly there were many needy widows in Israel in Elijah's time, when the heavens were closed for three and a half years, and a severe famine devastated the land. [26]Yet Elijah was not sent to any of them. He was sent instead to a foreigner—a widow of Zarephath in the land of Sidon. [27]And there were many lepers in Israel in the time of the prophet Elisha, but the only one healed was Naaman, a Syrian."

[28]When they heard this, the people in the synagogue were furious. [29]Jumping up, they mobbed him and forced him to the edge of the hill on which the town was built. They intended to push him over the cliff, [30]but he passed right through the crowd and went on his way.

Jesus Casts Out a Demon

[31]Then Jesus went to Capernaum, a town in Galilee, and taught there in the synagogue every Sabbath day. [32]There, too, the people were amazed at his teaching, for he spoke with authority.

[33]Once when he was in the synagogue, a man possessed by a demon—an evil* spirit—began shouting at Jesus, [34]"Go away! Why are you interfering with us, Jesus of Nazareth? Have you come to destroy us? I know who you are—the Holy One of God!"

[35]Jesus cut him short. "Be quiet! Come out of the man," he ordered. At that, the demon threw the man to the floor as the crowd watched; then it came out of him without hurting him further.

[36]Amazed, the people exclaimed, "What authority and power this man's words possess! Even evil spirits obey him, and they flee at his command!" [37]The news about Jesus spread through every village in the entire region.

Jesus Heals Many People

[38]After leaving the synagogue that day, Jesus went to Simon's home, where he found Simon's mother-in-law very sick with a high fever. "Please heal her," everyone begged. [39]Standing at her bedside, he rebuked the fever, and it left her. And she got up at once and prepared a meal for them.

[40]As the sun went down that evening, people throughout the village brought sick family members to Jesus. No matter what their diseases were, the touch of his hand healed every one. [41]Many were possessed by demons; and the demons came out at his command, shouting, "You are the Son of God!" But because they knew he was the Messiah, he rebuked them and refused to let them speak.

Jesus Continues to Preach

[42]Early the next morning Jesus went out to an isolated place. The crowds searched everywhere for him, and when they finally found him, they begged him not to leave them. [43]But he replied, "I must preach the Good News of the Kingdom of God in other towns, too, because that is why I was sent." [44]So he continued to travel around, preaching in synagogues throughout Judea.*

The First Disciples

5 One day as Jesus was preaching on the shore of the Sea of Galilee,* great crowds pressed in on him to listen to the word of God. [2]He noticed two empty boats at the water's edge, for the fishermen had left them and were washing their nets. [3]Stepping into one of the boats, Jesus asked Simon,* its owner, to push it out into the water. So he sat in the boat and taught the crowds from there.

[4]When he had finished speaking, he said to Simon, "Now go out where it is deeper, and let down your nets to catch some fish."

[5]"Master," Simon replied, "we worked hard all last night and didn't catch a thing. But if you say so, I'll let the nets down again." [6]And this time their nets were so full of fish they began to tear! [7]A shout for help brought their partners in the other boat, and soon both boats were filled with fish and on the verge of sinking.

[8]When Simon Peter realized what had happened, he fell to his knees before Jesus and said, "Oh, Lord, please leave me—I'm too much of a

---

4:18-19 Or *and to proclaim the acceptable year of the LORD.* Isa 61:1-2 (Greek version); 58:6.　**4:33** Greek *unclean;* also in 4:36.　**4:44** Some manuscripts read *Galilee.*　**5:1** Greek *Lake Gennesaret,* another name for the Sea of Galilee.　**5:3** *Simon* is called "Peter" in 6:14 and thereafter.

sinner to be around you." ⁹For he was awestruck by the number of fish they had caught, as were the others with him. ¹⁰His partners, James and John, the sons of Zebedee, were also amazed.

Jesus replied to Simon, "Don't be afraid! From now on you'll be fishing for people!" ¹¹And as soon as they landed, they left everything and followed Jesus.

Jesus Heals a Man with Leprosy

¹²In one of the villages, Jesus met a man with an advanced case of leprosy. When the man saw Jesus, he bowed with his face to the ground, begging to be healed. "Lord," he said, "if you are willing, you can heal me and make me clean."

¹³Jesus reached out and touched him. "I am willing," he said. "Be healed!" And instantly the leprosy disappeared. ¹⁴Then Jesus instructed him not to tell anyone what had happened. He said, "Go to the priest and let him examine you. Take along the offering required in the law of Moses for those who have been healed of leprosy.* This will be a public testimony that you have been cleansed."

¹⁵But despite Jesus' instructions, the report of his power spread even faster, and vast crowds came to hear him preach and to be healed of their diseases. ¹⁶But Jesus often withdrew to the wilderness for prayer.

Jesus Heals a Paralyzed Man

¹⁷One day while Jesus was teaching, some Pharisees and teachers of religious law were sitting nearby. (It seemed that these men showed up from every village in all Galilee and Judea, as well as from Jerusalem.) And the Lord's healing power was strongly with Jesus.

¹⁸Some men came carrying a paralyzed man on a sleeping mat. They tried to take him inside to Jesus, ¹⁹but they couldn't reach him because of the crowd. So they went up to the roof and took off some tiles. Then they lowered the sick man on his mat down into the crowd, right in front of Jesus. ²⁰Seeing their faith, Jesus said to the man, "Young man, your sins are forgiven."

²¹But the Pharisees and teachers of religious law said to themselves, "Who does he think he is? That's blasphemy! Only God can forgive sins!"

²²Jesus knew what they were thinking, so he asked them, "Why do you question this in your hearts? ²³Is it easier to say 'Your sins are forgiven,' or 'Stand up and walk'? ²⁴So I will prove to you that the Son of Man* has the authority on earth to forgive sins." Then Jesus turned to the paralyzed man and said, "Stand up, pick up your mat, and go home!"

²⁵And immediately, as everyone watched, the man jumped up, picked up his mat, and went home praising God. ²⁶Everyone was gripped with great wonder and awe, and they praised God, exclaiming, "We have seen amazing things today!"

Jesus Calls Levi (Matthew)

²⁷Later, as Jesus left the town, he saw a tax collector named Levi sitting at his tax collector's booth. "Follow me and be my disciple," Jesus said to him. ²⁸So Levi got up, left everything, and followed him.

²⁹Later, Levi held a banquet in his home with Jesus as the guest of honor. Many of Levi's fellow tax collectors and other guests also ate with them. ³⁰But the Pharisees and their teachers of religious law complained bitterly to Jesus' disciples, "Why do you eat and drink with such scum?*"

³¹Jesus answered them, "Healthy people don't need a doctor—sick people do. ³²I have come to call not those who think they are righteous, but those who know they are sinners and need to repent."

A Discussion about Fasting

³³One day some people said to Jesus, "John the Baptist's disciples fast and pray regularly, and so do the disciples of the Pharisees. Why are your disciples always eating and drinking?"

³⁴Jesus responded, "Do wedding guests fast while celebrating with the groom? Of course not. ³⁵But someday the groom will be taken away from them, and then they will fast."

³⁶Then Jesus gave them this illustration: "No one tears a piece of cloth from a new garment and uses it to patch an old garment. For then the new garment would be ruined, and the new patch wouldn't even match the old garment. ³⁷And no one puts new wine into old wineskins. For the new wine would burst the wineskins, spilling the wine and ruining the skins. ³⁸New wine must be stored in new wineskins. ³⁹But no one who drinks the old wine seems to want the new wine. 'The old is just fine,' they say."

A Discussion about the Sabbath

6 One Sabbath day as Jesus was walking through some grainfields, his disciples broke off heads of grain, rubbed off the husks in their hands, and ate the grain. ²But some Pharisees said, "Why are you breaking the law by harvesting grain on the Sabbath?"

³Jesus replied, "Haven't you read in the Scriptures what David did when he and his companions were hungry? ⁴He went into the house of God and broke the law by eating the sacred loaves of bread that only the priests can eat. He also gave some to his companions." ⁵And Jesus added, "The Son of Man* is Lord, even over the Sabbath."

5:14 See Lev 14:2-32. **5:24** "Son of Man" is a title Jesus used for himself. **5:30** Greek *with tax collectors and sinners?* **6:5** "Son of Man" is a title Jesus used for himself.

Jesus Heals on the Sabbath

⁶On another Sabbath day, a man with a deformed right hand was in the synagogue while Jesus was teaching. ⁷The teachers of religious law and the Pharisees watched Jesus closely. If he healed the man's hand, they planned to accuse him of working on the Sabbath.

⁸But Jesus knew their thoughts. He said to the man with the deformed hand, "Come and stand in front of everyone." So the man came forward. ⁹Then Jesus said to his critics, "I have a question for you. Does the law permit good deeds on the Sabbath, or is it a day for doing evil? Is this a day to save life or to destroy it?"

¹⁰He looked around at them one by one and then said to the man, "Hold out your hand." So the man held out his hand, and it was restored! ¹¹At this, the enemies of Jesus were wild with rage and began to discuss what to do with him.

Jesus Chooses the Twelve Apostles

¹²One day soon afterward Jesus went up on a mountain to pray, and he prayed to God all night. ¹³At daybreak he called together all of his disciples and chose twelve of them to be apostles. Here are their names:

¹⁴ Simon (whom he named Peter),
Andrew (Peter's brother),
James,
John,
Philip,
Bartholomew,
¹⁵ Matthew,
Thomas,
James (son of Alphaeus),
Simon (who was called the zealot),
¹⁶ Judas (son of James),
Judas Iscariot (who later betrayed him).

Crowds Follow Jesus

¹⁷When they came down from the mountain, the disciples stood with Jesus on a large, level area, surrounded by many of his followers and by the crowds. There were people from all over Judea and from Jerusalem and from as far north as the seacoasts of Tyre and Sidon. ¹⁸They had come to hear him and to be healed of their diseases; and those troubled by evil* spirits were healed. ¹⁹Everyone tried to touch him, because healing power went out from him, and he healed everyone.

The Beatitudes

²⁰Then Jesus turned to his disciples and said,

"God blesses you who are poor,
for the Kingdom of God is yours.
²¹ God blesses you who are hungry now,
for you will be satisfied.
God blesses you who weep now,
for in due time you will laugh.

²²What blessings await you when people hate you and exclude you and mock you and curse you as evil because you follow the Son of Man. ²³When that happens, be happy! Yes, leap for joy! For a great reward awaits you in heaven. And remember, their ancestors treated the ancient prophets that same way.

Sorrows Foretold

²⁴ "What sorrow awaits you who are rich,
for you have your only happiness now.
²⁵ What sorrow awaits you who are fat and
prosperous now,
for a time of awful hunger awaits you.
What sorrow awaits you who laugh now,
for your laughing will turn to mourning
and sorrow.
²⁶ What sorrow awaits you who are praised by
the crowds,
for their ancestors also praised false
prophets.

Love for Enemies

²⁷"But to you who are willing to listen, I say, love your enemies! Do good to those who hate you. ²⁸Bless those who curse you. Pray for those who hurt you. ²⁹If someone slaps you on one cheek, offer the other cheek also. If someone demands your coat, offer your shirt also. ³⁰Give to anyone who asks; and when things are taken away from you, don't try to get them back. ³¹Do to others as you would like them to do to you.

³²"If you love only those who love you, why should you get credit for that? Even sinners love those who love them! ³³And if you do good only to those who do good to you, why should you get credit? Even sinners do that much! ³⁴And if you lend money only to those who can repay you, why should you get credit? Even sinners will lend to other sinners for a full return.

³⁵"Love your enemies! Do good to them. Lend to them without expecting to be repaid. Then your reward from heaven will be very great, and you will truly be acting as children of the Most High, for he is kind to those who are unthankful and wicked. ³⁶You must be compassionate, just as your Father is compassionate.

Do Not Judge Others

³⁷"Do not judge others, and you will not be judged. Do not condemn others, or it will all come back against you. Forgive others, and you will be forgiven. ³⁸Give, and you will receive. Your gift will return to you in full—pressed down, shaken together to make room for more, running over, and poured into your lap. The amount you give will determine the amount you get back.*"

³⁹Then Jesus gave the following illustration: "Can one blind person lead another? Won't they

6:18 Greek *unclean.*   **6:38** Or *The measure you give will be the measure you get back.*

both fall into a ditch? [40]Students* are not greater than their teacher. But the student who is fully trained will become like the teacher.

[41]"And why worry about a speck in your friend's eye* when you have a log in your own? [42]How can you think of saying, 'Friend,* let me help you get rid of that speck in your eye,' when you can't see past the log in your own eye? Hypocrite! First get rid of the log in your own eye; then you will see well enough to deal with the speck in your friend's eye.

The Tree and Its Fruit

[43]"A good tree can't produce bad fruit, and a bad tree can't produce good fruit. [44]A tree is identified by its fruit. Figs are never gathered from thornbushes, and grapes are not picked from bramble bushes. [45]A good person produces good things from the treasury of a good heart, and an evil person produces evil things from the treasury of an evil heart. What you say flows from what is in your heart.

Building on a Solid Foundation

[46]"So why do you keep calling me 'Lord, Lord!' when you don't do what I say? [47]I will show you what it's like when someone comes to me, listens to my teaching, and then follows it. [48]It is like a person building a house who digs deep and lays the foundation on solid rock. When the floodwaters rise and break against that house, it stands firm because it is well built. [49]But anyone who hears and doesn't obey is like a person who builds a house without a foundation. When the floods sweep down against that house, it will collapse into a heap of ruins."

The Faith of a Roman Officer

7 When Jesus had finished saying all this to the people, he returned to Capernaum. [2]At that time the highly valued slave of a Roman officer* was sick and near death. [3]When the officer heard about Jesus, he sent some respected Jewish elders to ask him to come and heal his slave. [4]So they earnestly begged Jesus to help the man. "If anyone deserves your help, he does," they said, [5]"for he loves the Jewish people and even built a synagogue for us."

[6]So Jesus went with them. But just before they arrived at the house, the officer sent some friends to say, "Lord, don't trouble yourself by coming to my home, for I am not worthy of such an honor. [7]I am not even worthy to come and meet you. Just say the word from where you are, and my servant will be healed. [8]I know this because I am under the authority of my superior officers, and I have authority over my soldiers. I only need to say, 'Go,' and they go, or 'Come,' and they come. And if I say to my slaves, 'Do this,' they do it."

[9]When Jesus heard this, he was amazed. Turning to the crowd that was following him, he said, "I tell you, I haven't seen faith like this in all Israel!" [10]And when the officer's friends returned to his house, they found the slave completely healed.

Jesus Raises a Widow's Son

[11]Soon afterward Jesus went with his disciples to the village of Nain, and a large crowd followed him. [12]A funeral procession was coming out as he approached the village gate. The young man who had died was a widow's only son, and a large crowd from the village was with her. [13]When the Lord saw her, his heart overflowed with compassion. "Don't cry!" he said. [14]Then he walked over to the coffin and touched it, and the bearers stopped. "Young man," he said, "I tell you, get up." [15]Then the dead boy sat up and began to talk! And Jesus gave him back to his mother.

[16]Great fear swept the crowd, and they praised God, saying, "A mighty prophet has risen among us," and "God has visited his people today." [17]And the news about Jesus spread throughout Judea and the surrounding countryside.

Jesus and John the Baptist

[18]The disciples of John the Baptist told John about everything Jesus was doing. So John called for two of his disciples, [19]and he sent them to the Lord to ask him, "Are you the Messiah we've been expecting,* or should we keep looking for someone else?"

[20]John's two disciples found Jesus and said to him, "John the Baptist sent us to ask, 'Are you the Messiah we've been expecting, or should we keep looking for someone else?'"

[21]At that very time, Jesus cured many people of their diseases, illnesses, and evil spirits, and he restored sight to many who were blind. [22]Then he told John's disciples, "Go back to John and tell him what you have seen and heard—the blind see, the lame walk, the lepers are cured, the deaf hear, the dead are raised to life, and the Good News is being preached to the poor. [23]And tell him, 'God blesses those who do not turn away because of me.*'"

[24]After John's disciples left, Jesus began talking about him to the crowds. "What kind of man did you go into the wilderness to see? Was he a weak reed, swayed by every breath of wind? [25]Or were you expecting to see a man dressed in expensive clothes? No, people who wear beautiful clothes and live in luxury are found in palaces. [26]Were you looking for a prophet? Yes, and he is more than a prophet. [27]John is the man to whom the Scriptures refer when they say,

> 'Look, I am sending my messenger ahead
>   of you,
> and he will prepare your way before you.'*

6:40 Or *Disciples.*   **6:41** Greek *your brother's eye;* also in 6:42.   **6:42** Greek *Brother.*   **7:2** Greek *a centurion;* similarly in 7:6.
7:19 Greek *Are you the one who is coming?* Also in 7:20.   **7:23** Or *who are not offended by me.*   **7:27** Mal 3:1.

²⁸I tell you, of all who have ever lived, none is greater than John. Yet even the least person in the Kingdom of God is greater than he is!"

²⁹When they heard this, all the people—even the tax collectors—agreed that God's way was right,* for they had been baptized by John. ³⁰But the Pharisees and experts in religious law rejected God's plan for them, for they had refused John's baptism.

³¹"To what can I compare the people of this generation?" Jesus asked. "How can I describe them? ³²They are like children playing a game in the public square. They complain to their friends,

'We played wedding songs,
    and you didn't dance,
so we played funeral songs,
    and you didn't weep.'

³³For John the Baptist didn't spend his time eating bread or drinking wine, and you say, 'He's possessed by a demon.' ³⁴The Son of Man,* on the other hand, feasts and drinks, and you say, 'He's a glutton and a drunkard, and a friend of tax collectors and other sinners!' ³⁵But wisdom is shown to be right by the lives of those who follow it.*"

Jesus Anointed by a Sinful Woman

³⁶One of the Pharisees asked Jesus to have dinner with him, so Jesus went to his home and sat down to eat.* ³⁷When a certain immoral woman from that city heard he was eating there, she brought a beautiful alabaster jar filled with expensive perfume. ³⁸Then she knelt behind him at his feet, weeping. Her tears fell on his feet, and she wiped them off with her hair. Then she kept kissing his feet and putting perfume on them.

³⁹When the Pharisee who had invited him saw this, he said to himself, "If this man were a prophet, he would know what kind of woman were touching him. She's a sinner!"

⁴⁰Then Jesus answered his thoughts. "Simon," he said to the Pharisee, "I have something to say to you."

"Go ahead, Teacher," Simon replied.

⁴¹Then Jesus told him this story: "A man loaned money to two people—500 pieces of silver* to one and 50 pieces to the other. ⁴²But neither of them could repay him, so he kindly forgave them both, canceling their debts. Who do you suppose loved him more after that?"

⁴³Simon answered, "I suppose the one for whom he canceled the larger debt."

"That's right," Jesus said. ⁴⁴Then he turned to the woman and said to Simon, "Look at this woman kneeling here. When I entered your home, you didn't offer me water to wash the dust from my feet, but she has washed them with her tears and wiped them with her hair.

⁴⁵You didn't greet me with a kiss, but from the time I first came in, she has not stopped kissing my feet. ⁴⁶You neglected the courtesy of olive oil to anoint my head, but she has anointed my feet with rare perfume.

⁴⁷"I tell you, her sins—and they are many—have been forgiven, so she has shown me much love. But a person who is forgiven little shows only little love." ⁴⁸Then Jesus said to the woman, "Your sins are forgiven."

⁴⁹The men at the table said among themselves, "Who is this man, that he goes around forgiving sins?"

⁵⁰And Jesus said to the woman, "Your faith has saved you; go in peace."

Women Who Followed Jesus

8 Soon afterward Jesus began a tour of the nearby towns and villages, preaching and announcing the Good News about the Kingdom of God. He took his twelve disciples with him, ²along with some women who had been cured of evil spirits and diseases. Among them were Mary Magdalene, from whom he had cast out seven demons; ³Joanna, the wife of Chuza, Herod's business manager; Susanna; and many others who were contributing from their own resources to support Jesus and his disciples.

Parable of the Farmer Scattering Seed

⁴One day Jesus told a story in the form of a parable to a large crowd that had gathered from many towns to hear him: ⁵"A farmer went out to plant his seed. As he scattered it across his field, some seed fell on a footpath, where it was stepped on, and the birds ate it. ⁶Other seed fell among rocks. It began to grow, but the plant soon wilted and died for lack of moisture. ⁷Other seed fell among thorns that grew up with it and choked out the tender plants. ⁸Still other seed fell on fertile soil. This seed grew and produced a crop that was a hundred times as much as had been planted!" When he had said this, he called out, "Anyone with ears to hear should listen and understand."

⁹His disciples asked him what this parable meant. ¹⁰He replied, "You are permitted to understand the secrets* of the Kingdom of God. But I use parables to teach the others so that the Scriptures might be fulfilled:

'When they look, they won't really see.
    When they hear, they won't understand.'*

¹¹"This is the meaning of the parable: The seed is God's word. ¹²The seeds that fell on the footpath represent those who hear the message, only to have the devil come and take it away from their hearts and prevent them from believing and being saved. ¹³The seeds on the rocky

soil represent those who hear the message and receive it with joy. But since they don't have deep roots, they believe for a while, then they fall away when they face temptation. [14]The seeds that fell among the thorns represent those who hear the message, but all too quickly the message is crowded out by the cares and riches and pleasures of this life. And so they never grow into maturity. [15]And the seeds that fell on the good soil represent honest, good-hearted people who hear God's word, cling to it, and patiently produce a huge harvest.

Parable of the Lamp
[16]"No one lights a lamp and then covers it with a bowl or hides it under a bed. A lamp is placed on a stand, where its light can be seen by all who enter the house. [17]For all that is secret will eventually be brought into the open, and everything that is concealed will be brought to light and made known to all.

[18]"So pay attention to how you hear. To those who listen to my teaching, more understanding will be given. But for those who are not listening, even what they think they understand will be taken away from them."

The True Family of Jesus
[19]Then Jesus' mother and brothers came to see him, but they couldn't get to him because of the crowd. [20]Someone told Jesus, "Your mother and your brothers are outside, and they want to see you."

[21]Jesus replied, "My mother and my brothers are all those who hear God's word and obey it."

Jesus Calms the Storm
[22]One day Jesus said to his disciples, "Let's cross to the other side of the lake." So they got into a boat and started out. [23]As they sailed across, Jesus settled down for a nap. But soon a fierce storm came down on the lake. The boat was filling with water, and they were in real danger.

[24]The disciples went and woke him up, shouting, "Master, Master, we're going to drown!"

When Jesus woke up, he rebuked the wind and the raging waves. Suddenly the storm stopped and all was calm. [25]Then he asked them, "Where is your faith?"

The disciples were terrified and amazed. "Who is this man?" they asked each other. "When he gives a command, even the wind and waves obey him!"

Jesus Heals a Demon-Possessed Man
[26]So they arrived in the region of the Gerasenes,* across the lake from Galilee. [27]As Jesus was climbing out of the boat, a man who was possessed by demons came out to meet him. For a long time he had been homeless and naked, living in a cemetery outside the town.

[28]As soon as he saw Jesus, he shrieked and fell down in front of him. Then he screamed, "Why are you interfering with me, Jesus, Son of the Most High God? Please, I beg you, don't torture me!" [29]For Jesus had already commanded the evil* spirit to come out of him. This spirit had often taken control of the man. Even when he was placed under guard and put in chains and shackles, he simply broke them and rushed out into the wilderness, completely under the demon's power.

[30]Jesus demanded, "What is your name?"

"Legion," he replied, for he was filled with many demons. [31]The demons kept begging Jesus not to send them into the bottomless pit.*

[32]There happened to be a large herd of pigs feeding on the hillside nearby, and the demons begged him to let them enter into the pigs. So Jesus gave them permission. [33]Then the demons came out of the man and entered the pigs, and the entire herd plunged down the steep hillside into the lake and drowned.

[34]When the herdsmen saw it, they fled to the nearby town and the surrounding countryside, spreading the news as they ran. [35]People rushed out to see what had happened. A crowd soon gathered around Jesus, and they saw the man who had been freed from the demons. He was sitting at Jesus' feet, fully clothed and perfectly sane, and they were all afraid. [36]Then those who had seen what happened told the others how the demon-possessed man had been healed. [37]And all the people in the region of the Gerasenes begged Jesus to go away and leave them alone, for a great wave of fear swept over them.

So Jesus returned to the boat and left, crossing back to the other side of the lake. [38]The man who had been freed from the demons begged to go with him. But Jesus sent him home, saying, [39]"No, go back to your family, and tell them everything God has done for you." So he went all through the town proclaiming the great things Jesus had done for him.

Jesus Heals in Response to Faith
[40]On the other side of the lake the crowds welcomed Jesus, because they had been waiting for him. [41]Then a man named Jairus, a leader of the local synagogue, came and fell at Jesus' feet, pleading with him to come home with him. [42]His only daughter,* who was about twelve years old, was dying.

As Jesus went with him, he was surrounded by the crowds. [43]A woman in the crowd had suffered for twelve years with constant bleeding,* and she could find no cure. [44]Coming up behind

8:26 Other manuscripts read *Gadarenes;* still others read *Gergesenes;* also in 8:37. See Matt 8:28; Mark 5:1. **8:29** Greek *unclean.* **8:31** Or *The abyss,* or *the underworld.* **8:42** Or *His only child, a daughter.* **8:43** Some manuscripts add *having spent everything she had on doctors.*

Jesus, she touched the fringe of his robe. Immediately, the bleeding stopped.

⁴⁵"Who touched me?" Jesus asked.

Everyone denied it, and Peter said, "Master, this whole crowd is pressing up against you."

⁴⁶But Jesus said, "Someone deliberately touched me, for I felt healing power go out from me." ⁴⁷When the woman realized that she could not stay hidden, she began to tremble and fell to her knees in front of him. The whole crowd heard her explain why she had touched him and that she had been immediately healed. ⁴⁸"Daughter," he said to her, "your faith has made you well. Go in peace."

⁴⁹While he was still speaking to her, a messenger arrived from the home of Jairus, the leader of the synagogue. He told him, "Your daughter is dead. There's no use troubling the Teacher now."

⁵⁰But when Jesus heard what had happened, he said to Jairus, "Don't be afraid. Just have faith, and she will be healed."

⁵¹When they arrived at the house, Jesus wouldn't let anyone go in with him except Peter, John, James, and the little girl's father and mother. ⁵²The house was filled with people weeping and wailing, but he said, "Stop the weeping! She isn't dead; she's only asleep."

⁵³But the crowd laughed at him because they all knew she had died. ⁵⁴Then Jesus took her by the hand and said in a loud voice, "My child, get up!" ⁵⁵And at that moment her life* returned, and she immediately stood up! Then Jesus told them to give her something to eat. ⁵⁶Her parents were overwhelmed, but Jesus insisted that they not tell anyone what had happened.

Jesus Sends Out the Twelve Disciples

9 One day Jesus called together his twelve disciples* and gave them power and authority to cast out all demons and to heal all diseases. ²Then he sent them out to tell everyone about the Kingdom of God and to heal the sick. ³"Take nothing for your journey," he instructed them. "Don't take a walking stick, a traveler's bag, food, money,* or even a change of clothes. ⁴Wherever you go, stay in the same house until you leave town. ⁵And if a town refuses to welcome you, shake its dust from your feet as you leave to show that you have abandoned those people to their fate."

⁶So they began their circuit of the villages, preaching the Good News and healing the sick.

Herod's Confusion

⁷When Herod Antipas, the ruler of Galilee,* heard about everything Jesus was doing, he was puzzled. Some were saying that John the Baptist had been raised from the dead. ⁸Others thought Jesus was Elijah or one of the other prophets risen from the dead.

⁹"I beheaded John," Herod said, "so who is this man about whom I hear such stories?" And he kept trying to see him.

Jesus Feeds Five Thousand

¹⁰When the apostles returned, they told Jesus everything they had done. Then he slipped quietly away with them toward the town of Bethsaida. ¹¹But the crowds found out where he was going, and they followed him. He welcomed them and taught them about the Kingdom of God, and he healed those who were sick.

¹²Late in the afternoon the twelve disciples came to him and said, "Send the crowds away to the nearby villages and farms, so they can find food and lodging for the night. There is nothing to eat here in this remote place."

¹³But Jesus said, "You feed them."

"But we have only five loaves of bread and two fish," they answered. "Or are you expecting us to go and buy enough food for this whole crowd?" ¹⁴For there were about 5,000 men there.

Jesus replied, "Tell them to sit down in groups of about fifty each." ¹⁵So the people all sat down. ¹⁶Jesus took the five loaves and two fish, looked up toward heaven, and blessed them. Then, breaking the loaves into pieces, he kept giving the bread and fish to the disciples so they could distribute it to the people. ¹⁷They all ate as much as they wanted, and afterward, the disciples picked up twelve baskets of leftovers!

Peter's Declaration about Jesus

¹⁸One day Jesus left the crowds to pray alone. Only his disciples were with him, and he asked them, "Who do people say I am?"

¹⁹"Well," they replied, "some say John the Baptist, some say Elijah, and others say you are one of the other ancient prophets risen from the dead."

²⁰Then he asked them, "But who do you say I am?"

Peter replied, "You are the Messiah* sent from God!"

Jesus Predicts His Death

²¹Jesus warned his disciples not to tell anyone who he was. ²²"The Son of Man* must suffer many terrible things," he said. "He will be rejected by the elders, the leading priests, and the teachers of religious law. He will be killed, but on the third day he will be raised from the dead."

²³Then he said to the crowd, "If any of you wants to be my follower, you must turn from

8:55 Or *her spirit.* **9:1** Greek *the Twelve;* other manuscripts read *the twelve apostles.* **9:3** Or *silver coins.* **9:7** Greek *Herod the tetrarch.* Herod Antipas was a son of King Herod and was ruler over Galilee. **9:20** Or *the Christ. Messiah* (a Hebrew term) and *Christ* (a Greek term) both mean "the anointed one." **9:22** "Son of Man" is a title Jesus used for himself.

your selfish ways, take up your cross daily, and follow me. ²⁴If you try to hang on to your life, you will lose it. But if you give up your life for my sake, you will save it. ²⁵And what do you benefit if you gain the whole world but are yourself lost or destroyed? ²⁶If anyone is ashamed of me and my message, the Son of Man will be ashamed of that person when he returns in his glory and in the glory of the Father and the holy angels. ²⁷I tell you the truth, some standing here right now will not die before they see the Kingdom of God."

The Transfiguration

²⁸About eight days later Jesus took Peter, John, and James up on a mountain to pray. ²⁹And as he was praying, the appearance of his face was transformed, and his clothes became dazzling white. ³⁰Suddenly, two men, Moses and Elijah, appeared and began talking with Jesus. ³¹They were glorious to see. And they were speaking about his exodus from this world, which was about to be fulfilled in Jerusalem.

³²Peter and the others had fallen asleep. When they woke up, they saw Jesus' glory and the two men standing with him. ³³As Moses and Elijah were starting to leave, Peter, not even knowing what he was saying, blurted out, "Master, it's wonderful for us to be here! Let's make three shelters as memorials*—one for you, one for Moses, and one for Elijah." ³⁴But even as he was saying this, a cloud overshadowed them, and terror gripped them as the cloud covered them.

³⁵Then a voice from the cloud said, "This is my Son, my Chosen One.* Listen to him." ³⁶When the voice finished, Jesus was there alone. They didn't tell anyone at that time what they had seen.

Jesus Heals a Demon-Possessed Boy

³⁷The next day, after they had come down the mountain, a large crowd met Jesus. ³⁸A man in the crowd called out to him, "Teacher, I beg you to look at my son, my only child. ³⁹An evil spirit keeps seizing him, making him scream. It throws him into convulsions so that he foams at the mouth. It batters him and hardly ever leaves him alone. ⁴⁰I begged your disciples to cast out the spirit, but they couldn't do it."

⁴¹Jesus said, "You faithless and corrupt people! How long must I be with you and put up with you?" Then he said to the man, "Bring your son here."

⁴²As the boy came forward, the demon knocked him to the ground and threw him into a violent convulsion. But Jesus rebuked the evil* spirit and healed the boy. Then he gave him back to his father. ⁴³Awe gripped the peo-

ple as they saw this majestic display of God's power.

Jesus Again Predicts His Death

While everyone was marveling at everything he was doing, Jesus said to his disciples, ⁴⁴"Listen to me and remember what I say. The Son of Man is going to be betrayed into the hands of his enemies." ⁴⁵But they didn't know what he meant. Its significance was hidden from them, so they couldn't understand it, and they were afraid to ask him about it.

The Greatest in the Kingdom

⁴⁶Then his disciples began arguing about which of them was the greatest. ⁴⁷But Jesus knew their thoughts, so he brought a little child to his side. ⁴⁸Then he said to them, "Anyone who welcomes a little child like this on my behalf* welcomes me, and anyone who welcomes me also welcomes my Father who sent me. Whoever is the least among you is the greatest."

Using the Name of Jesus

⁴⁹John said to Jesus, "Master, we saw someone using your name to cast out demons, but we told him to stop because he isn't in our group."

⁵⁰But Jesus said, "Don't stop him! Anyone who is not against you is for you."

Opposition from Samaritans

⁵¹As the time drew near for him to ascend to heaven, Jesus resolutely set out for Jerusalem. ⁵²He sent messengers ahead to a Samaritan village to prepare for his arrival. ⁵³But the people of the village did not welcome Jesus because he was on his way to Jerusalem. ⁵⁴When James and John saw this, they said to Jesus, "Lord, should we call down fire from heaven to burn them up*?" ⁵⁵But Jesus turned and rebuked them.* ⁵⁶So they went on to another village.

The Cost of Following Jesus

⁵⁷As they were walking along, someone said to Jesus, "I will follow you wherever you go."

⁵⁸But Jesus replied, "Foxes have dens to live in, and birds have nests, but the Son of Man has no place even to lay his head."

⁵⁹He said to another person, "Come, follow me."

The man agreed, but he said, "Lord, first let me return home and bury my father."

⁶⁰But Jesus told him, "Let the spiritually dead bury their own dead!* Your duty is to go and preach about the Kingdom of God."

⁶¹Another said, "Yes, Lord, I will follow you, but first let me say good-bye to my family."

⁶²But Jesus told him, "Anyone who puts a hand to the plow and then looks back is not fit for the Kingdom of God."

9:33 Greek *three tabernacles.* **9:35** Some manuscripts read *This is my dearly loved Son.* **9:42** Greek *unclean.* **9:48** Greek *in my name.* **9:54** Some manuscripts add *as Elijah did.* **9:55** Some manuscripts add an expanded conclusion to verse 55 and an additional sentence in verse 56: *And he said, "You don't realize what your hearts are like. ⁵⁶For the Son of Man has not come to destroy people's lives, but to save them."* **9:60** Greek *Let the dead bury their own dead.*

Jesus Sends Out His Disciples

10 The Lord now chose seventy-two* other disciples and sent them ahead in pairs to all the towns and places he planned to visit. ²These were his instructions to them: "The harvest is great, but the workers are few. So pray to the Lord who is in charge of the harvest; ask him to send more workers into his fields. ³Now go, and remember that I am sending you out as lambs among wolves. ⁴Don't take any money with you, nor a traveler's bag, nor an extra pair of sandals. And don't stop to greet anyone on the road.

⁵"Whenever you enter someone's home, first say, 'May God's peace be on this house.' ⁶If those who live there are peaceful, the blessing will stand; if they are not, the blessing will return to you. ⁷Don't move around from home to home. Stay in one place, eating and drinking what they provide. Don't hesitate to accept hospitality, because those who work deserve their pay.

⁸"If you enter a town and it welcomes you, eat whatever is set before you. ⁹Heal the sick, and tell them, 'The Kingdom of God is near you now.' ¹⁰But if a town refuses to welcome you, go out into its streets and say, ¹¹'We wipe even the dust of your town from our feet to show that we have abandoned you to your fate. And know this—the Kingdom of God is near!' ¹²I assure you, even wicked Sodom will be better off than such a town on judgment day.

¹³"What sorrow awaits you, Korazin and Bethsaida! For if the miracles I did in you had been done in wicked Tyre and Sidon, their people would have repented of their sins long ago, clothing themselves in burlap and throwing ashes on their heads to show their remorse. ¹⁴Yes, Tyre and Sidon will be better off on judgment day than you. ¹⁵And you people of Capernaum, will you be honored in heaven? No, you will go down to the place of the dead.*"

¹⁶Then he said to the disciples, "Anyone who accepts your message is also accepting me. And anyone who rejects you is rejecting me. And anyone who rejects me is rejecting God, who sent me."

¹⁷When the seventy-two disciples returned, they joyfully reported to him, "Lord, even the demons obey us when we use your name!"

¹⁸"Yes," he told them, "I saw Satan fall from heaven like lightning! ¹⁹Look, I have given you authority over all the power of the enemy, and you can walk among snakes and scorpions and crush them. Nothing will injure you. ²⁰But don't rejoice because evil spirits obey you; rejoice because your names are registered in heaven."

Jesus' Prayer of Thanksgiving

²¹At that same time Jesus was filled with the joy of the Holy Spirit, and he said, "O Father, Lord of heaven and earth, thank you for hiding these things from those who think themselves wise and clever, and for revealing them to the childlike. Yes, Father, it pleased you to do it this way.

²²"My Father has entrusted everything to me. No one truly knows the Son except the Father, and no one truly knows the Father except the Son and those to whom the Son chooses to reveal him."

²³Then when they were alone, he turned to the disciples and said, "Blessed are the eyes that see what you have seen. ²⁴I tell you, many prophets and kings longed to see what you see, but they didn't see it. And they longed to hear what you hear, but they didn't hear it."

The Most Important Commandment

²⁵One day an expert in religious law stood up to test Jesus by asking him this question: "Teacher, what should I do to inherit eternal life?"

²⁶Jesus replied, "What does the law of Moses say? How do you read it?"

²⁷The man answered, " 'You must love the LORD your God with all your heart, all your soul, all your strength, and all your mind.' And, 'Love your neighbor as yourself.'"*

²⁸"Right!" Jesus told him. "Do this and you will live!"

²⁹The man wanted to justify his actions, so he asked Jesus, "And who is my neighbor?"

Parable of the Good Samaritan

³⁰Jesus replied with a story: "A Jewish man was traveling from Jerusalem down to Jericho, and he was attacked by bandits. They stripped him of his clothes, beat him up, and left him half dead beside the road.

³¹"By chance a priest came along. But when he saw the man lying there, he crossed to the other side of the road and passed him by. ³²A Temple assistant* walked over and looked at him lying there, but he also passed by on the other side.

³³"Then a despised Samaritan came along, and when he saw the man, he felt compassion for him. ³⁴Going over to him, the Samaritan soothed his wounds with olive oil and wine and bandaged them. Then he put the man on his own donkey and took him to an inn, where he took care of him. ³⁵The next day he handed the innkeeper two silver coins,* telling him, 'Take care of this man. If his bill runs higher than this, I'll pay you the next time I'm here.'

³⁶"Now which of these three would you say was a neighbor to the man who was attacked by bandits?" Jesus asked.

³⁷The man replied, "The one who showed him mercy."

Then Jesus said, "Yes, now go and do the same."

10:1 Some manuscripts read *seventy;* also in 10:17.   **10:15** Greek *to Hades.*   **10:27** Deut 6:5; Lev 19:18.   **10:32** Greek *A Levite.*
10:35 Greek *two denarii.* A denarius was equivalent to a laborer's full day's wage.

Jesus Visits Martha and Mary

³⁸As Jesus and the disciples continued on their way to Jerusalem, they came to a certain village where a woman named Martha welcomed him into her home. ³⁹Her sister, Mary, sat at the Lord's feet, listening to what he taught. ⁴⁰But Martha was distracted by the big dinner she was preparing. She came to Jesus and said, "Lord, doesn't it seem unfair to you that my sister just sits here while I do all the work? Tell her to come and help me."

⁴¹But the Lord said to her, "My dear Martha, you are worried and upset over all these details! ⁴²There is only one thing worth being concerned about. Mary has discovered it, and it will not be taken away from her."

Teaching about Prayer

11 Once Jesus was in a certain place praying. As he finished, one of his disciples came to him and said, "Lord, teach us to pray, just as John taught his disciples."

²Jesus said, "This is how you should pray:*

"Father, may your name be kept holy.
　May your Kingdom come soon.
³ Give us each day the food we need,*
⁴ and forgive us our sins,
　　as we forgive those who sin against us.
　And don't let us yield to temptation.*"

⁵Then, teaching them more about prayer, he used this story: "Suppose you went to a friend's house at midnight, wanting to borrow three loaves of bread. You say to him, ⁶'A friend of mine has just arrived for a visit, and I have nothing for him to eat.' ⁷And suppose he calls out from his bedroom, 'Don't bother me. The door is locked for the night, and my family and I are all in bed. I can't help you.' ⁸But I tell you this—though he won't do it for friendship's sake, if you keep knocking long enough, he will get up and give you whatever you need because of your shameless persistence.*

⁹"And so I tell you, keep on asking, and you will receive what you ask for. Keep on seeking, and you will find. Keep on knocking, and the door will be opened to you. ¹⁰For everyone who asks, receives. Everyone who seeks, finds. And to everyone who knocks, the door will be opened.

¹¹"You fathers—if your children ask* for a fish, do you give them a snake instead? ¹²Or if they ask for an egg, do you give them a scorpion? Of course not! ¹³So if you sinful people know how to give good gifts to your children, how much more will your heavenly Father give the Holy Spirit to those who ask him."

Jesus and the Prince of Demons

¹⁴One day Jesus cast out a demon from a man who couldn't speak, and when the demon was gone, the man began to speak. The crowds were amazed, ¹⁵but some of them said, "No wonder he can cast out demons. He gets his power from Satan,* the prince of demons." ¹⁶Others, trying to test Jesus, demanded that he show them a miraculous sign from heaven to prove his authority.

¹⁷He knew their thoughts, so he said, "Any kingdom divided by civil war is doomed. A family splintered by feuding will fall apart. ¹⁸You say I am empowered by Satan. But if Satan is divided and fighting against himself, how can his kingdom survive? ¹⁹And if I am empowered by Satan, what about your own exorcists? They cast out demons, too, so they will condemn you for what you have said. ²⁰But if I am casting out demons by the power of God,* then the Kingdom of God has arrived among you. ²¹For when a strong man like Satan is fully armed and guards his palace, his possessions are safe—²²until someone even stronger attacks and overpowers him, strips him of his weapons, and carries off his belongings.

²³"Anyone who isn't with me opposes me, and anyone who isn't working with me is actually working against me.

²⁴"When an evil* spirit leaves a person, it goes into the desert, searching for rest. But when it finds none, it says, 'I will return to the person I came from.' ²⁵So it returns and finds that its former home is all swept and in order. ²⁶Then the spirit finds seven other spirits more evil than itself, and they all enter the person and live there. And so that person is worse off than before."

²⁷As he was speaking, a woman in the crowd called out, "God bless your mother—the womb from which you came, and the breasts that nursed you!"

²⁸Jesus replied, "But even more blessed are all who hear the word of God and put it into practice."

The Sign of Jonah

²⁹As the crowd pressed in on Jesus, he said, "This evil generation keeps asking me to show them a miraculous sign. But the only sign I will give them is the sign of Jonah. ³⁰What happened to him was a sign to the people of Nineveh that God had sent him. What happens to the Son of Man* will be a sign to these people that he was sent by God.

³¹"The queen of Sheba* will stand up against this generation on judgment day and condemn it, for she came from a distant land to hear the wisdom of Solomon. Now someone greater than Solomon is here—but you refuse to listen. ³²The

---

11:2 Some manuscripts add additional phrases from the Lord's Prayer as it reads in Matt 6:9-13.　　**11:3** Or *Give us each day our food for the day;* or *Give us each day our food for tomorrow.*　　**11:4** Or *And keep us from being tested.*　　**11:8** Or *in order to avoid shame,* or *so his reputation won't be damaged.*　　**11:11** Some manuscripts add *for bread, do you give them a stone? Or [if they ask].*　　**11:15** Greek *Beelzeboul;* also in 11:18, 19. Other manuscripts read *Beezeboul;* Latin version reads *Beelzebub.*　　**11:20** Greek *by the finger of God.*　　**11:24** Greek *unclean.*　　**11:30** "Son of Man" is a title Jesus used for himself.　　**11:31** Greek *The queen of the south.*

people of Nineveh will also stand up against this generation on judgment day and condemn it, for they repented of their sins at the preaching of Jonah. Now someone greater than Jonah is here—but you refuse to repent.

Receiving the Light

33"No one lights a lamp and then hides it or puts it under a basket.* Instead, a lamp is placed on a stand, where its light can be seen by all who enter the house.

34"Your eye is a lamp that provides light for your body. When your eye is good, your whole body is filled with light. But when it is bad, your body is filled with darkness. 35Make sure that the light you think you have is not actually darkness. 36If you are filled with light, with no dark corners, then your whole life will be radiant, as though a floodlight were filling you with light."

Jesus Criticizes the Religious Leaders

37As Jesus was speaking, one of the Pharisees invited him home for a meal. So he went in and took his place at the table.* 38His host was amazed to see that he sat down to eat without first performing the hand-washing ceremony required by Jewish custom. 39Then the Lord said to him, "You Pharisees are so careful to clean the outside of the cup and the dish, but inside you are filthy—full of greed and wickedness! 40Fools! Didn't God make the inside as well as the outside? 41So clean the inside by giving gifts to the poor, and you will be clean all over.

42"What sorrow awaits you Pharisees! For you are careful to tithe even the tiniest income from your herb gardens,* but you ignore justice and the love of God. You should tithe, yes, but do not neglect the more important things.

43"What sorrow awaits you Pharisees! For you love to sit in the seats of honor in the synagogues and receive respectful greetings as you walk in the marketplaces. 44Yes, what sorrow awaits you! For you are like hidden graves in a field. People walk over them without knowing the corruption they are stepping on."

45"Teacher," said an expert in religious law, "you have insulted us, too, in what you just said."

46"Yes," said Jesus, "what sorrow also awaits you experts in religious law! For you crush people with unbearable religious demands, and you never lift a finger to ease the burden. 47What sorrow awaits you! For you build monuments for the prophets your own ancestors killed long ago. 48But in fact, you stand as witnesses who agree with what your ancestors did. They killed the prophets, and you join in their crime by building the monuments! 49This is what God in his wisdom said about you:* 'I will send proph-

ets and apostles to them, but they will kill some and persecute the others.'

50"As a result, this generation will be held responsible for the murder of all God's prophets from the creation of the world—51from the murder of Abel to the murder of Zechariah, who was killed between the altar and the sanctuary. Yes, it will certainly be charged against this generation.

52"What sorrow awaits you experts in religious law! For you remove the key to knowledge from the people. You don't enter the Kingdom yourselves, and you prevent others from entering."

53As Jesus was leaving, the teachers of religious law and the Pharisees became hostile and tried to provoke him with many questions. 54They wanted to trap him into saying something they could use against him.

A Warning against Hypocrisy

12 Meanwhile, the crowds grew until thousands were milling about and stepping on each other. Jesus turned first to his disciples and warned them, "Beware of the yeast of the Pharisees—their hypocrisy. 2The time is coming when everything that is covered up will be revealed, and all that is secret will be made known to all. 3Whatever you have said in the dark will be heard in the light, and what you have whispered behind closed doors will be shouted from the housetops for all to hear!

4"Dear friends, don't be afraid of those who want to kill your body; they cannot do any more to you after that. 5But I'll tell you whom to fear. Fear God, who has the power to kill you and then throw you into hell.* Yes, he's the one to fear.

6"What is the price of five sparrows—two copper coins*? Yet God does not forget a single one of them. 7And the very hairs on your head are all numbered. So don't be afraid; you are more valuable to God than a whole flock of sparrows.

8"I tell you the truth, everyone who acknowledges me publicly here on earth, the Son of Man* will also acknowledge in the presence of God's angels. 9But anyone who denies me here on earth will be denied before God's angels. 10Anyone who speaks against the Son of Man can be forgiven, but anyone who blasphemes the Holy Spirit will not be forgiven.

11"And when you are brought to trial in the synagogues and before rulers and authorities, don't worry about how to defend yourself or what to say, 12for the Holy Spirit will teach you at that time what needs to be said."

Parable of the Rich Fool

13Then someone called from the crowd, "Teacher, please tell my brother to divide our father's estate with me."

11:33 Some manuscripts do not include *or puts it under a basket, and every herb.* **11:37** Or *and reclined.* **11:42** Greek *tithe the mint, the rue,* **11:49** Greek *Therefore, the wisdom of God said.* **12:5** Greek *Gehenna.* **12:6** Greek *two assaria* [Roman coins equal to ¹⁄₁₆ of a denarius]. **12:8** "Son of Man" is a title Jesus used for himself.

[14]Jesus replied, "Friend, who made me a judge over you to decide such things as that?" [15]Then he said, "Beware! Guard against every kind of greed. Life is not measured by how much you own."

[16]Then he told them a story: "A rich man had a fertile farm that produced fine crops. [17]He said to himself, 'What should I do? I don't have room for all my crops.' [18]Then he said, 'I know! I'll tear down my barns and build bigger ones. Then I'll have room enough to store all my wheat and other goods. [19]And I'll sit back and say to myself, "My friend, you have enough stored away for years to come. Now take it easy! Eat, drink, and be merry!"'

[20]"But God said to him, 'You fool! You will die this very night. Then who will get everything you worked for?'

[21]"Yes, a person is a fool to store up earthly wealth but not have a rich relationship with God."

Teaching about Money and Possessions

[22]Then, turning to his disciples, Jesus said, "That is why I tell you not to worry about everyday life—whether you have enough food to eat or enough clothes to wear. [23]For life is more than food, and your body more than clothing. [24]Look at the ravens. They don't plant or harvest or store food in barns, for God feeds them. And you are far more valuable to him than any birds! [25]Can all your worries add a single moment to your life? [26]And if worry can't accomplish a little thing like that, what's the use of worrying over bigger things?

[27]"Look at the lilies and how they grow. They don't work or make their clothing, yet Solomon in all his glory was not dressed as beautifully as they are. [28]And if God cares so wonderfully for flowers that are here today and thrown into the fire tomorrow, he will certainly care for you. Why do you have so little faith?

[29]"And don't be concerned about what to eat and what to drink. Don't worry about such things. [30]These things dominate the thoughts of unbelievers all over the world, but your Father already knows your needs. [31]Seek the Kingdom of God above all else, and he will give you everything you need.

[32]"So don't be afraid, little flock. For it gives your Father great happiness to give you the Kingdom.

[33]"Sell your possessions and give to those in need. This will store up treasure for you in heaven! And the purses of heaven never get old or develop holes. Your treasure will be safe; no thief can steal it and no moth can destroy it. [34]Wherever your treasure is, there the desires of your heart will also be.

Be Ready for the Lord's Coming

[35]"Be dressed for service and keep your lamps burning, [36]as though you were waiting for your master to return from the wedding feast. Then you will be ready to open the door and let him in the moment he arrives and knocks. [37]The servants who are ready and waiting for his return will be rewarded. I tell you the truth, he himself will seat them, put on an apron, and serve them as they sit and eat! [38]He may come in the middle of the night or just before dawn.* But whenever he comes, he will reward the servants who are ready.

[39]"Understand this: If a homeowner knew exactly when a burglar was coming, he would not permit his house to be broken into. [40]You also must be ready all the time, for the Son of Man will come when least expected."

[41]Peter asked, "Lord, is that illustration just for us or for everyone?"

[42]And the Lord replied, "A faithful, sensible servant is one to whom the master can give the responsibility of managing his other household servants and feeding them. [43]If the master returns and finds that the servant has done a good job, there will be a reward. [44]I tell you the truth, the master will put that servant in charge of all he owns. [45]But what if the servant thinks, 'My master won't be back for a while,' and he begins beating the other servants, partying, and getting drunk? [46]The master will return unannounced and unexpected, and he will cut the servant in pieces and banish him with the unfaithful.

[47]"And a servant who knows what the master wants, but isn't prepared and doesn't carry out those instructions, will be severely punished. [48]But someone who does not know, and then does something wrong, will be punished only lightly. When someone has been given much, much will be required in return; and when someone has been entrusted with much, even more will be required.

Jesus Causes Division

[49]"I have come to set the world on fire, and I wish it were already burning! [50]I have a terrible baptism of suffering ahead of me, and I am under a heavy burden until it is accomplished. [51]Do you think I have come to bring peace to the earth? No, I have come to divide people against each other! [52]From now on families will be split apart, three in favor of me, and two against—or two in favor and three against.

[53] 'Father will be divided against son
 and son against father;
mother against daughter
 and daughter against mother;
and mother-in-law against daughter-in-law
 and daughter-in-law against
  mother-in-law.'*"

12:38 Greek *in the second or third watch.* **12:53** Mic 7:6.

54Then Jesus turned to the crowd and said, "When you see clouds beginning to form in the west, you say, 'Here comes a shower.' And you are right. 55When the south wind blows, you say, 'Today will be a scorcher.' And it is. 56You fools! You know how to interpret the weather signs of the earth and sky, but you don't know how to interpret the present times.

57"Why can't you decide for yourselves what is right? 58When you are on the way to court with your accuser, try to settle the matter before you get there. Otherwise, your accuser may drag you before the judge, who will hand you over to an officer, who will throw you into prison. 59And if that happens, you won't be free again until you have paid the very last penny.*"

A Call to Repentance

13 About this time Jesus was informed that Pilate had murdered some people from Galilee as they were offering sacrifices at the Temple. 2"Do you think those Galileans were worse sinners than all the other people from Galilee?" Jesus asked. "Is that why they suffered? 3Not at all! And you will perish, too, unless you repent of your sins and turn to God. 4And what about the eighteen people who died when the tower in Siloam fell on them? Were they the worst sinners in Jerusalem? 5No, and I tell you again that unless you repent, you will perish, too."

Parable of the Barren Fig Tree

6Then Jesus told this story: "A man planted a fig tree in his garden and came again and again to see if there was any fruit on it, but he was always disappointed. 7Finally, he said to his gardener, 'I've waited three years, and there hasn't been a single fig! Cut it down. It's just taking up space in the garden.'

8"The gardener answered, 'Sir, give it one more chance. Leave it another year, and I'll give it special attention and plenty of fertilizer. 9If we get figs next year, fine. If not, then you can cut it down.'"

Jesus Heals on the Sabbath

10One Sabbath day as Jesus was teaching in a synagogue, 11he saw a woman who had been crippled by an evil spirit. She had been bent double for eighteen years and was unable to stand up straight. 12When Jesus saw her, he called her over and said, "Dear woman, you are healed of your sickness!" 13Then he touched her, and instantly she could stand straight. How she praised God!

14But the leader in charge of the synagogue was indignant that Jesus had healed her on the Sabbath day. "There are six days of the week for working," he said to the crowd. "Come on those days to be healed, not on the Sabbath."

15But the Lord replied, "You hypocrites! Each of you works on the Sabbath day! Don't you untie your ox or your donkey from its stall on the Sabbath and lead it out for water? 16This dear woman, a daughter of Abraham, has been held in bondage by Satan for eighteen years. Isn't it right that she be released, even on the Sabbath?"

17This shamed his enemies, but all the people rejoiced at the wonderful things he did.

Parable of the Mustard Seed

18Then Jesus said, "What is the Kingdom of God like? How can I illustrate it? 19It is like a tiny mustard seed that a man planted in a garden; it grows and becomes a tree, and the birds make nests in its branches."

Parable of the Yeast

20He also asked, "What else is the Kingdom of God like? 21It is like the yeast a woman used in making bread. Even though she put only a little yeast in three measures of flour, it permeated every part of the dough."

The Narrow Door

22Jesus went through the towns and villages, teaching as he went, always pressing on toward Jerusalem. 23Someone asked him, "Lord, will only a few be saved?"

He replied, 24"Work hard to enter the narrow door to God's Kingdom, for many will try to enter but will fail. 25When the master of the house has locked the door, it will be too late. You will stand outside knocking and pleading, 'Lord, open the door for us!' But he will reply, 'I don't know you or where you come from.' 26Then you will say, 'But we ate and drank with you, and you taught in our streets.' 27And he will reply, 'I tell you, I don't know you or where you come from. Get away from me, all you who do evil.'

28"There will be weeping and gnashing of teeth, for you will see Abraham, Isaac, Jacob, and all the prophets in the Kingdom of God, but you will be thrown out. 29And people will come from all over the world—from east and west, north and south—to take their places in the Kingdom of God. 30And note this: Some who seem least important now will be the greatest then, and some who are the greatest now will be least important then.*"

Jesus Grieves over Jerusalem

31At that time some Pharisees said to him, "Get away from here if you want to live! Herod Antipas wants to kill you!"

32Jesus replied, "Go tell that fox that I will keep on casting out demons and healing people today and tomorrow; and the third day I will accomplish my purpose. 33Yes, today, tomorrow, and the next day I must proceed on my way. For

12:59 Greek *last lepton* [the smallest Jewish coin].   **13:30** Greek *Some are last who will be first, and some are first who will be last.*

it wouldn't do for a prophet of God to be killed except in Jerusalem!

³⁴"O Jerusalem, Jerusalem, the city that kills the prophets and stones God's messengers! How often I have wanted to gather your children together as a hen protects her chicks beneath her wings, but you wouldn't let me. ³⁵And now, look, your house is abandoned. And you will never see me again until you say, 'Blessings on the one who comes in the name of the LORD!'*"

Jesus Heals on the Sabbath

14 One Sabbath day Jesus went to eat dinner in the home of a leader of the Pharisees, and the people were watching him closely. ²There was a man there whose arms and legs were swollen.* ³Jesus asked the Pharisees and experts in religious law, "Is it permitted in the law to heal people on the Sabbath day, or not?" ⁴When they refused to answer, Jesus touched the sick man and healed him and sent him away. ⁵Then he turned to them and said, "Which of you doesn't work on the Sabbath? If your son* or your cow falls into a pit, don't you rush to get him out?" ⁶Again they could not answer.

Jesus Teaches about Humility

⁷When Jesus noticed that all who had come to the dinner were trying to sit in the seats of honor near the head of the table, he gave them this advice: ⁸"When you are invited to a wedding feast, don't sit in the seat of honor. What if someone who is more distinguished than you has also been invited? ⁹The host will come and say, 'Give this person your seat.' Then you will be embarrassed, and you will have to take whatever seat is left at the foot of the table!

¹⁰"Instead, take the lowest place at the foot of the table. Then when your host sees you, he will come and say, 'Friend, we have a better place for you!' Then you will be honored in front of all the other guests. ¹¹For those who exalt themselves will be humbled, and those who humble themselves will be exalted."

¹²Then he turned to his host. "When you put on a luncheon or a banquet," he said, "don't invite your friends, brothers, relatives, and rich neighbors. For they will invite you back, and that will be your only reward. ¹³Instead, invite the poor, the crippled, the lame, and the blind. ¹⁴Then at the resurrection of the righteous, God will reward you for inviting those who could not repay you."

Parable of the Great Feast

¹⁵Hearing this, a man sitting at the table with Jesus exclaimed, "What a blessing it will be to attend a banquet* in the Kingdom of God!"

¹⁶Jesus replied with this story: "A man prepared a great feast and sent out many invitations. ¹⁷When the banquet was ready, he sent his servant to tell the guests, 'Come, the banquet is ready.' ¹⁸But they all began making excuses. One said, 'I have just bought a field and must inspect it. Please excuse me.' ¹⁹Another said, 'I have just bought five pairs of oxen, and I want to try them out. Please excuse me.' ²⁰Another said, 'I now have a wife, so I can't come.'

²¹"The servant returned and told his master what they had said. His master was furious and said, 'Go quickly into the streets and alleys of the town and invite the poor, the crippled, the blind, and the lame.' ²²After the servant had done this, he reported, 'There is still room for more.' ²³So his master said, 'Go out into the country lanes and behind the hedges and urge anyone you find to come, so that the house will be full. ²⁴For none of those I first invited will get even the smallest taste of my banquet.'"

The Cost of Being a Disciple

²⁵A large crowd was following Jesus. He turned around and said to them, ²⁶"If you want to be my disciple, you must hate everyone else by comparison—your father and mother, wife and children, brothers and sisters—yes, even your own life. Otherwise, you cannot be my disciple. ²⁷And if you do not carry your own cross and follow me, you cannot be my disciple.

²⁸"But don't begin until you count the cost. For who would begin construction of a building without first calculating the cost to see if there is enough money to finish it? ²⁹Otherwise, you might complete only the foundation before running out of money, and then everyone would laugh at you. ³⁰They would say, 'There's the person who started that building and couldn't afford to finish it!'

³¹"Or what king would go to war against another king without first sitting down with his counselors to discuss whether his army of 10,000 could defeat the 20,000 soldiers marching against him? ³²And if he can't, he will send a delegation to discuss terms of peace while the enemy is still far away. ³³So you cannot become my disciple without giving up everything you own.

³⁴"Salt is good for seasoning. But if it loses its flavor, how do you make it salty again? ³⁵Flavorless salt is good neither for the soil nor for the manure pile. It is thrown away. Anyone with ears to hear should listen and understand!"

Parable of the Lost Sheep

15 Tax collectors and other notorious sinners often came to listen to Jesus teach. ²This made the Pharisees and teachers of religious law complain that he was associating with such sinful people—even eating with them!

³So Jesus told them this story: ⁴"If a man has a hundred sheep and one of them gets lost, what

13:35 Ps 118:26.   **14:2** Or *who had dropsy.*   **14:5** Some manuscripts read *donkey.*   **14:15** Greek *to eat bread.*

will he do? Won't he leave the ninety-nine others in the wilderness and go to search for the one that is lost until he finds it? ⁵And when he has found it, he will joyfully carry it home on his shoulders. ⁶When he arrives, he will call together his friends and neighbors, saying, 'Rejoice with me because I have found my lost sheep.' ⁷In the same way, there is more joy in heaven over one lost sinner who repents and returns to God than over ninety-nine others who are righteous and haven't strayed away!

Parable of the Lost Coin

⁸"Or suppose a woman has ten silver coins* and loses one. Won't she light a lamp and sweep the entire house and search carefully until she finds it? ⁹And when she finds it, she will call in her friends and neighbors and say, 'Rejoice with me because I have found my lost coin.' ¹⁰In the same way, there is joy in the presence of God's angels when even one sinner repents."

Parable of the Lost Son

¹¹To illustrate the point further, Jesus told them this story: "A man had two sons. ¹²The younger son told his father, 'I want my share of your estate now before you die.' So his father agreed to divide his wealth between his sons.

¹³"A few days later this younger son packed all his belongings and moved to a distant land, and there he wasted all his money in wild living. ¹⁴About the time his money ran out, a great famine swept over the land, and he began to starve. ¹⁵He persuaded a local farmer to hire him, and the man sent him into his fields to feed the pigs. ¹⁶The young man became so hungry that even the pods he was feeding the pigs looked good to him. But no one gave him anything.

¹⁷"When he finally came to his senses, he said to himself, 'At home even the hired servants have food enough to spare, and here I am dying of hunger! ¹⁸I will go home to my father and say, "Father, I have sinned against both heaven and you, ¹⁹and I am no longer worthy of being called your son. Please take me on as a hired servant."'

²⁰"So he returned home to his father. And while he was still a long way off, his father saw him coming. Filled with love and compassion, he ran to his son, embraced him, and kissed him. ²¹His son said to him, 'Father, I have sinned against both heaven and you, and I am no longer worthy of being called your son.*'

²²"But his father said to the servants, 'Quick! Bring the finest robe in the house and put it on him. Get a ring for his finger and sandals for his feet. ²³And kill the calf we have been fattening. We must celebrate with a feast, ²⁴for this son of mine was dead and has now returned to life. He was lost, but now he is found.' So the party began.

²⁵"Meanwhile, the older son was in the fields working. When he returned home, he heard music and dancing in the house, ²⁶and he asked one of the servants what was going on. ²⁷'Your brother is back,' he was told, 'and your father has killed the fattened calf. We are celebrating because of his safe return.'

²⁸"The older brother was angry and wouldn't go in. His father came out and begged him, ²⁹but he replied, 'All these years I've slaved for you and never once refused to do a single thing you told me to. And in all that time you never gave me even one young goat for a feast with my friends. ³⁰Yet when this son of yours comes back after squandering your money on prostitutes, you celebrate by killing the fattened calf!'

³¹"His father said to him, 'Look, dear son, you have always stayed by me, and everything I have is yours. ³²We had to celebrate this happy day. For your brother was dead and has come back to life! He was lost, but now he is found!'"

Parable of the Shrewd Manager

16 Jesus told this story to his disciples: "There was a certain rich man who had a manager handling his affairs. One day a report came that the manager was wasting his employer's money. ²So the employer called him in and said, 'What's this I hear about you? Get your report in order, because you are going to be fired.'

³"The manager thought to himself, 'Now what? My boss has fired me. I don't have the strength to dig ditches, and I'm too proud to beg. ⁴Ah, I know how to ensure that I'll have plenty of friends who will give me a home when I am fired.'

⁵"So he invited each person who owed money to his employer to come and discuss the situation. He asked the first one, 'How much do you owe him?' ⁶The man replied, 'I owe him 800 gallons of olive oil.' So the manager told him, 'Take the bill and quickly change it to 400 gallons.*'

⁷"'And how much do you owe my employer?' he asked the next man. 'I owe him 1,000 bushels of wheat,' was the reply. 'Here,' the manager said, 'take the bill and change it to 800 bushels.*'

⁸"The rich man had to admire the dishonest rascal for being so shrewd. And it is true that the children of this world are more shrewd in dealing with the world around them than are the children of the light. ⁹Here's the lesson: Use your worldly resources to benefit others and make friends. Then, when your earthly possessions are gone, they will welcome you to an eternal home.*

¹⁰"If you are faithful in little things, you will be faithful in large ones. But if you are dishonest in little things, you won't be honest with greater responsibilities. ¹¹And if you are untrustworthy about worldly wealth, who will trust you with the

15:8 Greek *ten drachmas.* A drachma was the equivalent of a full day's wage. **15:21** Some manuscripts add *Please take me on as a hired servant.* **16:6** Greek *100 baths . . . 50 [baths].* **16:7** Greek *100 korous . . . 80 [korous].* **16:9** Or *you will be welcomed into eternal homes.*

true riches of heaven? ¹²And if you are not faithful with other people's things, why should you be trusted with things of your own?

¹³"No one can serve two masters. For you will hate one and love the other; you will be devoted to one and despise the other. You cannot serve both God and money."

¹⁴The Pharisees, who dearly loved their money, heard all this and scoffed at him. ¹⁵Then he said to them, "You like to appear righteous in public, but God knows your hearts. What this world honors is detestable in the sight of God.

¹⁶"Until John the Baptist, the law of Moses and the messages of the prophets were your guides. But now the Good News of the Kingdom of God is preached, and everyone is eager to get in.* ¹⁷But that doesn't mean that the law has lost its force. It is easier for heaven and earth to disappear than for the smallest point of God's law to be overturned.

¹⁸"For example, a man who divorces his wife and marries someone else commits adultery. And anyone who marries a woman divorced from her husband commits adultery."

Parable of the Rich Man and Lazarus

¹⁹Jesus said, "There was a certain rich man who was splendidly clothed in purple and fine linen and who lived each day in luxury. ²⁰At his gate lay a poor man named Lazarus who was covered with sores. ²¹As Lazarus lay there longing for scraps from the rich man's table, the dogs would come and lick his open sores.

²²"Finally, the poor man died and was carried by the angels to be with Abraham.* The rich man also died and was buried, ²³and his soul went to the place of the dead.* There, in torment, he saw Abraham in the far distance with Lazarus at his side.

²⁴"The rich man shouted, 'Father Abraham, have some pity! Send Lazarus over here to dip the tip of his finger in water and cool my tongue. I am in anguish in these flames.'

²⁵"But Abraham said to him, 'Son, remember that during your lifetime you had everything you wanted, and Lazarus had nothing. So now he is here being comforted, and you are in anguish. ²⁶And besides, there is a great chasm separating us. No one can cross over to you from here, and no one can cross over to us from there.'

²⁷"Then the rich man said, 'Please, Father Abraham, at least send him to my father's home. ²⁸For I have five brothers, and I want him to warn them so they don't end up in this place of torment.'

²⁹"But Abraham said, 'Moses and the prophets have warned them. Your brothers can read what they wrote.'

³⁰"The rich man replied, 'No, Father Abraham! But if someone is sent to them from the dead, then they will repent of their sins and turn to God.'

³¹"But Abraham said, 'If they won't listen to Moses and the prophets, they won't listen even if someone rises from the dead.'"

Teachings about Forgiveness and Faith

17 One day Jesus said to his disciples, "There will always be temptations to sin, but what sorrow awaits the person who does the tempting! ²It would be better to be thrown into the sea with a millstone hung around your neck than to cause one of these little ones to fall into sin. ³So watch yourselves!

"If another believer* sins, rebuke that person; then if there is repentance, forgive. ⁴Even if that person wrongs you seven times a day and each time turns again and asks forgiveness, you must forgive."

⁵The apostles said to the Lord, "Show us how to increase our faith."

⁶The Lord answered, "If you had faith even as small as a mustard seed, you could say to this mulberry tree, 'May you be uprooted and thrown into the sea,' and it would obey you!

⁷"When a servant comes in from plowing or taking care of sheep, does his master say, 'Come in and eat with me'? ⁸No, he says, 'Prepare my meal, put on your apron, and serve me while I eat. Then you can eat later.' ⁹And does the master thank the servant for doing what he was told to do? Of course not. ¹⁰In the same way, when you obey me you should say, 'We are unworthy servants who have simply done our duty.'"

Ten Healed of Leprosy

¹¹As Jesus continued on toward Jerusalem, he reached the border between Galilee and Samaria. ¹²As he entered a village there, ten lepers stood at a distance, ¹³crying out, "Jesus, Master, have mercy on us!"

¹⁴He looked at them and said, "Go show yourselves to the priests."* And as they went, they were cleansed of their leprosy.

¹⁵One of them, when he saw that he was healed, came back to Jesus, shouting, "Praise God!" ¹⁶He fell to the ground at Jesus' feet, thanking him for what he had done. This man was a Samaritan.

¹⁷Jesus asked, "Didn't I heal ten men? Where are the other nine? ¹⁸Has no one returned to give glory to God except this foreigner?" ¹⁹And Jesus said to the man, "Stand up and go. Your faith has healed you.*"

The Coming of the Kingdom

²⁰One day the Pharisees asked Jesus, "When will the Kingdom of God come?"

Jesus replied, "The Kingdom of God can't be

16:16 Or *everyone is urged to enter in.* **16:22** Greek *into Abraham's bosom.* **16:23** Greek *to Hades.* **17:3** Greek *If your brother.* **17:14** See Lev 14:2-32. **17:19** Or *Your faith has saved you.*

detected by visible signs.* ²¹You won't be able to say, 'Here it is!' or 'It's over there!' For the Kingdom of God is already among you.*"

²²Then he said to his disciples, "The time is coming when you will long to see the day when the Son of Man returns,* but you won't see it. ²³People will tell you, 'Look, there is the Son of Man,' or 'Here he is,' but don't go out and follow them. ²⁴For as the lightning flashes and lights up the sky from one end to the other, so it will be on the day when the Son of Man comes. ²⁵But first the Son of Man must suffer terribly* and be rejected by this generation.

²⁶"When the Son of Man returns, it will be like it was in Noah's day. ²⁷In those days, the people enjoyed banquets and parties and weddings right up to the time Noah entered his boat and the flood came and destroyed them all.

²⁸"And the world will be as it was in the days of Lot. People went about their daily business—eating and drinking, buying and selling, farming and building—²⁹until the morning Lot left Sodom. Then fire and burning sulfur rained down from heaven and destroyed them all. ³⁰Yes, it will be 'business as usual' right up to the day when the Son of Man is revealed. ³¹On that day a person out on the deck of a roof must not go down into the house to pack. A person out in the field must not return home. ³²Remember what happened to Lot's wife! ³³If you cling to your life, you will lose it, and if you let your life go, you will save it. ³⁴That night two people will be asleep in one bed; one will be taken, the other left. ³⁵Two women will be grinding flour together at the mill; one will be taken, the other left.*"

³⁷"Where will this happen, Lord?"* the disciples asked.

Jesus replied, "Just as the gathering of vultures shows there is a carcass nearby, so these signs indicate that the end is near."*

Parable of the Persistent Widow

18 One day Jesus told his disciples a story to show that they should always pray and never give up. ²"There was a judge in a certain city," he said, "who neither feared God nor cared about people. ³A widow of that city came to him repeatedly, saying, 'Give me justice in this dispute with my enemy.' ⁴The judge ignored her for a while, but finally he said to himself, 'I don't fear God or care about people, ⁵but this woman is driving me crazy. I'm going to see that she gets justice, because she is wearing me out with her constant requests!'"

⁶Then the Lord said, "Learn a lesson from this unjust judge. ⁷Even he rendered a just decision in the end. So don't you think God will

surely give justice to his chosen people who cry out to him day and night? Will he keep putting them off? ⁸I tell you, he will grant justice to them quickly! But when the Son of Man* returns, how many will he find on the earth who have faith?"

Parable of the Pharisee and Tax Collector

⁹Then Jesus told this story to some who had great confidence in their own righteousness and scorned everyone else: ¹⁰"Two men went to the Temple to pray. One was a Pharisee, and the other was a despised tax collector. ¹¹The Pharisee stood by himself and prayed this prayer*: 'I thank you, God, that I am not a sinner like everyone else. For I don't cheat, I don't sin, and I don't commit adultery. I'm certainly not like that tax collector! ¹²I fast twice a week, and I give you a tenth of my income.'

¹³"But the tax collector stood at a distance and dared not even lift his eyes to heaven as he prayed. Instead, he beat his chest in sorrow, saying, 'O God, be merciful to me, for I am a sinner.' ¹⁴I tell you, this sinner, not the Pharisee, returned home justified before God. For those who exalt themselves will be humbled, and those who humble themselves will be exalted."

Jesus Blesses the Children

¹⁵One day some parents brought their little children to Jesus so he could touch and bless them. But when the disciples saw this, they scolded the parents for bothering him.

¹⁶Then Jesus called for the children and said to the disciples, "Let the children come to me. Don't stop them! For the Kingdom of God belongs to those who are like these children. ¹⁷I tell you the truth, anyone who doesn't receive the Kingdom of God like a child will never enter it."

The Rich Man

¹⁸Once a religious leader asked Jesus this question: "Good Teacher, what should I do to inherit eternal life?"

¹⁹"Why do you call me good?" Jesus asked him. "Only God is truly good. ²⁰But to answer your question, you know the commandments: 'You must not commit adultery. You must not murder. You must not steal. You must not testify falsely. Honor your father and mother.'*"

²¹The man replied, "I've obeyed all these commandments since I was young."

²²When Jesus heard his answer, he said, "There is still one thing you haven't done. Sell all your possessions and give the money to the poor, and you will have treasure in heaven. Then come, follow me."

17:20 Or *by your speculations.*   **17:21** Or *is within you,* or *is in your grasp.*   **17:22** Or *long for even one day with the Son of Man.* "Son of Man" is a title Jesus used for himself.   **17:25** Or *suffer many things.*   **17:35** Some manuscripts add verse 36, *Two men will be working in the field; one will be taken, the other left.* Compare Matt 24:40.   **17:37a** Greek *"Where, Lord?"*   **17:37b** Greek *"Wherever the carcass is, the vultures gather."*   **18:8** "Son of Man" is a title Jesus used for himself.   **18:11** Some manuscripts read *stood and prayed this prayer to himself.*   **18:20** Exod 20:12-16; Deut 5:16-20.

23But when the man heard this he became very sad, for he was very rich.

24When Jesus saw this,* he said, "How hard it is for the rich to enter the Kingdom of God! 25In fact, it is easier for a camel to go through the eye of a needle than for a rich person to enter the Kingdom of God!"

26Those who heard this said, "Then who in the world can be saved?"

27He replied, "What is impossible for people is possible with God."

28Peter said, "We've left our homes to follow you."

29"Yes," Jesus replied, "and I assure you that everyone who has given up house or wife or brothers or parents or children, for the sake of the Kingdom of God, 30will be repaid many times over in this life, and will have eternal life in the world to come."

Jesus Again Predicts His Death

31Taking the twelve disciples aside, Jesus said, "Listen, we're going up to Jerusalem, where all the predictions of the prophets concerning the Son of Man will come true. 32He will be handed over to the Romans,* and he will be mocked, treated shamefully, and spit upon. 33They will flog him with a whip and kill him, but on the third day he will rise again."

34But they didn't understand any of this. The significance of his words was hidden from them, and they failed to grasp what he was talking about.

Jesus Heals a Blind Beggar

35As Jesus approached Jericho, a blind beggar was sitting beside the road. 36When he heard the noise of a crowd going past, he asked what was happening. 37They told him that Jesus the Nazarene* was going by. 38So he began shouting, "Jesus, Son of David, have mercy on me!"

39"Be quiet!" the people in front yelled at him.

But he only shouted louder, "Son of David, have mercy on me!"

40When Jesus heard him, he stopped and ordered that the man be brought to him. As the man came near, Jesus asked him, 41"What do you want me to do for you?"

"Lord," he said, "I want to see!"

42And Jesus said, "All right, receive your sight! Your faith has healed you." 43Instantly the man could see, and he followed Jesus, praising God. And all who saw it praised God, too.

Jesus and Zacchaeus

19 Jesus entered Jericho and made his way through the town. 2There was a man there named Zacchaeus. He was the chief tax collector in the region, and he had become very rich. 3He tried to get a look at Jesus, but he was too short to see over the crowd. 4So he ran ahead and climbed a sycamore-fig tree beside the road, for Jesus was going to pass that way.

5When Jesus came by, he looked up at Zacchaeus and called him by name. "Zacchaeus!" he said. "Quick, come down! I must be a guest in your home today."

6Zacchaeus quickly climbed down and took Jesus to his house in great excitement and joy. 7But the people were displeased. "He has gone to be the guest of a notorious sinner," they grumbled.

8Meanwhile, Zacchaeus stood before the Lord and said, "I will give half my wealth to the poor, Lord, and if I have cheated people on their taxes, I will give them back four times as much!"

9Jesus responded, "Salvation has come to this home today, for this man has shown himself to be a true son of Abraham. 10For the Son of Man* came to seek and save those who are lost."

Parable of the Ten Servants

11The crowd was listening to everything Jesus said. And because he was nearing Jerusalem, he told them a story to correct the impression that the Kingdom of God would begin right away. 12He said, "A nobleman was called away to a distant empire to be crowned king and then return. 13Before he left, he called together ten of his servants and divided among them ten pounds of silver,* saying, 'Invest this for me while I am gone.' 14But his people hated him and sent a delegation after him to say, 'We do not want him to be our king.'

15"After he was crowned king, he returned and called in the servants to whom he had given the money. He wanted to find out what their profits were. 16The first servant reported, 'Master, I invested your money and made ten times the original amount!'

17"'Well done!' the king exclaimed. 'You are a good servant. You have been faithful with the little I entrusted to you, so you will be governor of ten cities as your reward.'

18"The next servant reported, 'Master, I invested your money and made five times the original amount.'

19"'Well done!' the king said. 'You will be governor over five cities.'

20"But the third servant brought back only the original amount of money and said, 'Master, I hid your money and kept it safe. 21I was afraid because you are a hard man to deal with, taking what isn't yours and harvesting crops you didn't plant.'

22"'You wicked servant!' the king roared. 'Your own words condemn you. If you knew that I'm a hard man who takes what isn't mine and harvests crops I didn't plant, 23why didn't you deposit my money in the bank? At least I could have gotten some interest on it.'

18:24 Some manuscripts read *When Jesus saw how sad the man was.* **18:32** Greek *the Gentiles.* **18:37** Or *Jesus of Nazareth.* **19:10** "Son of Man" is a title Jesus used for himself. **19:13** Greek *ten minas;* one mina was worth about three months' wages.

²⁴"Then, turning to the others standing nearby, the king ordered, 'Take the money from this servant, and give it to the one who has ten pounds.'

²⁵" 'But, master,' they said, 'he already has ten pounds!'

²⁶"'Yes,' the king replied, 'and to those who use well what they are given, even more will be given. But from those who do nothing, even what little they have will be taken away. ²⁷And as for these enemies of mine who didn't want me to be their king—bring them in and execute them right here in front of me.'"

Jesus' Triumphant Entry

²⁸After telling this story, Jesus went on toward Jerusalem, walking ahead of his disciples. ²⁹As he came to the towns of Bethphage and Bethany on the Mount of Olives, he sent two disciples ahead. ³⁰"Go into that village over there," he told them. "As you enter it, you will see a young donkey tied there that no one has ever ridden. Untie it and bring it here. ³¹If anyone asks, 'Why are you untying that colt?' just say, 'The Lord needs it.'"

³²So they went and found the colt, just as Jesus had said. ³³And sure enough, as they were untying it, the owners asked them, "Why are you untying that colt?"

³⁴And the disciples simply replied, "The Lord needs it." ³⁵So they brought the colt to Jesus and threw their garments over it for him to ride on.

³⁶As he rode along, the crowds spread out their garments on the road ahead of him. ³⁷When he reached the place where the road started down the Mount of Olives, all of his followers began to shout and sing as they walked along, praising God for all the wonderful miracles they had seen.

³⁸ "Blessings on the King who comes in the
name of the Lᴏʀᴅ!
Peace in heaven, and glory in highest
heaven!"*

³⁹But some of the Pharisees among the crowd said, "Teacher, rebuke your followers for saying things like that!"

⁴⁰He replied, "If they kept quiet, the stones along the road would burst into cheers!"

Jesus Weeps over Jerusalem

⁴¹But as he came closer to Jerusalem and saw the city ahead, he began to weep. ⁴²"How I wish today that you of all people would understand the way to peace. But now it is too late, and peace is hidden from your eyes. ⁴³Before long your enemies will build ramparts against your walls and encircle you and close in on you from every side. ⁴⁴They will crush you into the ground, and your children with you. Your enemies will not leave a single stone in place, because you did not accept your opportunity for salvation."

Jesus Clears the Temple

⁴⁵Then Jesus entered the Temple and began to drive out the people selling animals for sacrifices. ⁴⁶He said to them, "The Scriptures declare, 'My Temple will be a house of prayer,' but you have turned it into a den of thieves."*

⁴⁷After that, he taught daily in the Temple, but the leading priests, the teachers of religious law, and the other leaders of the people began planning how to kill him. ⁴⁸But they could think of nothing, because all the people hung on every word he said.

The Authority of Jesus Challenged

20 One day as Jesus was teaching the people and preaching the Good News in the Temple, the leading priests, the teachers of religious law, and the elders came up to him. ²They demanded, "By what authority are you doing all these things? Who gave you the right?"

³"Let me ask you a question first," he replied. ⁴"Did John's authority to baptize come from heaven, or was it merely human?"

⁵They talked it over among themselves. "If we say it was from heaven, he will ask why we didn't believe John. ⁶But if we say it was merely human, the people will stone us because they are convinced John was a prophet." ⁷So they finally replied that they didn't know.

⁸And Jesus responded, "Then I won't tell you by what authority I do these things."

Parable of the Evil Farmers

⁹Now Jesus turned to the people again and told them this story: "A man planted a vineyard, leased it to tenant farmers, and moved to another country to live for several years. ¹⁰At the time of the grape harvest, he sent one of his servants to collect his share of the crop. But the farmers attacked the servant, beat him up, and sent him back empty-handed. ¹¹So the owner sent another servant, but they also insulted him, beat him up, and sent him away empty-handed. ¹²A third man was sent, and they wounded him and chased him away.

¹³"'What will I do?' the owner asked himself. 'I know! I'll send my cherished son. Surely they will respect him.'

¹⁴"But when the tenant farmers saw his son, they said to each other, 'Here comes the heir to this estate. Let's kill him and get the estate for ourselves!' ¹⁵So they dragged him out of the vineyard and murdered him.

"What do you suppose the owner of the vineyard will do to them?" Jesus asked. ¹⁶"I'll tell you—he will come and kill those farmers and lease the vineyard to others."

19:38 Pss 118:26; 148:1.   **19:46** Isa 56:7; Jer 7:11.

"How terrible that such a thing should ever happen," his listeners protested.

[17]Jesus looked at them and said, "Then what does this Scripture mean?

'The stone that the builders rejected
has now become the cornerstone.'*

[18]Everyone who stumbles over that stone will be broken to pieces, and it will crush anyone it falls on."

[19]The teachers of religious law and the leading priests wanted to arrest Jesus immediately because they realized he was telling the story against them—they were the wicked farmers. But they were afraid of the people's reaction.

Taxes for Caesar

[20]Watching for their opportunity, the leaders sent spies pretending to be honest men. They tried to get Jesus to say something that could be reported to the Roman governor so he would arrest Jesus. [21]"Teacher," they said, "we know that you speak and teach what is right and are not influenced by what others think. You teach the way of God truthfully. [22]Now tell us—is it right for us to pay taxes to Caesar or not?"

[23]He saw through their trickery and said, [24]"Show me a Roman coin.* Whose picture and title are stamped on it?"

"Caesar's," they replied.

[25]"Well then," he said, "give to Caesar what belongs to Caesar, and give to God what belongs to God."

[26]So they failed to trap him by what he said in front of the people. Instead, they were amazed by his answer, and they became silent.

Discussion about Resurrection

[27]Then Jesus was approached by some Sadducees—religious leaders who say there is no resurrection from the dead. [28]They posed this question: "Teacher, Moses gave us a law that if a man dies, leaving a wife but no children, his brother should marry the widow and have a child who will carry on the brother's name.* [29]Well, suppose there were seven brothers. The oldest one married and then died without children. [30]So the second brother married the widow, but he also died. [31]Then the third brother married her. This continued with all seven of them, who died without children. [32]Finally, the woman also died. [33]So tell us, whose wife will she be in the resurrection? For all seven were married to her!"

[34]Jesus replied, "Marriage is for people here on earth. [35]But in the age to come, those worthy of being raised from the dead will neither marry nor be given in marriage. [36]And they will never die again. In this respect they will be like angels. They are children of God and children of the resurrection.

[37]"But now, as to whether the dead will be raised—even Moses proved this when he wrote about the burning bush. Long after Abraham, Isaac, and Jacob had died, he referred to the Lord* as 'the God of Abraham, the God of Isaac, and the God of Jacob.'* [38]So he is the God of the living, not the dead, for they are all alive to him."

[39]"Well said, Teacher!" remarked some of the teachers of religious law who were standing there. [40]And then no one dared to ask him any more questions.

Whose Son Is the Messiah?

[41]Then Jesus presented them with a question. "Why is it," he asked, "that the Messiah is said to be the son of David? [42]For David himself wrote in the book of Psalms:

'The Lord said to my Lord,
Sit in the place of honor at my right hand
[43] until I humble your enemies,
making them a footstool under your feet.'*

[44]Since David called the Messiah 'Lord,' how can the Messiah be his son?"

[45]Then, with the crowds listening, he turned to his disciples and said, [46]"Beware of these teachers of religious law! For they like to parade around in flowing robes and love to receive respectful greetings as they walk in the marketplaces. And how they love the seats of honor in the synagogues and the head table at banquets. [47]Yet they shamelessly cheat widows out of their property and then pretend to be pious by making long prayers in public. Because of this, they will be severely punished."

The Widow's Offering

21 While Jesus was in the Temple, he watched the rich people dropping their gifts in the collection box. [2]Then a poor widow came by and dropped in two small coins.*

[3]"I tell you the truth," Jesus said, "this poor widow has given more than all the rest of them. [4]For they have given a tiny part of their surplus, but she, poor as she is, has given everything she has."

Jesus Foretells the Future

[5]Some of his disciples began talking about the majestic stonework of the Temple and the memorial decorations on the walls. But Jesus said, [6]"The time is coming when all these things will be completely demolished. Not one stone will be left on top of another!"

[7]"Teacher," they asked, "when will all this

20:17 Ps 118:22.   **20:24** Greek *a denarius.*   **20:28** See Deut 25:5-6.   **20:37a** Greek *when he wrote about the bush. He referred to the Lord.*   **20:37b** Exod 3:6.   **20:42-43** Ps 110:1.   **21:2** Greek *two lepta* (the smallest of Jewish coins).

LUKE 22 . . . page 72

happen? What sign will show us that these things are about to take place?"

⁸He replied, "Don't let anyone mislead you, for many will come in my name, claiming, 'I am the Messiah,'* and saying, 'The time has come!' But don't believe them. ⁹And when you hear of wars and insurrections, don't panic. Yes, these things must take place first, but the end won't follow immediately." ¹⁰Then he added, "Nation will go to war against nation, and kingdom against kingdom. ¹¹There will be great earthquakes, and there will be famines and plagues in many lands, and there will be terrifying things and great miraculous signs from heaven.

¹²"But before all this occurs, there will be a time of great persecution. You will be dragged into synagogues and prisons, and you will stand trial before kings and governors because you are my followers. ¹³But this will be your opportunity to tell them about me.* ¹⁴So don't worry in advance about how to answer the charges against you, ¹⁵for I will give you the right words and such wisdom that none of your opponents will be able to reply or refute you! ¹⁶Even those closest to you—your parents, brothers, relatives, and friends—will betray you. They will even kill some of you. ¹⁷And everyone will hate you because you are my followers.* ¹⁸But not a hair of your head will perish! ¹⁹By standing firm, you will win your souls.

²⁰"And when you see Jerusalem surrounded by armies, then you will know that the time of its destruction has arrived. ²¹Then those in Judea must flee to the hills. Those in Jerusalem must get out, and those out in the country should not return to the city. ²²For those will be days of God's vengeance, and the prophetic words of the Scriptures will be fulfilled. ²³How terrible it will be for pregnant women and for nursing mothers in those days. For there will be disaster in the land and great anger against this people. ²⁴They will be killed by the sword or sent away as captives to all the nations of the world. And Jerusalem will be trampled down by the Gentiles until the period of the Gentiles comes to an end.

²⁵"And there will be strange signs in the sun, moon, and stars. And here on earth the nations will be in turmoil, perplexed by the roaring seas and strange tides. ²⁶People will be terrified at what they see coming upon the earth, for the powers in the heavens will be shaken. ²⁷Then everyone will see the Son of Man* coming on a cloud with power and great glory.* ²⁸So when all these things begin to happen, stand and look up, for your salvation is near!"

²⁹Then he gave them this illustration: "Notice the fig tree, or any other tree. ³⁰When the leaves come out, you know without being told that summer is near. ³¹In the same way, when you see

all these things taking place, you can know that the Kingdom of God is near. ³²I tell you the truth, this generation will not pass from the scene until all these things have taken place. ³³Heaven and earth will disappear, but my words will never disappear.

³⁴"Watch out! Don't let your hearts be dulled by carousing and drunkenness, and by the worries of this life. Don't let that day catch you unaware, ³⁵like a trap. For that day will come upon everyone living on the earth. ³⁶Keep alert at all times. And pray that you might be strong enough to escape these coming horrors and stand before the Son of Man."

³⁷Every day Jesus went to the Temple to teach, and each evening he returned to spend the night on the Mount of Olives. ³⁸The crowds gathered at the Temple early each morning to hear him.

Judas Agrees to Betray Jesus

22 The Festival of Unleavened Bread, which is also called Passover, was approaching. ²The leading priests and teachers of religious law were plotting how to kill Jesus, but they were afraid of the people's reaction.

³Then Satan entered into Judas Iscariot, who was one of the twelve disciples, ⁴and he went to the leading priests and captains of the Temple guard to discuss the best way to betray Jesus to them. ⁵They were delighted, and they promised to give him money. ⁶So he agreed and began looking for an opportunity to betray Jesus so they could arrest him when the crowds weren't around.

The Last Supper

⁷Now the Festival of Unleavened Bread arrived, when the Passover lamb is sacrificed. ⁸Jesus sent Peter and John ahead and said, "Go and prepare the Passover meal, so we can eat it together."

⁹"Where do you want us to prepare it?" they asked him.

¹⁰He replied, "As soon as you enter Jerusalem, a man carrying a pitcher of water will meet you. Follow him. At the house he enters, ¹¹say to the owner, 'The Teacher asks: Where is the guest room where I can eat the Passover meal with my disciples?' ¹²He will take you upstairs to a large room that is already set up. That is where you should prepare our meal." ¹³They went off to the city and found everything just as Jesus had said, and they prepared the Passover meal there.

¹⁴When the time came, Jesus and the apostles sat down together at the table.* ¹⁵Jesus said, "I have been very eager to eat this Passover meal with you before my suffering begins. ¹⁶For I tell you now that I won't eat this meal again until its meaning is fulfilled in the Kingdom of God."

¹⁷Then he took a cup of wine and gave thanks

21:8 Greek *claiming, 'I am.'*   21:13 Or *This will be your testimony against them.*   21:17 Greek *on account of my name.*
21:27a "Son of Man" is a title Jesus used for himself.   21:27b See Dan 7:13.   22:14 Or *reclined together.*

to God for it. Then he said, "Take this and share it among yourselves. [18]For I will not drink wine again until the Kingdom of God has come."

[19]He took some bread and gave thanks to God for it. Then he broke it in pieces and gave it to the disciples, saying, "This is my body, which is given for you. Do this to remember me."

[20]After supper he took another cup of wine and said, "This cup is the new covenant between God and his people—an agreement confirmed with my blood, which is poured out as a sacrifice for you.*

[21]"But here at this table, sitting among us as a friend, is the man who will betray me. [22]For it has been determined that the Son of Man* must die. But what sorrow awaits the one who betrays him." [23]The disciples began to ask each other which of them would ever do such a thing.

[24]Then they began to argue among themselves about who would be the greatest among them. [25]Jesus told them, "In this world the kings and great men lord it over their people, yet they are called 'friends of the people.' [26]But among you it will be different. Those who are the greatest among you should take the lowest rank, and the leader should be like a servant. [27]Who is more important, the one who sits at the table or the one who serves? The one who sits at the table, of course. But not here! For I am among you as one who serves.

[28]"You have stayed with me in my time of trial. [29]And just as my Father has granted me a Kingdom, I now grant you the right [30]to eat and drink at my table in my Kingdom. And you will sit on thrones, judging the twelve tribes of Israel.

Jesus Predicts Peter's Denial

[31]"Simon, Simon, Satan has asked to sift each of you like wheat. [32]But I have pleaded in prayer for you, Simon, that your faith should not fail. So when you have repented and turned to me again, strengthen your brothers."

[33]Peter said, "Lord, I am ready to go to prison with you, and even to die with you."

[34]But Jesus said, "Peter, let me tell you something. Before the rooster crows tomorrow morning, you will deny three times that you even know me."

[35]Then Jesus asked them, "When I sent you out to preach the Good News and you did not have money, a traveler's bag, or an extra pair of sandals, did you need anything?"

"No," they replied.

[36]"But now," he said, "take your money and a traveler's bag. And if you don't have a sword, sell your cloak and buy one! [37]For the time has come for this prophecy about me to be fulfilled: 'He was counted among the rebels.'* Yes, everything written about me by the prophets will come true."

[38]"Look, Lord," they replied, "we have two swords among us."

"That's enough," he said.

Jesus Prays on the Mount of Olives

[39]Then, accompanied by the disciples, Jesus left the upstairs room and went as usual to the Mount of Olives. [40]There he told them, "Pray that you will not give in to temptation."

[41]He walked away, about a stone's throw, and knelt down and prayed, [42]"Father, if you are willing, please take this cup of suffering away from me. Yet I want your will to be done, not mine." [43]Then an angel from heaven appeared and strengthened him. [44]He prayed more fervently, and he was in such agony of spirit that his sweat fell to the ground like great drops of blood.*

[45]At last he stood up again and returned to the disciples, only to find them asleep, exhausted from grief. [46]"Why are you sleeping?" he asked them. "Get up and pray, so that you will not give in to temptation."

Jesus Is Betrayed and Arrested

[47]But even as Jesus said this, a crowd approached, led by Judas, one of the twelve disciples. Judas walked over to Jesus to greet him with a kiss. [48]But Jesus said, "Judas, would you betray the Son of Man with a kiss?"

[49]When the other disciples saw what was about to happen, they exclaimed, "Lord, should we fight? We brought the swords!" [50]And one of them struck at the high priest's slave, slashing off his right ear.

[51]But Jesus said, "No more of this." And he touched the man's ear and healed him.

[52]Then Jesus spoke to the leading priests, the captains of the Temple guard, and the elders who had come for him. "Am I some dangerous revolutionary," he asked, "that you come with swords and clubs to arrest me? [53]Why didn't you arrest me in the Temple? I was there every day. But this is your moment, the time when the power of darkness reigns."

Peter Denies Jesus

[54]So they arrested him and led him to the high priest's home. And Peter followed at a distance. [55]The guards lit a fire in the middle of the courtyard and sat around it, and Peter joined them there. [56]A servant girl noticed him in the firelight and began staring at him. Finally she said, "This man was one of Jesus' followers!"

[57]But Peter denied it. "Woman," he said, "I don't even know him!"

[58]After a while someone else looked at him and said, "You must be one of them!"

"No, man, I'm not!" Peter retorted.

[59]About an hour later someone else insisted,

22:19-20 Some manuscripts do not include 22:19b-20, *which is given for you . . . which is poured out as a sacrifice for you.*   **22:22** "Son of Man" is a title Jesus used for himself.   **22:37** Isa 53:12.   **22:43-44** Verses 43 and 44 are not included in many ancient manuscripts.

"This must be one of them, because he is a Galilean, too."

⁶⁰But Peter said, "Man, I don't know what you are talking about." And immediately, while he was still speaking, the rooster crowed.

⁶¹At that moment the Lord turned and looked at Peter. Suddenly, the Lord's words flashed through Peter's mind: "Before the rooster crows tomorrow morning, you will deny three times that you even know me." ⁶²And Peter left the courtyard, weeping bitterly.

⁶³The guards in charge of Jesus began mocking and beating him. ⁶⁴They blindfolded him and said, "Prophesy to us! Who hit you that time?" ⁶⁵And they hurled all sorts of terrible insults at him.

Jesus before the Council

⁶⁶At daybreak all the elders of the people assembled, including the leading priests and the teachers of religious law. Jesus was led before this high council,* ⁶⁷and they said, "Tell us, are you the Messiah?"

But he replied, "If I tell you, you won't believe me. ⁶⁸And if I ask you a question, you won't answer. ⁶⁹But from now on the Son of Man will be seated in the place of power at God's right hand.*"

⁷⁰They all shouted, "So, are you claiming to be the Son of God?"

And he replied, "You say that I am."

⁷¹"Why do we need other witnesses?" they said. "We ourselves heard him say it."

Jesus' Trial before Pilate

23 Then the entire council took Jesus to Pilate, the Roman governor. ²They began to state their case: "This man has been leading our people astray by telling them not to pay their taxes to the Roman government and by claiming he is the Messiah, a king."

³So Pilate asked him, "Are you the king of the Jews?"

Jesus replied, "You have said it."

⁴Pilate turned to the leading priests and to the crowd and said, "I find nothing wrong with this man!"

⁵Then they became insistent. "But he is causing riots by his teaching wherever he goes—all over Judea, from Galilee to Jerusalem!"

⁶"Oh, is he a Galilean?" Pilate asked. ⁷When they said that he was, Pilate sent him to Herod Antipas, because Galilee was under Herod's jurisdiction, and Herod happened to be in Jerusalem at the time.

⁸Herod was delighted at the opportunity to see Jesus, because he had heard about him and had been hoping for a long time to see him perform a miracle. ⁹He asked Jesus question after question, but Jesus refused to answer. ¹⁰Meanwhile, the leading priests and the teachers of religious law stood there shouting their accusations. ¹¹Then Herod and his soldiers began mocking and ridiculing Jesus. Finally, they put a royal robe on him and sent him back to Pilate. ¹²(Herod and Pilate, who had been enemies before, became friends that day.)

¹³Then Pilate called together the leading priests and other religious leaders, along with the people, ¹⁴and he announced his verdict. "You brought this man to me, accusing him of leading a revolt. I have examined him thoroughly on this point in your presence and find him innocent. ¹⁵Herod came to the same conclusion and sent him back to us. Nothing this man has done calls for the death penalty. ¹⁶So I will have him flogged, and then I will release him."*

¹⁸Then a mighty roar rose from the crowd, and with one voice they shouted, "Kill him, and release Barabbas to us!" ¹⁹(Barabbas was in prison for taking part in an insurrection in Jerusalem against the government, and for murder.) ²⁰Pilate argued with them, because he wanted to release Jesus. ²¹But they kept shouting, "Crucify him! Crucify him!"

²²For the third time he demanded, "Why? What crime has he committed? I have found no reason to sentence him to death. So I will have him flogged, and then I will release him."

²³But the mob shouted louder and louder, demanding that Jesus be crucified, and their voices prevailed. ²⁴So Pilate sentenced Jesus to die as they demanded. ²⁵As they had requested, he released Barabbas, the man in prison for insurrection and murder. But he turned Jesus over to them to do as they wished.

The Crucifixion

²⁶As they led Jesus away, a man named Simon, who was from Cyrene,* happened to be coming in from the countryside. The soldiers seized him and put the cross on him and made him carry it behind Jesus. ²⁷A large crowd trailed behind, including many grief-stricken women. ²⁸But Jesus turned and said to them, "Daughters of Jerusalem, don't weep for me, but weep for yourselves and for your children. ²⁹For the days are coming when they will say, 'Fortunate indeed are the women who are childless, the wombs that have not borne a child and the breasts that have never nursed.' ³⁰People will beg the mountains, 'Fall on us,' and plead with the hills, 'Bury us.'* ³¹For if these things are done when the tree is green, what will happen when it is dry?*"

³²Two others, both criminals, were led out to be executed with him. ³³When they came to a

place called The Skull,* they nailed him to the cross. And the criminals were also crucified—one on his right and one on his left.

³⁴Jesus said, "Father, forgive them, for they don't know what they are doing."* And the soldiers gambled for his clothes by throwing dice.*

³⁵The crowd watched and the leaders scoffed. "He saved others," they said, "let him save himself if he is really God's Messiah, the Chosen One." ³⁶The soldiers mocked him, too, by offering him a drink of sour wine. ³⁷They called out to him, "If you are the King of the Jews, save yourself!" ³⁸A sign was fastened above him with these words: "This is the King of the Jews."

³⁹One of the criminals hanging beside him scoffed, "So you're the Messiah, are you? Prove it by saving yourself—and us, too, while you're at it!"

⁴⁰But the other criminal protested, "Don't you fear God even when you have been sentenced to die? ⁴¹We deserve to die for our crimes, but this man hasn't done anything wrong." ⁴²Then he said, "Jesus, remember me when you come into your Kingdom."

⁴³And Jesus replied, "I assure you, today you will be with me in paradise."

The Death of Jesus

⁴⁴By this time it was about noon, and darkness fell across the whole land until three o'clock. ⁴⁵The light from the sun was gone. And suddenly, the curtain in the sanctuary of the Temple was torn down the middle. ⁴⁶Then Jesus shouted, "Father, I entrust my spirit into your hands!"* And with those words he breathed his last.

⁴⁷When the Roman officer* overseeing the execution saw what had happened, he worshiped God and said, "Surely this man was innocent.*" ⁴⁸And when all the crowd that came to see the crucifixion saw what had happened, they went home in deep sorrow.* ⁴⁹But Jesus' friends, including the women who had followed him from Galilee, stood at a distance watching.

The Burial of Jesus

⁵⁰Now there was a good and righteous man named Joseph. He was a member of the Jewish high council, ⁵¹but he had not agreed with the decision and actions of the other religious leaders. He was from the town of Arimathea in Judea, and he was waiting for the Kingdom of God to come. ⁵²He went to Pilate and asked for Jesus' body. ⁵³Then he took the body down from the cross and wrapped it in a long sheet of linen cloth and laid it in a new tomb that had been carved out of rock. ⁵⁴This was done late on Friday afternoon, the day of preparation,* as the Sabbath was about to begin.

⁵⁵As his body was taken away, the women from Galilee followed and saw the tomb where his body was placed. ⁵⁶Then they went home and prepared spices and ointments to anoint his body. But by the time they were finished the Sabbath had begun, so they rested as required by the law.

The Resurrection

24 But very early on Sunday morning* the women went to the tomb, taking spices they had prepared. ²They found that the stone had been rolled away from the entrance. ³So they went in, but they didn't find the body of the Lord Jesus. ⁴As they stood there puzzled, two men suddenly appeared to them, clothed in dazzling robes.

⁵The women were terrified and bowed with their faces to the ground. Then the men asked, "Why are you looking among the dead for someone who is alive? ⁶He isn't here! He is risen from the dead! Remember what he told you back in Galilee, ⁷that the Son of Man* must be betrayed into the hands of sinful men and be crucified, and that he would rise again on the third day."

⁸Then they remembered that he had said this. ⁹So they rushed back from the tomb to tell his eleven disciples—and everyone else—what had happened. ¹⁰It was Mary Magdalene, Joanna, Mary the mother of James, and several other women who told the apostles what had happened. ¹¹But the story sounded like nonsense to the men, so they didn't believe it. ¹²However, Peter jumped up and ran to the tomb to look. Stooping, he peered in and saw the empty linen wrappings; then he went home again, wondering what had happened.

The Walk to Emmaus

¹³That same day two of Jesus' followers were walking to the village of Emmaus, seven miles* from Jerusalem. ¹⁴As they walked along they were talking about everything that had happened. ¹⁵As they talked and discussed these things, Jesus himself suddenly came and began walking with them. ¹⁶But God kept them from recognizing him.

¹⁷He asked them, "What are you discussing so intently as you walk along?"

They stopped short, sadness written across their faces. ¹⁸Then one of them, Cleopas, replied, "You must be the only person in Jerusalem who hasn't heard about all the things that have happened there the last few days."

¹⁹"What things?" Jesus asked.

"The things that happened to Jesus, the man from Nazareth," they said. "He was a prophet who did powerful miracles, and he was a mighty

---

23:33 Sometimes rendered *Calvary*, which comes from the Latin word for "skull." 23:34a This sentence is not included in many ancient manuscripts. 23:34b Greek *by casting lots.* See Ps 22:18. 23:46 Ps 31:5. 23:47a Greek *the centurion.* 23:47b Or *righteous.* 23:48 Greek *went home beating their breasts.* 23:54 Greek *It was the day of preparation.* 24:1 Greek *But on the first day of the week, very early in the morning.* 24:7 "Son of Man" is a title Jesus used for himself. 24:13 Greek *60 stadia* [11.1 kilometers].

teacher in the eyes of God and all the people. 20But our leading priests and other religious leaders handed him over to be condemned to death, and they crucified him. 21We had hoped he was the Messiah who had come to rescue Israel. This all happened three days ago.

22"Then some women from our group of his followers were at his tomb early this morning, and they came back with an amazing report. 23They said his body was missing, and they had seen angels who told them Jesus is alive! 24Some of our men ran out to see, and sure enough, his body was gone, just as the women had said."

25Then Jesus said to them, "You foolish people! You find it so hard to believe all that the prophets wrote in the Scriptures. 26Wasn't it clearly predicted that the Messiah would have to suffer all these things before entering his glory?" 27Then Jesus took them through the writings of Moses and all the prophets, explaining from all the Scriptures the things concerning himself.

28By this time they were nearing Emmaus and the end of their journey. Jesus acted as if he were going on, 29but they begged him, "Stay the night with us, since it is getting late." So he went home with them. 30As they sat down to eat,* he took the bread and blessed it. Then he broke it and gave it to them. 31Suddenly, their eyes were opened, and they recognized him. And at that moment he disappeared!

32They said to each other, "Didn't our hearts burn within us as he talked with us on the road and explained the Scriptures to us?" 33And within the hour they were on their way back to Jerusalem. There they found the eleven disciples and the others who had gathered with them, 34who said, "The Lord has really risen! He appeared to Peter.*"

Jesus Appears to the Disciples

35Then the two from Emmaus told their story of how Jesus had appeared to them as they were walking along the road, and how they had recognized him as he was breaking the bread. 36And just as they were telling about it, Jesus himself was suddenly standing there among them. "Peace be with you," he said. 37But the whole group was startled and frightened, thinking they were seeing a ghost!

38"Why are you frightened?" he asked. "Why are your hearts filled with doubt? 39Look at my hands. Look at my feet. You can see that it's really me. Touch me and make sure that I am not a ghost, because ghosts don't have bodies, as you see that I do." 40As he spoke, he showed them his hands and his feet.

41Still they stood there in disbelief, filled with joy and wonder. Then he asked them, "Do you have anything here to eat?" 42They gave him a piece of broiled fish, 43and he ate it as they watched.

44Then he said, "When I was with you before, I told you that everything written about me in the law of Moses and the prophets and in the Psalms must be fulfilled." 45Then he opened their minds to understand the Scriptures. 46And he said, "Yes, it was written long ago that the Messiah would suffer and die and rise from the dead on the third day. 47It was also written that this message would be proclaimed in the authority of his name to all the nations,* beginning in Jerusalem: 'There is forgiveness of sins for all who repent.' 48You are witnesses of all these things.

49"And now I will send the Holy Spirit, just as my Father promised. But stay here in the city until the Holy Spirit comes and fills you with power from heaven."

The Ascension

50Then Jesus led them to Bethany, and lifting his hands to heaven, he blessed them. 51While he was blessing them, he left them and was taken up to heaven. 52So they worshiped him and then returned to Jerusalem filled with great joy. 53And they spent all of their time in the Temple, praising God.

24:30 Or *As they reclined.*   **24:34** Greek *Simon.*   **24:47** Or *all peoples.*

DOUG JARVIS
Assistant Coach Boston Bruins, NHL
Winner of 6 Stanley Cups
NHL's All Time Ironman

Even though I came to a realization of God's love for me personally and accepted Christ at a young age, it is still a constant struggle to keep my life priorities in the proper order. It often seems that so many things are constantly competing to take our focus off our faith relationship with God. A lot of our time is filled with the urgency of our careers, earning a living, and the day-to-day concerns that tend to dominate our lives. For me, this includes wanting to take control of these things. This usually ends up in a lot of worry and anxiety, instead of peace that comes through trusting and depending on God to be in control of all these situations on a daily basis.

However, as we grow in our faith and allow God to work and have His rightful place in our lives, we can experience the confidence and peace that comes from His directing our lives. As our faith develops, we come to realize that His promises are real, that He is always with us, that He came to give us abundant and eternal life now and that He will meet our daily needs beyond what we could ask or think.

" . . . His promises are real—He is with us always . . . "

The Bible continually supports and strengthens my faith by increasing my knowledge and understanding of who God is and how He relates to my day-to-day living. Proverbs 3:5-6 is a passage that helps me when I face the uncertainties that come in life and in the game of hockey. *"Trust in The Lord with all your heart; do not lean on your own understanding. Seek his will in all you do and he will show you the path to take."* When I consciously choose to trust God and put my confidence in Him to lead me rather than bearing this responsibility on my own, then I experience a genuine sense of freedom and peace. My personal relationship with Christ offers me this opportunity to continually lean into God's strong, all-knowing and all-sufficient being.

GLEN AND JOSH WESLEY

The Bible plays a significant role in strengthening my faith. I dig for God's truth through personal study of the Scriptures and small group discussions. While I don't know the challenges I will face each day, I know God will guide me as I pray, listen and read His Word and am submissive to His will.

One passage that has impacted me is John 8:12, where Jesus states: *"I am the light of the world. He who follows me shall not walk in darkness but shall have the light of life."* I was walking in darkness before I began following Christ. He has given me light and it will never flicker. This happened in 1995. I was traded from Boston to Hartford shortly after my wife Barb lost her mom to cancer and I lost my dad to Lou Gehrig's disease. I watched as the Lord worked in Barb's life, leading her to rededicate her life to Christ. Her example inspired me to intensify my search for the real meaning in life, and one Sunday morning I accepted our youth pastor's invitation to receive Christ as my personal Savior. It was official . . . I was on the God squad! My name is now written in the Lamb's book of life, and I know I will see Christ face to face one day and spend eternity in heaven with fellow believers from around the world.

It was official . . . I was on the God Squad.

Church is so important. Each week, our souls are fed and we are challenged to take what we have learned from the sermon and apply it to our lives. This devotion to Christ motivates me to be spiritually disciplined, which helps me handle temptation and inspires me to train physically. Christian hockey players are not wimps. With God in our lives, we are strengthened. I now live for Him and not for me. While we can be mocked at times, the most important thing is that we are standing for Christ. I always wanted my teammates to see Christ in me.

JOSH WESLEY
Defense, United States National Team
Development Program

2006 Stanley Cup Champion Glen Wesley passed down far more than hockey talent to his son, Josh. He also passed on the family legacy of faith. "I've been going to church and hearing about Jesus since I was little. When I was 14 I got a grasp of how Christ works in my life and I dedicated my life to the Lord.

One of the changing moments in my life was when I got cut by a team for which I really wanted to play. This helped me to grow closer to God. I left it up to Him . . . the very next day I got a call to play for another team . . . I started great friendships with some of the players and was able to share the Gospel with most of the players.

The Bible plays a huge role in my life. Every time I open it I learn something new. Whenever I go through a hard time in hockey or in life, it's amazing that I always find an answer right away to whatever I'm struggling with. Reading the verses and doing my daily devotions shows me God is there and always working.

"Getting cut from a team . . . helped me to grow closer to God."

My favorite Bible verse is 1 Corinthians 9:25. *'Everyone who competes in the games goes into strict training. They do it to get a crown that will not last; but we do it to get a crown that will last forever.'* It is saying we are not playing for financial riches that will eventually turn into garbage, but we are playing for God, and the crown we get when we are with Him will last forever.

Being with Christ is so important to me; I know that He is there all the time. In the good times and bad times, both on and off the ice, I have peace because I know He will never leave me."

John

Prologue: Christ, the Eternal Word

1 ¹ In the beginning the Word already existed.
The Word was with God,
and the Word was God.

² He existed in the beginning with God.

³ God created everything through him,
and nothing was created except through
him.

⁴ The Word gave life to everything that was
created,*
and his life brought light to everyone.

⁵ The light shines in the darkness,
and the darkness can never extinguish it.*

⁶God sent a man, John the Baptist,* ⁷to tell about the light so that everyone might believe because of his testimony. ⁸John himself was not the light; he was simply a witness to tell about the light. ⁹The one who is the true light, who gives light to everyone, was coming into the world.

¹⁰He came into the very world he created, but the world didn't recognize him. ¹¹He came to his own people, and even they rejected him. ¹²But to all who believed him and accepted him, he gave the right to become children of God. ¹³They are reborn—not with a physical birth resulting from human passion or plan, but a birth that comes from God.

¹⁴So the Word became human* and made his home among us. He was full of unfailing love and faithfulness.* And we have seen his glory, the glory of the Father's one and only Son.

¹⁵John testified about him when he shouted to the crowds, "This is the one I was talking about when I said, 'Someone is coming after me who is far greater than I am, for he existed long before me.'"

¹⁶From his abundance we have all received one gracious blessing after another.* ¹⁷For the law was given through Moses, but God's unfailing love and faithfulness came through Jesus Christ. ¹⁸No one has ever seen God. But the unique One, who is himself God,* is near to the Father's heart. He has revealed God to us.

The Testimony of John the Baptist

¹⁹This was John's testimony when the Jewish leaders sent priests and Temple assistants* from Jerusalem to ask John, "Who are you?" ²⁰He came right out and said, "I am not the Messiah."

²¹"Well then, who are you?" they asked. "Are you Elijah?"

"No," he replied.

"Are you the Prophet we are expecting?"*

"No."

²²"Then who are you? We need an answer for those who sent us. What do you have to say about yourself?"

²³John replied in the words of the prophet Isaiah:

"I am a voice shouting in the wilderness,
'Clear the way for the LORD's coming!'"*

²⁴Then the Pharisees who had been sent ²⁵asked him, "If you aren't the Messiah or Elijah or the Prophet, what right do you have to baptize?"

²⁶John told them, "I baptize with* water, but right here in the crowd is someone you do not recognize. ²⁷Though his ministry follows mine, I'm not even worthy to be his slave and untie the straps of his sandal."

²⁸This encounter took place in Bethany, an area east of the Jordan River, where John was baptizing.

Jesus, the Lamb of God

²⁹The next day John saw Jesus coming toward him and said, "Look! The Lamb of God who takes away the sin of the world! ³⁰He is the one I was talking about when I said, 'A man is coming after me who is far greater than I am, for he existed long before me.' ³¹I did not recognize him as the Messiah, but I have been baptizing with water so that he might be revealed to Israel."

³²Then John testified, "I saw the Holy Spirit descending like a dove from heaven and resting upon him. ³³I didn't know he was the one, but when God sent me to baptize with water, he told me, 'The one on whom you see the Spirit descend and rest is the one who will baptize with the Holy Spirit.' ³⁴I saw this happen to Jesus, so I testify that he is the Chosen One of God.*"

The First Disciples

35The following day John was again standing with two of his disciples. 36As Jesus walked by, John looked at him and declared, "Look! There is the Lamb of God!" 37When John's two disciples heard this, they followed Jesus.

38Jesus looked around and saw them following. "What do you want?" he asked them.

They replied, "Rabbi" (which means "Teacher"), "where are you staying?"

39"Come and see," he said. It was about four o'clock in the afternoon when they went with him to the place where he was staying, and they remained with him the rest of the day.

40Andrew, Simon Peter's brother, was one of these men who heard what John said and then followed Jesus. 41Andrew went to find his brother, Simon, and told him, "We have found the Messiah" (which means "Christ"*).

42Then Andrew brought Simon to meet Jesus. Looking intently at Simon, Jesus said, "Your name is Simon, son of John—but you will be called Cephas" (which means "Peter"*).

43The next day Jesus decided to go to Galilee. He found Philip and said to him, "Come, follow me." 44Philip was from Bethsaida, Andrew and Peter's hometown.

45Philip went to look for Nathanael and told him, "We have found the very person Moses* and the prophets wrote about! His name is Jesus, the son of Joseph from Nazareth."

46"Nazareth!" exclaimed Nathanael. "Can anything good come from Nazareth?"

"Come and see for yourself," Philip replied.

47As they approached, Jesus said, "Now here is a genuine son of Israel—a man of complete integrity."

48"How do you know about me?" Nathanael asked.

Jesus replied, "I could see you under the fig tree before Philip found you."

49Then Nathanael exclaimed, "Rabbi, you are the Son of God—the King of Israel!"

50Jesus asked him, "Do you believe this just because I told you I had seen you under the fig tree? You will see greater things than this." 51Then he said, "I tell you the truth, you will all see heaven open and the angels of God going up and down on the Son of Man, the one who is the stairway between heaven and earth.*"

The Wedding at Cana

2 The next day* there was a wedding celebration in the village of Cana in Galilee. Jesus' mother was there, 2and Jesus and his disciples were also invited to the celebration. 3The wine supply ran out during the festivities, so Jesus' mother told him, "They have no more wine."

4"Dear woman, that's not our problem," Jesus replied. "My time has not yet come."

5But his mother told the servants, "Do whatever he tells you."

6Standing nearby were six stone water jars, used for Jewish ceremonial washing. Each could hold twenty to thirty gallons.* 7Jesus told the servants, "Fill the jars with water." When the jars had been filled, 8he said, "Now dip some out, and take it to the master of ceremonies." So the servants followed his instructions.

9When the master of ceremonies tasted the water that was now wine, not knowing where it had come from (though, of course, the servants knew), he called the bridegroom over. 10"A host always serves the best wine first," he said. "Then, when everyone has had a lot to drink, he brings out the less expensive wine. But you have kept the best until now!"

11This miraculous sign at Cana in Galilee was the first time Jesus revealed his glory. And his disciples believed in him.

12After the wedding he went to Capernaum for a few days with his mother, his brothers, and his disciples.

Jesus Clears the Temple

13It was nearly time for the Jewish Passover celebration, so Jesus went to Jerusalem. 14In the Temple area he saw merchants selling cattle, sheep, and doves for sacrifices; he also saw dealers at tables exchanging foreign money. 15Jesus made a whip from some ropes and chased them all out of the Temple. He drove out the sheep and cattle, scattered the money changers' coins over the floor, and turned over their tables. 16Then, going over to the people who sold doves, he told them, "Get these things out of here. Stop turning my Father's house into a marketplace!"

17Then his disciples remembered this prophecy from the Scriptures: "Passion for God's house will consume me."*

18But the Jewish leaders demanded, "What are you doing? If God gave you authority to do this, show us a miraculous sign to prove it."

19"All right," Jesus replied. "Destroy this temple, and in three days I will raise it up."

20"What!" they exclaimed. "It has taken forty-six years to build this Temple, and you can rebuild it in three days?" 21But when Jesus said "this temple," he meant his own body. 22After he was raised from the dead, his disciples remembered he had said this, and they believed both the Scriptures and what Jesus had said.

Jesus and Nicodemus

23Because of the miraculous signs Jesus did in Jerusalem at the Passover celebration, many be-

---

1:41 *Messiah* (a Hebrew term) and *Christ* (a Greek term) both mean "the anointed one." **1:42** The names *Cephas* (from Aramaic) and *Peter* (from Greek) both mean "rock." **1:45** Greek *Moses in the law.* **1:51** Greek *going up and down on the Son of Man;* see Gen 28:10-17. "Son of Man" is a title Jesus used for himself. **2:1** Greek *On the third day;* see 1:35, 43. **2:6** Greek *2 or 3 measures* [75 to 113 liters]. **2:17** Or *"Concern for God's house will be my undoing."* Ps 69:9.

gan to trust in him. [24]But Jesus didn't trust them, because he knew human nature. [25]No one needed to tell him what mankind is really like.

3 There was a man named Nicodemus, a Jewish religious leader who was a Pharisee. [2]After dark one evening, he came to speak with Jesus. "Rabbi," he said, "we all know that God has sent you to teach us. Your miraculous signs are evidence that God is with you."

[3]Jesus replied, "I tell you the truth, unless you are born again,* you cannot see the Kingdom of God."

[4]"What do you mean?" exclaimed Nicodemus. "How can an old man go back into his mother's womb and be born again?"

[5]Jesus replied, "I assure you, no one can enter the Kingdom of God without being born of water and the Spirit.* [6]Humans can reproduce only human life, but the Holy Spirit gives birth to spiritual life.* [7]So don't be surprised when I say, 'You* must be born again.' [8]The wind blows wherever it wants. Just as you can hear the wind but can't tell where it comes from or where it is going, so you can't explain how people are born of the Spirit."

[9]"How are these things possible?" Nicodemus asked.

[10]Jesus replied, "You are a respected Jewish teacher, and yet you don't understand these things? [11]I assure you, we tell you what we know and have seen, and yet you won't believe our testimony. [12]But if you don't believe me when I tell you about earthly things, how can you possibly believe if I tell you about heavenly things? [13]No one has ever gone to heaven and returned. But the Son of Man* has come down from heaven. [14]And as Moses lifted up the bronze snake on a pole in the wilderness, so the Son of Man must be lifted up, [15]so that everyone who believes in him will have eternal life.*

[16]"For God loved the world so much that he gave his one and only Son, so that everyone who believes in him will not perish but have eternal life. [17]God sent his Son into the world not to judge the world, but to save the world through him.

[18]"There is no judgment against anyone who believes in him. But anyone who does not believe in him has already been judged for not believing in God's one and only Son. [19]And the judgment is based on this fact: God's light came into the world, but people loved the darkness more than the light, for their actions were evil. [20]All who do evil hate the light and refuse to go near it for fear their sins will be exposed. [21]But those who do what is right come to the light so others can see that they are doing what God wants.*"

John the Baptist Exalts Jesus

[22]Then Jesus and his disciples left Jerusalem and went into the Judean countryside. Jesus spent some time with them there, baptizing people.

[23]At this time John the Baptist was baptizing at Aenon, near Salim, because there was plenty of water there; and people kept coming to him for baptism. [24](This was before John was thrown into prison.) [25]A debate broke out between John's disciples and a certain Jew* over ceremonial cleansing. [26]So John's disciples came to him and said, "Rabbi, the man you met on the other side of the Jordan River, the one you identified as the Messiah, is also baptizing people. And everybody is going to him instead of coming to us."

[27]John replied, "No one can receive anything unless God gives it from heaven. [28]You yourselves know how plainly I told you, 'I am not the Messiah. I am only here to prepare the way for him.' [29]It is the bridegroom who marries the bride, and the best man is simply glad to stand with him and hear his vows. Therefore, I am filled with joy at his success. [30]He must become greater and greater, and I must become less and less.

[31]"He has come from above and is greater than anyone else. We are of the earth, and we speak of earthly things, but he has come from heaven and is greater than anyone else.* [32]He testifies about what he has seen and heard, but how few believe what he tells them! [33]Anyone who accepts his testimony can affirm that God is true. [34]For he is sent by God. He speaks God's words, for God gives him the Spirit without limit. [35]The Father loves his Son and has put everything into his hands. [36]And anyone who believes in God's Son has eternal life. Anyone who doesn't obey the Son will never experience eternal life but remains under God's angry judgment."

Jesus and the Samaritan Woman

4 Jesus* knew the Pharisees had heard that he was baptizing and making more disciples than John [2](though Jesus himself didn't baptize them—his disciples did). [3]So he left Judea and returned to Galilee.

[4]He had to go through Samaria on the way. [5]Eventually he came to the Samaritan village of Sychar, near the field that Jacob gave to his son Joseph. [6]Jacob's well was there; and Jesus, tired from the long walk, sat wearily beside the well about noontime. [7]Soon a Samaritan woman came to draw water, and Jesus said to her, "Please give me a drink." [8]He was alone at the time because his disciples had gone into the village to buy some food.

[9]The woman was surprised, for Jews refuse to have anything to do with Samaritans.* She said

---

3:3 Or *born from above;* also in 3:7.   **3:5** Or *and spirit.* The Greek word for *Spirit* can also be translated *wind;* see 3:8.   **3:6** Greek *what is born of the Spirit is spirit.*   **3:7** The Greek word for *you* is plural; also in 3:12.   **3:13** Some manuscripts add *who lives in heaven.* "Son of Man" is a title Jesus used for himself.   **3:15** Or *everyone who believes will have eternal life in him.*   **3:21** Or *can see God at work in what he is doing.*   **3:25** Some manuscripts read *some Jews.*   **3:31** Some manuscripts do not include *and is greater than anyone else.*   **4:1** Some manuscripts read *The Lord.*   **4:9** Some manuscripts do not include this sentence.

to Jesus, "You are a Jew, and I am a Samaritan woman. Why are you asking me for a drink?"

10Jesus replied, "If you only knew the gift God has for you and who you are speaking to, you would ask me, and I would give you living water."

11"But sir, you don't have a rope or a bucket," she said, "and this well is very deep. Where would you get this living water? 12And besides, do you think you're greater than our ancestor Jacob, who gave us this well? How can you offer better water than he and his sons and his animals enjoyed?"

13Jesus replied, "Anyone who drinks this water will soon become thirsty again. 14But those who drink the water I give will never be thirsty again. It becomes a fresh, bubbling spring within them, giving them eternal life."

15"Please, sir," the woman said, "give me this water! Then I'll never be thirsty again, and I won't have to come here to get water."

16"Go and get your husband," Jesus told her.

17"I don't have a husband," the woman replied.

Jesus said, "You're right! You don't have a husband—18for you have had five husbands, and you aren't even married to the man you're living with now. You certainly spoke the truth!"

19"Sir," the woman said, "you must be a prophet. 20So tell me, why is it that you Jews insist that Jerusalem is the only place of worship, while we Samaritans claim it is here at Mount Gerizim,* where our ancestors worshiped?"

21Jesus replied, "Believe me, dear woman, the time is coming when it will no longer matter whether you worship the Father on this mountain or in Jerusalem. 22You Samaritans know very little about the one you worship, while we Jews know all about him, for salvation comes through the Jews. 23But the time is coming—indeed it's here now—when true worshipers will worship the Father in spirit and in truth. The Father is looking for those who will worship him that way. 24For God is Spirit, so those who worship him must worship in spirit and in truth."

25The woman said, "I know the Messiah is coming—the one who is called Christ. When he comes, he will explain everything to us."

26Then Jesus told her, "I Am the Messiah!"*

27Just then his disciples came back. They were shocked to find him talking to a woman, but none of them had the nerve to ask, "What do you want with her?" or "Why are you talking to her?" 28The woman left her water jar beside the well and ran back to the village, telling everyone, 29"Come and see a man who told me everything I ever did! Could he possibly be the Messiah?" 30So the people came streaming from the village to see him.

31Meanwhile, the disciples were urging Jesus, "Rabbi, eat something."

32But Jesus replied, "I have a kind of food you know nothing about."

33"Did someone bring him food while we were gone?" the disciples asked each other.

34Then Jesus explained: "My nourishment comes from doing the will of God, who sent me, and from finishing his work. 35You know the saying, 'Four months between planting and harvest.' But I say, wake up and look around. The fields are already ripe* for harvest. 36The harvesters are paid good wages, and the fruit they harvest is people brought to eternal life. What joy awaits both the planter and the harvester alike! 37You know the saying, 'One plants and another harvests.' And it's true. 38I sent you to harvest where you didn't plant; others had already done the work, and now you will get to gather the harvest."

Many Samaritans Believe

39Many Samaritans from the village believed in Jesus because the woman had said, "He told me everything I ever did!" 40When they came out to see him, they begged him to stay in their village. So he stayed for two days, 41long enough for many more to hear his message and believe. 42Then they said to the woman, "Now we believe, not just because of what you told us, but because we have heard him ourselves. Now we know that he is indeed the Savior of the world."

Jesus Heals an Official's Son

43At the end of the two days, Jesus went on to Galilee. 44He himself had said that a prophet is not honored in his own hometown. 45Yet the Galileans welcomed him, for they had been in Jerusalem at the Passover celebration and had seen everything he did there.

46As he traveled through Galilee, he came to Cana, where he had turned the water into wine. There was a government official in nearby Capernaum whose son was very sick. 47When he heard that Jesus had come from Judea to Galilee, he went and begged Jesus to come to Capernaum to heal his son, who was about to die.

48Jesus asked, "Will you never believe in me unless you see miraculous signs and wonders?"

49The official pleaded, "Lord, please come now before my little boy dies."

50Then Jesus told him, "Go back home. Your son will live!" And the man believed what Jesus said and started home.

51While the man was on his way, some of his servants met him with the news that his son was alive and well. 52He asked them when the boy had begun to get better, and they replied, "Yesterday afternoon at one o'clock his fever suddenly disappeared!" 53Then the father realized that that was the very time Jesus had told him, "Your son will live." And he and his entire house-

---

4:20 Greek *on this mountain.*   4:26 Or *"The 'I Am' is here"*; or *"I am the Lord"*; Greek reads *"I am, the one speaking to you."* See Exod 3:14.   4:35 Greek *white.*

hold believed in Jesus. [54]This was the second miraculous sign Jesus did in Galilee after coming from Judea.

Jesus Heals a Lame Man

5 Afterward Jesus returned to Jerusalem for one of the Jewish holy days. [2]Inside the city, near the Sheep Gate, was the pool of Bethesda,* with five covered porches. [3]Crowds of sick people—blind, lame, or paralyzed—lay on the porches.* [5]One of the men lying there had been sick for thirty-eight years. [6]When Jesus saw him and knew he had been ill for a long time, he asked him, "Would you like to get well?"

[7]"I can't, sir," the sick man said, "for I have no one to put me into the pool when the water bubbles up. Someone else always gets there ahead of me."

[8]Jesus told him, "Stand up, pick up your mat, and walk!"

[9]Instantly, the man was healed! He rolled up his sleeping mat and began walking! But this miracle happened on the Sabbath, [10]so the Jewish leaders objected. They said to the man who was cured, "You can't work on the Sabbath! The law doesn't allow you to carry that sleeping mat!"

[11]But he replied, "The man who healed me told me, 'Pick up your mat and walk.'"

[12]"Who said such a thing as that?" they demanded.

[13]The man didn't know, for Jesus had disappeared into the crowd. [14]But afterward Jesus found him in the Temple and told him, "Now you are well; so stop sinning, or something even worse may happen to you." [15]Then the man went and told the Jewish leaders that it was Jesus who had healed him.

Jesus Claims to Be the Son of God

[16]So the Jewish leaders began harassing* Jesus for breaking the Sabbath rules. [17]But Jesus replied, "My Father is always working, and so am I." [18]So the Jewish leaders tried all the harder to find a way to kill him. For he not only broke the Sabbath, he called God his Father, thereby making himself equal with God.

[19]So Jesus explained, "I tell you the truth, the Son can do nothing by himself. He does only what he sees the Father doing. Whatever the Father does, the Son also does. [20]For the Father loves the Son and shows him everything he is doing. In fact, the Father will show him how to do even greater works than healing this man. Then you will truly be astonished. [21]For just as the Father gives life to those he raises from the dead, so the Son gives life to anyone he wants. [22]In addition, the Father judges no one. Instead, he has given the Son absolute authority to judge,

[23]so that everyone will honor the Son, just as they honor the Father. Anyone who does not honor the Son is certainly not honoring the Father who sent him.

[24]"I tell you the truth, those who listen to my message and believe in God who sent me have eternal life. They will never be condemned for their sins, but they have already passed from death into life.

[25]"And I assure you that the time is coming, indeed it's here now, when the dead will hear my voice—the voice of the Son of God. And those who listen will live. [26]The Father has life in himself, and he has granted that same life-giving power to his Son. [27]And he has given him authority to judge everyone because he is the Son of Man.* [28]Don't be so surprised! Indeed, the time is coming when all the dead in their graves will hear the voice of God's Son, [29]and they will rise again. Those who have done good will rise to experience eternal life, and those who have continued in evil will rise to experience judgment. [30]I can do nothing on my own. I judge as God tells me. Therefore, my judgment is just, because I carry out the will of the one who sent me, not my own will.

Witnesses to Jesus

[31]"If I were to testify on my own behalf, my testimony would not be valid. [32]But someone else is also testifying about me, and I assure you that everything he says about me is true. [33]In fact, you sent investigators to listen to John the Baptist, and his testimony about me was true. [34]Of course, I have no need of human witnesses, but I say these things so you might be saved. [35]John was like a burning and shining lamp, and you were excited for a while about his message. [36]But I have a greater witness than John—my teachings and my miracles. The Father gave me these works to accomplish, and they prove that he sent me. [37]And the Father who sent me has testified about me himself. You have never heard his voice or seen him face to face, [38]and you do not have his message in your hearts, because you do not believe me—the one he sent to you.

[39]"You search the Scriptures because you think they give you eternal life. But the Scriptures point to me! [40]Yet you refuse to come to me to receive this life.

[41]"Your approval means nothing to me, [42]because I know you don't have God's love within you. [43]For I have come to you in my Father's name, and you have rejected me. Yet if others come in their own name, you gladly welcome them. [44]No wonder you can't believe! For you gladly honor each other, but you don't care about the honor that comes from the one who alone is God.*

5:2 Other manuscripts read *Beth-zatha;* still others read *Bethsaida.* 5:3 Some manuscripts add an expanded conclusion to verse 3 and all of verse 4: *waiting for a certain movement of the water, 'for an angel of the Lord came from time to time and stirred up the water. And the first person to step in after the water was stirred was healed of whatever disease he had.* 5:16 Or *persecuting.* 5:27 "Son of Man" is a title Jesus used for himself. 5:44 Some manuscripts read *from the only One.*

45"Yet it isn't I who will accuse you before the Father. Moses will accuse you! Yes, Moses, in whom you put your hopes. 46If you really believed Moses, you would believe me, because he wrote about me. 47But since you don't believe what he wrote, how will you believe what I say?"

Jesus Feeds Five Thousand

6 After this, Jesus crossed over to the far side of the Sea of Galilee, also known as the Sea of Tiberias. 2A huge crowd kept following him wherever he went, because they saw his miraculous signs as he healed the sick. 3Then Jesus climbed a hill and sat down with his disciples around him. 4(It was nearly time for the Jewish Passover celebration.) 5Jesus soon saw a huge crowd of people coming to look for him. Turning to Philip, he asked, "Where can we buy bread to feed all these people?" 6He was testing Philip, for he already knew what he was going to do.

7Philip replied, "Even if we worked for months, we wouldn't have enough money* to feed them!"

8Then Andrew, Simon Peter's brother, spoke up. 9"There's a young boy here with five barley loaves and two fish. But what good is that with this huge crowd?"

10"Tell everyone to sit down," Jesus said. So they all sat down on the grassy slopes. (The men alone numbered about 5,000.) 11Then Jesus took the loaves, gave thanks to God, and distributed them to the people. Afterward he did the same with the fish. And they all ate as much as they wanted. 12After everyone was full, Jesus told his disciples, "Now gather the leftovers, so that nothing is wasted." 13So they picked up the pieces and filled twelve baskets with scraps left by the people who had eaten from the five barley loaves.

14When the people saw him* do this miraculous sign, they exclaimed, "Surely, he is the Prophet we have been expecting!"* 15When Jesus saw that they were ready to force him to be their king, he slipped away into the hills by himself.

Jesus Walks on Water

16That evening Jesus' disciples went down to the shore to wait for him. 17But as darkness fell and Jesus still hadn't come back, they got into the boat and headed across the lake toward Capernaum. 18Soon a gale swept down upon them, and the sea grew very rough. 19They had rowed three or four miles* when suddenly they saw Jesus walking on the water toward the boat. They were terrified, 20but he called out to them, "Don't be afraid. I am here!"* 21Then they were eager to let him in the boat, and immediately they arrived at their destination!

Jesus, the Bread of Life

22The next day the crowd that had stayed on the far shore saw that the disciples had taken the only boat, and they realized Jesus had not gone with them. 23Several boats from Tiberias landed near the place where the Lord had blessed the bread and the people had eaten. 24So when the crowd saw that neither Jesus nor his disciples were there, they got into the boats and went across to Capernaum to look for him. 25They found him on the other side of the lake and asked, "Rabbi, when did you get here?"

26Jesus replied, "I tell you the truth, you want to be with me because I fed you, not because you understood the miraculous signs. 27But don't be so concerned about perishable things like food. Spend your energy seeking the eternal life that the Son of Man* can give you. For God the Father has given me the seal of his approval."

28They replied, "We want to perform God's works, too. What should we do?"

29Jesus told them, "This is the only work God wants from you: Believe in the one he has sent."

30They answered, "Show us a miraculous sign if you want us to believe in you. What can you do? 31After all, our ancestors ate manna while they journeyed through the wilderness! The Scriptures say, 'Moses gave them bread from heaven to eat.'*"

32Jesus said, "I tell you the truth, Moses didn't give you bread from heaven. My Father did. And now he offers you the true bread from heaven. 33The true bread of God is the one who comes down from heaven and gives life to the world."

34"Sir," they said, "give us that bread every day."

35Jesus replied, "I am the bread of life. Whoever comes to me will never be hungry again. Whoever believes in me will never be thirsty. 36But you haven't believed in me even though you have seen me. 37However, those the Father has given me will come to me, and I will never reject them. 38For I have come down from heaven to do the will of God who sent me, not to do my own will. 39And this is the will of God, that I should not lose even one of all those he has given me, but that I should raise them up at the last day. 40For it is my Father's will that all who see his Son and believe in him should have eternal life. I will raise them up at the last day."

41Then the people* began to murmur in disagreement because he had said, "I am the bread that came down from heaven." 42They said, "Isn't this Jesus, the son of Joseph? We know his father and mother. How can he say, 'I came down from heaven'?"

43But Jesus replied, "Stop complaining about what I said. 44For no one can come to me unless

6:7 Greek *Two hundred denarii would not be enough.* A denarius was equivalent to a laborer's full day's wage. 6:14a Some manuscripts read *Jesus.* 6:14b See Deut 18:15, 18; Mal 4:5-6. 6:19 Greek *25 or 30 stadia* [4.6 or 5.5 kilometers]. 6:20 Or The '*I Am' is here;* Greek reads *I am.* See Exod 3:14. 6:27 "Son of Man" is a title Jesus used for himself. 6:31 Exod 16:4; Ps 78:24. 6:41 Greek *Jewish people;* also in 6:52.

the Father who sent me draws them to me, and at the last day I will raise them up. ⁴⁵As it is written in the Scriptures,* 'They will all be taught by God.' Everyone who listens to the Father and learns from him comes to me. ⁴⁶(Not that anyone has ever seen the Father; only I, who was sent from God, have seen him.)

⁴⁷"I tell you the truth, anyone who believes has eternal life. ⁴⁸Yes, I am the bread of life! ⁴⁹Your ancestors ate manna in the wilderness, but they all died. ⁵⁰Anyone who eats the bread from heaven, however, will never die. ⁵¹I am the living bread that came down from heaven. Anyone who eats this bread will live forever; and this bread, which I will offer so the world may live, is my flesh."

⁵²Then the people began arguing with each other about what he meant. "How can this man give us his flesh to eat?" they asked.

⁵³So Jesus said again, "I tell you the truth, unless you eat the flesh of the Son of Man and drink his blood, you cannot have eternal life within you. ⁵⁴But anyone who eats my flesh and drinks my blood has eternal life, and I will raise that person at the last day. ⁵⁵For my flesh is true food, and my blood is true drink. ⁵⁶Anyone who eats my flesh and drinks my blood remains in me, and I in him. ⁵⁷I live because of the living Father who sent me; in the same way, anyone who feeds on me will live because of me. ⁵⁸I am the true bread that came down from heaven. Anyone who eats this bread will not die as your ancestors did (even though they ate the manna) but will live forever."

⁵⁹He said these things while he was teaching in the synagogue in Capernaum.

Many Disciples Desert Jesus

⁶⁰Many of his disciples said, "This is very hard to understand. How can anyone accept it?"

⁶¹Jesus was aware that his disciples were complaining, so he said to them, "Does this offend you? ⁶²Then what will you think if you see the Son of Man ascend to heaven again? ⁶³The Spirit alone gives eternal life. Human effort accomplishes nothing. And the very words I have spoken to you are spirit and life. ⁶⁴But some of you do not believe me." (For Jesus knew from the beginning which ones didn't believe, and he knew who would betray him.) ⁶⁵Then he said, "That is why I said that people can't come to me unless the Father gives them to me."

⁶⁶At this point many of his disciples turned away and deserted him. ⁶⁷Then Jesus turned to the Twelve and asked, "Are you also going to leave?"

⁶⁸Simon Peter replied, "Lord, to whom would we go? You have the words that give eternal life. ⁶⁹We believe, and we know you are the Holy One of God.*"

⁷⁰Then Jesus said, "I chose the twelve of you, but one is a devil." ⁷¹He was speaking of Judas, son of Simon Iscariot, one of the Twelve, who would later betray him.

Jesus and His Brothers

7 After this, Jesus traveled around Galilee. He wanted to stay out of Judea, where the Jewish leaders were plotting his death. ²But soon it was time for the Jewish Festival of Shelters, ³and Jesus' brothers said to him, "Leave here and go to Judea, where your followers can see your miracles! ⁴You can't become famous if you hide like this! If you can do such wonderful things, show yourself to the world!" ⁵For even his brothers didn't believe in him.

⁶Jesus replied, "Now is not the right time for me to go, but you can go anytime. ⁷The world can't hate you, but it does hate me because I accuse it of doing evil. ⁸You go on. I'm not going* to this festival, because my time has not yet come." ⁹After saying these things, Jesus remained in Galilee.

Jesus Teaches Openly at the Temple

¹⁰But after his brothers left for the festival, Jesus also went, though secretly, staying out of public view. ¹¹The Jewish leaders tried to find him at the festival and kept asking if anyone had seen him. ¹²There was a lot of grumbling about him among the crowds. Some argued, "He's a good man," but others said, "He's nothing but a fraud who deceives the people." ¹³But no one had the courage to speak favorably about him in public, for they were afraid of getting in trouble with the Jewish leaders.

¹⁴Then, midway through the festival, Jesus went up to the Temple and began to teach. ¹⁵The people* were surprised when they heard him. "How does he know so much when he hasn't been trained?" they asked.

¹⁶So Jesus told them, "My message is not my own; it comes from God who sent me. ¹⁷Anyone who wants to do the will of God will know whether my teaching is from God or is merely my own. ¹⁸Those who speak for themselves want glory only for themselves, but a person who seeks to honor the one who sent him speaks truth, not lies. ¹⁹Moses gave you the law, but none of you obeys it! In fact, you are trying to kill me."

²⁰The crowd replied, "You're demon possessed! Who's trying to kill you?"

²¹Jesus replied, "I did one miracle on the Sabbath, and you were amazed. ²²But you work on the Sabbath, too, when you obey Moses' law of circumcision. (Actually, this tradition of circumcision began with the patriarchs, long before the law of Moses.) ²³For if the correct time for circumcising your son falls on the Sabbath, you go

---

6:45 Greek *in the prophets.* Isa 54:13.　**6:69** Other manuscripts read *you are the Christ, the Holy One of God;* still others read *you are the Christ, the Son of God;* and still others read *you are the Christ, the Son of the living God.*　**7:8** Some manuscripts read *not yet going.*　**7:15** Greek *Jewish people.*

ahead and do it so as not to break the law of Moses. So why should you be angry with me for healing a man on the Sabbath? ²⁴Look beneath the surface so you can judge correctly."

Is Jesus the Messiah?

²⁵Some of the people who lived in Jerusalem started to ask each other, "Isn't this the man they are trying to kill? ²⁶But here he is, speaking in public, and they say nothing to him. Could our leaders possibly believe that he is the Messiah? ²⁷But how could he be? For we know where this man comes from. When the Messiah comes, he will simply appear; no one will know where he comes from."

²⁸While Jesus was teaching in the Temple, he called out, "Yes, you know me, and you know where I come from. But I'm not here on my own. The one who sent me is true, and you don't know him. ²⁹But I know him because I come from him, and he sent me to you." ³⁰Then the leaders tried to arrest him; but no one laid a hand on him, because his time* had not yet come.

³¹Many among the crowds at the Temple believed in him. "After all," they said, "would you expect the Messiah to do more miraculous signs than this man has done?"

³²When the Pharisees heard that the crowds were whispering such things, they and the leading priests sent Temple guards to arrest Jesus. ³³But Jesus told them, "I will be with you only a little longer. Then I will return to the one who sent me. ³⁴You will search for me but not find me. And you cannot go where I am going."

³⁵The Jewish leaders were puzzled by this statement. "Where is he planning to go?" they asked. "Is he thinking of leaving the country and going to the Jews in other lands?* Maybe he will even teach the Greeks! ³⁶What does he mean when he says, 'You will search for me but not find me,' and 'You cannot go where I am going'?"

Jesus Promises Living Water

³⁷On the last day, the climax of the festival, Jesus stood and shouted to the crowds, "Anyone who is thirsty may come to me! ³⁸Anyone who believes in me may come and drink! For the Scriptures declare, 'Rivers of living water will flow from his heart.'"* ³⁹(When he said "living water," he was speaking of the Spirit, who would be given to everyone believing in him. But the Spirit had not yet been given,* because Jesus had not yet entered into his glory.)

Division and Unbelief

⁴⁰When the crowds heard him say this, some of them declared, "Surely this man is the Prophet

we've been expecting."* ⁴¹Others said, "He is the Messiah." Still others said, "But he can't be! Will the Messiah come from Galilee? ⁴²For the Scriptures clearly state that the Messiah will be born of the royal line of David, in Bethlehem, the village where King David was born."* ⁴³So the crowd was divided about him. ⁴⁴Some even wanted him arrested, but no one laid a hand on him.

⁴⁵When the Temple guards returned without having arrested Jesus, the leading priests and Pharisees demanded, "Why didn't you bring him in?"

⁴⁶"We have never heard anyone speak like this!" the guards responded.

⁴⁷"Have you been led astray, too?" the Pharisees mocked. ⁴⁸"Is there a single one of us rulers or Pharisees who believes in him? ⁴⁹This foolish crowd follows him, but they are ignorant of the law. God's curse is on them!"

⁵⁰Then Nicodemus, the leader who had met with Jesus earlier, spoke up. ⁵¹"Is it legal to convict a man before he is given a hearing?" he asked.

⁵²They replied, "Are you from Galilee, too? Search the Scriptures and see for yourself—no prophet ever comes* from Galilee!"

[The most ancient Greek manuscripts do not include John 7:53–8:11.]

⁵³Then the meeting broke up, and everybody went home.

A Woman Caught in Adultery

8 Jesus returned to the Mount of Olives, ²but early the next morning he was back again at the Temple. A crowd soon gathered, and he sat down and taught them. ³As he was speaking, the teachers of religious law and the Pharisees brought a woman who had been caught in the act of adultery. They put her in front of the crowd.

⁴"Teacher," they said to Jesus, "this woman was caught in the act of adultery. ⁵The law of Moses says to stone her. What do you say?"

⁶They were trying to trap him into saying something they could use against him, but Jesus stooped down and wrote in the dust with his finger. ⁷They kept demanding an answer, so he stood up again and said, "All right, but let the one who has never sinned throw the first stone!" ⁸Then he stooped down again and wrote in the dust.

⁹When the accusers heard this, they slipped away one by one, beginning with the oldest, until only Jesus was left in the middle of the crowd with the woman. ¹⁰Then Jesus stood up again and said to the woman, "Where are your accusers? Didn't even one of them condemn you?"

7:30 Greek *his hour.*   **7:35** Or *the Jews who live among the Greeks?*   **7:37-38** Or *"Let anyone who is thirsty come to me and drink.* ³⁸*For the Scriptures declare, 'Rivers of living water will flow from the heart of anyone who believes in me.'"*   **7:39** Some manuscripts read *But as yet there was no Spirit.* Still others read *But as yet there was no Holy Spirit.*   **7:40** See Deut 18:15, 18; Mal 4:5-6.   **7:42** See Mic 5:2.   **7:52** Some manuscripts read *the prophet does not come.*

¹¹"No, Lord," she said.

And Jesus said, "Neither do I. Go and sin no more."

Jesus, the Light of the World

¹²Jesus spoke to the people once more and said, "I am the light of the world. If you follow me, you won't have to walk in darkness, because you will have the light that leads to life."

¹³The Pharisees replied, "You are making those claims about yourself! Such testimony is not valid."

¹⁴Jesus told them, "These claims are valid even though I make them about myself. For I know where I came from and where I am going, but you don't know this about me. ¹⁵You judge me by human standards, but I do not judge anyone. ¹⁶And if I did, my judgment would be correct in every respect because I am not alone. The Father* who sent me is with me. ¹⁷Your own law says that if two people agree about something, their witness is accepted as fact.* ¹⁸I am one witness, and my Father who sent me is the other."

¹⁹"Where is your father?" they asked.

Jesus answered, "Since you don't know who I am, you don't know who my Father is. If you knew me, you would also know my Father." ²⁰Jesus made these statements while he was teaching in the section of the Temple known as the Treasury. But he was not arrested, because his time* had not yet come.

The Unbelieving People Warned

²¹Later Jesus said to them again, "I am going away. You will search for me but will die in your sin. You cannot come where I am going."

²²The people* asked, "Is he planning to commit suicide? What does he mean, 'You cannot come where I am going'?"

²³Jesus continued, "You are from below; I am from above. You belong to this world; I do not. ²⁴That is why I said that you will die in your sins; for unless you believe that I AM who I claim to be,* you will die in your sins."

²⁵"Who are you?" they demanded.

Jesus replied, "The one I have always claimed to be.* ²⁶I have much to say about you and much to condemn, but I won't. For I say only what I have heard from the one who sent me, and he is completely truthful." ²⁷But they still didn't understand that he was talking about his Father.

²⁸So Jesus said, "When you have lifted up the Son of Man on the cross, then you will understand that I AM he.* I do nothing on my own but say only what the Father taught me. ²⁹And the one who sent me is with me—he has not deserted me. For I always do what pleases him."

³⁰Then many who heard him say these things believed in him.

Jesus and Abraham

³¹Jesus said to the people who believed in him, "You are truly my disciples if you remain faithful to my teachings. ³²And you will know the truth, and the truth will set you free."

³³"But we are descendants of Abraham," they said. "We have never been slaves to anyone. What do you mean, 'You will be set free'?"

³⁴Jesus replied, "I tell you the truth, everyone who sins is a slave of sin. ³⁵A slave is not a permanent member of the family, but a son is part of the family forever. ³⁶So if the Son sets you free, you are truly free. ³⁷Yes, I realize that you are descendants of Abraham. And yet some of you are trying to kill me because there's no room in your hearts for my message. ³⁸I am telling you what I saw when I was with my Father. But you are following the advice of your father."

³⁹"Our father is Abraham!" they declared.

"No," Jesus replied, "for if you were really the children of Abraham, you would follow his example.* ⁴⁰Instead, you are trying to kill me because I told you the truth, which I heard from God. Abraham never did such a thing. ⁴¹No, you are imitating your real father."

They replied, "We aren't illegitimate children! God himself is our true Father."

⁴²Jesus told them, "If God were your Father, you would love me, because I have come to you from God. I am not here on my own, but he sent me. ⁴³Why can't you understand what I am saying? It's because you can't even hear me! ⁴⁴For you are the children of your father the devil, and you love to do the evil things he does. He was a murderer from the beginning. He has always hated the truth, because there is no truth in him. When he lies, it is consistent with his character; for he is a liar and the father of lies. ⁴⁵So when I tell the truth, you just naturally don't believe me! ⁴⁶Which of you can truthfully accuse me of sin? And since I am telling you the truth, why don't you believe me? ⁴⁷Anyone who belongs to God listens gladly to the words of God. But you don't listen because you don't belong to God."

⁴⁸The people retorted, "You Samaritan devil! Didn't we say all along that you were possessed by a demon?"

⁴⁹"No," Jesus said, "I have no demon in me. For I honor my Father—and you dishonor me. ⁵⁰And though I have no wish to glorify myself, God is going to glorify me. He is the true judge. ⁵¹I tell you the truth, anyone who obeys my teaching will never die!"

⁵²The people said, "Now we know you are possessed by a demon. Even Abraham and the

---

8:16 Some manuscripts read *The One.*   **8:17** See Deut 19:15.   **8:20** Greek *his hour.*   **8:22** Greek *Jewish people;* also in 8:31, 48, 52, 57.   **8:24** Greek *unless you believe that I am.* See Exod 3:14.   **8:25** Or *Why do I speak to you at all?*   **8:28** Greek *When you have lifted up the Son of Man, then you will know that I am.* "Son of Man" is a title Jesus used for himself.   **8:39** Some manuscripts read *if you are really the children of Abraham, follow his example.*

prophets died, but you say, 'Anyone who obeys my teaching will never die!' ⁵³Are you greater than our father Abraham? He died, and so did the prophets. Who do you think you are?"

⁵⁴Jesus answered, "If I want glory for myself, it doesn't count. But it is my Father who will glorify me. You say, 'He is our God,'* ⁵⁵but you don't even know him. I know him. If I said otherwise, I would be as great a liar as you! But I do know him and obey him. ⁵⁶Your father Abraham rejoiced as he looked forward to my coming. He saw it and was glad."

⁵⁷The people said, "You aren't even fifty years old. How can you say you have seen Abraham?*"

⁵⁸Jesus answered, "I tell you the truth, before Abraham was even born, I Am!*" ⁵⁹At that point they picked up stones to throw at him. But Jesus was hidden from them and left the Temple.

Jesus Heals a Man Born Blind

9 As Jesus was walking along, he saw a man who had been blind from birth. ²"Rabbi," his disciples asked him, "why was this man born blind? Was it because of his own sins or his parents' sins?"

³"It was not because of his sins or his parents' sins," Jesus answered. "This happened so the power of God could be seen in him. ⁴We must quickly carry out the tasks assigned us by the one who sent us.* The night is coming, and then no one can work. ⁵But while I am here in the world, I am the light of the world."

⁶Then he spit on the ground, made mud with the saliva, and spread the mud over the blind man's eyes. ⁷He told him, "Go wash yourself in the pool of Siloam" (Siloam means "sent"). So the man went and washed and came back seeing!

⁸His neighbors and others who knew him as a blind beggar asked each other, "Isn't this the man who used to sit and beg?" ⁹Some said he was, and others said, "No, he just looks like him!"

But the beggar kept saying, "Yes, I am the same one!"

¹⁰They asked, "Who healed you? What happened?"

¹¹He told them, "The man they call Jesus made mud and spread it over my eyes and told me, 'Go to the pool of Siloam and wash yourself.' So I went and washed, and now I can see!"

¹²"Where is he now?" they asked.

"I don't know," he replied.

¹³Then they took the man who had been blind to the Pharisees, ¹⁴because it was on the Sabbath that Jesus had made the mud and healed him. ¹⁵The Pharisees asked the man all about it. So he told them, "He put the mud over my eyes, and when I washed it away, I could see!"

¹⁶Some of the Pharisees said, "This man Jesus is not from God, for he is working on the Sabbath." Others said, "But how could an ordinary sinner do such miraculous signs?" So there was a deep division of opinion among them.

¹⁷Then the Pharisees again questioned the man who had been blind and demanded, "What's your opinion about this man who healed you?"

The man replied, "I think he must be a prophet."

¹⁸The Jewish leaders still refused to believe the man had been blind and could now see, so they called in his parents. ¹⁹They asked them, "Is this your son? Was he born blind? If so, how can he now see?"

²⁰His parents replied, "We know this is our son and that he was born blind, ²¹but we don't know how he can see or who healed him. Ask him. He is old enough to speak for himself." ²²His parents said this because they were afraid of the Jewish leaders, who had announced that anyone saying Jesus was the Messiah would be expelled from the synagogue. ²³That's why they said, "He is old enough. Ask him."

²⁴So for the second time they called in the man who had been blind and told him, "God should get the glory for this,* because we know this man Jesus is a sinner."

²⁵"I don't know whether he is a sinner," the man replied. "But I know this: I was blind, and now I can see!"

²⁶"But what did he do?" they asked. "How did he heal you?"

²⁷"Look!" the man exclaimed. "I told you once. Didn't you listen? Why do you want to hear it again? Do you want to become his disciples, too?"

²⁸Then they cursed him and said, "You are his disciple, but we are disciples of Moses! ²⁹We know God spoke to Moses, but we don't even know where this man comes from."

³⁰"Why, that's very strange!" the man replied. "He healed my eyes, and yet you don't know where he comes from? ³¹We know that God doesn't listen to sinners, but he is ready to hear those who worship him and do his will. ³²Ever since the world began, no one has been able to open the eyes of someone born blind. ³³If this man were not from God, he couldn't have done it."

³⁴"You were born a total sinner!" they answered. "Are you trying to teach us?" And they threw him out of the synagogue.

Spiritual Blindness

³⁵When Jesus heard what had happened, he found the man and asked, "Do you believe in the Son of Man?*"

³⁶The man answered, "Who is he, sir? I want to believe in him."

³⁷"You have seen him," Jesus said, "and he is speaking to you!"

³⁸"Yes, Lord, I believe!" the man said. And he worshiped Jesus.

³⁹Then Jesus told him,* "I entered this world to render judgment—to give sight to the blind and to show those who think they see* that they are blind."

⁴⁰Some Pharisees who were standing nearby heard him and asked, "Are you saying we're blind?"

⁴¹"If you were blind, you wouldn't be guilty," Jesus replied. "But you remain guilty because you claim you can see.

The Good Shepherd and His Sheep

10 "I tell you the truth, anyone who sneaks over the wall of a sheepfold, rather than going through the gate, must surely be a thief and a robber! ²But the one who enters through the gate is the shepherd of the sheep. ³The gatekeeper opens the gate for him, and the sheep recognize his voice and come to him. He calls his own sheep by name and leads them out. ⁴After he has gathered his own flock, he walks ahead of them, and they follow him because they know his voice. ⁵They won't follow a stranger; they will run from him because they don't know his voice."

⁶Those who heard Jesus use this illustration didn't understand what he meant, ⁷so he explained it to them: "I tell you the truth, I am the gate for the sheep. ⁸All who came before me* were thieves and robbers. But the true sheep did not listen to them. ⁹Yes, I am the gate. Those who come in through me will be saved.* They will come and go freely and will find good pastures. ¹⁰The thief's purpose is to steal and kill and destroy. My purpose is to give them a rich and satisfying life.

¹¹"I am the good shepherd. The good shepherd sacrifices his life for the sheep. ¹²A hired hand will run when he sees a wolf coming. He will abandon the sheep because they don't belong to him and he isn't their shepherd. And so the wolf attacks them and scatters the flock. ¹³The hired hand runs away because he's working only for the money and doesn't really care about the sheep.

¹⁴"I am the good shepherd; I know my own sheep, and they know me, ¹⁵just as my Father knows me and I know the Father. So I sacrifice my life for the sheep. ¹⁶I have other sheep, too, that are not in this sheepfold. I must bring them also. They will listen to my voice, and there will be one flock with one shepherd.

¹⁷"The Father loves me because I sacrifice my life so I may take it back again. ¹⁸No one can take my life from me. I sacrifice it voluntarily. For I have the authority to lay it down when I want to and also to take it up again. For this is what my Father has commanded."

¹⁹When he said these things, the people* were again divided in their opinions about him. ²⁰Some said, "He's demon possessed and out of his mind. Why listen to a man like that?" ²¹Others said, "This doesn't sound like a man possessed by a demon! Can a demon open the eyes of the blind?"

Jesus Claims to Be the Son of God

²²It was now winter, and Jesus was in Jerusalem at the time of Hanukkah, the Festival of Dedication. ²³He was in the Temple, walking through the section known as Solomon's Colonnade. ²⁴The people surrounded him and asked, "How long are you going to keep us in suspense? If you are the Messiah, tell us plainly."

²⁵Jesus replied, "I have already told you, and you don't believe me. The proof is the work I do in my Father's name. ²⁶But you don't believe me because you are not my sheep. ²⁷My sheep listen to my voice; I know them, and they follow me. ²⁸I give them eternal life, and they will never perish. No one can snatch them away from me, ²⁹for my Father has given them to me, and he is more powerful than anyone else.* No one can snatch them from the Father's hand. ³⁰The Father and I are one."

³¹Once again the people picked up stones to kill him. ³²Jesus said, "At my Father's direction I have done many good works. For which one are you going to stone me?"

³³They replied, "We're stoning you not for any good work, but for blasphemy! You, a mere man, claim to be God."

³⁴Jesus replied, "It is written in your own Scriptures* that God said to certain leaders of the people, 'I say, you are gods!'* ³⁵And you know that the Scriptures cannot be altered. So if those people who received God's message were called 'gods,' ³⁶why do you call it blasphemy when I say, 'I am the Son of God'? After all, the Father set me apart and sent me into the world. ³⁷Don't believe me unless I carry out my Father's work. ³⁸But if I do his work, believe in the evidence of the miraculous works I have done, even if you don't believe me. Then you will know and understand that the Father is in me, and I am in the Father."

³⁹Once again they tried to arrest him, but he got away and left them. ⁴⁰He went beyond the Jordan River near the place where John was first baptizing and stayed there awhile. ⁴¹And many

9:38-39a Some manuscripts do not include *"Yes, Lord, I believe!" the man said. And he worshiped Jesus. Then Jesus told him.*
9:39b Greek *those who see.*   10:8 Some manuscripts do not include *before me.*   10:9 Or *will find safety.*   10:19 Greek *Jewish people;* also in 10:24, 31.   10:29 Other manuscripts read *for what my Father has given me is more powerful than anything;* still others read *for regarding that which my Father has given me, he is greater than all.*   10:34a Greek *your own law.*   10:34b Ps 82:6.

followed him. "John didn't perform miraculous signs," they remarked to one another, "but everything he said about this man has come true." [42]And many who were there believed in Jesus.

The Raising of Lazarus

11 A man named Lazarus was sick. He lived in Bethany with his sisters, Mary and Martha. [2]This is the Mary who later poured the expensive perfume on the Lord's feet and wiped them with her hair.* Her brother, Lazarus, was sick. [3]So the two sisters sent a message to Jesus telling him, "Lord, your dear friend is very sick."

[4]But when Jesus heard about it he said, "Lazarus's sickness will not end in death. No, it happened for the glory of God so that the Son of God will receive glory from this." [5]So although Jesus loved Martha, Mary, and Lazarus, [6]he stayed where he was for the next two days. [7]Finally, he said to his disciples, "Let's go back to Judea."

[8]But his disciples objected. "Rabbi," they said, "only a few days ago the people* in Judea were trying to stone you. Are you going there again?"

[9]Jesus replied, "There are twelve hours of daylight every day. During the day people can walk safely. They can see because they have the light of this world. [10]But at night there is danger of stumbling because they have no light." [11]Then he said, "Our friend Lazarus has fallen asleep, but now I will go and wake him up."

[12]The disciples said, "Lord, if he is sleeping, he will soon get better!" [13]They thought Jesus meant Lazarus was simply sleeping, but Jesus meant Lazarus had died.

[14]So he told them plainly, "Lazarus is dead. [15]And for your sakes, I'm glad I wasn't there, for now you will really believe. Come, let's go see him."

[16]Thomas, nicknamed the Twin,* said to his fellow disciples, "Let's go, too—and die with Jesus."

[17]When Jesus arrived at Bethany, he was told that Lazarus had already been in his grave for four days. [18]Bethany was only a few miles* down the road from Jerusalem, [19]and many of the people had come to console Martha and Mary in their loss. [20]When Martha got word that Jesus was coming, she went to meet him. But Mary stayed in the house. [21]Martha said to Jesus, "Lord, if only you had been here, my brother would not have died. [22]But even now I know that God will give you whatever you ask."

[23]Jesus told her, "Your brother will rise again."

[24]"Yes," Martha said, "he will rise when everyone else rises, at the last day."

[25]Jesus told her, "I am the resurrection and the life.* Anyone who believes in me will live, even after dying. [26]Everyone who lives in me and believes in me will never ever die. Do you believe this, Martha?"

[27]"Yes, Lord," she told him. "I have always believed you are the Messiah, the Son of God, the one who has come into the world from God."

[28]Then she returned to Mary. She called Mary aside from the mourners and told her, "The Teacher is here and wants to see you." [29]So Mary immediately went to him.

[30]Jesus had stayed outside the village, at the place where Martha met him. [31]When the people who were at the house consoling Mary saw her leave so hastily, they assumed she was going to Lazarus's grave to weep. So they followed her there. [32]When Mary arrived and saw Jesus, she fell at his feet and said, "Lord, if only you had been here, my brother would not have died."

[33]When Jesus saw her weeping and saw the other people wailing with her, a deep anger welled up within him,* and he was deeply troubled. [34]"Where have you put him?" he asked them.

They told him, "Lord, come and see." [35]Then Jesus wept. [36]The people who were standing nearby said, "See how much he loved him!" [37]But some said, "This man healed a blind man. Couldn't he have kept Lazarus from dying?"

[38]Jesus was still angry as he arrived at the tomb, a cave with a stone rolled across its entrance. [39]"Roll the stone aside," Jesus told them.

But Martha, the dead man's sister, protested, "Lord, he has been dead for four days. The smell will be terrible."

[40]Jesus responded, "Didn't I tell you that you would see God's glory if you believe?" [41]So they rolled the stone aside. Then Jesus looked up to heaven and said, "Father, thank you for hearing me. [42]You always hear me, but I said it out loud for the sake of all these people standing here, so that they will believe you sent me." [43]Then Jesus shouted, "Lazarus, come out!" [44]And the dead man came out, his hands and feet bound in graveclothes, his face wrapped in a headcloth. Jesus told them, "Unwrap him and let him go!"

The Plot to Kill Jesus

[45]Many of the people who were with Mary believed in Jesus when they saw this happen. [46]But some went to the Pharisees and told them what Jesus had done. [47]Then the leading priests and Pharisees called the high council* together. "What are we going to do?" they asked each other. "This man certainly performs many miraculous signs. [48]If we allow him to go on like this, soon everyone will believe in him. Then the Roman army will come and destroy both our Temple* and our nation."

11:2 This incident is recorded in chapter 12.   11:8 Greek *Jewish people;* also in 11:19, 31, 33, 36, 45, 54.   11:16 Greek *Thomas, who was called Didymus.*   11:18 Greek *was about 15 stadia* (about 2.8 kilometers).   11:25 Some manuscripts do not include *and the life.*   11:33 Or *he was angry in his spirit.*   11:47 Greek *the Sanhedrin.*   11:48 Or *our position;* Greek reads *our place.*

⁴⁹Caiaphas, who was high priest at that time,* said, "You don't know what you're talking about! ⁵⁰You don't realize that it's better for you that one man should die for the people than for the whole nation to be destroyed."

⁵¹He did not say this on his own; as high priest at that time he was led to prophesy that Jesus would die for the entire nation. ⁵²And not only for that nation, but to bring together and unite all the children of God scattered around the world.

⁵³So from that time on, the Jewish leaders began to plot Jesus' death. ⁵⁴As a result, Jesus stopped his public ministry among the people and left Jerusalem. He went to a place near the wilderness, to the village of Ephraim, and stayed there with his disciples.

⁵⁵It was now almost time for the Jewish Passover celebration, and many people from all over the country arrived in Jerusalem several days early so they could go through the purification ceremony before Passover began. ⁵⁶They kept looking for Jesus, but as they stood around in the Temple, they said to each other, "What do you think? He won't come for Passover, will he?" ⁵⁷Meanwhile, the leading priests and Pharisees had publicly ordered that anyone seeing Jesus must report it immediately so they could arrest him.

Jesus Anointed at Bethany

12 Six days before the Passover celebration began, Jesus arrived in Bethany, the home of Lazarus—the man he had raised from the dead. ²A dinner was prepared in Jesus' honor. Martha served, and Lazarus was among those who ate* with him. ³Then Mary took a twelve-ounce jar* of expensive perfume made from essence of nard, and she anointed Jesus' feet with it, wiping his feet with her hair. The house was filled with the fragrance.

⁴But Judas Iscariot, the disciple who would soon betray him, said, ⁵"That perfume was worth a year's wages.* It should have been sold and the money given to the poor." ⁶Not that he cared for the poor—he was a thief, and since he was in charge of the disciples' money, he often stole some for himself.

⁷Jesus replied, "Leave her alone. She did this in preparation for my burial. ⁸You will always have the poor among you, but you will not always have me."

⁹When all the people* heard of Jesus' arrival, they flocked to see him and also to see Lazarus, the man Jesus had raised from the dead. ¹⁰Then the leading priests decided to kill Lazarus, too, ¹¹for it was because of him that many of the people had deserted them* and believed in Jesus.

Jesus' Triumphant Entry

¹²The next day, the news that Jesus was on the way to Jerusalem swept through the city. A large crowd of Passover visitors ¹³took palm branches and went down the road to meet him. They shouted,

> "Praise God!*
> Blessings on the one who comes in the name
>   of the Lord!
> Hail to the King of Israel!"*

¹⁴Jesus found a young donkey and rode on it, fulfilling the prophecy that said:

¹⁵ "Don't be afraid, people of Jerusalem.*
Look, your King is coming,
     riding on a donkey's colt."*

¹⁶His disciples didn't understand at the time that this was a fulfillment of prophecy. But after Jesus entered into his glory, they remembered what had happened and realized that these things had been written about him.

¹⁷Many in the crowd had seen Jesus call Lazarus from the tomb, raising him from the dead, and they were telling others* about it. ¹⁸That was the reason so many went out to meet him—because they had heard about this miraculous sign. ¹⁹Then the Pharisees said to each other, "There's nothing we can do. Look, everyone* has gone after him!"

Jesus Predicts His Death

²⁰Some Greeks who had come to Jerusalem for the Passover celebration ²¹paid a visit to Philip, who was from Bethsaida in Galilee. They said, "Sir, we want to meet Jesus." ²²Philip told Andrew about it, and they went together to ask Jesus.

²³Jesus replied, "Now the time has come for the Son of Man* to enter into his glory. ²⁴I tell you the truth, unless a kernel of wheat is planted in the soil and dies, it remains alone. But its death will produce many new kernels—a plentiful harvest of new lives. ²⁵Those who love their life in this world will lose it. Those who care nothing for their life in this world will keep it for eternity. ²⁶Anyone who wants to be my disciple must follow me, because my servants must be where I am. And the Father will honor anyone who serves me.

²⁷"Now my soul is deeply troubled. Should I pray, 'Father, save me from this hour'? But this is the very reason I came! ²⁸Father, bring glory to your name."

Then a voice spoke from heaven, saying, "I have already brought glory to my name, and I will do so again." ²⁹When the crowd heard the voice, some thought it was thunder, while others declared an angel had spoken to him.

³⁰Then Jesus told them, "The voice was for your benefit, not mine. ³¹The time for judging this world has come, when Satan, the ruler of this world, will be cast out. ³²And when I am lifted up from the earth, I will draw everyone to myself." ³³He said this to indicate how he was going to die.

³⁴The crowd responded, "We understood from Scripture* that the Messiah would live forever. How can you say the Son of Man will die? Just who is this Son of Man, anyway?"

³⁵Jesus replied, "My light will shine for you just a little longer. Walk in the light while you can, so the darkness will not overtake you. Those who walk in the darkness cannot see where they are going. ³⁶Put your trust in the light while there is still time; then you will become children of the light."

After saying these things, Jesus went away and was hidden from them.

The Unbelief of the People

³⁷But despite all the miraculous signs Jesus had done, most of the people still did not believe in him. ³⁸This is exactly what Isaiah the prophet had predicted:

> "Lᴏʀᴅ, who has believed our message?
>   To whom has the Lᴏʀᴅ revealed his
>   powerful arm?"*

³⁹But the people couldn't believe, for as Isaiah also said,

⁴⁰ "The Lord has blinded their eyes
>   and hardened their hearts—
> so that their eyes cannot see,
>   and their hearts cannot understand,
> and they cannot turn to me
>   and have me heal them."*

⁴¹Isaiah was referring to Jesus when he said this, because he saw the future and spoke of the Messiah's glory. ⁴²Many people did believe in him, however, including some of the Jewish leaders. But they wouldn't admit it for fear that the Pharisees would expel them from the synagogue. ⁴³For they loved human praise more than the praise of God.

⁴⁴Jesus shouted to the crowds, "If you trust me, you are trusting not only me, but also God who sent me. ⁴⁵For when you see me, you are seeing the one who sent me. ⁴⁶I have come as a light to shine in this dark world, so that all who put their trust in me will no longer remain in the dark. ⁴⁷I will not judge those who hear me but don't obey me, for I have come to save the world and not to judge it. ⁴⁸But all who reject me and my message will be judged on the day of judgment by the truth I have spoken. ⁴⁹I don't speak on my own authority. The Father who sent me

has commanded me what to say and how to say it. ⁵⁰And I know his commands lead to eternal life; so I say whatever the Father tells me to say."

Jesus Washes His Disciples' Feet

13 Before the Passover celebration, Jesus knew that his hour had come to leave this world and return to his Father. He had loved his disciples during his ministry on earth, and now he loved them to the very end.* ²It was time for supper, and the devil had already prompted Judas,* son of Simon Iscariot, to betray Jesus. ³Jesus knew that the Father had given him authority over everything and that he had come from God and would return to God. ⁴So he got up from the table, took off his robe, wrapped a towel around his waist, ⁵and poured water into a basin. Then he began to wash the disciples' feet, drying them with the towel he had around him.

⁶When Jesus came to Simon Peter, Peter said to him, "Lord, are you going to wash my feet?"

⁷Jesus replied, "You don't understand now what I am doing, but someday you will."

⁸"No," Peter protested, "you will never ever wash my feet!"

Jesus replied, "Unless I wash you, you won't belong to me."

⁹Simon Peter exclaimed, "Then wash my hands and head as well, Lord, not just my feet!"

¹⁰Jesus replied, "A person who has bathed all over does not need to wash, except for the feet,* to be entirely clean. And you disciples are clean, but not all of you." ¹¹For Jesus knew who would betray him. That is what he meant when he said, "Not all of you are clean."

¹²After washing their feet, he put on his robe again and sat down and asked, "Do you understand what I was doing? ¹³You call me 'Teacher' and 'Lord,' and you are right, because that's what I am. ¹⁴And since I, your Lord and Teacher, have washed your feet, you ought to wash each other's feet. ¹⁵I have given you an example to follow. Do as I have done to you. ¹⁶I tell you the truth, slaves are not greater than their master. Nor is the messenger more important than the one who sends the message. ¹⁷Now that you know these things, God will bless you for doing them.

Jesus Predicts His Betrayal

¹⁸"I am not saying these things to all of you; I know the ones I have chosen. But this fulfills the Scripture that says, 'The one who eats my food has turned against me.'* ¹⁹I tell you this beforehand, so that when it happens you will believe that I Aᴍ the Messiah.* ²⁰I tell you the truth, anyone who welcomes my messenger is welcoming me, and anyone who welcomes me is welcoming the Father who sent me."

²¹Now Jesus was deeply troubled,* and he ex-

12:34 Greek *from the law.*   **12:38** Isa 53:1.   **12:40** Isa 6:10.   **13:1** Or *he showed them the full extent of his love.*   **13:2** Or *the devil had already intended for Judas.*   **13:10** Some manuscripts do not include *except for the feet.*   **13:18** Ps 41:9.   **13:19** Or *that the 'I Aᴍ' has come;* or *that I am the Lᴏʀᴅ;* Greek reads *that I am.* See Exod 3:14.   **13:21** Greek *was troubled in his spirit.*

claimed, "I tell you the truth, one of you will betray me!"

²²The disciples looked at each other, wondering whom he could mean. ²³The disciple Jesus loved was sitting next to Jesus at the table.* ²⁴Simon Peter motioned to him to ask, "Who's he talking about?" ²⁵So that disciple leaned over to Jesus and asked, "Lord, who is it?"

²⁶Jesus responded, "It is the one to whom I give the bread I dip in the bowl." And when he had dipped it, he gave it to Judas, son of Simon Iscariot. ²⁷When Judas had eaten the bread, Satan entered into him. Then Jesus told him, "Hurry and do what you're going to do." ²⁸None of the others at the table knew what Jesus meant. ²⁹Since Judas was their treasurer, some thought Jesus was telling him to go and pay for the food or to give some money to the poor. ³⁰So Judas left at once, going out into the night.

Jesus Predicts Peter's Denial

³¹As soon as Judas left the room, Jesus said, "The time has come for the Son of Man* to enter into his glory, and God will be glorified because of him. ³²And since God receives glory because of the Son,* he will soon give glory to the Son. ³³Dear children, I will be with you only a little longer. And as I told the Jewish leaders, you will search for me, but you can't come where I am going. ³⁴So now I am giving you a new commandment: Love each other. Just as I have loved you, you should love each other. ³⁵Your love for one another will prove to the world that you are my disciples."

³⁶Simon Peter asked, "Lord, where are you going?"

And Jesus replied, "You can't go with me now, but you will follow me later."

³⁷"But why can't I come now, Lord?" he asked. "I'm ready to die for you."

³⁸Jesus answered, "Die for me? I tell you the truth, Peter—before the rooster crows tomorrow morning, you will deny three times that you even know me.

Jesus, the Way to the Father

14 "Don't let your hearts be troubled. Trust in God, and trust also in me. ²There is more than enough room in my Father's home.* If this were not so, would I have told you that I am going to prepare a place for you?* ³When everything is ready, I will come and get you, so that you will always be with me where I am. ⁴And you know the way to where I am going."

⁵"No, we don't know, Lord," Thomas said. "We have no idea where you are going, so how can we know the way?"

⁶Jesus told him, "I am the way, the truth, and the life. No one can come to the Father except through me. ⁷If you had really known me, you would know who my Father is.* From now on, you do know him and have seen him!"

⁸Philip said, "Lord, show us the Father, and we will be satisfied."

⁹Jesus replied, "Have I been with you all this time, Philip, and yet you still don't know who I am? Anyone who has seen me has seen the Father! So why are you asking me to show him to you? ¹⁰Don't you believe that I am in the Father and the Father is in me? The words I speak are not my own, but my Father who lives in me does his work through me. ¹¹Just believe that I am in the Father and the Father is in me. Or at least believe because of the work you have seen me do.

¹²"I tell you the truth, anyone who believes in me will do the same works I have done, and even greater works, because I am going to be with the Father. ¹³You can ask for anything in my name, and I will do it, so that the Son can bring glory to the Father. ¹⁴Yes, ask me for anything in my name, and I will do it!

Jesus Promises the Holy Spirit

¹⁵"If you love me, obey* my commandments. ¹⁶And I will ask the Father, and he will give you another Advocate,* who will never leave you. ¹⁷He is the Holy Spirit, who leads into all truth. The world cannot receive him, because it isn't looking for him and doesn't recognize him. But you know him, because he lives with you now and later will be in you.* ¹⁸No, I will not abandon you as orphans—I will come to you. ¹⁹Soon the world will no longer see me, but you will see me. Since I live, you also will live. ²⁰When I am raised to life again, you will know that I am in my Father, and you are in me, and I am in you. ²¹Those who accept my commandments and obey them are the ones who love me. And because they love me, my Father will love them. And I will love them and reveal myself to each of them."

²²Judas (not Judas Iscariot, but the other disciple with that name) said to him, "Lord, why are you going to reveal yourself only to us and not to the world at large?"

²³Jesus replied, "All who love me will do what I say. My Father will love them, and we will come and make our home with each of them. ²⁴Anyone who doesn't love me will not obey me. And remember, my words are not my own. What I am telling you is from the Father who sent me. ²⁵I am telling you these things now while I am still with you. ²⁶But when the Father sends the Advocate as my representative—that is, the Holy

---

13:23 Greek *was reclining on Jesus' bosom.* The "disciple Jesus loved" was probably John.   **13:31** "Son of Man" is a title Jesus used for himself.   **13:32** Some manuscripts do not include *And since God receives glory because of the Son.*   **14:2a** Or *There are many rooms in my Father's house.*   **14:2b** Or *If this were not so, I would have told you that I am going to prepare a place for you.* Some manuscripts read *If this were not so, I would have told you. I am going to prepare a place for you.*   **14:7** Some manuscripts read *If you have really known me, you will know who my Father is.*   **14:15** Other manuscripts read *you will obey;* still others read *you should obey.*   **14:16** Or *Comforter,* or *Encourager,* or *Counselor.* Greek reads *Paraclete;* also in 14:26.   **14:17** Some manuscripts read *and is in you.*

Spirit—he will teach you everything and will remind you of everything I have told you.

²⁷"I am leaving you with a gift—peace of mind and heart. And the peace I give is a gift the world cannot give. So don't be troubled or afraid. ²⁸Remember what I told you: I am going away, but I will come back to you again. If you really loved me, you would be happy that I am going to the Father, who is greater than I am. ²⁹I have told you these things before they happen so that when they do happen, you will believe.

³⁰"I don't have much more time to talk to you, because the ruler of this world approaches. He has no power over me, ³¹but I will do what the Father requires of me, so that the world will know that I love the Father. Come, let's be going.

Jesus, the True Vine

15 "I am the true grapevine, and my Father is the gardener. ²He cuts off every branch of mine that doesn't produce fruit, and he prunes the branches that do bear fruit so they will produce even more. ³You have already been pruned and purified by the message I have given you. ⁴Remain in me, and I will remain in you. For a branch cannot produce fruit if it is severed from the vine, and you cannot be fruitful unless you remain in me.

⁵"Yes, I am the vine; you are the branches. Those who remain in me, and I in them, will produce much fruit. For apart from me you can do nothing. ⁶Anyone who does not remain in me is thrown away like a useless branch and withers. Such branches are gathered into a pile to be burned. ⁷But if you remain in me and my words remain in you, you may ask for anything you want, and it will be granted! ⁸When you produce much fruit, you are my true disciples. This brings great glory to my Father.

⁹"I have loved you even as the Father has loved me. Remain in my love. ¹⁰When you obey my commandments, you remain in my love, just as I obey my Father's commandments and remain in his love. ¹¹I have told you these things so that you will be filled with my joy. Yes, your joy will overflow! ¹²This is my commandment: Love each other in the same way I have loved you. ¹³There is no greater love than to lay down one's life for one's friends. ¹⁴You are my friends if you do what I command. ¹⁵I no longer call you slaves, because a master doesn't confide in his slaves. Now you are my friends, since I have told you everything the Father told me. ¹⁶You didn't choose me. I chose you. I appointed you to go and produce lasting fruit, so that the Father will give you whatever you ask for, using my name. ¹⁷This is my command: Love each other.

The World's Hatred

¹⁸"If the world hates you, remember that it hated me first. ¹⁹The world would love you as one of its own if you belonged to it, but you are no longer part of the world. I chose you to come out of the world, so it hates you. ²⁰Do you remember what I told you? 'A slave is not greater than the master.' Since they persecuted me, naturally they will persecute you. And if they had listened to me, they would listen to you. ²¹They will do all this to you because of me, for they have rejected the one who sent me. ²²They would not be guilty if I had not come and spoken to them. But now they have no excuse for their sin. ²³Anyone who hates me also hates my Father. ²⁴If I hadn't done such miraculous signs among them that no one else could do, they would not be guilty. But as it is, they have seen everything I did, yet they still hate me and my Father. ²⁵This fulfills what is written in their Scriptures*: 'They hated me without cause.'

²⁶"But I will send you the Advocate*—the Spirit of truth. He will come to you from the Father and will testify all about me. ²⁷And you must also testify about me because you have been with me from the beginning of my ministry.

16 "I have told you these things so that you won't abandon your faith. ²For you will be expelled from the synagogues, and the time is coming when those who kill you will think they are doing a holy service for God. ³This is because they have never known the Father or me. ⁴Yes, I'm telling you these things now, so that when they happen, you will remember my warning. I didn't tell you earlier because I was going to be with you for a while longer.

The Work of the Holy Spirit

⁵"But now I am going away to the one who sent me, and not one of you is asking where I am going. ⁶Instead, you grieve because of what I've told you. ⁷But in fact, it is best for you that I go away, because if I don't, the Advocate* won't come. If I do go away, then I will send him to you. ⁸And when he comes, he will convict the world of its sin, and of God's righteousness, and of the coming judgment. ⁹The world's sin is that it refuses to believe in me. ¹⁰Righteousness is available because I go to the Father, and you will see me no more. ¹¹Judgment will come because the ruler of this world has already been judged.

¹²"There is so much more I want to tell you, but you can't bear it now. ¹³When the Spirit of truth comes, he will guide you into all truth. He will not speak on his own but will tell you what he has heard. He will tell you about the future. ¹⁴He will bring me glory by telling you whatever he receives from me. ¹⁵All that belongs to the

---

15:25 Greek *in their law.* Pss 35:19; 69:4. **15:26** Or *Comforter,* or *Encourager,* or *Counselor.* Greek reads *Paraclete.*
16:7 Or *Comforter,* or *Encourager,* or *Counselor.* Greek reads *Paraclete.*

Father is mine; this is why I said, 'The Spirit will tell you whatever he receives from me.'

Sadness Will Be Turned to Joy

16"In a little while you won't see me anymore. But a little while after that, you will see me again."

17Some of the disciples asked each other, "What does he mean when he says, 'In a little while you won't see me, but then you will see me,' and 'I am going to the Father'? 18And what does he mean by 'a little while'? We don't understand."

19Jesus realized they wanted to ask him about it, so he said, "Are you asking yourselves what I meant? I said in a little while you won't see me, but a little while after that you will see me again. 20I tell you the truth, you will weep and mourn over what is going to happen to me, but the world will rejoice. You will grieve, but your grief will suddenly turn to wonderful joy. 21It will be like a woman suffering the pains of labor. When her child is born, her anguish gives way to joy because she has brought a new baby into the world. 22So you have sorrow now, but I will see you again; then you will rejoice, and no one can rob you of that joy. 23At that time you won't need to ask me for anything. I tell you the truth, you will ask the Father directly, and he will grant your request because you use my name. 24You haven't done this before. Ask, using my name, and you will receive, and you will have abundant joy.

25"I have spoken of these matters in figures of speech, but soon I will stop speaking figuratively and will tell you plainly all about the Father. 26Then you will ask in my name. I'm not saying I will ask the Father on your behalf, 27for the Father himself loves you dearly because you love me and believe that I came from God.* 28Yes, I came from the Father into the world, and now I will leave the world and return to the Father."

29Then his disciples said, "At last you are speaking plainly and not figuratively. 30Now we understand that you know everything, and there's no need to question you. From this we believe that you came from God."

31Jesus asked, "Do you finally believe? 32But the time is coming—indeed it's here now—when you will be scattered, each one going his own way, leaving me alone. Yet I am not alone because the Father is with me. 33I have told you all this so that you may have peace in me. Here on earth you will have many trials and sorrows. But take heart, because I have overcome the world."

The Prayer of Jesus

17 After saying all these things, Jesus looked up to heaven and said, "Father, the hour has come. Glorify your Son so he can give glory back to you. 2For you have given him authority over everyone. He gives eternal life to each one you have given him. 3And this is the way to have eternal life—to know you, the only true God, and Jesus Christ, the one you sent to earth. 4I brought glory to you here on earth by completing the work you gave me to do. 5Now, Father, bring me into the glory we shared before the world began.

6"I have revealed you* to the ones you gave me from this world. They were always yours. You gave them to me, and they have kept your word. 7Now they know that everything I have is a gift from you, 8for I have passed on to them the message you gave me. They accepted it and know that I came from you, and they believe you sent me.

9"My prayer is not for the world, but for those you have given me, because they belong to you. 10All who are mine belong to you, and you have given them to me, so they bring me glory. 11Now I am departing from the world; they are staying in this world, but I am coming to you. Holy Father, you have given me your name;* now protect them by the power of your name so that they will be united just as we are. 12During my time here, I protected them by the power of the name you gave me.* I guarded them so that not one was lost, except the one headed for destruction, as the Scriptures foretold.

13"Now I am coming to you. I told them many things while I was with them in this world so they would be filled with my joy. 14I have given them your word. And the world hates them because they do not belong to the world, just as I do not belong to the world. 15I'm not asking you to take them out of the world, but to keep them safe from the evil one. 16They do not belong to this world any more than I do. 17Make them holy by your truth; teach them your word, which is truth. 18Just as you sent me into the world, I am sending them into the world. 19And I give myself as a holy sacrifice for them so they can be made holy by your truth.

20"I am praying not only for these disciples but also for all who will ever believe in me through their message. 21I pray that they will all be one, just as you and I are one—as you are in me, Father, and I am in you. And may they be in us so that the world will believe you sent me.

22"I have given them the glory you gave me, so they may be one as we are one. 23I am in them and you are in me. May they experience such perfect unity that the world will know that you sent me and that you love them as much as you love me. 24Father, I want these whom you have given me to be with me where I am. Then they can see all the glory you gave me because you loved me even before the world began!

25"O righteous Father, the world doesn't know you, but I do; and these disciples know you sent me. 26I have revealed you to them, and

16:27 Some manuscripts read *from the Father.* **17:6** Greek *have revealed your name;* also in 17:26. **17:11** Some manuscripts read *you have given me these [disciples].* **17:12** Some manuscripts read *I protected those you gave me, by the power of your name.*

I will continue to do so. Then your love for me will be in them, and I will be in them."

Jesus Is Betrayed and Arrested

18 After saying these things, Jesus crossed the Kidron Valley with his disciples and entered a grove of olive trees. ²Judas, the betrayer, knew this place, because Jesus had often gone there with his disciples. ³The leading priests and Pharisees had given Judas a contingent of Roman soldiers and Temple guards to accompany him. Now with blazing torches, lanterns, and weapons, they arrived at the olive grove.

⁴Jesus fully realized all that was going to happen to him, so he stepped forward to meet them. "Who are you looking for?" he asked.

⁵"Jesus the Nazarene,"* they replied.

"I Am he,"* Jesus said. (Judas, who betrayed him, was standing with them.) ⁶As Jesus said "I Am he," they all drew back and fell to the ground! ⁷Once more he asked them, "Who are you looking for?"

And again they replied, "Jesus the Nazarene."

⁸"I told you that I Am he," Jesus said. "And since I am the one you want, let these others go." ⁹He did this to fulfill his own statement: "I did not lose a single one of those you have given me."*

¹⁰Then Simon Peter drew a sword and slashed off the right ear of Malchus, the high priest's slave. ¹¹But Jesus said to Peter, "Put your sword back into its sheath. Shall I not drink from the cup of suffering the Father has given me?"

Jesus at the High Priest's House

¹²So the soldiers, their commanding officer, and the Temple guards arrested Jesus and tied him up. ¹³First they took him to Annas, the father-in-law of Caiaphas, the high priest at that time.* ¹⁴Caiaphas was the one who had told the other Jewish leaders, "It's better that one man should die for the people."

Peter's First Denial

¹⁵Simon Peter followed Jesus, as did another of the disciples. That other disciple was acquainted with the high priest, so he was allowed to enter the high priest's courtyard with Jesus. ¹⁶Peter had to stay outside the gate. Then the disciple who knew the high priest spoke to the woman watching at the gate, and she let Peter in. ¹⁷The woman asked Peter, "You're not one of that man's disciples, are you?"

"No," he said, "I am not."

¹⁸Because it was cold, the household servants and the guards had made a charcoal fire. They stood around it, warming themselves, and Peter stood with them, warming himself.

The High Priest Questions Jesus

¹⁹Inside, the high priest began asking Jesus about his followers and what he had been teaching them. ²⁰Jesus replied, "Everyone knows what I teach. I have preached regularly in the synagogues and the Temple, where the people* gather. I have not spoken in secret. ²¹Why are you asking me this question? Ask those who heard me. They know what I said."

²²Then one of the Temple guards standing nearby slapped Jesus across the face. "Is that the way to answer the high priest?" he demanded.

²³Jesus replied, "If I said anything wrong, you must prove it. But if I'm speaking the truth, why are you beating me?"

²⁴Then Annas bound Jesus and sent him to Caiaphas, the high priest.

Peter's Second and Third Denials

²⁵Meanwhile, as Simon Peter was standing by the fire warming himself, they asked him again, "You're not one of his disciples, are you?"

He denied it, saying, "No, I am not."

²⁶But one of the household slaves of the high priest, a relative of the man whose ear Peter had cut off, asked, "Didn't I see you out there in the olive grove with Jesus?" ²⁷Again Peter denied it. And immediately a rooster crowed.

Jesus' Trial before Pilate

²⁸Jesus' trial before Caiaphas ended in the early hours of the morning. Then he was taken to the headquarters of the Roman governor.* His accusers didn't go inside because it would defile them, and they wouldn't be allowed to celebrate the Passover. ²⁹So Pilate, the governor, went out to them and asked, "What is your charge against this man?"

³⁰"We wouldn't have handed him over to you if he weren't a criminal!" they retorted.

³¹"Then take him away and judge him by your own law," Pilate told them.

"Only the Romans are permitted to execute someone," the Jewish leaders replied. ³²(This fulfilled Jesus' prediction about the way he would die.*)

³³Then Pilate went back into his headquarters and called for Jesus to be brought to him. "Are you the king of the Jews?" he asked him.

³⁴Jesus replied, "Is this your own question, or did others tell you about me?"

³⁵"Am I a Jew?" Pilate retorted. "Your own people and their leading priests brought you to me for trial. Why? What have you done?"

³⁶Jesus answered, "My Kingdom is not an earthly kingdom. If it were, my followers would fight to keep me from being handed over to the Jewish leaders. But my Kingdom is not of this world."

18:5a Or *Jesus of Nazareth;* also in 18:7. **18:5b** Or *"The 'I Am' is here";* or *"I am the LORD";* Greek reads *I am;* also in 18:6, 8. See Exod 3:14. **18:9** See John 6:39 and 17:12. **18:13** Greek *that year.* **18:20** Greek *Jewish people;* also in 18:38. **18:28** Greek *to the Praetorium;* also in 18:33. **18:32** See John 12:32-33.

³⁷Pilate said, "So you are a king?"

Jesus responded, "You say I am a king. Actually, I was born and came into the world to testify to the truth. All who love the truth recognize that what I say is true."

³⁸"What is truth?" Pilate asked. Then he went out again to the people and told them, "He is not guilty of any crime. ³⁹But you have a custom of asking me to release one prisoner each year at Passover. Would you like me to release this 'King of the Jews'?"

⁴⁰But they shouted back, "No! Not this man. We want Barabbas!" (Barabbas was a revolutionary.)

Jesus Sentenced to Death

19 Then Pilate had Jesus flogged with a lead-tipped whip. ²The soldiers wove a crown of thorns and put it on his head, and they put a purple robe on him. ³"Hail! King of the Jews!" they mocked, as they slapped him across the face.

⁴Pilate went outside again and said to the people, "I am going to bring him out to you now, but understand clearly that I find him not guilty." ⁵Then Jesus came out wearing the crown of thorns and the purple robe. And Pilate said, "Look, here is the man!"

⁶When they saw him, the leading priests and Temple guards began shouting, "Crucify him! Crucify him!"

"Take him yourselves and crucify him," Pilate said. "I find him not guilty."

⁷The Jewish leaders replied, "By our law he ought to die because he called himself the Son of God."

⁸When Pilate heard this, he was more frightened than ever. ⁹He took Jesus back into the headquarters* again and asked him, "Where are you from?" But Jesus gave no answer. ¹⁰"Why don't you talk to me?" Pilate demanded. "Don't you realize that I have the power to release you or crucify you?"

¹¹Then Jesus said, "You would have no power over me at all unless it were given to you from above. So the one who handed me over to you has the greater sin."

¹²Then Pilate tried to release him, but the Jewish leaders shouted, "If you release this man, you are no 'friend of Caesar.'* Anyone who declares himself a king is a rebel against Caesar."

¹³When they said this, Pilate brought Jesus out to them again. Then Pilate sat down on the judgment seat on the platform that is called the Stone Pavement (in Hebrew, *Gabbatha*). ¹⁴It was now about noon on the day of preparation for the Passover. And Pilate said to the people,* "Look, here is your king!"

¹⁵"Away with him," they yelled. "Away with him! Crucify him!"

"What? Crucify your king?" Pilate asked.

"We have no king but Caesar," the leading priests shouted back.

¹⁶Then Pilate turned Jesus over to them to be crucified.

The Crucifixion

So they took Jesus away. ¹⁷Carrying the cross by himself, he went to the place called Place of the Skull (in Hebrew, *Golgotha*). ¹⁸There they nailed him to the cross. Two others were crucified with him, one on either side, with Jesus between them. ¹⁹And Pilate posted a sign on the cross that read, "Jesus of Nazareth,* the King of the Jews." ²⁰The place where Jesus was crucified was near the city, and the sign was written in Hebrew, Latin, and Greek, so that many people could read it.

²¹Then the leading priests objected and said to Pilate, "Change it from 'The King of the Jews' to 'He said, I am King of the Jews.'"

²²Pilate replied, "No, what I have written, I have written."

²³When the soldiers had crucified Jesus, they divided his clothes among the four of them. They also took his robe, but it was seamless, woven in one piece from top to bottom. ²⁴So they said, "Rather than tearing it apart, let's throw dice* for it." This fulfilled the Scripture that says, "They divided my garments among themselves and threw dice for my clothing."* So that is what they did.

²⁵Standing near the cross were Jesus' mother, and his mother's sister, Mary (the wife of Clopas), and Mary Magdalene. ²⁶When Jesus saw his mother standing there beside the disciple he loved, he said to her, "Dear woman, here is your son." ²⁷And he said to this disciple, "Here is your mother." And from then on this disciple took her into his home.

The Death of Jesus

²⁸Jesus knew that his mission was now finished, and to fulfill Scripture he said, "I am thirsty."* ²⁹A jar of sour wine was sitting there, so they soaked a sponge in it, put it on a hyssop branch, and held it up to his lips. ³⁰When Jesus had tasted it, he said, "It is finished!" Then he bowed his head and released his spirit.

³¹It was the day of preparation, and the Jewish leaders didn't want the bodies hanging there the next day, which was the Sabbath (and a very special Sabbath, because it was the Passover). So they asked Pilate to hasten their deaths by ordering that their legs be broken. Then their bodies could be taken down. ³²So the soldiers came and broke the legs of the two men crucified with Jesus. ³³But when they came to Jesus, they saw that he was already dead, so they didn't break his legs. ³⁴One of the soldiers, however, pierced his side with a spear, and immediately blood and

19:9 Greek *the Praetorium.*   **19:12** "Friend of Caesar" is a technical term that refers to an ally of the emperor.   **19:14** Greek *Jewish people;* also in 19:20.   **19:19** Or *Jesus the Nazarene.*   **19:24a** Greek *cast lots.*   **19:24b** Ps 22:18.   **19:28** See Pss 22:15; 69:21.

water flowed out. ³⁵(This report is from an eyewitness giving an accurate account. He speaks the truth so that you also can believe.*) ³⁶These things happened in fulfillment of the Scriptures that say, "Not one of his bones will be broken,"* ³⁷and "They will look on the one they pierced."*

The Burial of Jesus

³⁸Afterward Joseph of Arimathea, who had been a secret disciple of Jesus (because he feared the Jewish leaders), asked Pilate for permission to take down Jesus' body. When Pilate gave permission, Joseph came and took the body away. ³⁹With him came Nicodemus, the man who had come to Jesus at night. He brought about seventy-five pounds* of perfumed ointment made from myrrh and aloes. ⁴⁰Following Jewish burial custom, they wrapped Jesus' body with the spices in long sheets of linen cloth. ⁴¹The place of crucifixion was near a garden, where there was a new tomb, never used before. ⁴²And so, because it was the day of preparation for the Jewish Passover* and since the tomb was close at hand, they laid Jesus there.

The Resurrection

20 Early on Sunday morning,* while it was still dark, Mary Magdalene came to the tomb and found that the stone had been rolled away from the entrance. ²She ran and found Simon Peter and the other disciple, the one whom Jesus loved. She said, "They have taken the Lord's body out of the tomb, and we don't know where they have put him!"

³Peter and the other disciple started out for the tomb. ⁴They were both running, but the other disciple outran Peter and reached the tomb first. ⁵He stooped and looked in and saw the linen wrappings lying there, but he didn't go in. ⁶Then Simon Peter arrived and went inside. He also noticed the linen wrappings lying there, ⁷while the cloth that had covered Jesus' head was folded up and lying apart from the other wrappings. ⁸Then the disciple who had reached the tomb first also went in, and he saw and believed—⁹for until then they still hadn't understood the Scriptures that said Jesus must rise from the dead. ¹⁰Then they went home.

Jesus Appears to Mary Magdalene

¹¹Mary was standing outside the tomb crying, and as she wept, she stooped and looked in. ¹²She saw two white-robed angels, one sitting at the head and the other at the foot of the place where the body of Jesus had been lying. ¹³"Dear woman, why are you crying?" the angels asked her.

"Because they have taken away my Lord," she replied, "and I don't know where they have put him."

¹⁴She turned to leave and saw someone standing there. It was Jesus, but she didn't recognize him. ¹⁵"Dear woman, why are you crying?" Jesus asked her. "Who are you looking for?"

She thought he was the gardener. "Sir," she said, "if you have taken him away, tell me where you have put him, and I will go and get him."

¹⁶"Mary!" Jesus said.

She turned to him and cried out, "Rabboni!" (which is Hebrew for "Teacher").

¹⁷"Don't cling to me," Jesus said, "for I haven't yet ascended to the Father. But go find my brothers and tell them, 'I am ascending to my Father and your Father, to my God and your God.' "

¹⁸Mary Magdalene found the disciples and told them, "I have seen the Lord!" Then she gave them his message.

Jesus Appears to His Disciples

¹⁹That Sunday evening* the disciples were meeting behind locked doors because they were afraid of the Jewish leaders. Suddenly, Jesus was standing there among them! "Peace be with you," he said. ²⁰As he spoke, he showed them the wounds in his hands and his side. They were filled with joy when they saw the Lord! ²¹Again he said, "Peace be with you. As the Father has sent me, so I am sending you." ²²Then he breathed on them and said, "Receive the Holy Spirit. ²³If you forgive anyone's sins, they are forgiven. If you do not forgive them, they are not forgiven."

Jesus Appears to Thomas

²⁴One of the twelve disciples, Thomas (nicknamed the Twin),* was not with the others when Jesus came. ²⁵They told him, "We have seen the Lord!"

But he replied, "I won't believe it unless I see the nail wounds in his hands, put my fingers into them, and place my hand into the wound in his side."

²⁶Eight days later the disciples were together again, and this time Thomas was with them. The doors were locked; but suddenly, as before, Jesus was standing among them. "Peace be with you," he said. ²⁷Then he said to Thomas, "Put your finger here, and look at my hands. Put your hand into the wound in my side. Don't be faithless any longer. Believe!"

²⁸"My Lord and my God!" Thomas exclaimed.

²⁹Then Jesus told him, "You believe because you have seen me. Blessed are those who believe without seeing me."

Purpose of the Book

³⁰The disciples saw Jesus do many other miraculous signs in addition to the ones recorded in this book. ³¹But these are written so that you

---

19:35 Some manuscripts read *can continue to believe.* **19:36** Exod 12:46; Num 9:12; Ps 34:20. **19:37** Zech 12:10. **19:39** Greek *100 litras* [32.7 kilograms]. **19:42** Greek *because of the Jewish day of preparation.* **20:1** Greek *On the first day of the week.* **20:19** Greek *In the evening of that day, the first day of the week.* **20:24** Greek *Thomas, who was called Didymus.*

may continue to believe* that Jesus is the Messiah, the Son of God, and that by believing in him you will have life by the power of his name.

Epilogue: Jesus Appears to Seven Disciples

21 Later, Jesus appeared again to the disciples beside the Sea of Galilee.* This is how it happened. ²Several of the disciples were there—Simon Peter, Thomas (nicknamed the Twin),* Nathanael from Cana in Galilee, the sons of Zebedee, and two other disciples.

³Simon Peter said, "I'm going fishing."

"We'll come, too," they all said. So they went out in the boat, but they caught nothing all night.

⁴At dawn Jesus was standing on the beach, but the disciples couldn't see who he was. ⁵He called out, "Fellows,* have you caught any fish?"

"No," they replied.

⁶Then he said, "Throw out your net on the right-hand side of the boat, and you'll get some!" So they did, and they couldn't haul in the net because there were so many fish in it.

⁷Then the disciple Jesus loved said to Peter, "It's the Lord!" When Simon Peter heard that it was the Lord, he put on his tunic (for he had stripped for work), jumped into the water, and headed to shore. ⁸The others stayed with the boat and pulled the loaded net to the shore, for they were only about a hundred yards* from shore. ⁹When they got there, they found breakfast waiting for them—fish cooking over a charcoal fire, and some bread.

¹⁰"Bring some of the fish you've just caught," Jesus said. ¹¹So Simon Peter went aboard and dragged the net to the shore. There were 153 large fish, and yet the net hadn't torn.

¹²"Now come and have some breakfast!" Jesus said. None of the disciples dared to ask him, "Who are you?" They knew it was the Lord. ¹³Then Jesus served them the bread and the fish. ¹⁴This was the third time Jesus had appeared to his disciples since he had been raised from the dead.

¹⁵After breakfast Jesus asked Simon Peter, "Simon son of John, do you love me more than these?*"

"Yes, Lord," Peter replied, "you know I love you."

"Then feed my lambs," Jesus told him.

¹⁶Jesus repeated the question: "Simon son of John, do you love me?"

"Yes, Lord," Peter said, "you know I love you."

"Then take care of my sheep," Jesus said.

¹⁷A third time he asked him, "Simon son of John, do you love me?"

Peter was hurt that Jesus asked the question a third time. He said, "Lord, you know everything. You know that I love you."

Jesus said, "Then feed my sheep.

¹⁸"I tell you the truth, when you were young, you were able to do as you liked; you dressed yourself and went wherever you wanted to go. But when you are old, you will stretch out your hands, and others* will dress you and take you where you don't want to go." ¹⁹Jesus said this to let him know by what kind of death he would glorify God. Then Jesus told him, "Follow me."

²⁰Peter turned around and saw behind them the disciple Jesus loved—the one who had leaned over to Jesus during supper and asked, "Lord, who will betray you?" ²¹Peter asked Jesus, "What about him, Lord?"

²²Jesus replied, "If I want him to remain alive until I return, what is that to you? As for you, follow me." ²³So the rumor spread among the community of believers* that this disciple wouldn't die. But that isn't what Jesus said at all. He only said, "If I want him to remain alive until I return, what is that to you?"

²⁴This disciple is the one who testifies to these events and has recorded them here. And we know that his account of these things is accurate.

²⁵Jesus also did many other things. If they were all written down, I suppose the whole world could not contain the books that would be written.

20:31 Some manuscripts read *that you may believe.* **21:1** Greek *Sea of Tiberias,* another name for the Sea of Galilee. **21:2** Greek *Thomas, who was called Didymus.* **21:5** Greek *Children.* **21:8** Greek *200 cubits* [90 meters]. **21:15** Or *more than these others do?* **21:18** Some manuscripts read *and another one.* **21:23** Greek *the brothers.*

JIM NILL
Vice President & Assistant General Manager,
Detroit Red Wings, NHL

I struggled to get to the point where I finally accepted Christ.

I was fortunate to be friends with Laurie Boschman and Doug Smail while playing in Winnipeg. The way they lived their lives had a strong influence on me. I wanted what they had. During those years I attended an HMI hockey camp in Saskatchewan with Doug. I witnessed the changes that took place during the week in the campers' lives. This tugged very hard on my heart.

The biggest influence on my coming to personal faith in Christ was experiencing the blessings of my beautiful wife and our children. Rebecca prayed for 20 years for God's grace to come into my life and those prayers were answered. My children were raised in this Christian environment, and watching them live out God's Word changed my life.

As a player I was quick to judge and react, not always in a positive manner. Now that I am in management and have accepted Christ as my Savior, I handle situations so differently. I have a better understanding of situations and the importance of relationships. The everyday emotions are not as high and the times in the valley are not as low.

" . . . God will never forget us or give up on us."

The Bible has played a key role in strengthening my faith. It is all I need to guide me on a daily basis. Each time I pick up the Bible I seem to find a new favorite verse, but the one verse that always sticks with me is Philippians 4:13, *"I can do all things through him who gives me strength."* Every day there are going to be trials, struggles, and decisions to make, but to know that God is always there to give me strength is all I really need. Another passage that has been meaningful is James 1:2-18, which talks about dealing with trials and temptations.

Looking back on my career there were so many twists and turns, but now I understand that God had His plan and purpose for me all along.

TREVOR NILL
Forward, Michigan State Spartans 2008-2012,
drafted by St. Louis Blues 2007

Like father, like son . . . Trevor Nill talks about how his dad shaped his faith from an early age.

The concept of death scared me. I didn't understand what it meant until my father explained that true believers in Jesus Christ will go to heaven after they die. Since that day, going to church and believing in Christ has had new meaning for me. While I may stress at times I now realize that I have a God who is looking after me and is walking with me wherever I go.

The Bible has been instrumental in strengthening my faith. It is a guiding light for me. I know that no matter what situation I am facing, I can turn to the Bible and there will be an answer. Both my dad and I find the following verses very helpful. They have always given me hope. Knowing that the challenges I go through have a purpose inspires me to persevere and come out as a better person, hockey player, and Christ follower.

" . . . knowing God is with me gives me the confidence . . . "

James 1:2-4 says: *"My friends, consider yourselves fortunate when all kinds of trials come your way, for you know that when your faith succeeds in facing such trials, the result is the ability to endure. Make sure that your endurance carries you all the way without failing, so that you may be perfect and complete, lacking nothing."*

My devotion to Jesus has not only enabled me to handle the temptations of life in hockey but has also given me an opportunity to reach out to my teammates. Knowing God is with me gives me the confidence to stand behind my decisions.

My faith has always guided my career, and to this day I believe it is God's will for me to mentor young hockey players, just as I was encouraged to stay strong in Christ in hockey by players like David Booth and Jeff Petry.

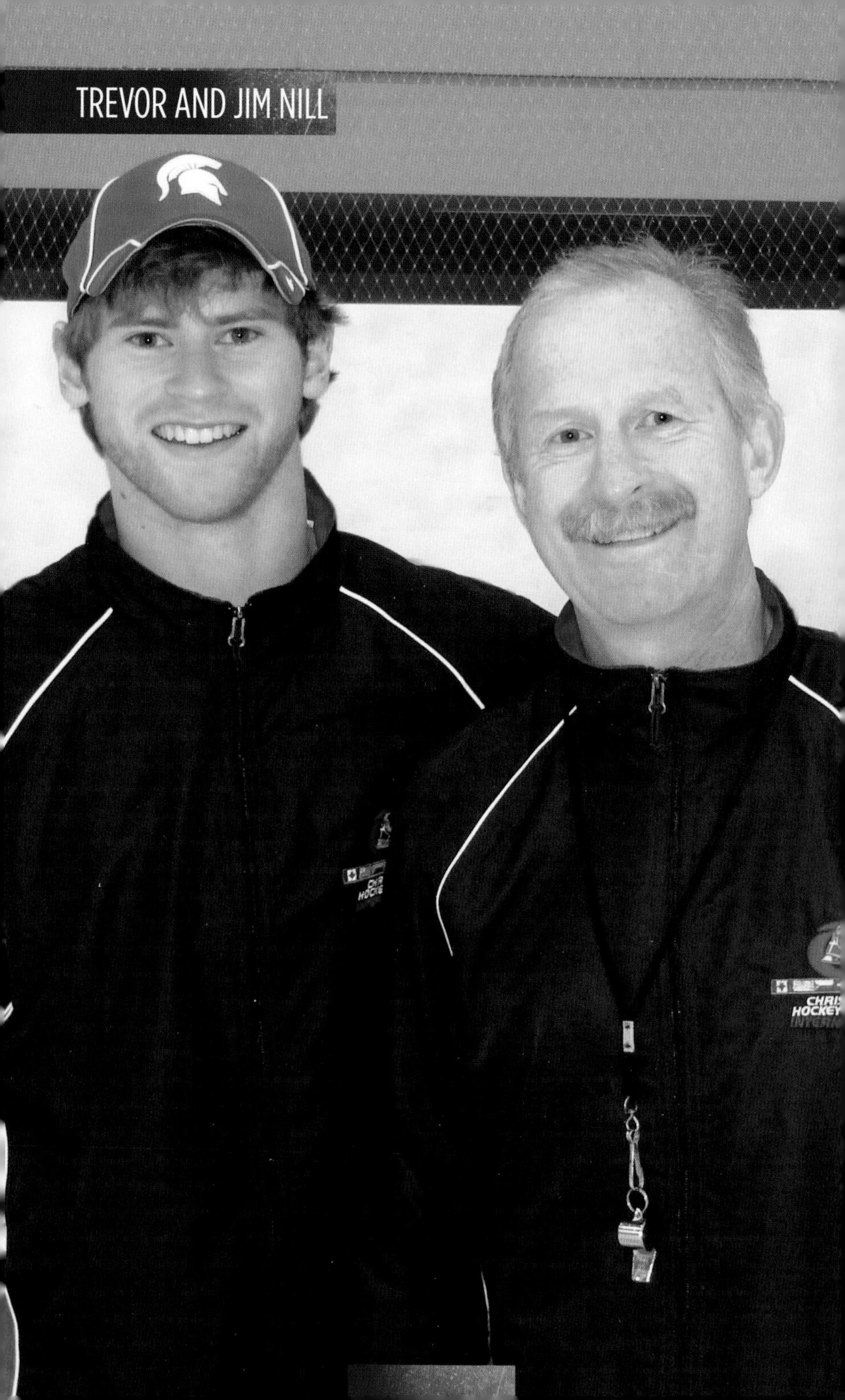

TREVOR AND JIM NILL

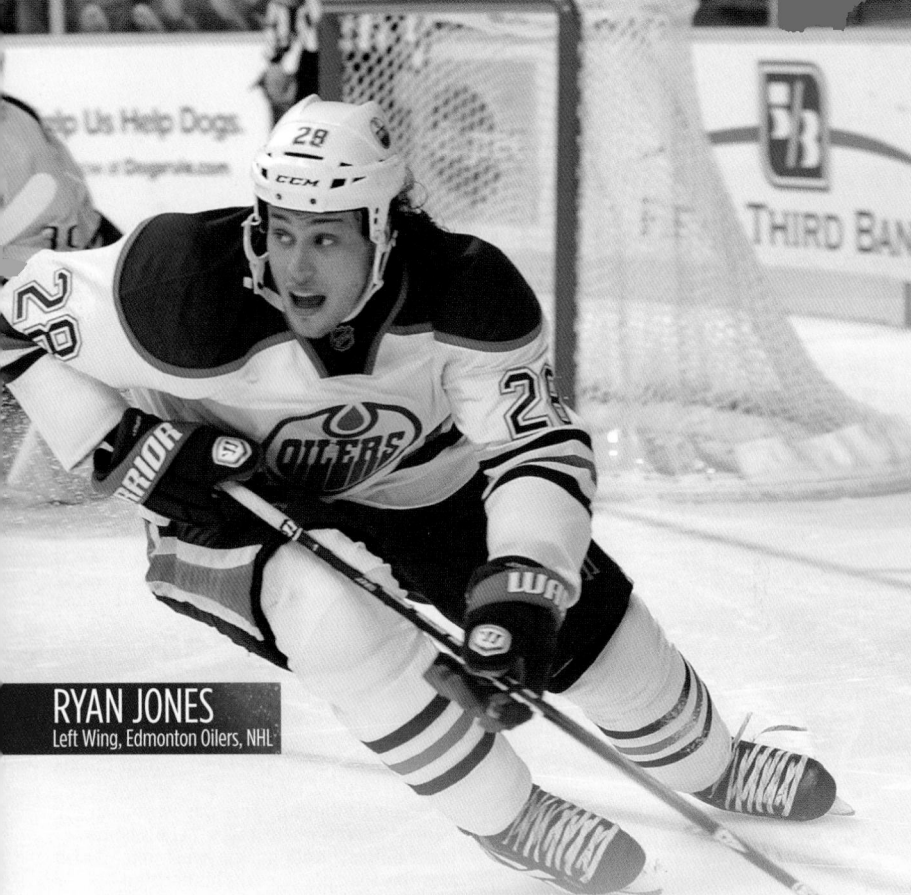

RYAN JONES
Left Wing, Edmonton Oilers, NHL

"It's easy to find God when things are going right. If you're happy and things are going well, you can say it's a blessing and a gift from God. But when you get down, there are two ways you can go. You can blame God and turn your back on Him because he let something bad happen or you can be thankful for what you have."

On New Year's Eve 2012 while skating with a group of players, Ryan was hit with a puck and sustained a serious eye injury. What way would the young Edmonton forward go?

"When this happened to me, my first thoughts were whether or not I would play again. I quickly realized there was only one Person who knew the answer. I made the choice to be thankful that I still had my eye and looked for what I could learn. I wasn't mad at God, not even the slightest. When I asked God to be in my life again a few years ago, that meant that I was fully accepting His plan for me. I may not totally understand why He does things, but I am not supposed to. In the Bible, God never said He wouldn't let anything bad happen to us; He just says He'll be there. I believe He's at my side. His grace gives me comfort to know I'm never going to be alone.

"When you get down there are two ways you can go."

Everything that has been given to me has been given to me by Him. If for some reason a part of me had forgotten that, this accident reminded me who I truly owe for everything.

Matthew 17:20 is a very meaningful verse. Jesus said: *". . . if you have faith as small as a mustard seed, you can say to this mountain, 'Move from here to there' and it will move. Nothing will be impossible for you."* To me, this verse says if you have faith in the Lord, no matter how big or small, you can accomplish anything through Him. Whether or not I get the outcome I want, ultimately He's going to lead me . . . "

Acts

The Promise of the Holy Spirit

1 In my first book* I told you, Theophilus, about everything Jesus began to do and teach ²until the day he was taken up to heaven after giving his chosen apostles further instructions through the Holy Spirit. ³During the forty days after his crucifixion, he appeared to the apostles from time to time, and he proved to them in many ways that he was actually alive. And he talked to them about the Kingdom of God.

⁴Once when he was eating with them, he commanded them, "Do not leave Jerusalem until the Father sends you the gift he promised, as I told you before. ⁵John baptized with* water, but in just a few days you will be baptized with the Holy Spirit."

The Ascension of Jesus

⁶So when the apostles were with Jesus, they kept asking him, "Lord, has the time come for you to free Israel and restore our kingdom?"

⁷He replied, "The Father alone has the authority to set those dates and times, and they are not for you to know. ⁸But you will receive power when the Holy Spirit comes upon you. And you will be my witnesses, telling people about me everywhere—in Jerusalem, throughout Judea, in Samaria, and to the ends of the earth."

⁹After saying this, he was taken up into a cloud while they were watching, and they could no longer see him. ¹⁰As they strained to see him rising into heaven, two white-robed men suddenly stood among them. ¹¹"Men of Galilee," they said, "why are you standing here staring into heaven? Jesus has been taken from you into heaven, but someday he will return from heaven in the same way you saw him go!"

Matthias Replaces Judas

¹²Then the apostles returned to Jerusalem from the Mount of Olives, a distance of half a mile.* ¹³When they arrived, they went to the upstairs room of the house where they were staying.

Here are the names of those who were present: Peter, John, James, Andrew, Philip, Thomas, Bartholomew, Matthew, James (son of Alphaeus), Simon (the Zealot), and Judas (son of James).

¹⁴They all met together and were constantly united in prayer, along with Mary the mother of Jesus, several other women, and the brothers of Jesus.

¹⁵During this time, when about 120 believers* were together in one place, Peter stood up and addressed them. ¹⁶"Brothers," he said, "the Scriptures had to be fulfilled concerning Judas, who guided those who arrested Jesus. This was predicted long ago by the Holy Spirit, speaking through King David. ¹⁷Judas was one of us and shared in the ministry with us."

¹⁸(Judas had bought a field with the money he received for his treachery. Falling headfirst there, his body split open, spilling out all his intestines. ¹⁹The news of his death spread to all the people of Jerusalem, and they gave the place the Aramaic name *Akeldama,* which means "Field of Blood.")

²⁰Peter continued, "This was written in the book of Psalms, where it says, 'Let his home become desolate, with no one living in it.' It also says, 'Let someone else take his position.'*

²¹"So now we must choose a replacement for Judas from among the men who were with us the entire time we were traveling with the Lord Jesus—²²from the time he was baptized by John until the day he was taken from us. Whoever is chosen will join us as a witness of Jesus' resurrection."

²³So they nominated two men: Joseph called Barsabbas (also known as Justus) and Matthias. ²⁴Then they all prayed, "O Lord, you know every heart. Show us which of these men you have chosen ²⁵as an apostle to replace Judas in this ministry, for he has deserted us and gone where he belongs." ²⁶Then they cast lots, and Matthias was selected to become an apostle with the other eleven.

The Holy Spirit Comes

2 On the day of Pentecost* all the believers were meeting together in one place. ²Suddenly, there was a sound from heaven like the roaring of a mighty windstorm, and it filled the house where they were sitting. ³Then, what looked like flames or tongues of fire appeared and settled on each of them. ⁴And everyone

---

1:1 The reference is to the Gospel of Luke.　**1:5** Or *in;* also in 1:5b.　**1:12** Greek *a Sabbath day's journey.*　**1:15** Greek *brothers.* **1:20** Pss 69:25; 109:8.　**2:1** The Festival of Pentecost came 50 days after Passover (when Jesus was crucified).

present was filled with the Holy Spirit and began speaking in other languages,* as the Holy Spirit gave them this ability.

5At that time there were devout Jews from every nation living in Jerusalem. 6When they heard the loud noise, everyone came running, and they were bewildered to hear their own languages being spoken by the believers.

7They were completely amazed. "How can this be?" they exclaimed. "These people are all from Galilee, 8and yet we hear them speaking in our own native languages! 9Here we are—Parthians, Medes, Elamites, people from Mesopotamia, Judea, Cappadocia, Pontus, the province of Asia, 10Phrygia, Pamphylia, Egypt, and the areas of Libya around Cyrene, visitors from Rome 11(both Jews and converts to Judaism), Cretans, and Arabs. And we all hear these people speaking in our own languages about the wonderful things God has done!" 12They stood there amazed and perplexed. "What can this mean?" they asked each other.

13But others in the crowd ridiculed them, saying, "They're just drunk, that's all!"

Peter Preaches to the Crowd

14Then Peter stepped forward with the eleven other apostles and shouted to the crowd, "Listen carefully, all of you, fellow Jews and residents of Jerusalem! Make no mistake about this. 15These people are not drunk, as some of you are assuming. Nine o'clock in the morning is much too early for that. 16No, what you see was predicted long ago by the prophet Joel:

17 'In the last days,' God says,
   'I will pour out my Spirit upon all people.
   Your sons and daughters will prophesy.
   Your young men will see visions,
   and your old men will dream dreams.
18 In those days I will pour out my Spirit
   even on my servants—men and women
      alike—
   and they will prophesy.
19 And I will cause wonders in the heavens
      above
   and signs on the earth below—
   blood and fire and clouds of smoke.
20 The sun will become dark,
   and the moon will turn blood red
   before that great and glorious day of the
      LORD arrives.
21 But everyone who calls on the name of the
      LORD
   will be saved.'*

22"People of Israel, listen! God publicly endorsed Jesus the Nazarene* by doing powerful miracles, wonders, and signs through him, as you well know. 23But God knew what would hap-

pen, and his prearranged plan was carried out when Jesus was betrayed. With the help of lawless Gentiles, you nailed him to a cross and killed him. 24But God released him from the horrors of death and raised him back to life, for death could not keep him in its grip. 25King David said this about him:

'I see that the LORD is always with me.
   I will not be shaken, for he is right
      beside me.
26 No wonder my heart is glad,
   and my tongue shouts his praises!
   My body rests in hope.
27 For you will not leave my soul among the
      dead*
   or allow your Holy One to rot in the grave.
28 You have shown me the way of life,
   and you will fill me with the joy of your
      presence.'*

29"Dear brothers, think about this! You can be sure that the patriarch David wasn't referring to himself, for he died and was buried, and his tomb is still here among us. 30But he was a prophet, and he knew God had promised with an oath that one of David's own descendants would sit on his throne. 31David was looking into the future and speaking of the Messiah's resurrection. He was saying that God would not leave him among the dead or allow his body to rot in the grave.

32"God raised Jesus from the dead, and we are all witnesses of this. 33Now he is exalted to the place of highest honor in heaven, at God's right hand. And the Father, as he had promised, gave him the Holy Spirit to pour out upon us, just as you see and hear today. 34For David himself never ascended into heaven, yet he said,

'The LORD said to my Lord,
   "Sit in the place of honor at my right hand
35 until I humble your enemies,
   making them a footstool under your
      feet."'*

36"So let everyone in Israel know for certain that God has made this Jesus, whom you crucified, to be both Lord and Messiah!"

37Peter's words pierced their hearts, and they said to him and to the other apostles, "Brothers, what should we do?"

38Peter replied, "Each of you must repent of your sins and turn to God, and be baptized in the name of Jesus Christ for the forgiveness of your sins. Then you will receive the gift of the Holy Spirit. 39This promise is to you, and to your children, and even to the Gentiles*—all who have been called by the Lord our God." 40Then Peter continued preaching for a long time, strongly urging all his listeners, "Save yourselves from this crooked generation!"

2:4 Or *in other tongues.* **2:17-21** Joel 2:28-32. **2:22** Or *Jesus of Nazareth.* **2:27** Greek *in Hades;* also in 2:31. **2:25-28** Ps 16:8-11 (Greek version). **2:34-35** Ps 110:1. **2:39** Or *and to people far in the future;* Greek reads *and to those far away.*

[41]Those who believed what Peter said were baptized and added to the church that day—about 3,000 in all.

The Believers Form a Community

[42]All the believers devoted themselves to the apostles' teaching, and to fellowship, and to sharing in meals (including the Lord's Supper*), and to prayer.

[43]A deep sense of awe came over them all, and the apostles performed many miraculous signs and wonders. [44]And all the believers met together in one place and shared everything they had. [45]They sold their property and possessions and shared the money with those in need. [46]They worshiped together at the Temple each day, met in homes for the Lord's Supper, and shared their meals with great joy and generosity*—[47]all the while praising God and enjoying the goodwill of all the people. And each day the Lord added to their fellowship those who were being saved.

Peter Heals a Crippled Beggar

3 Peter and John went to the Temple one afternoon to take part in the three o'clock prayer service. [2]As they approached the Temple, a man lame from birth was being carried in. Each day he was put beside the Temple gate, the one called the Beautiful Gate, so he could beg from the people going into the Temple. [3]When he saw Peter and John about to enter, he asked them for some money.

[4]Peter and John looked at him intently, and Peter said, "Look at us!" [5]The lame man looked at them eagerly, expecting some money. [6]But Peter said, "I don't have any silver or gold for you. But I'll give you what I have. In the name of Jesus Christ the Nazarene,* get up and* walk!"

[7]Then Peter took the lame man by the right hand and helped him up. And as he did, the man's feet and ankles were instantly healed and strengthened. [8]He jumped up, stood on his feet, and began to walk! Then, walking, leaping, and praising God, he went into the Temple with them.

[9]All the people saw him walking and heard him praising God. [10]When they realized he was the lame beggar they had seen so often at the Beautiful Gate, they were absolutely astounded! [11]They all rushed out in amazement to Solomon's Colonnade, where the man was holding tightly to Peter and John.

Peter Preaches in the Temple

[12]Peter saw his opportunity and addressed the crowd. "People of Israel," he said, "what is so surprising about this? And why stare at us as though we had made this man walk by our own power or godliness? [13]For it is the God of Abraham, Isaac, and Jacob—the God of all our ancestors—who has brought glory to his servant Jesus by doing this. This is the same Jesus whom you handed over and rejected before Pilate, despite Pilate's decision to release him. [14]You rejected this holy, righteous one and instead demanded the release of a murderer. [15]You killed the author of life, but God raised him from the dead. And we are witnesses of this fact!

[16]"Through faith in the name of Jesus, this man was healed—and you know how crippled he was before. Faith in Jesus' name has healed him before your very eyes.

[17]"Friends,* I realize that what you and your leaders did to Jesus was done in ignorance. [18]But God was fulfilling what all the prophets had foretold about the Messiah—that he must suffer these things. [19]Now repent of your sins and turn to God, so that your sins may be wiped away. [20]Then times of refreshment will come from the presence of the Lord, and he will again send you Jesus, your appointed Messiah. [21]For he must remain in heaven until the time for the final restoration of all things, as God promised long ago through his holy prophets. [22]Moses said, 'The LORD your God will raise up for you a Prophet like me from among your own people. Listen carefully to everything he tells you.'* [23]Then Moses said, 'Anyone who will not listen to that Prophet will be completely cut off from God's people.'*

[24]"Starting with Samuel, every prophet spoke about what is happening today. [25]You are the children of those prophets, and you are included in the covenant God promised to your ancestors. For God said to Abraham, 'Through your descendants* all the families on earth will be blessed.' [26]When God raised up his servant, Jesus, he sent him first to you people of Israel, to bless you by turning each of you back from your sinful ways."

Peter and John before the Council

4 While Peter and John were speaking to the people, they were confronted by the priests, the captain of the Temple guard, and some of the Sadducees. [2]These leaders were very disturbed that Peter and John were teaching the people that through Jesus there is a resurrection of the dead. [3]They arrested them and, since it was already evening, put them in jail until morning. [4]But many of the people who heard their message believed it, so the number of believers now totaled about 5,000 men, not counting women and children.*

[5]The next day the council of all the rulers and elders and teachers of religious law met in Jerusalem. [6]Annas the high priest was there, along with Caiaphas, John, Alexander, and other relatives of the high priest. [7]They brought in the two disciples and demanded, "By what power, or in whose name, have you done this?"

2:42 Greek *the breaking of bread;* also in 2:46. **2:46** Or *and sincere hearts.* **3:6a** Or *Jesus Christ of Nazareth.* **3:6b** Some manuscripts do not include *get up and.* **3:17** Greek *Brothers.* **3:22** Deut 18:15. **3:23** Deut 18:19; Lev 23:29. **3:25** Greek *your seed;* see Gen 12:3; 22:18. **4:4** Greek *5,000 adult males.*

⁸Then Peter, filled with the Holy Spirit, said to them, "Rulers and elders of our people, ⁹are we being questioned today because we've done a good deed for a crippled man? Do you want to know how he was healed? ¹⁰Let me clearly state to all of you and to all the people of Israel that he was healed by the powerful name of Jesus Christ the Nazarene,* the man you crucified but whom God raised from the dead. ¹¹For Jesus is the one referred to in the Scriptures, where it says,

'The stone that you builders rejected
  has now become the cornerstone.'*

¹²There is salvation in no one else! God has given no other name under heaven by which we must be saved."

¹³The members of the council were amazed when they saw the boldness of Peter and John, for they could see that they were ordinary men with no special training in the Scriptures. They also recognized them as men who had been with Jesus. ¹⁴But since they could see the man who had been healed standing right there among them, there was nothing the council could say. ¹⁵So they ordered Peter and John out of the council chamber* and conferred among themselves.

¹⁶"What should we do with these men?" they asked each other. "We can't deny that they have performed a miraculous sign, and everybody in Jerusalem knows about it. ¹⁷But to keep them from spreading their propaganda any further, we must warn them not to speak to anyone in Jesus' name again." ¹⁸So they called the apostles back in and commanded them never again to speak or teach in the name of Jesus.

¹⁹But Peter and John replied, "Do you think God wants us to obey you rather than him? ²⁰We cannot stop telling about everything we have seen and heard."

²¹The council then threatened them further, but they finally let them go because they didn't know how to punish them without starting a riot. For everyone was praising God ²²for this miraculous sign—the healing of a man who had been lame for more than forty years.

The Believers Pray for Courage

²³As soon as they were freed, Peter and John returned to the other believers and told them what the leading priests and elders had said. ²⁴When they heard the report, all the believers lifted their voices together in prayer to God: "O Sovereign Lord, Creator of heaven and earth, the sea, and everything in them—²⁵you spoke long ago by the Holy Spirit through our ancestor David, your servant, saying,

'Why were the nations so angry?
  Why did they waste their time with futile
    plans?

²⁶ The kings of the earth prepared for battle;
  the rulers gathered together
against the LORD
  and against his Messiah.'*

²⁷"In fact, this has happened here in this very city! For Herod Antipas, Pontius Pilate the governor, the Gentiles, and the people of Israel were all united against Jesus, your holy servant, whom you anointed. ²⁸But everything they did was determined beforehand according to your will. ²⁹And now, O Lord, hear their threats, and give us, your servants, great boldness in preaching your word. ³⁰Stretch out your hand with healing power; may miraculous signs and wonders be done through the name of your holy servant Jesus."

³¹After this prayer, the meeting place shook, and they were all filled with the Holy Spirit. Then they preached the word of God with boldness.

The Believers Share Their Possessions

³²All the believers were united in heart and mind. And they felt that what they owned was not their own, so they shared everything they had. ³³The apostles testified powerfully to the resurrection of the Lord Jesus, and God's great blessing was upon them all. ³⁴There were no needy people among them, because those who owned land or houses would sell them ³⁵and bring the money to the apostles to give to those in need.

³⁶For instance, there was Joseph, the one the apostles nicknamed Barnabas (which means "Son of Encouragement"). He was from the tribe of Levi and came from the island of Cyprus. ³⁷He sold a field he owned and brought the money to the apostles.

Ananias and Sapphira

5 But there was a certain man named Ananias who, with his wife, Sapphira, sold some property. ²He brought part of the money to the apostles, claiming it was the full amount. With his wife's consent, he kept the rest.

³Then Peter said, "Ananias, why have you let Satan fill your heart? You lied to the Holy Spirit, and you kept some of the money for yourself. ⁴The property was yours to sell or not sell, as you wished. And after selling it, the money was also yours to give away. How could you do a thing like this? You weren't lying to us but to God!"

⁵As soon as Ananias heard these words, he fell to the floor and died. Everyone who heard about it was terrified. ⁶Then some young men got up, wrapped him in a sheet, and took him out and buried him.

⁷About three hours later his wife came in, not knowing what had happened. ⁸Peter asked her, "Was this the price you and your husband received for your land?"

4:10 Or *Jesus Christ of Nazareth.*   **4:11** Ps 118:22.   **4:15** Greek *the Sanhedrin.*   **4:25-26** Or *his anointed one;* or *his Christ.* Ps 2:1-2.

"Yes," she replied, "that was the price."

⁹And Peter said, "How could the two of you even think of conspiring to test the Spirit of the Lord like this? The young men who buried your husband are just outside the door, and they will carry you out, too."

¹⁰Instantly, she fell to the floor and died. When the young men came in and saw that she was dead, they carried her out and buried her beside her husband. ¹¹Great fear gripped the entire church and everyone else who heard what had happened.

The Apostles Heal Many

¹²The apostles were performing many miraculous signs and wonders among the people. And all the believers were meeting regularly at the Temple in the area known as Solomon's Colonnade. ¹³But no one else dared to join them, even though all the people had high regard for them. ¹⁴Yet more and more people believed and were brought to the Lord—crowds of both men and women. ¹⁵As a result of the apostles' work, sick people were brought out into the streets on beds and mats so that Peter's shadow might fall across some of them as he went by. ¹⁶Crowds came from the villages around Jerusalem, bringing their sick and those possessed by evil* spirits, and they were all healed.

The Apostles Meet Opposition

¹⁷The high priest and his officials, who were Sadducees, were filled with jealousy. ¹⁸They arrested the apostles and put them in the public jail. ¹⁹But an angel of the Lord came at night, opened the gates of the jail, and brought them out. Then he told them, ²⁰"Go to the Temple and give the people this message of life!"

²¹So at daybreak the apostles entered the Temple, as they were told, and immediately began teaching.

When the high priest and his officials arrived, they convened the high council*—the full assembly of the elders of Israel. Then they sent for the apostles to be brought from the jail for trial. ²²But when the Temple guards went to the jail, the men were gone. So they returned to the council and reported, ²³"The jail was securely locked, with the guards standing outside, but when we opened the gates, no one was there!"

²⁴When the captain of the Temple guard and the leading priests heard this, they were perplexed, wondering where it would all end. ²⁵Then someone arrived with startling news: "The men you put in jail are standing in the Temple, teaching the people!"

²⁶The captain went with his Temple guards and arrested the apostles, but without violence, for they were afraid the people would stone them. ²⁷Then they brought the apostles before the high council, where the high priest confronted them. ²⁸"Didn't we tell you never again to teach in this man's name?" he demanded. "Instead, you have filled all Jerusalem with your teaching about him, and you want to make us responsible for his death!"

²⁹But Peter and the apostles replied, "We must obey God rather than any human authority. ³⁰The God of our ancestors raised Jesus from the dead after you killed him by hanging him on a cross.* ³¹Then God put him in the place of honor at his right hand as Prince and Savior. He did this so the people of Israel would repent of their sins and be forgiven. ³²We are witnesses of these things and so is the Holy Spirit, who is given by God to those who obey him."

³³When they heard this, the high council was furious and decided to kill them. ³⁴But one member, a Pharisee named Gamaliel, who was an expert in religious law and respected by all the people, stood up and ordered that the men be sent outside the council chamber for a while. ³⁵Then he said to his colleagues, "Men of Israel, take care what you are planning to do to these men! ³⁶Some time ago there was that fellow Theudas, who pretended to be someone great. About 400 others joined him, but he was killed, and all his followers went their various ways. The whole movement came to nothing. ³⁷After him, at the time of the census, there was Judas of Galilee. He got people to follow him, but he was killed, too, and all his followers were scattered.

³⁸"So my advice is, leave these men alone. Let them go. If they are planning and doing these things merely on their own, it will soon be overthrown. ³⁹But if it is from God, you will not be able to overthrow them. You may even find yourselves fighting against God!"

⁴⁰The others accepted his advice. They called in the apostles and had them flogged. Then they ordered them never again to speak in the name of Jesus, and they let them go.

⁴¹The apostles left the high council rejoicing that God had counted them worthy to suffer disgrace for the name of Jesus.* ⁴²And every day, in the Temple and from house to house, they continued to teach and preach this message: "Jesus is the Messiah."

Seven Men Chosen to Serve

6 But as the believers* rapidly multiplied, there were rumblings of discontent. The Greek-speaking believers complained about the Hebrew-speaking believers, saying that their widows were being discriminated against in the daily distribution of food.

²So the Twelve called a meeting of all the believers. They said, "We apostles should spend our time teaching the word of God, not running a food program. ³And so, brothers, select seven

---

5:16 Greek *unclean.*   5:21 Greek *Sanhedrin;* also in 5:27, 41.   5:30 Greek *on a tree.*   5:41 Greek *for the name.*   6:1 Greek *disciples;* also in 6:2, 7.

men who are well respected and are full of the Spirit and wisdom. We will give them this responsibility. ⁴Then we apostles can spend our time in prayer and teaching the word."

⁵Everyone liked this idea, and they chose the following: Stephen (a man full of faith and the Holy Spirit), Philip, Procorus, Nicanor, Timon, Parmenas, and Nicolas of Antioch (an earlier convert to the Jewish faith). ⁶These seven were presented to the apostles, who prayed for them as they laid their hands on them.

⁷So God's message continued to spread. The number of believers greatly increased in Jerusalem, and many of the Jewish priests were converted, too.

Stephen Is Arrested

⁸Stephen, a man full of God's grace and power, performed amazing miracles and signs among the people. ⁹But one day some men from the Synagogue of Freed Slaves, as it was called, started to debate with him. They were Jews from Cyrene, Alexandria, Cilicia, and the province of Asia. ¹⁰None of them could stand against the wisdom and the Spirit with which Stephen spoke.

¹¹So they persuaded some men to lie about Stephen, saying, "We heard him blaspheme Moses, and even God." ¹²This roused the people, the elders, and the teachers of religious law. So they arrested Stephen and brought him before the high council.*

¹³The lying witnesses said, "This man is always speaking against the holy Temple and against the law of Moses. ¹⁴We have heard him say that this Jesus of Nazareth* will destroy the Temple and change the customs Moses handed down to us."

¹⁵At this point everyone in the high council stared at Stephen, because his face became as bright as an angel's.

Stephen Addresses the Council

7 Then the high priest asked Stephen, "Are these accusations true?"

²This was Stephen's reply: "Brothers and fathers, listen to me. Our glorious God appeared to our ancestor Abraham in Mesopotamia before he settled in Haran.* ³God told him, 'Leave your native land and your relatives, and come into the land that I will show you.'* ⁴So Abraham left the land of the Chaldeans and lived in Haran until his father died. Then God brought him here to the land where you now live.

⁵"But God gave him no inheritance here, not even one square foot of land. God did promise, however, that eventually the whole land would belong to Abraham and his descendants—even though he had no children yet. ⁶God also told him that his descendants would live in a foreign

land, where they would be oppressed as slaves for 400 years. ⁷'But I will punish the nation that enslaves them,' God said, 'and in the end they will come out and worship me here in this place.'*

⁸"God also gave Abraham the covenant of circumcision at that time. So when Abraham became the father of Isaac, he circumcised him on the eighth day. And the practice was continued when Isaac became the father of Jacob, and when Jacob became the father of the twelve patriarchs of the Israelite nation.

⁹"These patriarchs were jealous of their brother Joseph, and they sold him to be a slave in Egypt. But God was with him ¹⁰and rescued him from all his troubles. And God gave him favor before Pharaoh, king of Egypt. God also gave Joseph unusual wisdom, so that Pharaoh appointed him governor over all of Egypt and put him in charge of the palace.

¹¹"But a famine came upon Egypt and Canaan. There was great misery, and our ancestors ran out of food. ¹²Jacob heard that there was still grain in Egypt, so he sent his sons—our ancestors—to buy some. ¹³The second time they went, Joseph revealed his identity to his brothers,* and they were introduced to Pharaoh. ¹⁴Then Joseph sent for his father, Jacob, and all his relatives to come to Egypt, seventy-five persons in all. ¹⁵So Jacob went to Egypt. He died there, as did our ancestors. ¹⁶Their bodies were taken to Shechem and buried in the tomb Abraham had bought for a certain price from Hamor's sons in Shechem.

¹⁷"As the time drew near when God would fulfill his promise to Abraham, the number of our people in Egypt greatly increased. ¹⁸But then a new king came to the throne of Egypt who knew nothing about Joseph. ¹⁹This king exploited our people and oppressed them, forcing parents to abandon their newborn babies so they would die.

²⁰"At that time Moses was born—a beautiful child in God's eyes. His parents cared for him at home for three months. ²¹When they had to abandon him, Pharaoh's daughter adopted him and raised him as her own son. ²²Moses was taught all the wisdom of the Egyptians, and he was powerful in both speech and action.

²³"One day when Moses was forty years old, he decided to visit his relatives, the people of Israel. ²⁴He saw an Egyptian mistreating an Israelite. So Moses came to the man's defense and avenged him, killing the Egyptian. ²⁵Moses assumed his fellow Israelites would realize that God had sent him to rescue them, but they didn't.

²⁶"The next day he visited them again and saw two men of Israel fighting. He tried to be a peacemaker. 'Men,' he said, 'you are brothers. Why are you fighting each other?'

²⁷"But the man in the wrong pushed Moses aside. 'Who made you a ruler and judge over us?'

6:12 Greek *Sanhedrin;* also in 6:15.   **6:14** Or *Jesus the Nazarene.*   **7:2** *Mesopotamia* was the region now called Iraq. *Haran* was a city in what is now called Syria.   **7:3** Gen 12:1.   **7:5-7** Gen 12:7; 15:13-14; Exod 3:12.   **7:13** Other manuscripts read *Joseph was recognized by his brothers.*

he asked. 28"Are you going to kill me as you killed that Egyptian yesterday?' 29When Moses heard that, he fled the country and lived as a foreigner in the land of Midian. There his two sons were born.

30"Forty years later, in the desert near Mount Sinai, an angel appeared to Moses in the flame of a burning bush. 31When Moses saw it, he was amazed at the sight. As he went to take a closer look, the voice of the Lord called out to him, 32'I am the God of your ancestors—the God of Abraham, Isaac, and Jacob.' Moses shook with terror and did not dare to look.

33"Then the Lord said to him, 'Take off your sandals, for you are standing on holy ground. 34I have certainly seen the oppression of my people in Egypt. I have heard their groans and have come down to rescue them. Now go, for I am sending you back to Egypt.'*

35"So God sent back the same man his people had previously rejected when they demanded, 'Who made you a ruler and judge over us?' Through the angel who appeared to him in the burning bush, God sent Moses to be their ruler and savior. 36And by means of many wonders and miraculous signs, he led them out of Egypt, through the Red Sea, and through the wilderness for forty years.

37"Moses himself told the people of Israel, 'God will raise up for you a Prophet like me from among your own people.'* 38Moses was with our ancestors, the assembly of God's people in the wilderness, when the angel spoke to him at Mount Sinai. And there Moses received life-giving words to pass on to us.*

39"But our ancestors refused to listen to Moses. They rejected him and wanted to return to Egypt. 40They told Aaron, 'Make us some gods who can lead us, for we don't know what has become of this Moses, who brought us out of Egypt.' 41So they made an idol shaped like a calf, and they sacrificed to it and celebrated over this thing they had made. 42Then God turned away from them and abandoned them to serve the stars of heaven as their gods! In the book of the prophets it is written,

'Was it to me you were bringing sacrifices
    and offerings
        during those forty years in the wilderness,
        Israel?
43 No, you carried your pagan gods—
    the shrine of Molech,
    the star of your god Rephan,
    and the images you made to worship
        them.
So I will send you into exile
    as far away as Babylon.'*

44"Our ancestors carried the Tabernacle* with them through the wilderness. It was con-structed according to the plan God had shown to Moses. 45Years later, when Joshua led our ancestors in battle against the nations that God drove out of this land, the Tabernacle was taken with them into their new territory. And it stayed there until the time of King David.

46"David found favor with God and asked for the privilege of building a permanent Temple for the God of Jacob.* 47But it was Solomon who actually built it. 48However, the Most High doesn't live in temples made by human hands. As the prophet says,

49 'Heaven is my throne,
        and the earth is my footstool.
    Could you build me a temple as good as
        that?'
        asks the Lord.
    'Could you build me such a resting place?
50   Didn't my hands make both heaven and
        earth?'*

51"You stubborn people! You are heathen* at heart and deaf to the truth. Must you forever resist the Holy Spirit? That's what your ancestors did, and so do you! 52Name one prophet your ancestors didn't persecute! They even killed the ones who predicted the coming of the Righteous One—the Messiah whom you betrayed and murdered. 53You deliberately disobeyed God's law, even though you received it from the hands of angels."

54The Jewish leaders were infuriated by Stephen's accusation, and they shook their fists at him in rage.* 55But Stephen, full of the Holy Spirit, gazed steadily into heaven and saw the glory of God, and he saw Jesus standing in the place of honor at God's right hand. 56And he told them, "Look, I see the heavens opened and the Son of Man standing in the place of honor at God's right hand!"

57Then they put their hands over their ears and began shouting. They rushed at him 58and dragged him out of the city and began to stone him. His accusers took off their coats and laid them at the feet of a young man named Saul.*

59As they stoned him, Stephen prayed, "Lord Jesus, receive my spirit." 60He fell to his knees, shouting, "Lord, don't charge them with this sin!" And with that, he died.

8 Saul was one of the witnesses, and he agreed completely with the killing of Stephen.

Persecution Scatters the Believers

A great wave of persecution began that day, sweeping over the church in Jerusalem; and all the believers except the apostles were scattered through the regions of Judea and Samaria. 2(Some devout men came and buried Stephen

7:31-34 Exod 3:5-10.   7:37 Deut 18:15.   7:38 Some manuscripts read *to you.*   7:42-43 Amos 5:25-27 (Greek version).
7:44 Greek *the tent of witness.*   7:46 Some manuscripts read *the house of Jacob.*   7:49-50 Isa 66:1-2.   7:51 Greek *uncircumcised.*
7:54 Greek *they were grinding their teeth against him.*   7:58 *Saul* is later called Paul; see 13:9.

with great mourning.) ³But Saul was going everywhere to destroy the church. He went from house to house, dragging out both men and women to throw them into prison.

Philip Preaches in Samaria

⁴But the believers who were scattered preached the Good News about Jesus wherever they went. ⁵Philip, for example, went to the city of Samaria and told the people there about the Messiah. ⁶Crowds listened intently to Philip because they were eager to hear his message and see the miraculous signs he did. ⁷Many evil* spirits were cast out, screaming as they left their victims. And many who had been paralyzed or lame were healed. ⁸So there was great joy in that city.

⁹A man named Simon had been a sorcerer there for many years, amazing the people of Samaria and claiming to be someone great. ¹⁰Everyone, from the least to the greatest, often spoke of him as "the Great One—the Power of God." ¹¹They listened closely to him because for a long time he had astounded them with his magic.

¹²But now the people believed Philip's message of Good News concerning the Kingdom of God and the name of Jesus Christ. As a result, many men and women were baptized. ¹³Then Simon himself believed and was baptized. He began following Philip wherever he went, and he was amazed by the signs and great miracles Philip performed.

¹⁴When the apostles in Jerusalem heard that the people of Samaria had accepted God's message, they sent Peter and John there. ¹⁵As soon as they arrived, they prayed for these new believers to receive the Holy Spirit. ¹⁶The Holy Spirit had not yet come upon any of them, for they had only been baptized in the name of the Lord Jesus. ¹⁷Then Peter and John laid their hands upon these believers, and they received the Holy Spirit.

¹⁸When Simon saw that the Spirit was given when the apostles laid their hands on people, he offered them money to buy this power. ¹⁹"Let me have this power, too," he exclaimed, "so that when I lay my hands on people, they will receive the Holy Spirit!"

²⁰But Peter replied, "May your money be destroyed with you for thinking God's gift can be bought! ²¹You can have no part in this, for your heart is not right with God. ²²Repent of your wickedness and pray to the Lord. Perhaps he will forgive your evil thoughts, ²³for I can see that you are full of bitter jealousy and are held captive by sin."

²⁴"Pray to the Lord for me," Simon exclaimed, "that these terrible things you've said won't happen to me!"

²⁵After testifying and preaching the word of the Lord in Samaria, Peter and John returned to Jerusalem. And they stopped in many Samaritan villages along the way to preach the Good News.

Philip and the Ethiopian Eunuch

²⁶As for Philip, an angel of the Lord said to him, "Go south* down the desert road that runs from Jerusalem to Gaza." ²⁷So he started out, and he met the treasurer of Ethiopia, a eunuch of great authority under the Kandake, the queen of Ethiopia. The eunuch had gone to Jerusalem to worship, ²⁸and he was now returning. Seated in his carriage, he was reading aloud from the book of the prophet Isaiah.

²⁹The Holy Spirit said to Philip, "Go over and walk along beside the carriage."

³⁰Philip ran over and heard the man reading from the prophet Isaiah. Philip asked, "Do you understand what you are reading?"

³¹The man replied, "How can I, unless someone instructs me?" And he urged Philip to come up into the carriage and sit with him.

³²The passage of Scripture he had been reading was this:

"He was led like a sheep to the slaughter.
    And as a lamb is silent before the shearers,
    he did not open his mouth.
³³ He was humiliated and received no justice.
    Who can speak of his descendants?
    For his life was taken from the earth."*

³⁴The eunuch asked Philip, "Tell me, was the prophet talking about himself or someone else?" ³⁵So beginning with this same Scripture, Philip told him the Good News about Jesus.

³⁶As they rode along, they came to some water, and the eunuch said, "Look! There's some water! Why can't I be baptized?"* ³⁸He ordered the carriage to stop, and they went down into the water, and Philip baptized him.

³⁹When they came up out of the water, the Spirit of the Lord snatched Philip away. The eunuch never saw him again but went on his way rejoicing. ⁴⁰Meanwhile, Philip found himself farther north at the town of Azotus. He preached the Good News there and in every town along the way until he came to Caesarea.

Saul's Conversion

9 Meanwhile, Saul was uttering threats with every breath and was eager to kill the Lord's followers.* So he went to the high priest. ²He requested letters addressed to the synagogues in Damascus, asking for their cooperation in the arrest of any followers of the Way he found there. He wanted to bring them—both men and women—back to Jerusalem in chains.

³As he was approaching Damascus on this mission, a light from heaven suddenly shone down around him. ⁴He fell to the ground and

---

8:7 Greek *unclean.*   **8:26** Or *Go at noon.*   **8:32-33** Isa 53:7-8 (Greek version).   **8:36** Some manuscripts add verse 37,
"You can," Philip answered, "if you believe with all your heart." And the eunuch replied, "I believe that Jesus Christ is the Son of God."
9:1 Greek *disciples.*

heard a voice saying to him, "Saul! Saul! Why are you persecuting me?"

⁵"Who are you, lord?" Saul asked.

And the voice replied, "I am Jesus, the one you are persecuting! ⁶Now get up and go into the city, and you will be told what you must do."

⁷The men with Saul stood speechless, for they heard the sound of someone's voice but saw no one! ⁸Saul picked himself up off the ground, but when he opened his eyes he was blind. So his companions led him by the hand to Damascus. ⁹He remained there blind for three days and did not eat or drink.

¹⁰Now there was a believer* in Damascus named Ananias. The Lord spoke to him in a vision, calling, "Ananias!"

"Yes, Lord!" he replied.

¹¹The Lord said, "Go over to Straight Street, to the house of Judas. When you get there, ask for a man from Tarsus named Saul. He is praying to me right now. ¹²I have shown him a vision of a man named Ananias coming in and laying hands on him so he can see again."

¹³"But Lord," exclaimed Ananias, "I've heard many people talk about the terrible things this man has done to the believers* in Jerusalem! ¹⁴And he is authorized by the leading priests to arrest everyone who calls upon your name."

¹⁵But the Lord said, "Go, for Saul is my chosen instrument to take my message to the Gentiles and to kings, as well as to the people of Israel. ¹⁶And I will show him how much he must suffer for my name's sake."

¹⁷So Ananias went and found Saul. He laid his hands on him and said, "Brother Saul, the Lord Jesus, who appeared to you on the road, has sent me so that you might regain your sight and be filled with the Holy Spirit." ¹⁸Instantly something like scales fell from Saul's eyes, and he regained his sight. Then he got up and was baptized. ¹⁹Afterward he ate some food and regained his strength.

Saul in Damascus and Jerusalem

Saul stayed with the believers* in Damascus for a few days. ²⁰And immediately he began preaching about Jesus in the synagogues, saying, "He is indeed the Son of God!"

²¹All who heard him were amazed. "Isn't this the same man who caused such devastation among Jesus' followers in Jerusalem?" they asked. "And didn't he come here to arrest them and take them in chains to the leading priests?"

²²Saul's preaching became more and more powerful, and the Jews in Damascus couldn't refute his proofs that Jesus was indeed the Messiah. ²³After a while some of the Jews plotted together to kill him. ²⁴They were watching for him day and night at the city gate so they could murder him, but Saul was told about their plot.

²⁵So during the night, some of the other believers* lowered him in a large basket through an opening in the city wall.

²⁶When Saul arrived in Jerusalem, he tried to meet with the believers, but they were all afraid of him. They did not believe he had truly become a believer! ²⁷Then Barnabas brought him to the apostles and told them how Saul had seen the Lord on the way to Damascus and how the Lord had spoken to Saul. He also told them that Saul had preached boldly in the name of Jesus in Damascus.

²⁸So Saul stayed with the apostles and went all around Jerusalem with them, preaching boldly in the name of the Lord. ²⁹He debated with some Greek-speaking Jews, but they tried to murder him. ³⁰When the believers* heard about this, they took him down to Caesarea and sent him away to Tarsus, his hometown.

³¹The church then had peace throughout Judea, Galilee, and Samaria, and it became stronger as the believers lived in the fear of the Lord. And with the encouragement of the Holy Spirit, it also grew in numbers.

Peter Heals Aeneas and Raises Dorcas

³²Meanwhile, Peter traveled from place to place, and he came down to visit the believers in the town of Lydda. ³³There he met a man named Aeneas, who had been paralyzed and bedridden for eight years. ³⁴Peter said to him, "Aeneas, Jesus Christ heals you! Get up, and roll up your sleeping mat!" And he was healed instantly. ³⁵Then the whole population of Lydda and Sharon saw Aeneas walking around, and they turned to the Lord.

³⁶There was a believer in Joppa named Tabitha (which in Greek is Dorcas*). She was always doing kind things for others and helping the poor. ³⁷About this time she became ill and died. Her body was washed for burial and laid in an upstairs room. ³⁸But the believers had heard that Peter was nearby at Lydda, so they sent two men to beg him, "Please come as soon as possible!"

³⁹So Peter returned with them; and as soon as he arrived, they took him to the upstairs room. The room was filled with widows who were weeping and showing him the coats and other clothes Dorcas had made for them. ⁴⁰But Peter asked them all to leave the room; then he knelt and prayed. Turning to the body he said, "Get up, Tabitha." And she opened her eyes! When she saw Peter, she sat up! ⁴¹He gave her his hand and helped her up. Then he called in the widows and all the believers, and he presented her to them alive.

⁴²The news spread through the whole town, and many believed in the Lord. ⁴³And Peter stayed a long time in Joppa, living with Simon, a tanner of hides.

9:10 Greek *disciple;* also in 9:26, 36.　**9:13** Greek *God's holy people;* also in 9:32, 41.　**9:19** Greek *disciples;* also in 9:26, 38.
9:25 Greek *his disciples.*　**9:30** Greek *brothers.*　**9:36** The names *Tabitha* in Aramaic and *Dorcas* in Greek both mean "gazelle."

Cornelius Calls for Peter

10 In Caesarea there lived a Roman army officer* named Cornelius, who was a captain of the Italian Regiment. ²He was a devout, God-fearing man, as was everyone in his household. He gave generously to the poor and prayed regularly to God. ³One afternoon about three o'clock, he had a vision in which he saw an angel of God coming toward him. "Cornelius!" the angel said.

⁴Cornelius stared at him in terror. "What is it, sir?" he asked the angel.

And the angel replied, "Your prayers and gifts to the poor have been received by God as an offering! ⁵Now send some men to Joppa, and summon a man named Simon Peter. ⁶He is staying with Simon, a tanner who lives near the seashore."

⁷As soon as the angel was gone, Cornelius called two of his household servants and a devout soldier, one of his personal attendants. ⁸He told them what had happened and sent them off to Joppa.

Peter Visits Cornelius

⁹The next day as Cornelius's messengers were nearing the town, Peter went up on the flat roof to pray. It was about noon, ¹⁰and he was hungry. But while a meal was being prepared, he fell into a trance. ¹¹He saw the sky open, and something like a large sheet was let down by its four corners. ¹²In the sheet were all sorts of animals, reptiles, and birds. ¹³Then a voice said to him, "Get up, Peter; kill and eat them."

¹⁴"No, Lord," Peter declared. "I have never eaten anything that our Jewish laws have declared impure and unclean.*"

¹⁵But the voice spoke again: "Do not call something unclean if God has made it clean." ¹⁶The same vision was repeated three times. Then the sheet was suddenly pulled up to heaven.

¹⁷Peter was very perplexed. What could the vision mean? Just then the men sent by Cornelius found Simon's house. Standing outside the gate, ¹⁸they asked if a man named Simon Peter was staying there.

¹⁹Meanwhile, as Peter was puzzling over the vision, the Holy Spirit said to him, "Three men have come looking for you. ²⁰Get up, go downstairs, and go with them without hesitation. Don't worry, for I have sent them."

²¹So Peter went down and said, "I'm the man you are looking for. Why have you come?"

²²They said, "We were sent by Cornelius, a Roman officer. He is a devout and God-fearing man, well respected by all the Jews. A holy angel instructed him to summon you to his house so that he can hear your message." ²³So Peter invited the men to stay for the night. The next day he went with them, accompanied by some of the brothers from Joppa.

²⁴They arrived in Caesarea the following day. Cornelius was waiting for them and had called together his relatives and close friends. ²⁵As Peter entered his home, Cornelius fell at his feet and worshiped him. ²⁶But Peter pulled him up and said, "Stand up! I'm a human being just like you!" ²⁷So they talked together and went inside, where many others were assembled.

²⁸Peter told them, "You know it is against our laws for a Jewish man to enter a Gentile home like this or to associate with you. But God has shown me that I should no longer think of anyone as impure or unclean. ²⁹So I came without objection as soon as I was sent for. Now tell me why you sent for me."

³⁰Cornelius replied, "Four days ago I was praying in my house about this same time, three o'clock in the afternoon. Suddenly, a man in dazzling clothes was standing in front of me. ³¹He told me, 'Cornelius, your prayer has been heard, and your gifts to the poor have been noticed by God! ³²Now send messengers to Joppa, and summon a man named Simon Peter. He is staying in the home of Simon, a tanner who lives near the seashore.' ³³So I sent for you at once, and it was good of you to come. Now we are all here, waiting before God to hear the message the Lord has given you."

The Gentiles Hear the Good News

³⁴Then Peter replied, "I see very clearly that God shows no favoritism. ³⁵In every nation he accepts those who fear him and do what is right. ³⁶This is the message of Good News for the people of Israel—that there is peace with God through Jesus Christ, who is Lord of all. ³⁷You know what happened throughout Judea, beginning in Galilee, after John began preaching his message of baptism. ³⁸And you know that God anointed Jesus of Nazareth with the Holy Spirit and with power. Then Jesus went around doing good and healing all who were oppressed by the devil, for God was with him.

³⁹"And we apostles are witnesses of all he did throughout Judea and in Jerusalem. They put him to death by hanging him on a cross,* ⁴⁰but God raised him to life on the third day. Then God allowed him to appear, ⁴¹not to the general public,* but to us whom God had chosen in advance to be his witnesses. We were those who ate and drank with him after he rose from the dead. ⁴²And he ordered us to preach everywhere and to testify that Jesus is the one appointed by God to be the judge of all—the living and the dead. ⁴³He is the one all the prophets testified about, saying that everyone who believes in him will have their sins forgiven through his name."

10:1 Greek *a centurion;* similarly in 10:22. **10:14** Greek *anything common and unclean.* **10:39** Greek *on a tree.* **10:41** Greek *the people.*

The Gentiles Receive the Holy Spirit

⁴⁴Even as Peter was saying these things, the Holy Spirit fell upon all who were listening to the message. ⁴⁵The Jewish believers* who came with Peter were amazed that the gift of the Holy Spirit had been poured out on the Gentiles, too. ⁴⁶For they heard them speaking in other tongues* and praising God.

Then Peter asked, ⁴⁷"Can anyone object to their being baptized, now that they have received the Holy Spirit just as we did?" ⁴⁸So he gave orders for them to be baptized in the name of Jesus Christ. Afterward Cornelius asked him to stay with them for several days.

Peter Explains His Actions

11 Soon the news reached the apostles and other believers* in Judea that the Gentiles had received the word of God. ²But when Peter arrived back in Jerusalem, the Jewish believers* criticized him. ³"You entered the home of Gentiles* and even ate with them!" they said.

⁴Then Peter told them exactly what had happened. ⁵"I was in the town of Joppa," he said, "and while I was praying, I went into a trance and saw a vision. Something like a large sheet was let down by its four corners from the sky. And it came right down to me. ⁶When I looked inside the sheet, I saw all sorts of tame and wild animals, reptiles, and birds. ⁷And I heard a voice say, 'Get up, Peter; kill and eat them.'

⁸"'No, Lord,' I replied. 'I have never eaten anything that our Jewish laws have declared impure or unclean.*'

⁹"But the voice from heaven spoke again: 'Do not call something unclean if God has made it clean.' ¹⁰This happened three times before the sheet and all it contained was pulled back up to heaven.

¹¹"Just then three men who had been sent from Caesarea arrived at the house where we were staying. ¹²The Holy Spirit told me to go with them and not to worry that they were Gentiles. These six brothers here accompanied me, and we soon entered the home of the man who had sent for us. ¹³He told us how an angel had appeared to him in his home and had told him, 'Send messengers to Joppa, and summon a man named Simon Peter. ¹⁴He will tell you how you and everyone in your household can be saved!'

¹⁵"As I began to speak," Peter continued, "the Holy Spirit fell on them, just as he fell on us at the beginning. ¹⁶Then I thought of the Lord's words when he said, 'John baptized with* water, but you will be baptized with the Holy Spirit.' ¹⁷And since God gave these Gentiles the same gift he gave us when we believed in the Lord Jesus Christ, who was I to stand in God's way?"

¹⁸When the others heard this, they stopped objecting and began praising God. They said, "We can see that God has also given the Gentiles the privilege of repenting of their sins and receiving eternal life."

The Church in Antioch of Syria

¹⁹Meanwhile, the believers who had been scattered during the persecution after Stephen's death traveled as far as Phoenicia, Cyprus, and Antioch of Syria. They preached the word of God, but only to Jews. ²⁰However, some of the believers who went to Antioch from Cyprus and Cyrene began preaching to the Gentiles* about the Lord Jesus. ²¹The power of the Lord was with them, and a large number of these Gentiles believed and turned to the Lord.

²²When the church at Jerusalem heard what had happened, they sent Barnabas to Antioch. ²³When he arrived and saw this evidence of God's blessing, he was filled with joy, and he encouraged the believers to stay true to the Lord. ²⁴Barnabas was a good man, full of the Holy Spirit and strong in faith. And many people were brought to the Lord.

²⁵Then Barnabas went on to Tarsus to look for Saul. ²⁶When he found him, he brought him back to Antioch. Both of them stayed there with the church for a full year, teaching large crowds of people. (It was at Antioch that the believers* were first called Christians.)

²⁷During this time some prophets traveled from Jerusalem to Antioch. ²⁸One of them named Agabus stood up in one of the meetings and predicted by the Spirit that a great famine was coming upon the entire Roman world. (This was fulfilled during the reign of Claudius.) ²⁹So the believers in Antioch decided to send relief to the brothers and sisters* in Judea, everyone giving as much as they could. ³⁰This they did, entrusting their gifts to Barnabas and Saul to take to the elders of the church in Jerusalem.

James Is Killed and Peter Is Imprisoned

12 About that time King Herod Agrippa* began to persecute some believers in the church. ²He had the apostle James (John's brother) killed with a sword. ³When Herod saw how much this pleased the Jewish people, he also arrested Peter. (This took place during the Passover celebration.*) ⁴Then he imprisoned him, placing him under the guard of four squads of four soldiers each. Herod intended to bring Peter out for public trial after the Passover. ⁵But while Peter was in prison, the church prayed very earnestly for him.

10:45 Greek *The faithful ones of the circumcision.* 10:46 Or *in other languages.* 11:1 Greek *brothers.* 11:2 Greek *those of the circumcision.* 11:3 Greek *of uncircumcised men.* 11:8 Greek *anything common or unclean.* 11:16 Or *in;* also in 11:16b. 11:20 Greek *the Hellenists* (i.e., those who speak Greek); other manuscripts read *the Greeks.* 11:26 Greek *disciples;* also in 11:29. 11:29 Greek *the brothers.* 12:1 Greek *Herod the king.* He was the nephew of Herod Antipas and a grandson of Herod the Great. 12:3 Greek *the days of unleavened bread.*

Peter's Miraculous Escape from Prison

⁶The night before Peter was to be placed on trial, he was asleep, fastened with two chains between two soldiers. Others stood guard at the prison gate. ⁷Suddenly, there was a bright light in the cell, and an angel of the Lord stood before Peter. The angel struck him on the side to awaken him and said, "Quick! Get up!" And the chains fell off his wrists. ⁸Then the angel told him, "Get dressed and put on your sandals." And he did. "Now put on your coat and follow me," the angel ordered.

⁹So Peter left the cell, following the angel. But all the time he thought it was a vision. He didn't realize it was actually happening. ¹⁰They passed the first and second guard posts and came to the iron gate leading to the city, and this opened for them all by itself. So they passed through and started walking down the street, and then the angel suddenly left him.

¹¹Peter finally came to his senses. "It's really true!" he said. "The Lord has sent his angel and saved me from Herod and from what the Jewish leaders* had planned to do to me!"

¹²When he realized this, he went to the home of Mary, the mother of John Mark, where many were gathered for prayer. ¹³He knocked at the door in the gate, and a servant girl named Rhoda came to open it. ¹⁴When she recognized Peter's voice, she was so overjoyed that, instead of opening the door, she ran back inside and told everyone, "Peter is standing at the door!"

¹⁵"You're out of your mind!" they said. When she insisted, they decided, "It must be his angel."

¹⁶Meanwhile, Peter continued knocking. When they finally opened the door and saw him, they were amazed. ¹⁷He motioned for them to quiet down and told them how the Lord had led him out of prison. "Tell James and the other brothers what happened," he said. And then he went to another place.

¹⁸At dawn there was a great commotion among the soldiers about what had happened to Peter. ¹⁹Herod Agrippa ordered a thorough search for him. When he couldn't be found, Herod interrogated the guards and sentenced them to death. Afterward Herod left Judea to stay in Caesarea for a while.

The Death of Herod Agrippa

²⁰Now Herod was very angry with the people of Tyre and Sidon. So they sent a delegation to make peace with him because their cities were dependent upon Herod's country for food. The delegates won the support of Blastus, Herod's personal assistant, ²¹and an appointment with Herod was granted. When the day arrived, Herod put on his royal robes, sat on his throne, and made a speech to them. ²²The people gave him a great ovation, shouting, "It's the voice of a god, not of a man!"

²³Instantly, an angel of the Lord struck Herod with a sickness, because he accepted the people's worship instead of giving the glory to God. So he was consumed with worms and died.

²⁴Meanwhile, the word of God continued to spread, and there were many new believers.

²⁵When Barnabas and Saul had finished their mission to Jerusalem, they returned,* taking John Mark with them.

Barnabas and Saul Are Commissioned

13 Among the prophets and teachers of the church at Antioch of Syria were Barnabas, Simeon (called "the black man"*), Lucius (from Cyrene), Manaen (the childhood companion of King Herod Antipas*), and Saul. ²One day as these men were worshiping the Lord and fasting, the Holy Spirit said, "Dedicate Barnabas and Saul for the special work to which I have called them." ³So after more fasting and prayer, the men laid their hands on them and sent them on their way.

Paul's First Missionary Journey

⁴So Barnabas and Saul were sent out by the Holy Spirit. They went down to the seaport of Seleucia and then sailed for the island of Cyprus. ⁵There, in the town of Salamis, they went to the Jewish synagogues and preached the word of God. John Mark went with them as their assistant.

⁶Afterward they traveled from town to town across the entire island until finally they reached Paphos, where they met a Jewish sorcerer, a false prophet named Bar-Jesus. ⁷He had attached himself to the governor, Sergius Paulus, who was an intelligent man. The governor invited Barnabas and Saul to visit him, for he wanted to hear the word of God. ⁸But Elymas, the sorcerer (as his name means in Greek), interfered and urged the governor to pay no attention to what Barnabas and Saul said. He was trying to keep the governor from believing.

⁹Saul, also known as Paul, was filled with the Holy Spirit, and he looked the sorcerer in the eye. ¹⁰Then he said, "You son of the devil, full of every sort of deceit and fraud, and enemy of all that is good! Will you never stop perverting the true ways of the Lord? ¹¹Watch now, for the Lord has laid his hand of punishment upon you, and you will be struck blind. You will not see the sunlight for some time." Instantly mist and darkness came over the man's eyes, and he began groping around begging for someone to take his hand and lead him.

¹²When the governor saw what had happened, he became a believer, for he was astonished at the teaching about the Lord.

12:11 Or *the Jewish people.* **12:25** Or *mission, they returned to Jerusalem.* Other manuscripts read *mission, they returned from Jerusalem;* still others read *mission, they returned from Jerusalem to Antioch.* **13:1a** Greek *who was called Niger.* **13:1b** Greek *Herod the tetrarch.*

Paul Preaches in Antioch of Pisidia

¹³Paul and his companions then left Paphos by ship for Pamphylia, landing at the port town of Perga. There John Mark left them and returned to Jerusalem. ¹⁴But Paul and Barnabas traveled inland to Antioch of Pisidia.*

On the Sabbath they went to the synagogue for the services. ¹⁵After the usual readings from the books of Moses* and the prophets, those in charge of the service sent them this message: "Brothers, if you have any word of encouragement for the people, come and give it."

¹⁶So Paul stood, lifted his hand to quiet them, and started speaking. "Men of Israel," he said, "and you God-fearing Gentiles, listen to me.

¹⁷"The God of this nation of Israel chose our ancestors and made them multiply and grow strong during their stay in Egypt. Then with a powerful arm he led them out of their slavery. ¹⁸He put up with them* through forty years of wandering in the wilderness. ¹⁹Then he destroyed seven nations in Canaan and gave their land to Israel as an inheritance. ²⁰All this took about 450 years.

"After that, God gave them judges to rule until the time of Samuel the prophet. ²¹Then the people begged for a king, and God gave them Saul son of Kish, a man of the tribe of Benjamin, who reigned for forty years. ²²But God removed Saul and replaced him with David, a man about whom God said, 'I have found David son of Jesse, a man after my own heart. He will do everything I want him to do.'*

²³"And it is one of King David's descendants, Jesus, who is God's promised Savior of Israel! ²⁴Before he came, John the Baptist preached that all the people of Israel needed to repent of their sins and turn to God and be baptized. ²⁵As John was finishing his ministry he asked, 'Do you think I am the Messiah? No, I am not! But he is coming soon—and I'm not even worthy to be his slave and untie the sandals on his feet.'

²⁶"Brothers—you sons of Abraham, and also you God-fearing Gentiles—this message of salvation has been sent to us! ²⁷The people in Jerusalem and their leaders did not recognize Jesus as the one the prophets had spoken about. Instead, they condemned him, and in doing this they fulfilled the prophets' words that are read every Sabbath. ²⁸They found no legal reason to execute him, but they asked Pilate to have him killed anyway.

²⁹"When they had done all that the prophecies said about him, they took him down from the cross* and placed him in a tomb. ³⁰But God raised him from the dead! ³¹And over a period of many days he appeared to those who had gone with him from Galilee to Jerusalem. They are now his witnesses to the people of Israel.

³²"And now we are here to bring you this Good News. The promise was made to our ancestors, ³³and God has now fulfilled it for us, their descendants, by raising Jesus. This is what the second psalm says about Jesus:

'You are my Son.
    Today I have become your Father.*'

³⁴For God had promised to raise him from the dead, not leaving him to rot in the grave. He said, 'I will give you the sacred blessings I promised to David.'* ³⁵Another psalm explains it more fully: 'You will not allow your Holy One to rot in the grave.'* ³⁶This is not a reference to David, for after David had done the will of God in his own generation, he died and was buried with his ancestors, and his body decayed. ³⁷No, it was a reference to someone else—someone whom God raised and whose body did not decay.

³⁸*"Brothers, listen! We are here to proclaim that through this man Jesus there is forgiveness for your sins. ³⁹Everyone who believes in him is declared right with God—something the law of Moses could never do. ⁴⁰Be careful! Don't let the prophets' words apply to you. For they said,

⁴¹ 'Look, you mockers,
    be amazed and die!
For I am doing something in your own day,
    something you wouldn't believe
    even if someone told you about it.'*"

⁴²As Paul and Barnabas left the synagogue that day, the people begged them to speak about these things again the next week. ⁴³Many Jews and devout converts to Judaism followed Paul and Barnabas, and the two men urged them to continue to rely on the grace of God.

Paul Turns to the Gentiles

⁴⁴The following week almost the entire city turned out to hear them preach the word of the Lord. ⁴⁵But when some of the Jews saw the crowds, they were jealous; so they slandered Paul and argued against whatever he said.

⁴⁶Then Paul and Barnabas spoke out boldly and declared, "It was necessary that we first preach the word of God to you Jews. But since you have rejected it and judged yourselves unworthy of eternal life, we will offer it to the Gentiles. ⁴⁷For the Lord gave us this command when he said,

'I have made you a light to the Gentiles,
    to bring salvation to the farthest corners of
    the earth.'*"

⁴⁸When the Gentiles heard this, they were very glad and thanked the Lord for his message; and all who were chosen for eternal life became

13:13-14 *Pamphylia* and *Pisidia* were districts in what is now Turkey.   13:15 Greek *from the law.*   13:18 Some manuscripts read *He cared for them;* compare Deut 1:31.   13:22 1 Sam 13:14.   13:29 Greek *from the tree.*   13:33 Or *Today I reveal you as my Son.* Ps 2:7.   13:34 Isa 55:3.   13:35 Ps 16:10.   13:38 English translations divide verses 38 and 39 in various ways.   13:41 Hab 1:5 (Greek version).   13:47 Isa 49:6.

believers. ⁴⁹So the Lord's message spread throughout that region.

⁵⁰Then the Jews stirred up the influential religious women and the leaders of the city, and they incited a mob against Paul and Barnabas and ran them out of town. ⁵¹So they shook the dust from their feet as a sign of rejection and went to the town of Iconium. ⁵²And the believers* were filled with joy and with the Holy Spirit.

Paul and Barnabas in Iconium

14 The same thing happened in Iconium.* Paul and Barnabas went to the Jewish synagogue and preached with such power that a great number of both Jews and Greeks became believers. ²Some of the Jews, however, spurned God's message and poisoned the minds of the Gentiles against Paul and Barnabas. ³But the apostles stayed there a long time, preaching boldly about the grace of the Lord. And the Lord proved their message was true by giving them power to do miraculous signs and wonders. ⁴But the people of the town were divided in their opinion about them. Some sided with the Jews, and some with the apostles.

⁵Then a mob of Gentiles and Jews, along with their leaders, decided to attack and stone them. ⁶When the apostles learned of it, they fled to the region of Lycaonia—to the towns of Lystra and Derbe and the surrounding area. ⁷And there they preached the Good News.

Paul and Barnabas in Lystra and Derbe

⁸While they were at Lystra, Paul and Barnabas came upon a man with crippled feet. He had been that way from birth, so he had never walked. He was sitting ⁹and listening as Paul preached. Looking straight at him, Paul realized he had faith to be healed. ¹⁰So Paul called to him in a loud voice, "Stand up!" And the man jumped to his feet and started walking.

¹¹When the crowd saw what Paul had done, they shouted in their local dialect, "These men are gods in human form!" ¹²They decided that Barnabas was the Greek god Zeus and that Paul was Hermes, since he was the chief speaker. ¹³Now the temple of Zeus was located just outside the town. So the priest of the temple and the crowd brought bulls and wreaths of flowers to the town gates, and they prepared to offer sacrifices to the apostles.

¹⁴But when the apostles Barnabas and Paul heard what was happening, they tore their clothing in dismay and ran out among the people, shouting, ¹⁵"Friends,* why are you doing this? We are merely human beings—just like you! We have come to bring you the Good News that you should turn from these worthless things and turn to the living God, who made heaven and earth, the sea, and everything in them. ¹⁶In the past he permitted all the nations to go their own ways, ¹⁷but he never left them without evidence of himself and his goodness. For instance, he sends you rain and good crops and gives you food and joyful hearts." ¹⁸But even with these words, Paul and Barnabas could scarcely restrain the people from sacrificing to them.

¹⁹Then some Jews arrived from Antioch and Iconium and won the crowds to their side. They stoned Paul and dragged him out of town, thinking he was dead. ²⁰But as the believers* gathered around him, he got up and went back into the town. The next day he left with Barnabas for Derbe.

Paul and Barnabas Return to Antioch of Syria

²¹After preaching the Good News in Derbe and making many disciples, Paul and Barnabas returned to Lystra, Iconium, and Antioch of Pisidia, ²²where they strengthened the believers. They encouraged them to continue in the faith, reminding them that we must suffer many hardships to enter the Kingdom of God. ²³Paul and Barnabas also appointed elders in every church. With prayer and fasting, they turned the elders over to the care of the Lord, in whom they had put their trust. ²⁴Then they traveled back through Pisidia to Pamphylia. ²⁵They preached the word in Perga, then went down to Attalia.

²⁶Finally, they returned by ship to Antioch of Syria, where their journey had begun. The believers there had entrusted them to the grace of God to do the work they had now completed. ²⁷Upon arriving in Antioch, they called the church together and reported everything God had done through them and how he had opened the door of faith to the Gentiles, too. ²⁸And they stayed there with the believers for a long time.

The Council at Jerusalem

15 While Paul and Barnabas were at Antioch of Syria, some men from Judea arrived and began to teach the believers*: "Unless you are circumcised as required by the law of Moses, you cannot be saved." ²Paul and Barnabas disagreed with them, arguing vehemently. Finally, the church decided to send Paul and Barnabas to Jerusalem, accompanied by some local believers, to talk to the apostles and elders about this question. ³The church sent the delegates to Jerusalem, and they stopped along the way in Phoenicia and Samaria to visit the believers. They told them—much to everyone's joy—that the Gentiles, too, were being converted.

⁴When they arrived in Jerusalem, Barnabas and Paul were welcomed by the whole church, including the apostles and elders. They reported everything God had done through them. ⁵But then some of the believers who belonged to the sect of the Pharisees stood up and insisted, "The

13:52 Greek *the disciples.* **14:1** *Iconium,* as well as *Lystra* and *Derbe* (14:6), were towns in what is now Turkey. **14:15** Greek *Men.* **14:20** Greek *disciples;* also in 14:22, 28. **15:1** Greek *brothers;* also in 15:3, 23, 32, 33, 36, 40.

Gentile converts must be circumcised and required to follow the law of Moses."

6So the apostles and elders met together to resolve this issue. 7At the meeting, after a long discussion, Peter stood and addressed them as follows: "Brothers, you all know that God chose me from among you some time ago to preach to the Gentiles so that they could hear the Good News and believe. 8God knows people's hearts, and he confirmed that he accepts Gentiles by giving them the Holy Spirit, just as he did to us. 9He made no distinction between us and them, for he cleansed their hearts through faith. 10So why are you now challenging God by burdening the Gentile believers* with a yoke that neither we nor our ancestors were able to bear? 11We believe that we are all saved the same way, by the undeserved grace of the Lord Jesus."

12Everyone listened quietly as Barnabas and Paul told about the miraculous signs and wonders God had done through them among the Gentiles.

13When they had finished, James stood and said, "Brothers, listen to me. 14Peter* has told you about the time God first visited the Gentiles to take from them a people for himself. 15And this conversion of Gentiles is exactly what the prophets predicted. As it is written:

16 'Afterward I will return
    and restore the fallen house*
        of David.
    I will rebuild its ruins
        and restore it,
17 so that the rest of humanity might seek
        the LORD,
    including the Gentiles—
        all those I have called to be mine.
    The LORD has spoken—
18   he who made these things known so
        long ago.'*

19"And so my judgment is that we should not make it difficult for the Gentiles who are turning to God. 20Instead, we should write and tell them to abstain from eating food offered to idols, from sexual immorality, from eating the meat of strangled animals, and from consuming blood. 21For these laws of Moses have been preached in Jewish synagogues in every city on every Sabbath for many generations."

The Letter for Gentile Believers

22Then the apostles and elders together with the whole church in Jerusalem chose delegates, and they sent them to Antioch of Syria with Paul and Barnabas to report on this decision. The men chosen were two of the church leaders*—Judas (also called Barsabbas) and Silas. 23This is the letter they took with them:

"This letter is from the apostles and elders, your brothers in Jerusalem. It is written to the Gentile believers in Antioch, Syria, and Cilicia. Greetings!

24"We understand that some men from here have troubled you and upset you with their teaching, but we did not send them! 25So we decided, having come to complete agreement, to send you official representatives, along with our beloved Barnabas and Paul, 26who have risked their lives for the name of our Lord Jesus Christ. 27We are sending Judas and Silas to confirm what we have decided concerning your question.

28"For it seemed good to the Holy Spirit and to us to lay no greater burden on you than these few requirements: 29You must abstain from eating food offered to idols, from consuming blood or the meat of strangled animals, and from sexual immorality. If you do this, you will do well. Farewell."

30The messengers went at once to Antioch, where they called a general meeting of the believers and delivered the letter. 31And there was great joy throughout the church that day as they read this encouraging message.

32Then Judas and Silas, both being prophets, spoke at length to the believers, encouraging and strengthening their faith. 33They stayed for a while, and then the believers sent them back to the church in Jerusalem with a blessing of peace.* 35Paul and Barnabas stayed in Antioch. They and many others taught and preached the word of the Lord there.

Paul and Barnabas Separate

36After some time Paul said to Barnabas, "Let's go back and visit each city where we previously preached the word of the Lord, to see how the new believers are doing." 37Barnabas agreed and wanted to take along John Mark. 38But Paul disagreed strongly, since John Mark had deserted them in Pamphylia and had not continued with them in their work. 39Their disagreement was so sharp that they separated. Barnabas took John Mark with him and sailed for Cyprus. 40Paul chose Silas, and as he left, the believers entrusted him to the Lord's gracious care. 41Then he traveled throughout Syria and Cilicia, strengthening the churches there.

Paul's Second Missionary Journey

16 Paul went first to Derbe and then to Lystra, where there was a young disciple named Timothy. His mother was a Jewish believer, but his father was a Greek. 2Timothy was well thought of by the believers* in Lystra and Iconium, 3so Paul wanted him to join them on

15:10 Greek disciples. 15:14 Greek Symeon. 15:16 Or kingdom; Greek reads tent. 15:16-18 Amos 9:11-12 (Greek version); Isa 45:21. 15:22 Greek were leaders among the brothers. 15:33 Some manuscripts add verse 34, But Silas decided to stay there. 16:2 Greek brothers; also in 16:40.

their journey. In deference to the Jews of the area, he arranged for Timothy to be circumcised before they left, for everyone knew that his father was a Greek. ⁴Then they went from town to town, instructing the believers to follow the decisions made by the apostles and elders in Jerusalem. ⁵So the churches were strengthened in their faith and grew larger every day.

A Call from Macedonia

⁶Next Paul and Silas traveled through the area of Phrygia and Galatia, because the Holy Spirit had prevented them from preaching the word in the province of Asia at that time. ⁷Then coming to the borders of Mysia, they headed north for the province of Bithynia,* but again the Spirit of Jesus did not allow them to go there. ⁸So instead, they went on through Mysia to the seaport of Troas.

⁹That night Paul had a vision: A man from Macedonia in northern Greece was standing there, pleading with him, "Come over to Macedonia and help us!" ¹⁰So we* decided to leave for Macedonia at once, having concluded that God was calling us to preach the Good News there.

Lydia of Philippi Believes in Jesus

¹¹We boarded a boat at Troas and sailed straight across to the island of Samothrace, and the next day we landed at Neapolis. ¹²From there we reached Philippi, a major city of that district of Macedonia and a Roman colony. And we stayed there several days.

¹³On the Sabbath we went a little way outside the city to a riverbank, where we thought people would be meeting for prayer, and we sat down to speak with some women who had gathered there. ¹⁴One of them was Lydia from Thyatira, a merchant of expensive purple cloth, who worshiped God. As she listened to us, the Lord opened her heart, and she accepted what Paul was saying. ¹⁵She was baptized along with other members of her household, and she asked us to be her guests. "If you agree that I am a true believer in the Lord," she said, "come and stay at my home." And she urged us until we agreed.

Paul and Silas in Prison

¹⁶One day as we were going down to the place of prayer, we met a demon-possessed slave girl. She was a fortune-teller who earned a lot of money for her masters. ¹⁷She followed Paul and the rest of us, shouting, "These men are servants of the Most High God, and they have come to tell you how to be saved."

¹⁸This went on day after day until Paul got so exasperated that he turned and said to the demon within her, "I command you in the name of Jesus Christ to come out of her." And instantly it left her.

¹⁹Her masters' hopes of wealth were now shattered, so they grabbed Paul and Silas and dragged them before the authorities at the marketplace. ²⁰"The whole city is in an uproar because of these Jews!" they shouted to the city officials. ²¹"They are teaching customs that are illegal for us Romans to practice."

²²A mob quickly formed against Paul and Silas, and the city officials ordered them stripped and beaten with wooden rods. ²³They were severely beaten, and then they were thrown into prison. The jailer was ordered to make sure they didn't escape. ²⁴So the jailer put them into the inner dungeon and clamped their feet in the stocks.

²⁵Around midnight Paul and Silas were praying and singing hymns to God, and the other prisoners were listening. ²⁶Suddenly, there was a massive earthquake, and the prison was shaken to its foundations. All the doors immediately flew open, and the chains of every prisoner fell off! ²⁷The jailer woke up to see the prison doors wide open. He assumed the prisoners had escaped, so he drew his sword to kill himself. ²⁸But Paul shouted to him, "Stop! Don't kill yourself! We are all here!"

²⁹The jailer called for lights and ran to the dungeon and fell down trembling before Paul and Silas. ³⁰Then he brought them out and asked, "Sirs, what must I do to be saved?"

³¹They replied, "Believe in the Lord Jesus and you will be saved, along with everyone in your household." ³²And they shared the word of the Lord with him and with all who lived in his household. ³³Even at that hour of the night, the jailer cared for them and washed their wounds. Then he and everyone in his household were immediately baptized. ³⁴He brought them into his house and set a meal before them, and he and his entire household rejoiced because they all believed in God.

³⁵The next morning the city officials sent the police to tell the jailer, "Let those men go!" ³⁶So the jailer told Paul, "The city officials have said you and Silas are free to leave. Go in peace."

³⁷But Paul replied, "They have publicly beaten us without a trial and put us in prison—and we are Roman citizens. So now they want us to leave secretly? Certainly not! Let them come themselves to release us!"

³⁸When the police reported this, the city officials were alarmed to learn that Paul and Silas were Roman citizens. ³⁹So they came to the jail and apologized to them. Then they brought them out and begged them to leave the city. ⁴⁰When Paul and Silas left the prison, they returned to the home of Lydia. There they met with the believers and encouraged them once more. Then they left town.

16:6-7 *Phrygia, Galatia, Asia, Mysia,* and *Bithynia* were all districts in what is now Turkey.　**16:10** Luke, the writer of this book, here joined Paul and accompanied him on his journey.

Paul Preaches in Thessalonica

17 Paul and Silas then traveled through the towns of Amphipolis and Apollonia and came to Thessalonica, where there was a Jewish synagogue. ²As was Paul's custom, he went to the synagogue service, and for three Sabbaths in a row he used the Scriptures to reason with the people. ³He explained the prophecies and proved that the Messiah must suffer and rise from the dead. He said, "This Jesus I'm telling you about is the Messiah." ⁴Some of the Jews who listened were persuaded and joined Paul and Silas, along with many God-fearing Greek men and quite a few prominent women.*

⁵But some of the Jews were jealous, so they gathered some troublemakers from the marketplace to form a mob and start a riot. They attacked the home of Jason, searching for Paul and Silas so they could drag them out to the crowd.* ⁶Not finding them there, they dragged out Jason and some of the other believers* instead and took them before the city council. "Paul and Silas have caused trouble all over the world," they shouted, "and now they are here disturbing our city, too. ⁷And Jason has welcomed them into his home. They are all guilty of treason against Caesar, for they profess allegiance to another king, named Jesus."

⁸The people of the city, as well as the city council, were thrown into turmoil by these reports. ⁹So the officials forced Jason and the other believers to post bond, and then they released them.

Paul and Silas in Berea

¹⁰That very night the believers sent Paul and Silas to Berea. When they arrived there, they went to the Jewish synagogue. ¹¹And the people of Berea were more open-minded than those in Thessalonica, and they listened eagerly to Paul's message. They searched the Scriptures day after day to see if Paul and Silas were teaching the truth. ¹²As a result, many Jews believed, as did many of the prominent Greek women and men.

¹³But when some Jews in Thessalonica learned that Paul was preaching the word of God in Berea, they went there and stirred up trouble. ¹⁴The believers acted at once, sending Paul on to the coast, while Silas and Timothy remained behind. ¹⁵Those escorting Paul went with him all the way to Athens; then they returned to Berea with instructions for Silas and Timothy to hurry and join him.

Paul Preaches in Athens

¹⁶While Paul was waiting for them in Athens, he was deeply troubled by all the idols he saw everywhere in the city. ¹⁷He went to the synagogue to reason with the Jews and the God-fearing Gentiles, and he spoke daily in the public square to all who happened to be there.

¹⁸He also had a debate with some of the Epicurean and Stoic philosophers. When he told them about Jesus and his resurrection, they said, "What's this babbler trying to say with these strange ideas he's picked up?" Others said, "He seems to be preaching about some foreign gods."

¹⁹Then they took him to the high council of the city.* "Come and tell us about this new teaching," they said. ²⁰"You are saying some rather strange things, and we want to know what it's all about." ²¹(It should be explained that all the Athenians as well as the foreigners in Athens seemed to spend all their time discussing the latest ideas.)

²²So Paul, standing before the council,* addressed them as follows: "Men of Athens, I notice that you are very religious in every way, ²³for as I was walking along I saw your many shrines. And one of your altars had this inscription on it: 'To an Unknown God.' This God, whom you worship without knowing, is the one I'm telling you about.

²⁴"He is the God who made the world and everything in it. Since he is Lord of heaven and earth, he doesn't live in man-made temples, ²⁵and human hands can't serve his needs—for he has no needs. He himself gives life and breath to everything, and he satisfies every need. ²⁶From one man* he created all the nations throughout the whole earth. He decided beforehand when they should rise and fall, and he determined their boundaries.

²⁷"His purpose was for the nations to seek after God and perhaps feel their way toward him and find him—though he is not far from any one of us. ²⁸For in him we live and move and exist. As some of your* own poets have said, 'We are his offspring.' ²⁹And since this is true, we shouldn't think of God as an idol designed by craftsmen from gold or silver or stone.

³⁰"God overlooked people's ignorance about these things in earlier times, but now he commands everyone everywhere to repent of their sins and turn to him. ³¹For he has set a day for judging the world with justice by the man he has appointed, and he proved to everyone who this is by raising him from the dead."

³²When they heard Paul speak about the resurrection of the dead, some laughed in contempt, but others said, "We want to hear more about this later." ³³That ended Paul's discussion with them, ³⁴but some joined him and became believers. Among them were Dionysius, a member of the council,* a woman named Damaris, and others with them.

17:4 Some manuscripts read *quite a few of the wives of the leading men.*   **17:5** Or *the city council.*   **17:6** Greek *brothers;* also in 17:10, 14.   **17:19** Or *the most learned society of philosophers in the city.* Greek reads *the Areopagus.*   **17:22** Traditionally rendered *standing in the middle of Mars Hill;* Greek reads *standing in the middle of the Areopagus.*   **17:26** Greek *From one;* other manuscripts read *From one blood.*   **17:28** Some manuscripts read *our.*   **17:34** Greek *an Areopagite.*

Paul Meets Priscilla and Aquila in Corinth

18 Then Paul left Athens and went to Corinth.* ²There he became acquainted with a Jew named Aquila, born in Pontus, who had recently arrived from Italy with his wife, Priscilla. They had left Italy when Claudius Caesar deported all Jews from Rome. ³Paul lived and worked with them, for they were tentmakers* just as he was.

⁴Each Sabbath found Paul at the synagogue, trying to convince the Jews and Greeks alike. ⁵And after Silas and Timothy came down from Macedonia, Paul spent all his time preaching the word. He testified to the Jews that Jesus was the Messiah. ⁶But when they opposed and insulted him, Paul shook the dust from his clothes and said, "Your blood is upon your own heads—I am innocent. From now on I will go preach to the Gentiles."

⁷Then he left and went to the home of Titius Justus, a Gentile who worshiped God and lived next door to the synagogue. ⁸Crispus, the leader of the synagogue, and everyone in his household believed in the Lord. Many others in Corinth also heard Paul, became believers, and were baptized.

⁹One night the Lord spoke to Paul in a vision and told him, "Don't be afraid! Speak out! Don't be silent! ¹⁰For I am with you, and no one will attack and harm you, for many people in this city belong to me." ¹¹So Paul stayed there for the next year and a half, teaching the word of God.

¹²But when Gallio became governor of Achaia, some Jews rose up together against Paul and brought him before the governor for judgment. ¹³They accused Paul of "persuading people to worship God in ways that are contrary to our law."

¹⁴But just as Paul started to make his defense, Gallio turned to Paul's accusers and said, "Listen, you Jews, if this were a case involving some wrongdoing or a serious crime, I would have a reason to accept your case. ¹⁵But since it is merely a question of words and names and your Jewish law, take care of it yourselves. I refuse to judge such matters." ¹⁶And he threw them out of the courtroom.

¹⁷The crowd* then grabbed Sosthenes, the leader of the synagogue, and beat him right there in the courtroom. But Gallio paid no attention.

Paul Returns to Antioch of Syria

¹⁸Paul stayed in Corinth for some time after that, then said good-bye to the brothers and sisters* and went to nearby Cenchrea. There he shaved his head according to Jewish custom, marking the end of a vow. Then he set sail for Syria, taking Priscilla and Aquila with him.

¹⁹They stopped first at the port of Ephesus, where Paul left the others behind. While he was there, he went to the synagogue to reason with the Jews. ²⁰They asked him to stay longer, but he declined. ²¹As he left, however, he said, "I will come back later,* God willing." Then he set sail from Ephesus. ²²The next stop was at the port of Caesarea. From there he went up and visited the church at Jerusalem* and then went back to Antioch.

²³After spending some time in Antioch, Paul went back through Galatia and Phrygia, visiting and strengthening all the believers.*

Apollos Instructed at Ephesus

²⁴Meanwhile, a Jew named Apollos, an eloquent speaker who knew the Scriptures well, had arrived in Ephesus from Alexandria in Egypt. ²⁵He had been taught the way of the Lord, and he taught others about Jesus with an enthusiastic spirit* and with accuracy. However, he knew only about John's baptism. ²⁶When Priscilla and Aquila heard him preaching boldly in the synagogue, they took him aside and explained the way of God even more accurately.

²⁷Apollos had been thinking about going to Achaia, and the brothers and sisters in Ephesus encouraged him to go. They wrote to the believers in Achaia, asking them to welcome him. When he arrived there, he proved to be of great benefit to those who, by God's grace, had believed. ²⁸He refuted the Jews with powerful arguments in public debate. Using the Scriptures, he explained to them that Jesus was the Messiah.

Paul's Third Missionary Journey

19 While Apollos was in Corinth, Paul traveled through the interior regions until he reached Ephesus, on the coast, where he found several believers.* ²"Did you receive the Holy Spirit when you believed?" he asked them.

"No," they replied, "we haven't even heard that there is a Holy Spirit."

³"Then what baptism did you experience?" he asked.

And they replied, "The baptism of John."

⁴Paul said, "John's baptism called for repentance from sin. But John himself told the people to believe in the one who would come later, meaning Jesus."

⁵As soon as they heard this, they were baptized in the name of the Lord Jesus. ⁶Then when Paul laid his hands on them, the Holy Spirit came on them, and they spoke in other tongues* and prophesied. ⁷There were about twelve men in all.

18:1 *Athens* and *Corinth* were major cities in Achaia, the region in the southern portion of the Greek peninsula. **18:3** Or *leather-workers.* **18:17** Greek *Everyone;* other manuscripts read *All the Greeks.* **18:18** Greek *brothers;* also in 18:27. **18:21** Some manuscripts read *"I must by all means be at Jerusalem for the upcoming festival, but I will come back later."* **18:22** Greek *the church.* **18:23** Greek *disciples;* also in 18:27. **18:25** Or *with enthusiasm in the Spirit.* **19:1** Greek *disciples;* also in 19:9, 30. **19:6** Or *in other languages.*

Paul Ministers in Ephesus

8Then Paul went to the synagogue and preached boldly for the next three months, arguing persuasively about the Kingdom of God. 9But some became stubborn, rejecting his message and publicly speaking against the Way. So Paul left the synagogue and took the believers with him. Then he held daily discussions at the lecture hall of Tyrannus. 10This went on for the next two years, so that people throughout the province of Asia—both Jews and Greeks—heard the word of the Lord.

11God gave Paul the power to perform unusual miracles. 12When handkerchiefs or aprons that had merely touched his skin were placed on sick people, they were healed of their diseases, and evil spirits were expelled.

13A group of Jews was traveling from town to town casting out evil spirits. They tried to use the name of the Lord Jesus in their incantation, saying, "I command you in the name of Jesus, whom Paul preaches, to come out!" 14Seven sons of Sceva, a leading priest, were doing this. 15But one time when they tried it, the evil spirit replied, "I know Jesus, and I know Paul, but who are you?" 16Then the man with the evil spirit leaped on them, overpowered them, and attacked them with such violence that they fled from the house, naked and battered.

17The story of what happened spread quickly all through Ephesus, to Jews and Greeks alike. A solemn fear descended on the city, and the name of the Lord Jesus was greatly honored. 18Many who became believers confessed their sinful practices. 19A number of them who had been practicing sorcery brought their incantation books and burned them at a public bonfire. The value of the books was several million dollars.* 20So the message about the Lord spread widely and had a powerful effect.

21Afterward Paul felt compelled by the Spirit* to go over to Macedonia and Achaia before going to Jerusalem. "And after that," he said, "I must go on to Rome!" 22He sent his two assistants, Timothy and Erastus, ahead to Macedonia while he stayed awhile longer in the province of Asia.

The Riot in Ephesus

23About that time, serious trouble developed in Ephesus concerning the Way. 24It began with Demetrius, a silversmith who had a large business manufacturing silver shrines of the Greek goddess Artemis.* He kept many craftsmen busy. 25He called them together, along with others employed in similar trades, and addressed them as follows:

"Gentlemen, you know that our wealth comes from this business. 26But as you have seen and heard, this man Paul has persuaded many people that handmade gods aren't really gods at all.

And he's done this not only here in Ephesus but throughout the entire province! 27Of course, I'm not just talking about the loss of public respect for our business. I'm also concerned that the temple of the great goddess Artemis will lose its influence and that Artemis—this magnificent goddess worshiped throughout the province of Asia and all around the world—will be robbed of her great prestige!"

28At this their anger boiled, and they began shouting, "Great is Artemis of the Ephesians!" 29Soon the whole city was filled with confusion. Everyone rushed to the amphitheater, dragging along Gaius and Aristarchus, who were Paul's traveling companions from Macedonia. 30Paul wanted to go in, too, but the believers wouldn't let him. 31Some of the officials of the province, friends of Paul, also sent a message to him, begging him not to risk his life by entering the amphitheater.

32Inside, the people were all shouting, some one thing and some another. Everything was in confusion. In fact, most of them didn't even know why they were there. 33The Jews in the crowd pushed Alexander forward and told him to explain the situation. He motioned for silence and tried to speak. 34But when the crowd realized he was a Jew, they started shouting again and kept it up for about two hours: "Great is Artemis of the Ephesians! Great is Artemis of the Ephesians!"

35At last the mayor was able to quiet them down enough to speak. "Citizens of Ephesus," he said. "Everyone knows that Ephesus is the official guardian of the temple of the great Artemis, whose image fell down to us from heaven. 36Since this is an undeniable fact, you should stay calm and not do anything rash. 37You have brought these men here, but they have stolen nothing from the temple and have not spoken against our goddess.

38"If Demetrius and the craftsmen have a case against them, the courts are in session and the officials can hear the case at once. Let them make formal charges. 39And if there are complaints about other matters, they can be settled in a legal assembly. 40I am afraid we are in danger of being charged with rioting by the Roman government, since there is no cause for all this commotion. And if Rome demands an explanation, we won't know what to say." 41*Then he dismissed them, and they dispersed.

Paul Goes to Macedonia and Greece

20 When the uproar was over, Paul sent for the believers* and encouraged them. Then he said good-bye and left for Macedonia. 2While there, he encouraged the believers in all the towns he passed through. Then he traveled down to Greece, 3where he stayed for three months. He was preparing to sail back to Syria

---

19:19 Greek *50,000 pieces of silver,* each of which was the equivalent of a day's wage.   19:21 Or *decided in his spirit.*
19:24 *Artemis* is otherwise known as Diana.   19:41 Some translations include verse 41 as part of verse 40.   20:1 Greek *disciples.*

when he discovered a plot by some Jews against his life, so he decided to return through Macedonia.

⁴Several men were traveling with him. They were Sopater son of Pyrrhus from Berea; Aristarchus and Secundus from Thessalonica; Gaius from Derbe; Timothy; and Tychicus and Trophimus from the province of Asia. ⁵They went on ahead and waited for us at Troas. ⁶After the Passover* ended, we boarded a ship at Philippi in Macedonia and five days later joined them in Troas, where we stayed a week.

Paul's Final Visit to Troas

⁷On the first day of the week, we gathered with the local believers to share in the Lord's Supper.* Paul was preaching to them, and since he was leaving the next day, he kept talking until midnight. ⁸The upstairs room where we met was lighted with many flickering lamps. ⁹As Paul spoke on and on, a young man named Eutychus, sitting on the windowsill, became very drowsy. Finally, he fell sound asleep and dropped three stories to his death below. ¹⁰Paul went down, bent over him, and took him into his arms. "Don't worry," he said, "he's alive!" ¹¹Then they all went back upstairs, shared in the Lord's Supper,* and ate together. Paul continued talking to them until dawn, and then he left. ¹²Meanwhile, the young man was taken home unhurt, and everyone was greatly relieved.

Paul Meets the Ephesian Elders

¹³Paul went by land to Assos, where he had arranged for us to join him, while we traveled by ship. ¹⁴He joined us there, and we sailed together to Mitylene. ¹⁵The next day we sailed past the island of Kios. The following day we crossed to the island of Samos, and* a day later we arrived at Miletus.

¹⁶Paul had decided to sail on past Ephesus, for he didn't want to spend any more time in the province of Asia. He was hurrying to get to Jerusalem, if possible, in time for the Festival of Pentecost. ¹⁷But when we landed at Miletus, he sent a message to the elders of the church at Ephesus, asking them to come and meet him.

¹⁸When they arrived he declared, "You know that from the day I set foot in the province of Asia until now ¹⁹I have done the Lord's work humbly and with many tears. I have endured the trials that came to me from the plots of the Jews. ²⁰I never shrank back from telling you what you needed to hear, either publicly or in your homes. ²¹I have had one message for Jews and Greeks alike—the necessity of repenting from sin and turning to God, and of having faith in our Lord Jesus.

²²"And now I am bound by the Spirit* to go to Jerusalem. I don't know what awaits me, ²³except that the Holy Spirit tells me in city after city that jail and suffering lie ahead. ²⁴But my life is worth nothing to me unless I use it for finishing the work assigned me by the Lord Jesus—the work of telling others the Good News about the wonderful grace of God.

²⁵"And now I know that none of you to whom I have preached the Kingdom will ever see me again. ²⁶I declare today that I have been faithful. If anyone suffers eternal death, it's not my fault,* ²⁷for I didn't shrink from declaring all that God wants you to know.

²⁸"So guard yourselves and God's people. Feed and shepherd God's flock—his church, purchased with his own blood*—over which the Holy Spirit has appointed you as elders.* ²⁹I know that false teachers, like vicious wolves, will come in among you after I leave, not sparing the flock. ³⁰Even some men from your own group will rise up and distort the truth in order to draw a following. ³¹Watch out! Remember the three years I was with you—my constant watch and care over you night and day, and my many tears for you.

³²"And now I entrust you to God and the message of his grace that is able to build you up and give you an inheritance with all those he has set apart for himself.

³³"I have never coveted anyone's silver or gold or fine clothes. ³⁴You know that these hands of mine have worked to supply my own needs and even the needs of those who were with me. ³⁵And I have been a constant example of how you can help those in need by working hard. You should remember the words of the Lord Jesus: 'It is more blessed to give than to receive.'"

³⁶When he had finished speaking, he knelt and prayed with them. ³⁷They all cried as they embraced and kissed him good-bye. ³⁸They were sad most of all because he had said that they would never see him again. Then they escorted him down to the ship.

Paul's Journey to Jerusalem

21 After saying farewell to the Ephesian elders, we sailed straight to the island of Cos. The next day we reached Rhodes and then went to Patara. ²There we boarded a ship sailing for Phoenicia. ³We sighted the island of Cyprus, passed it on our left, and landed at the harbor of Tyre, in Syria, where the ship was to unload its cargo.

⁴We went ashore, found the local believers,* and stayed with them a week. These believers prophesied through the Holy Spirit that Paul should not go on to Jerusalem. ⁵When we returned to the ship at the end of the week, the entire congregation, including women* and

---

20:6 Greek *the days of unleavened bread.* **20:7** Greek *to break bread.* **20:11** Greek *broke the bread.* **20:15** Some manuscripts read *and having stayed at Trogyllium.* **20:22** Or *by my spirit,* or *by an inner compulsion;* Greek reads *by the spirit.* **20:26** Greek *I am innocent of the blood of all.* **20:28a** Or *with the blood of his own [Son].* **20:28b** Greek *overseers.* **21:4** Greek *disciples;* also in 21:16. **21:5** Or *wives.*

children, left the city and came down to the shore with us. There we knelt, prayed, ⁶and said our farewells. Then we went aboard, and they returned home.

⁷The next stop after leaving Tyre was Ptolemais, where we greeted the brothers and sisters* and stayed for one day. ⁸The next day we went on to Caesarea and stayed at the home of Philip the Evangelist, one of the seven men who had been chosen to distribute food. ⁹He had four unmarried daughters who had the gift of prophecy.

¹⁰Several days later a man named Agabus, who also had the gift of prophecy, arrived from Judea. ¹¹He came over, took Paul's belt, and bound his own feet and hands with it. Then he said, "The Holy Spirit declares, 'So shall the owner of this belt be bound by the Jewish leaders in Jerusalem and turned over to the Gentiles.'" ¹²When we heard this, we and the local believers all begged Paul not to go on to Jerusalem.

¹³But he said, "Why all this weeping? You are breaking my heart! I am ready not only to be jailed at Jerusalem but even to die for the sake of the Lord Jesus." ¹⁴When it was clear that we couldn't persuade him, we gave up and said, "The Lord's will be done."

Paul Arrives at Jerusalem

¹⁵After this we packed our things and left for Jerusalem. ¹⁶Some believers from Caesarea accompanied us, and they took us to the home of Mnason, a man originally from Cyprus and one of the early believers. ¹⁷When we arrived, the brothers and sisters in Jerusalem welcomed us warmly.

¹⁸The next day Paul went with us to meet with James, and all the elders of the Jerusalem church were present. ¹⁹After greeting them, Paul gave a detailed account of the things God had accomplished among the Gentiles through his ministry.

²⁰After hearing this, they praised God. And then they said, "You know, dear brother, how many thousands of Jews have also believed, and they all follow the law of Moses very seriously. ²¹But the Jewish believers here in Jerusalem have been told that you are teaching all the Jews who live among the Gentiles to turn their backs on the laws of Moses. They've heard that you teach them not to circumcise their children or follow other Jewish customs. ²²What should we do? They will certainly hear that you have come.

²³"Here's what we want you to do. We have four men here who have completed their vow. ²⁴Go with them to the Temple and join them in the purification ceremony, paying for them to have their heads ritually shaved. Then everyone will know that the rumors are all false and that you yourself observe the Jewish laws. ²⁵As for the Gentile believers, they should do what we already told them in a letter: They should abstain from eating food offered to idols, from consuming blood or the meat of strangled animals, and from sexual immorality."

Paul Is Arrested

²⁶So Paul went to the Temple the next day with the other men. They had already started the purification ritual, so he publicly announced the date when their vows would end and sacrifices would be offered for each of them.

²⁷The seven days were almost ended when some Jews from the province of Asia saw Paul in the Temple and roused a mob against him. They grabbed him, ²⁸yelling, "Men of Israel, help us! This is the man who preaches against our people everywhere and tells everybody to disobey the Jewish laws. He speaks against the Temple—and even defiles this holy place by bringing in Gentiles.*" ²⁹(For earlier that day they had seen him in the city with Trophimus, a Gentile from Ephesus,* and they assumed Paul had taken him into the Temple.)

³⁰The whole city was rocked by these accusations, and a great riot followed. Paul was grabbed and dragged out of the Temple, and immediately the gates were closed behind him. ³¹As they were trying to kill him, word reached the commander of the Roman regiment that all Jerusalem was in an uproar. ³²He immediately called out his soldiers and officers* and ran down among the crowd. When the mob saw the commander and the troops coming, they stopped beating Paul.

³³Then the commander arrested him and ordered him bound with two chains. He asked the crowd who he was and what he had done. ³⁴Some shouted one thing and some another. Since he couldn't find out the truth in all the uproar and confusion, he ordered that Paul be taken to the fortress. ³⁵As Paul reached the stairs, the mob grew so violent the soldiers had to lift him to their shoulders to protect him. ³⁶And the crowd followed behind, shouting, "Kill him, kill him!"

Paul Speaks to the Crowd

³⁷As Paul was about to be taken inside, he said to the commander, "May I have a word with you?"

"Do you know Greek?" the commander asked, surprised. ³⁸"Aren't you the Egyptian who led a rebellion some time ago and took 4,000 members of the Assassins out into the desert?"

³⁹"No," Paul replied, "I am a Jew and a citizen of Tarsus in Cilicia, which is an important city. Please, let me talk to these people." ⁴⁰The commander agreed, so Paul stood on the stairs and motioned to the people to be quiet. Soon a deep silence enveloped the crowd, and he addressed them in their own language, Aramaic.*

21:7 Greek *brothers;* also in 21:17.   **21:28** Greek *Greeks.*   **21:29** Greek *Trophimus, the Ephesian.*   **21:32** Greek *centurions.*
21:40 Or *Hebrew.*

22 "Brothers and esteemed fathers," Paul said, "listen to me as I offer my defense." ²When they heard him speaking in their own language,* the silence was even greater.

³Then Paul said, "I am a Jew, born in Tarsus, a city in Cilicia, and I was brought up and educated here in Jerusalem under Gamaliel. As his student, I was carefully trained in our Jewish laws and customs. I became very zealous to honor God in everything I did, just like all of you today. ⁴And I persecuted the followers of the Way, hounding some to death, arresting both men and women and throwing them in prison. ⁵The high priest and the whole council of elders can testify that this is so. For I received letters from them to our Jewish brothers in Damascus, authorizing me to bring the Christians from there to Jerusalem, in chains, to be punished.

⁶"As I was on the road, approaching Damascus about noon, a very bright light from heaven suddenly shone down around me. ⁷I fell to the ground and heard a voice saying to me, 'Saul, Saul, why are you persecuting me?'

⁸"'Who are you, lord?' I asked.

"And the voice replied, 'I am Jesus the Nazarene,* the one you are persecuting.' ⁹The people with me saw the light but didn't understand the voice speaking to me.

¹⁰"I asked, 'What should I do, Lord?'

"And the Lord told me, 'Get up and go into Damascus, and there you will be told everything you are to do.'

¹¹"I was blinded by the intense light and had to be led by the hand to Damascus by my companions. ¹²A man named Ananias lived there. He was a godly man, deeply devoted to the law, and well regarded by all the Jews of Damascus. ¹³He came and stood beside me and said, 'Brother Saul, regain your sight.' And that very moment I could see him!

¹⁴"Then he told me, 'The God of our ancestors has chosen you to know his will and to see the Righteous One and hear him speak. ¹⁵For you are to be his witness, telling everyone what you have seen and heard. ¹⁶What are you waiting for? Get up and be baptized. Have your sins washed away by calling on the name of the Lord.'

¹⁷"After I returned to Jerusalem, I was praying in the Temple and fell into a trance. ¹⁸I saw a vision of Jesus* saying to me, 'Hurry! Leave Jerusalem, for the people here won't accept your testimony about me.'

¹⁹"'But Lord,' I argued, 'they certainly know that in every synagogue I imprisoned and beat those who believed in you. ²⁰And I was in complete agreement when your witness Stephen was killed. I stood by and kept the coats they took off when they stoned him.'

²¹"But the Lord said to me, 'Go, for I will send you far away to the Gentiles!'"

²²The crowd listened until Paul said that word. Then they all began to shout, "Away with such a fellow! He isn't fit to live!" ²³They yelled, threw off their coats, and tossed handfuls of dust into the air.

Paul Reveals His Roman Citizenship

²⁴The commander brought Paul inside and ordered him lashed with whips to make him confess his crime. He wanted to find out why the crowd had become so furious. ²⁵When they tied Paul down to lash him, Paul said to the officer* standing there, "Is it legal for you to whip a Roman citizen who hasn't even been tried?"

²⁶When the officer heard this, he went to the commander and asked, "What are you doing? This man is a Roman citizen!"

²⁷So the commander went over and asked Paul, "Tell me, are you a Roman citizen?"

"Yes, I certainly am," Paul replied.

²⁸"I am, too," the commander muttered, "and it cost me plenty!"

Paul answered, "But I am a citizen by birth!"

²⁹The soldiers who were about to interrogate Paul quickly withdrew when they heard he was a Roman citizen, and the commander was frightened because he had ordered him bound and whipped.

Paul before the High Council

³⁰The next day the commander ordered the leading priests into session with the Jewish high council.* He wanted to find out what the trouble was all about, so he released Paul to have him stand before them.

23 Gazing intently at the high council,* Paul began: "Brothers, I have always lived before God with a clear conscience!"

²Instantly Ananias the high priest commanded those close to Paul to slap him on the mouth. ³But Paul said to him, "God will slap you, you corrupt hypocrite!* What kind of judge are you to break the law yourself by ordering me struck like that?"

⁴Those standing near Paul said to him, "Do you dare to insult God's high priest?"

⁵"I'm sorry, brothers. I didn't realize he was the high priest," Paul replied, "for the Scriptures say, 'You must not speak evil of any of your rulers.'*"

⁶Paul realized that some members of the high council were Sadducees and some were Pharisees, so he shouted, "Brothers, I am a Pharisee, as were my ancestors! And I am on trial because my hope is in the resurrection of the dead!"

⁷This divided the council—the Pharisees against the Sadducees—⁸for the Sadducees say there is no resurrection or angels or spirits, but the Pharisees believe in all of these. ⁹So there

---

22:2 Greek *in Aramaic,* or *in Hebrew.*   **22:8** Or *Jesus of Nazareth.*   **22:18** Greek *him.*   **22:25** Greek *the centurion;* also in 22:26.
22:30 Greek *Sanhedrin.*   **23:1** Greek *Sanhedrin;* also in 23:6, 15, 20, 28.   **23:3** Greek *you whitewashed wall.*   **23:5** Exod 22:28.

was a great uproar. Some of the teachers of religious law who were Pharisees jumped up and began to argue forcefully. "We see nothing wrong with him," they shouted. "Perhaps a spirit or an angel spoke to him." ¹⁰As the conflict grew more violent, the commander was afraid they would tear Paul apart. So he ordered his soldiers to go and rescue him by force and take him back to the fortress.

¹¹That night the Lord appeared to Paul and said, "Be encouraged, Paul. Just as you have been a witness to me here in Jerusalem, you must preach the Good News in Rome as well."

The Plan to Kill Paul

¹²The next morning a group of Jews* got together and bound themselves with an oath not to eat or drink until they had killed Paul. ¹³There were more than forty of them in the conspiracy. ¹⁴They went to the leading priests and elders and told them, "We have bound ourselves with an oath to eat nothing until we have killed Paul. ¹⁵So you and the high council should ask the commander to bring Paul back to the council again. Pretend you want to examine his case more fully. We will kill him on the way."

¹⁶But Paul's nephew—his sister's son—heard of their plan and went to the fortress and told Paul. ¹⁷Paul called for one of the Roman officers* and said, "Take this young man to the commander. He has something important to tell him."

¹⁸So the officer did, explaining, "Paul, the prisoner, called me over and asked me to bring this young man to you because he has something to tell you."

¹⁹The commander took his hand, led him aside, and asked, "What is it you want to tell me?"

²⁰Paul's nephew told him, "Some Jews are going to ask you to bring Paul before the high council tomorrow, pretending they want to get some more information. ²¹But don't do it! There are more than forty men hiding along the way ready to ambush him. They have vowed not to eat or drink anything until they have killed him. They are ready now, just waiting for your consent."

²²"Don't let anyone know you told me this," the commander warned the young man.

Paul Is Sent to Caesarea

²³Then the commander called two of his officers and ordered, "Get 200 soldiers ready to leave for Caesarea at nine o'clock tonight. Also take 200 spearmen and 70 mounted troops. ²⁴Provide horses for Paul to ride, and get him safely to Governor Felix." ²⁵Then he wrote this letter to the governor:

²⁶"From Claudius Lysias, to his Excellency, Governor Felix: Greetings!

²⁷"This man was seized by some Jews, and they were about to kill him when I arrived with the troops. When I learned that he was a Roman citizen, I removed him to safety. ²⁸Then I took him to their high council to try to learn the basis of the accusations against him. ²⁹I soon discovered the charge was something regarding their religious law—certainly nothing worthy of imprisonment or death. ³⁰But when I was informed of a plot to kill him, I immediately sent him on to you. I have told his accusers to bring their charges before you."

³¹So that night, as ordered, the soldiers took Paul as far as Antipatris. ³²They returned to the fortress the next morning, while the mounted troops took him on to Caesarea. ³³When they arrived in Caesarea, they presented Paul and the letter to Governor Felix. ³⁴He read it and then asked Paul what province he was from. "Cilicia," Paul answered.

³⁵"I will hear your case myself when your accusers arrive," the governor told him. Then the governor ordered him kept in the prison at Herod's headquarters.*

Paul Appears before Felix

24 Five days later Ananias, the high priest, arrived with some of the Jewish elders and the lawyer* Tertullus, to present their case against Paul to the governor. ²When Paul was called in, Tertullus presented the charges against Paul in the following address to the governor:

"You have provided a long period of peace for us Jews and with foresight have enacted reforms for us. ³For all of this, Your Excellency, we are very grateful to you. ⁴But I don't want to bore you, so please give me your attention for only a moment. ⁵We have found this man to be a troublemaker who is constantly stirring up riots among the Jews all over the world. He is a ringleader of the cult known as the Nazarenes. ⁶Furthermore, he was trying to desecrate the Temple when we arrested him.* ⁸You can find out the truth of our accusations by examining him yourself." ⁹Then the other Jews chimed in, declaring that everything Tertullus said was true.

¹⁰The governor then motioned for Paul to speak. Paul said, "I know, sir, that you have been a judge of Jewish affairs for many years, so I gladly present my defense before you. ¹¹You can quickly discover that I arrived in Jerusalem no more than twelve days ago to worship at the Temple. ¹²My accusers never found me arguing with anyone in the Temple, nor stirring up a riot in any synagogue or on the streets of the city.

23:12 Greek *the Jews.*   **23:17** Greek *centurions;* also in 23:23.   **23:35** Greek *Herod's Praetorium.*   **24:1** Greek *some elders and an orator.*   **24:6** Some manuscripts add an expanded conclusion to verse 6, all of verse 7, and an additional phrase in verse 8: *We would have judged him by our law,* ⁷*but Lysias, the commander of the garrison, came and violently took him away from us,* ⁸*commanding his accusers to come before you.*

[13]These men cannot prove the things they accuse me of doing.

[14]"But I admit that I follow the Way, which they call a cult. I worship the God of our ancestors, and I firmly believe the Jewish law and everything written in the prophets. [15]I have the same hope in God that these men have, that he will raise both the righteous and the unrighteous. [16]Because of this, I always try to maintain a clear conscience before God and all people.

[17]"After several years away, I returned to Jerusalem with money to aid my people and to offer sacrifices to God. [18]My accusers saw me in the Temple as I was completing a purification ceremony. There was no crowd around me and no rioting. [19]But some Jews from the province of Asia were there—and they ought to be here to bring charges if they have anything against me! [20]Ask these men here what crime the Jewish high council* found me guilty of, [21]except for the one time I shouted out, 'I am on trial before you today because I believe in the resurrection of the dead!'"

[22]At that point Felix, who was quite familiar with the Way, adjourned the hearing and said, "Wait until Lysias, the garrison commander, arrives. Then I will decide the case." [23]He ordered an officer* to keep Paul in custody but to give him some freedom and allow his friends to visit him and take care of his needs.

[24]A few days later Felix came back with his wife, Drusilla, who was Jewish. Sending for Paul, they listened as he told them about faith in Christ Jesus. [25]As he reasoned with them about righteousness and self-control and the coming day of judgment, Felix became frightened. "Go away for now," he replied. "When it is more convenient, I'll call for you again." [26]He also hoped that Paul would bribe him, so he sent for him quite often and talked with him.

[27]After two years went by in this way, Felix was succeeded by Porcius Festus. And because Felix wanted to gain favor with the Jewish people, he left Paul in prison.

Paul Appears before Festus

25 Three days after Festus arrived in Caesarea to take over his new responsibilities, he left for Jerusalem, [2]where the leading priests and other Jewish leaders met with him and made their accusations against Paul. [3]They asked Festus as a favor to transfer Paul to Jerusalem (planning to ambush and kill him on the way). [4]But Festus replied that Paul was at Caesarea and he himself would be returning there soon. [5]So he said, "Those of you in authority can return with me. If Paul has done anything wrong, you can make your accusations."

[6]About eight or ten days later Festus returned to Caesarea, and on the following day he took his seat in court and ordered that Paul be brought in. [7]When Paul arrived, the Jewish leaders from Jerusalem gathered around and made many serious accusations they couldn't prove.

[8]Paul denied the charges. "I am not guilty of any crime against the Jewish laws or the Temple or the Roman government," he said.

[9]Then Festus, wanting to please the Jews, asked him, "Are you willing to go to Jerusalem and stand trial before me there?"

[10]But Paul replied, "No! This is the official Roman court, so I ought to be tried right here. You know very well I am not guilty of harming the Jews. [11]If I have done something worthy of death, I don't refuse to die. But if I am innocent, no one has a right to turn me over to these men to kill me. I appeal to Caesar!"

[12]Festus conferred with his advisers and then replied, "Very well! You have appealed to Caesar, and to Caesar you will go!"

[13]A few days later King Agrippa arrived with his sister, Bernice,* to pay their respects to Festus. [14]During their stay of several days, Festus discussed Paul's case with the king. "There is a prisoner here," he told him, "whose case was left for me by Felix. [15]When I was in Jerusalem, the leading priests and Jewish elders pressed charges against him and asked me to condemn him. [16]I pointed out to them that Roman law does not convict people without a trial. They must be given an opportunity to confront their accusers and defend themselves.

[17]"When his accusers came here for the trial, I didn't delay. I called the case the very next day and ordered Paul brought in. [18]But the accusations made against him weren't any of the crimes I expected. [19]Instead, it was something about their religion and a dead man named Jesus, who Paul insists is alive. [20]I was at a loss to know how to investigate these things, so I asked him whether he would be willing to stand trial on these charges in Jerusalem. [21]But Paul appealed to have his case decided by the emperor. So I ordered that he be held in custody until I could arrange to send him to Caesar."

[22]"I'd like to hear the man myself," Agrippa said.

And Festus replied, "You will—tomorrow!"

Paul Speaks to Agrippa

[23]So the next day Agrippa and Bernice arrived at the auditorium with great pomp, accompanied by military officers and prominent men of the city. Festus ordered that Paul be brought in. [24]Then Festus said, "King Agrippa and all who are here, this is the man whose death is demanded by all the Jews, both here and in Jerusalem. [25]But in my opinion he has done nothing deserving death. However, since he appealed his case to the emperor, I have decided to send him to Rome.

24:20 Greek *Sanhedrin.*   **24:23** Greek *a centurion.*   **25:13** Greek *Agrippa the king and Bernice arrived.*

26"But what shall I write the emperor? For there is no clear charge against him. So I have brought him before all of you, and especially you, King Agrippa, so that after we examine him, I might have something to write. 27For it makes no sense to send a prisoner to the emperor without specifying the charges against him!"

26 Then Agrippa said to Paul, "You may speak in your defense."

So Paul, gesturing with his hand, started his defense: 2"I am fortunate, King Agrippa, that you are the one hearing my defense today against all these accusations made by the Jewish leaders, 3for I know you are an expert on all Jewish customs and controversies. Now please listen to me patiently!

4"As the Jewish leaders are well aware, I was given a thorough Jewish training from my earliest childhood among my own people and in Jerusalem. 5If they would admit it, they know that I have been a member of the Pharisees, the strictest sect of our religion. 6Now I am on trial because of my hope in the fulfillment of God's promise made to our ancestors. 7In fact, that is why the twelve tribes of Israel zealously worship God night and day, and they share the same hope I have. Yet, Your Majesty, they accuse me for having this hope! 8Why does it seem incredible to any of you that God can raise the dead?

9"I used to believe that I ought to do everything I could to oppose the very name of Jesus the Nazarene.* 10Indeed, I did just that in Jerusalem. Authorized by the leading priests, I caused many believers* there to be sent to prison. And I cast my vote against them when they were condemned to death. 11Many times I had them punished in the synagogues to get them to curse Jesus.* I was so violently opposed to them that I even chased them down in foreign cities.

12"One day I was on such a mission to Damascus, armed with the authority and commission of the leading priests. 13About noon, Your Majesty, as I was on the road, a light from heaven brighter than the sun shone down on me and my companions. 14We all fell down, and I heard a voice saying to me in Aramaic,* 'Saul, Saul, why are you persecuting me? It is useless for you to fight against my will.*'

15"'Who are you, lord?' I asked.

"And the Lord replied, 'I am Jesus, the one you are persecuting. 16Now get to your feet! For I have appeared to you to appoint you as my servant and witness. You are to tell the world what you have seen and what I will show you in the future. 17And I will rescue you from both your own people and the Gentiles. Yes, I am sending you to the Gentiles 18to open their eyes, so they may turn from darkness to light and from the power

of Satan to God. Then they will receive forgiveness for their sins and be given a place among God's people, who are set apart by faith in me.'

19"And so, King Agrippa, I obeyed that vision from heaven. 20I preached first to those in Damascus, then in Jerusalem and throughout all Judea, and also to the Gentiles, that all must repent of their sins and turn to God—and prove they have changed by the good things they do. 21Some Jews arrested me in the Temple for preaching this, and they tried to kill me. 22But God has protected me right up to this present time so I can testify to everyone, from the least to the greatest. I teach nothing except what the prophets and Moses said would happen—23that the Messiah would suffer and be the first to rise from the dead, and in this way announce God's light to Jews and Gentiles alike."

24Suddenly, Festus shouted, "Paul, you are insane. Too much study has made you crazy!"

25But Paul replied, "I am not insane, Most Excellent Festus. What I am saying is the sober truth. 26And King Agrippa knows about these things. I speak boldly, for I am sure these events are all familiar to him, for they were not done in a corner! 27King Agrippa, do you believe the prophets? I know you do—"

28Agrippa interrupted him. "Do you think you can persuade me to become a Christian so quickly?"*

29Paul replied, "Whether quickly or not, I pray to God that both you and everyone here in this audience might become the same as I am, except for these chains."

30Then the king, the governor, Bernice, and all the others stood and left. 31As they went out, they talked it over and agreed, "This man hasn't done anything to deserve death or imprisonment."

32And Agrippa said to Festus, "He could have been set free if he hadn't appealed to Caesar."

Paul Sails for Rome

27 When the time came, we set sail for Italy. Paul and several other prisoners were placed in the custody of a Roman officer* named Julius, a captain of the Imperial Regiment. 2Aristarchus, a Macedonian from Thessalonica, was also with us. We left on a ship whose home port was Adramyttium on the northwest coast of the province of Asia;* it was scheduled to make several stops at ports along the coast of the province.

3The next day when we docked at Sidon, Julius was very kind to Paul and let him go ashore to visit with friends so they could provide for his needs. 4Putting out to sea from there, we encountered strong headwinds that made it difficult to keep the ship on course, so we sailed north of Cy-

26:9 Or *Jesus of Nazareth.* **26:10** Greek *many of God's holy people.* **26:11** Greek *to blaspheme.* **26:14a** Or *Hebrew.* **26:14b** Greek *It is hard for you to kick against the oxgoads.* **26:28** Or *"A little more, and your arguments would make me a Christian."* **27:1** Greek *centurion;* similarly in 27:6, 11, 31, 43. **27:2** *Asia* was a Roman province in what is now western Turkey.

prus between the island and the mainland. [5]Keeping to the open sea, we passed along the coast of Cilicia and Pamphylia, landing at Myra, in the province of Lycia. [6]There the commanding officer found an Egyptian ship from Alexandria that was bound for Italy, and he put us on board.

[7]We had several days of slow sailing, and after great difficulty we finally neared Cnidus. But the wind was against us, so we sailed across to Crete and along the sheltered coast of the island, past the cape of Salmone. [8]We struggled along the coast with great difficulty and finally arrived at Fair Havens, near the town of Lasea. [9]We had lost a lot of time. The weather was becoming dangerous for sea travel because it was so late in the fall,* and Paul spoke to the ship's officers about it.

[10]"Men," he said, "I believe there is trouble ahead if we go on—shipwreck, loss of cargo, and danger to our lives as well." [11]But the officer in charge of the prisoners listened more to the ship's captain and the owner than to Paul. [12]And since Fair Havens was an exposed harbor—a poor place to spend the winter—most of the crew wanted to go on to Phoenix, farther up the coast of Crete, and spend the winter there. Phoenix was a good harbor with only a southwest and northwest exposure.

The Storm at Sea

[13]When a light wind began blowing from the south, the sailors thought they could make it. So they pulled up anchor and sailed close to the shore of Crete. [14]But the weather changed abruptly, and a wind of typhoon strength (called a "northeaster") burst across the island and blew us out to sea. [15]The sailors couldn't turn the ship into the wind, so they gave up and let it run before the gale.

[16]We sailed along the sheltered side of a small island named Cauda,* where with great difficulty we hoisted aboard the lifeboat being towed behind us. [17]Then the sailors bound ropes around the hull of the ship to strengthen it. They were afraid of being driven across to the sandbars of Syrtis off the African coast, so they lowered the sea anchor to slow the ship and were driven before the wind.

[18]The next day, as gale-force winds continued to batter the ship, the crew began throwing the cargo overboard. [19]The following day they even took some of the ship's gear and threw it overboard. [20]The terrible storm raged for many days, blotting out the sun and the stars, until at last all hope was gone.

[21]No one had eaten for a long time. Finally, Paul called the crew together and said, "Men, you should have listened to me in the first place and not left Crete. You would have avoided all this damage and loss. [22]But take courage! None of you will lose your lives, even though the ship will go down. [23]For last night an angel of the God to whom I belong and whom I serve stood beside me, [24]and he said, 'Don't be afraid, Paul, for you will surely stand trial before Caesar! What's more, God in his goodness has granted safety to everyone sailing with you.' [25]So take courage! For I believe God. It will be just as he said. [26]But we will be shipwrecked on an island."

The Shipwreck

[27]About midnight on the fourteenth night of the storm, as we were being driven across the Sea of Adria,* the sailors sensed land was near. [28]They dropped a weighted line and found that the water was 120 feet deep. But a little later they measured again and found it was only 90 feet deep.* [29]At this rate they were afraid we would soon be driven against the rocks along the shore, so they threw out four anchors from the back of the ship and prayed for daylight.

[30]Then the sailors tried to abandon the ship; they lowered the lifeboat as though they were going to put out anchors from the front of the ship. [31]But Paul said to the commanding officer and the soldiers, "You will all die unless the sailors stay aboard." [32]So the soldiers cut the ropes to the lifeboat and let it drift away.

[33]Just as day was dawning, Paul urged everyone to eat. "You have been so worried that you haven't touched food for two weeks," he said. [34]"Please eat something now for your own good. For not a hair of your heads will perish." [35]Then he took some bread, gave thanks to God before them all, and broke off a piece and ate it. [36]Then everyone was encouraged and began to eat—[37]all 276 of us who were on board. [38]After eating, the crew lightened the ship further by throwing the cargo of wheat overboard.

[39]When morning dawned, they didn't recognize the coastline, but they saw a bay with a beach and wondered if they could get to shore by running the ship aground. [40]So they cut off the anchors and left them in the sea. Then they lowered the rudders, raised the foresail, and headed toward shore. [41]But they hit a shoal and ran the ship aground too soon. The bow of the ship stuck fast, while the stern was repeatedly smashed by the force of the waves and began to break apart.

[42]The soldiers wanted to kill the prisoners to make sure they didn't swim ashore and escape. [43]But the commanding officer wanted to spare Paul, so he didn't let them carry out their plan. Then he ordered all who could swim to jump overboard first and make for land. [44]The others held on to planks or debris from the broken ship.* So everyone escaped safely to shore.

27:9 Greek *because the fast was now already gone by.* This fast was associated with the Day of Atonement (*Yom Kippur*), which occurred in late September or early October.   **27:16** Some manuscripts read *Clauda.*   **27:27** The *Sea of Adria* includes the central portion of the Mediterranean.   **27:28** Greek *20 fathoms . . . 15 fathoms* [37 meters . . . 27 meters].   **27:44** Or *or were helped by members of the ship's crew.*

Paul on the Island of Malta

28 Once we were safe on shore, we learned that we were on the island of Malta. ²The people of the island were very kind to us. It was cold and rainy, so they built a fire on the shore to welcome us.

³As Paul gathered an armful of sticks and was laying them on the fire, a poisonous snake, driven out by the heat, bit him on the hand. ⁴The people of the island saw it hanging from his hand and said to each other, "A murderer, no doubt! Though he escaped the sea, justice will not permit him to live." ⁵But Paul shook off the snake into the fire and was unharmed. ⁶The people waited for him to swell up or suddenly drop dead. But when they had waited a long time and saw that he wasn't harmed, they changed their minds and decided he was a god.

⁷Near the shore where we landed was an estate belonging to Publius, the chief official of the island. He welcomed us and treated us kindly for three days. ⁸As it happened, Publius's father was ill with fever and dysentery. Paul went in and prayed for him, and laying his hands on him, he healed him. ⁹Then all the other sick people on the island came and were healed. ¹⁰As a result we were showered with honors, and when the time came to sail, people supplied us with everything we would need for the trip.

Paul Arrives at Rome

¹¹It was three months after the shipwreck that we set sail on another ship that had wintered at the island—an Alexandrian ship with the twin gods* as its figurehead. ¹²Our first stop was Syracuse,* where we stayed three days. ¹³From there we sailed across to Rhegium.* A day later a south wind began blowing, so the following day we sailed up the coast to Puteoli. ¹⁴There we found some believers,* who invited us to spend a week with them. And so we came to Rome. ¹⁵The brothers and sisters* in Rome had heard we were coming, and they came to meet us at the Forum* on the Appian Way. Others joined us at The Three Taverns.* When Paul saw them, he was encouraged and thanked God.

¹⁶When we arrived in Rome, Paul was permitted to have his own private lodging, though he was guarded by a soldier.

Paul Preaches at Rome under Guard

¹⁷Three days after Paul's arrival, he called together the local Jewish leaders. He said to them,

"Brothers, I was arrested in Jerusalem and handed over to the Roman government, even though I had done nothing against our people or the customs of our ancestors. ¹⁸The Romans tried me and wanted to release me, because they found no cause for the death sentence. ¹⁹But when the Jewish leaders protested the decision, I felt it necessary to appeal to Caesar, even though I had no desire to press charges against my own people. ²⁰I asked you to come here today so we could get acquainted and so I could explain to you that I am bound with this chain because I believe that the hope of Israel—the Messiah—has already come."

²¹They replied, "We have had no letters from Judea or reports against you from anyone who has come here. ²²But we want to hear what you believe, for the only thing we know about this movement is that it is denounced everywhere."

²³So a time was set, and on that day a large number of people came to Paul's lodging. He explained and testified about the Kingdom of God and tried to persuade them about Jesus from the Scriptures. Using the law of Moses and the books of the prophets, he spoke to them from morning until evening. ²⁴Some were persuaded by the things he said, but others did not believe. ²⁵And after they had argued back and forth among themselves, they left with this final word from Paul: "The Holy Spirit was right when he said to your ancestors through Isaiah the prophet,

²⁶ 'Go and say to this people:
When you hear what I say,
    you will not understand.
When you see what I do,
    you will not comprehend.
²⁷ For the hearts of these people are hardened,
    and their ears cannot hear,
    and they have closed their eyes—
so their eyes cannot see,
    and their ears cannot hear,
    and their hearts cannot understand,
and they cannot turn to me
    and let me heal them.'*

²⁸So I want you to know that this salvation from God has also been offered to the Gentiles, and they will accept it."*

³⁰For the next two years, Paul lived in Rome at his own expense.* He welcomed all who visited him, ³¹boldly proclaiming the Kingdom of God and teaching about the Lord Jesus Christ. And no one tried to stop him.

28:11 The *twin gods* were the Roman gods Castor and Pollux.   **28:12** *Syracuse* was on the island of Sicily.   **28:13** *Rhegium* was on the southern tip of Italy.   **28:14** Greek *brothers*.   **28:15a** Greek *brothers*.   **28:15b** *The Forum* was about 43 miles (70 kilometers) from Rome.   **28:15c** *The Three Taverns* was about 35 miles (57 kilometers) from Rome.   **28:26-27** Isa 6:9-10 (Greek version).
28:28 Some manuscripts add verse 29, *And when he had said these words, the Jews departed, greatly disagreeing with each other.*
28:30 Or *in his own rented quarters.*

Romans

Greetings from Paul

1 This letter is from Paul, a slave of Christ Jesus, chosen by God to be an apostle and sent out to preach his Good News. ²God promised this Good News long ago through his prophets in the holy Scriptures. ³The Good News is about his Son. In his earthly life he was born into King David's family line, ⁴and he was shown to be* the Son of God when he was raised from the dead by the power of the Holy Spirit.* He is Jesus Christ our Lord. ⁵Through Christ, God has given us the privilege* and authority as apostles to tell Gentiles everywhere what God has done for them, so that they will believe and obey him, bringing glory to his name.

⁶And you are included among those Gentiles who have been called to belong to Jesus Christ. ⁷I am writing to all of you in Rome who are loved by God and are called to be his own holy people.

May God our Father and the Lord Jesus Christ give you grace and peace.

God's Good News

⁸Let me say first that I thank my God through Jesus Christ for all of you, because your faith in him is being talked about all over the world. ⁹God knows how often I pray for you. Day and night I bring you and your needs in prayer to God, whom I serve with all my heart* by spreading the Good News about his Son.

¹⁰One of the things I always pray for is the opportunity, God willing, to come at last to see you. ¹¹For I long to visit you so I can bring you some spiritual gift that will help you grow strong in the Lord. ¹²When we get together, I want to encourage you in your faith, but I also want to be encouraged by yours.

¹³I want you to know, dear brothers and sisters,* that I planned many times to visit you, but I was prevented until now. I want to work among you and see spiritual fruit, just as I have seen among other Gentiles. ¹⁴For I have a great sense of obligation to people in both the civilized world and the rest of the world,* to the educated and uneducated alike. ¹⁵So I am eager to come to you in Rome, too, to preach the Good News.

¹⁶For I am not ashamed of this Good News about Christ. It is the power of God at work, saving everyone who believes—the Jew first and also the Gentile.* ¹⁷This Good News tells us how God makes us right in his sight. This is accomplished from start to finish by faith. As the Scriptures say, "It is through faith that a righteous person has life."*

God's Anger at Sin

¹⁸But God shows his anger from heaven against all sinful, wicked people who suppress the truth by their wickedness.* ¹⁹They know the truth about God because he has made it obvious to them. ²⁰For ever since the world was created, people have seen the earth and sky. Through everything God made, they can clearly see his invisible qualities—his eternal power and divine nature. So they have no excuse for not knowing God.

²¹Yes, they knew God, but they wouldn't worship him as God or even give him thanks. And they began to think up foolish ideas of what God was like. As a result, their minds became dark and confused. ²²Claiming to be wise, they instead became utter fools. ²³And instead of worshiping the glorious, ever-living God, they worshiped idols made to look like mere people and birds and animals and reptiles.

²⁴So God abandoned them to do whatever shameful things their hearts desired. As a result, they did vile and degrading things with each other's bodies. ²⁵They traded the truth about God for a lie. So they worshiped and served the things God created instead of the Creator himself, who is worthy of eternal praise! Amen. ²⁶That is why God abandoned them to their shameful desires. Even the women turned against the natural way to have sex and instead indulged in sex with each other. ²⁷And the men, instead of having normal sexual relations with women, burned with lust for each other. Men did shameful things with other men, and as a result of this sin, they suffered within themselves the penalty they deserved.

²⁸Since they thought it foolish to acknowledge God, he abandoned them to their foolish thinking and let them do things that should

---

1:4a Or *and was designated.*   **1:4b** Or *by the Spirit of holiness; or in the new realm of the Spirit.*   **1:5** Or *the grace.*   **1:9** Or *in my spirit.*   **1:13** Greek *brothers.*   **1:14** Greek *to Greeks and barbarians.*   **1:16** Greek *also the Greek.*   **1:17** Or *"The righteous will live by faith."* Hab 2:4.   **1:18** Or *who, by their wickedness, prevent the truth from being known.*

never be done. ²⁹Their lives became full of every kind of wickedness, sin, greed, hate, envy, murder, quarreling, deception, malicious behavior, and gossip. ³⁰They are backstabbers, haters of God, insolent, proud, and boastful. They invent new ways of sinning, and they disobey their parents. ³¹They refuse to understand, break their promises, are heartless, and have no mercy. ³²They know God's justice requires that those who do these things deserve to die, yet they do them anyway. Worse yet, they encourage others to do them, too.

God's Judgment of Sin

2 You may think you can condemn such people, but you are just as bad, and you have no excuse! When you say they are wicked and should be punished, you are condemning yourself, for you who judge others do these very same things. ²And we know that God, in his justice, will punish anyone who does such things. ³Since you judge others for doing these things, why do you think you can avoid God's judgment when you do the same things? ⁴Don't you see how wonderfully kind, tolerant, and patient God is with you? Does this mean nothing to you? Can't you see that his kindness is intended to turn you from your sin?

⁵But because you are stubborn and refuse to turn from your sin, you are storing up terrible punishment for yourself. For a day of anger is coming, when God's righteous judgment will be revealed. ⁶He will judge everyone according to what they have done. ⁷He will give eternal life to those who keep on doing good, seeking after the glory and honor and immortality that God offers. ⁸But he will pour out his anger and wrath on those who live for themselves, who refuse to obey the truth and instead live lives of wickedness. ⁹There will be trouble and calamity for everyone who keeps on doing what is evil—for the Jew first and also for the Gentile.* ¹⁰But there will be glory and honor and peace from God for all who do good—for the Jew first and also for the Gentile. ¹¹For God does not show favoritism.

¹²When the Gentiles sin, they will be destroyed, even though they never had God's written law. And the Jews, who do have God's law, will be judged by that law when they fail to obey it. ¹³For merely listening to the law doesn't make us right with God. It is obeying the law that makes us right in his sight. ¹⁴Even Gentiles, who do not have God's written law, show that they know his law when they instinctively obey it, even without having heard it. ¹⁵They demonstrate that God's law is written in their hearts, for their own conscience and thoughts either accuse them or tell them they are doing right. ¹⁶And this is the message I proclaim—that the day is coming when God, through Christ Jesus, will judge everyone's secret life.

The Jews and the Law

¹⁷You who call yourselves Jews are relying on God's law, and you boast about your special relationship with him. ¹⁸You know what he wants; you know what is right because you have been taught his law. ¹⁹You are convinced that you are a guide for the blind and a light for people who are lost in darkness. ²⁰You think you can instruct the ignorant and teach children the ways of God. For you are certain that God's law gives you complete knowledge and truth.

²¹Well then, if you teach others, why don't you teach yourself? You tell others not to steal, but do you steal? ²²You say it is wrong to commit adultery, but do you commit adultery? You condemn idolatry, but do you use items stolen from pagan temples?* ²³You are so proud of knowing the law, but you dishonor God by breaking it. ²⁴No wonder the Scriptures say, "The Gentiles blaspheme the name of God because of you."*

²⁵The Jewish ceremony of circumcision has value only if you obey God's law. But if you don't obey God's law, you are no better off than an uncircumcised Gentile. ²⁶And if the Gentiles obey God's law, won't God declare them to be his own people? ²⁷In fact, uncircumcised Gentiles who keep God's law will condemn you Jews who are circumcised and possess God's law but don't obey it.

²⁸For you are not a true Jew just because you were born of Jewish parents or because you have gone through the ceremony of circumcision. ²⁹No, a true Jew is one whose heart is right with God. And true circumcision is not merely obeying the letter of the law; rather, it is a change of heart produced by God's Spirit. And a person with a changed heart seeks praise* from God, not from people.

God Remains Faithful

3 Then what's the advantage of being a Jew? Is there any value in the ceremony of circumcision? ²Yes, there are great benefits! First of all, the Jews were entrusted with the whole revelation of God.*

³True, some of them were unfaithful; but just because they were unfaithful, does that mean God will be unfaithful? ⁴Of course not! Even if everyone else is a liar, God is true. As the Scriptures say about him,

"You will be proved right in what you say,
  and you will win your case in court."*

⁵"But," some might say, "our sinfulness serves a good purpose, for it helps people see how righteous God is. Isn't it unfair, then, for him to pun-

---

2:9 Greek *also for the Greek;* also in 2:10.   2:22 Greek *do you steal from temples?*   2:24 Isa 52:5 (Greek version).   2:29 Or *receives praise.*   3:2 Greek *the oracles of God.*   3:4 Ps 51:4 (Greek version).

ish us?" (This is merely a human point of view.) ⁶Of course not! If God were not entirely fair, how would he be qualified to judge the world? ⁷"But," someone might still argue, "how can God condemn me as a sinner if my dishonesty highlights his truthfulness and brings him more glory?" ⁸And some people even slander us by claiming that we say, "The more we sin, the better it is!" Those who say such things deserve to be condemned.

All People Are Sinners

⁹Well then, should we conclude that we Jews are better than others? No, not at all, for we have already shown that all people, whether Jews or Gentiles,* are under the power of sin. ¹⁰As the Scriptures say,

> "No one is righteous—
> not even one.
> ¹¹ No one is truly wise;
> no one is seeking God.
> ¹² All have turned away;
> all have become useless.
> No one does good,
> not a single one."*
> ¹³ "Their talk is foul, like the stench from an
> open grave.
> Their tongues are filled with lies."
> "Snake venom drips from their lips."*
> ¹⁴ "Their mouths are full of cursing and
> bitterness."*
> ¹⁵ "They rush to commit murder.
> ¹⁶ Destruction and misery always follow
> them.
> ¹⁷ They don't know where to find peace."*
> ¹⁸ "They have no fear of God at all."*

¹⁹Obviously, the law applies to those to whom it was given, for its purpose is to keep people from having excuses, and to show that the entire world is guilty before God. ²⁰For no one can ever be made right with God by doing what the law commands. The law simply shows us how sinful we are.

Christ Took Our Punishment

²¹But now God has shown us a way to be made right with him without keeping the requirements of the law, as was promised in the writings of Moses* and the prophets long ago. ²²We are made right with God by placing our faith in Jesus Christ. And this is true for everyone who believes, no matter who we are.

²³For everyone has sinned; we all fall short of God's glorious standard. ²⁴Yet God, with undeserved kindness, declares that we are righteous. He did this through Christ Jesus when he freed us from the penalty for our sins. ²⁵For God pre-

sented Jesus as the sacrifice for sin. People are made right with God when they believe that Jesus sacrificed his life, shedding his blood. This sacrifice shows that God was being fair when he held back and did not punish those who sinned in times past, ²⁶for he was looking ahead and including them in what he would do in this present time. God did this to demonstrate his righteousness, for he himself is fair and just, and he declares sinners to be right in his sight when they believe in Jesus.

²⁷Can we boast, then, that we have done anything to be accepted by God? No, because our acquittal is not based on obeying the law. It is based on faith. ²⁸So we are made right with God through faith and not by obeying the law.

²⁹After all, is God the God of the Jews only? Isn't he also the God of the Gentiles? Of course he is. ³⁰There is only one God, and he makes people right with himself only by faith, whether they are Jews or Gentiles.* ³¹Well then, if we emphasize faith, does this mean that we can forget about the law? Of course not! In fact, only when we have faith do we truly fulfill the law.

The Faith of Abraham

4 Abraham was, humanly speaking, the founder of our Jewish nation. What did he discover about being made right with God? ²If his good deeds had made him acceptable to God, he would have had something to boast about. But that was not God's way. ³For the Scriptures tell us, "Abraham believed God, and God counted him as righteous because of his faith."*

⁴When people work, their wages are not a gift, but something they have earned. ⁵But people are counted as righteous, not because of their work, but because of their faith in God who forgives sinners. ⁶David also spoke of this when he described the happiness of those who are declared righteous without working for it:

> ⁷ "Oh, what joy for those
> whose disobedience is forgiven,
> whose sins are put out of sight.
> ⁸ Yes, what joy for those
> whose record the Lord has cleared of
> sin."*

⁹Now, is this blessing only for the Jews, or is it also for uncircumcised Gentiles?* Well, we have been saying that Abraham was counted as righteous by God because of his faith. ¹⁰But how did this happen? Was he counted as righteous only after he was circumcised, or was it before he was circumcised? Clearly, God accepted Abraham before he was circumcised!

¹¹Circumcision was a sign that Abraham already had faith and that God had already

3:9 Greek *or Greeks.* **3:10-12** Pss 14:1-3; 53:1-3 (Greek version). **3:13** Pss 5:9 (Greek version); 140:3. **3:14** Ps 10:7 (Greek version). **3:15-17** Isa 59:7-8. **3:18** Ps 36:1. **3:21** Greek *in the law.* **3:30** Greek *whether they are circumcised or uncircumcised.* **4:3** Gen 15:6. **4:7-8** Ps 32:1-2 (Greek version). **4:9** Greek *is this blessing only for the circumcised, or is it also for the uncircumcised?*

accepted him and declared him to be righteous—even before he was circumcised. So Abraham is the spiritual father of those who have faith but have not been circumcised. They are counted as righteous because of their faith. 12And Abraham is also the spiritual father of those who have been circumcised, but only if they have the same kind of faith Abraham had before he was circumcised.

13Clearly, God's promise to give the whole earth to Abraham and his descendants was based not on his obedience to God's law, but on a right relationship with God that comes by faith. 14If God's promise is only for those who obey the law, then faith is not necessary and the promise is pointless. 15For the law always brings punishment on those who try to obey it. (The only way to avoid breaking the law is to have no law to break!)

16So the promise is received by faith. It is given as a free gift. And we are all certain to receive it, whether or not we live according to the law of Moses, if we have faith like Abraham's. For Abraham is the father of all who believe. 17That is what the Scriptures mean when God told him, "I have made you the father of many nations."* This happened because Abraham believed in the God who brings the dead back to life and who creates new things out of nothing.

18Even when there was no reason for hope, Abraham kept hoping—believing that he would become the father of many nations. For God had said to him, "That's how many descendants you will have!"* 19And Abraham's faith did not weaken, even though, at about 100 years of age, he figured his body was as good as dead—and so was Sarah's womb.

20Abraham never wavered in believing God's promise. In fact, his faith grew stronger, and in this he brought glory to God. 21He was fully convinced that God is able to do whatever he promises. 22And because of Abraham's faith, God counted him as righteous. 23And when God counted him as righteous, it wasn't just for Abraham's benefit. It was recorded 24for our benefit, too, assuring us that God will also count us as righteous if we believe in him, the one who raised Jesus our Lord from the dead. 25He was handed over to die because of our sins, and he was raised to life to make us right with God.

Faith Brings Joy

5 Therefore, since we have been made right in God's sight by faith, we have peace with God because of what Jesus Christ our Lord has done for us. 2Because of our faith, Christ has brought us into this place of undeserved privilege where we now stand, and we confidently and joyfully look forward to sharing God's glory.

3We can rejoice, too, when we run into problems and trials, for we know that they help us de-velop endurance. 4And endurance develops strength of character, and character strengthens our confident hope of salvation. 5And this hope will not lead to disappointment. For we know how dearly God loves us, because he has given us the Holy Spirit to fill our hearts with his love.

6When we were utterly helpless, Christ came at just the right time and died for us sinners. 7Now, most people would not be willing to die for an upright person, though someone might perhaps be willing to die for a person who is especially good. 8But God showed his great love for us by sending Christ to die for us while we were still sinners. 9And since we have been made right in God's sight by the blood of Christ, he will certainly save us from God's condemnation. 10For since our friendship with God was restored by the death of his Son while we were still his enemies, we will certainly be saved through the life of his Son. 11So now we can rejoice in our wonderful new relationship with God because our Lord Jesus Christ has made us friends of God.

Adam and Christ Contrasted

12When Adam sinned, sin entered the world. Adam's sin brought death, so death spread to everyone, for everyone sinned. 13Yes, people sinned even before the law was given. But it was not counted as sin because there was not yet any law to break. 14Still, everyone died—from the time of Adam to the time of Moses—even those who did not disobey an explicit commandment of God, as Adam did. Now Adam is a symbol, a representation of Christ, who was yet to come. 15But there is a great difference between Adam's sin and God's gracious gift. For the sin of this one man, Adam, brought death to many. But even greater is God's wonderful grace and his gift of forgiveness to many through this other man, Jesus Christ. 16And the result of God's gracious gift is very different from the result of that one man's sin. For Adam's sin led to condemnation, but God's free gift leads to our being made right with God, even though we are guilty of many sins. 17For the sin of this one man, Adam, caused death to rule over many. But even greater is God's wonderful grace and his gift of righteousness, for all who receive it will live in triumph over sin and death through this one man, Jesus Christ.

18Yes, Adam's one sin brings condemnation for everyone, but Christ's one act of righteousness brings a right relationship with God and new life for everyone. 19Because one person disobeyed God, many became sinners. But because one other person obeyed God, many will be made righteous.

20God's law was given so that all people could see how sinful they were. But as people sinned more and more, God's wonderful grace became more abundant. 21So just as sin ruled over all people and brought them to death, now God's wonderful grace rules instead, giving us right standing with God and resulting in eternal life through Jesus Christ our Lord.

Sin's Power Is Broken

6 Well then, should we keep on sinning so that God can show us more and more of his wonderful grace? ²Of course not! Since we have died to sin, how can we continue to live in it? ³Or have you forgotten that when we were joined with Christ Jesus in baptism, we joined him in his death? ⁴For we died and were buried with Christ by baptism. And just as Christ was raised from the dead by the glorious power of the Father, now we also may live new lives.

⁵Since we have been united with him in his death, we will also be raised to life as he was. ⁶We know that our old sinful selves were crucified with Christ so that sin might lose its power in our lives. We are no longer slaves to sin. ⁷For when we died with Christ we were set free from the power of sin. ⁸And since we died with Christ, we know we will also live with him. ⁹We are sure of this because Christ was raised from the dead, and he will never die again. Death no longer has any power over him. ¹⁰When he died, he died once to break the power of sin. But now that he lives, he lives for the glory of God. ¹¹So you also should consider yourselves to be dead to the power of sin and alive to God through Christ Jesus.

¹²Do not let sin control the way you live;* do not give in to sinful desires. ¹³Do not let any part of your body become an instrument of evil to serve sin. Instead, give yourselves completely to God, for you were dead, but now you have new life. So use your whole body as an instrument to do what is right for the glory of God. ¹⁴Sin is no longer your master, for you no longer live under the requirements of the law. Instead, you live under the freedom of God's grace.

¹⁵Well then, since God's grace has set us free from the law, does that mean we can go on sinning? Of course not! ¹⁶Don't you realize that you become the slave of whatever you choose to obey? You can be a slave to sin, which leads to death, or you can choose to obey God, which leads to righteous living. ¹⁷Thank God! Once you were slaves of sin, but now you wholeheartedly obey this teaching we have given you. ¹⁸Now you are free from your slavery to sin, and you have become slaves to righteous living.

¹⁹Because of the weakness of your human nature, I am using the illustration of slavery to help you understand all this. Previously, you let yourselves be slaves to impurity and lawlessness, which led ever deeper into sin. Now you must give yourselves to be slaves to righteous living so that you will become holy.

²⁰When you were slaves to sin, you were free from the obligation to do right. ²¹And what was the result? You are now ashamed of the things you used to do, things that end in eternal doom. ²²But now you are free from the power of sin and have become slaves of God. Now you do those things that lead to holiness and result in eternal life. ²³For the wages of sin is death, but the free gift of God is eternal life through Christ Jesus our Lord.

No Longer Bound to the Law

7 Now, dear brothers and sisters*—you who are familiar with the law—don't you know that the law applies only while a person is living? ²For example, when a woman marries, the law binds her to her husband as long as he is alive. But if he dies, the laws of marriage no longer apply to her. ³So while her husband is alive, she would be committing adultery if she married another man. But if her husband dies, she is free from that law and does not commit adultery when she remarries.

⁴So, my dear brothers and sisters, this is the point: You died to the power of the law when you died with Christ. And now you are united with the one who was raised from the dead. As a result, we can produce a harvest of good deeds for God. ⁵When we were controlled by our old nature,* sinful desires were at work within us, and the law aroused these evil desires that produced a harvest of sinful deeds, resulting in death. ⁶But now we have been released from the law, for we died to it and are no longer captive to its power. Now we can serve God, not in the old way of obeying the letter of the law, but in the new way of living in the Spirit.

God's Law Reveals Our Sin

⁷Well then, am I suggesting that the law of God is sinful? Of course not! In fact, it was the law that showed me my sin. I would never have known that coveting is wrong if the law had not said, "You must not covet."* ⁸But sin used this command to arouse all kinds of covetous desires within me! If there were no law, sin would not have that power. ⁹At one time I lived without understanding the law. But when I learned the command not to covet, for instance, the power of sin came to life, ¹⁰and I died. So I discovered that the law's commands, which were supposed to bring life, brought spiritual death instead. ¹¹Sin took advantage of those commands and deceived me; it used the commands to kill me. ¹²But still, the law itself is holy, and its commands are holy and right and good.

¹³But how can that be? Did the law, which is good, cause my death? Of course not! Sin used what was good to bring about my condemnation to death. So we can see how terrible sin really is.

6:12 Or *Do not let sin reign in your body, which is subject to death, the flesh.* **7:7** Exod 20:17; Deut 5:21.   **7:1** Greek *brothers;* also in 7:4.   **7:5** Greek *When we were in*

It uses God's good commands for its own evil purposes.

Struggling with Sin

[14]So the trouble is not with the law, for it is spiritual and good. The trouble is with me, for I am all too human, a slave to sin. [15]I don't really understand myself, for I want to do what is right, but I don't do it. Instead, I do what I hate. [16]But if I know that what I am doing is wrong, this shows that I agree that the law is good. [17]So I am not the one doing wrong; it is sin living in me that does it.

[18]And I know that nothing good lives in me, that is, in my sinful nature.* I want to do what is right, but I can't. [19]I want to do what is good, but I don't. I don't want to do what is wrong, but I do it anyway. [20]But if I do what I don't want to do, I am not really the one doing wrong; it is sin living in me that does it.

[21]I have discovered this principle of life—that when I want to do what is right, I inevitably do what is wrong. [22]I love God's law with all my heart. [23]But there is another power* within me that is at war with my mind. This power makes me a slave to the sin that is still within me. [24]Oh, what a miserable person I am! Who will free me from this life that is dominated by sin and death? [25]Thank God! The answer is in Jesus Christ our Lord. So you see how it is: In my mind I really want to obey God's law, but because of my sinful nature I am a slave to sin.

Life in the Spirit

8 So now there is no condemnation for those who belong to Christ Jesus. [2]And because you belong to him, the power* of the life-giving Spirit has freed you* from the power of sin that leads to death. [3]The law of Moses was unable to save us because of the weakness of our sinful nature.* So God did what the law could not do. He sent his own Son in a body like the bodies we sinners have. And in that body God declared an end to sin's control over us by giving his Son as a sacrifice for our sins. [4]He did this so that the just requirement of the law would be fully satisfied for us, who no longer follow our sinful nature but instead follow the Spirit.

[5]Those who are dominated by the sinful nature think about sinful things, but those who are controlled by the Holy Spirit think about things that please the Spirit. [6]So letting your sinful nature control your mind leads to death. But letting the Spirit control your mind leads to life and peace. [7]For the sinful nature is always hostile to God. It never did obey God's laws, and it never will. [8]That's why those who are still under the control of their sinful nature can never please God.

[9]But you are not controlled by your sinful nature. You are controlled by the Spirit if you have the Spirit of God living in you. (And remember that those who do not have the Spirit of Christ living in them do not belong to him at all.) [10]And Christ lives within you, so even though your body will die because of sin, the Spirit gives you life* because you have been made right with God. [11]The Spirit of God, who raised Jesus from the dead, lives in you. And just as God raised Christ Jesus from the dead, he will give life to your mortal bodies by this same Spirit living within you.

[12]Therefore, dear brothers and sisters,* you have no obligation to do what your sinful nature urges you to do. [13]For if you live by its dictates, you will die. But if through the power of the Spirit you put to death the deeds of your sinful nature,* you will live. [14]For all who are led by the Spirit of God are children* of God.

[15]So you have not received a spirit that makes you fearful slaves. Instead, you received God's Spirit when he adopted you as his own children.* Now we call him, "Abba, Father."* [16]For his Spirit joins with our spirit to affirm that we are God's children. [17]And since we are his children, we are his heirs. In fact, together with Christ we are heirs of God's glory. But if we are to share his glory, we must also share his suffering.

The Future Glory

[18]Yet what we suffer now is nothing compared to the glory he will reveal to us later. [19]For all creation is waiting eagerly for that future day when God will reveal who his children really are. [20]Against its will, all creation was subjected to God's curse. But with eager hope, [21]the creation looks forward to the day when it will join God's children in glorious freedom from death and decay. [22]For we know that all creation has been groaning as in the pains of childbirth right up to the present time. [23]And we believers also groan, even though we have the Holy Spirit within us as a foretaste of future glory, for we long for our bodies to be released from sin and suffering. We, too, wait with eager hope for the day when God will give us our full rights as his adopted children,* including the new bodies he has promised us. [24]We were given this hope when we were saved. (If we already have something, we don't need to hope* for it. [25]But if we look forward to something we don't yet have, we must wait patiently and confidently.)

[26]And the Holy Spirit helps us in our weakness. For example, we don't know what God wants us to pray for. But the Holy Spirit prays for us with groanings that cannot be expressed in words. [27]And the Father who knows all hearts

7:18 Greek *my flesh;* also in 7:25. **7:23** Greek *law;* also in 7:23b. **8:2a** Greek *the law;* also in 8:2b. **8:2b** Some manuscripts read *me.* **8:3** Greek *our flesh;* similarly in 8:4, 5, 6, 7, 8, 9, 12. **8:10** Or *your spirit is alive.* **8:12** Greek *brothers;* also in 8:29. **8:13** Greek *deeds of the body.* **8:14** Greek *sons;* also in 8:19. **8:15a** Greek *you received a spirit of sonship.* **8:15b** *Abba* is an Aramaic term for "father." **8:23** Greek *wait anxiously for sonship.* **8:24** Some manuscripts read *wait.*

knows what the Spirit is saying, for the Spirit pleads for us believers* in harmony with God's own will. ²⁸And we know that God causes everything to work together* for the good of those who love God and are called according to his purpose for them. ²⁹For God knew his people in advance, and he chose them to become like his Son, so that his Son would be the firstborn* among many brothers and sisters. ³⁰And having chosen them, he called them to come to him. And having called them, he gave them right standing with himself. And having given them right standing, he gave them his glory.

Nothing Can Separate Us from God's Love

³¹What shall we say about such wonderful things as these? If God is for us, who can ever be against us? ³²Since he did not spare even his own Son but gave him up for us all, won't he also give us everything else? ³³Who dares accuse us whom God has chosen for his own? No one—for God himself has given us right standing with himself. ³⁴Who then will condemn us? No one—for Christ Jesus died for us and was raised to life for us, and he is sitting in the place of honor at God's right hand, pleading for us.

³⁵Can anything ever separate us from Christ's love? Does it mean he no longer loves us if we have trouble or calamity, or are persecuted, or hungry, or destitute, or in danger, or threatened with death? ³⁶(As the Scriptures say, "For your sake we are killed every day; we are being slaughtered like sheep."*) ³⁷No, despite all these things, overwhelming victory is ours through Christ, who loved us.

³⁸And I am convinced that nothing can ever separate us from God's love. Neither death nor life, neither angels nor demons,* neither our fears for today nor our worries about tomorrow—not even the powers of hell can separate us from God's love. ³⁹No power in the sky above or in the earth below—indeed, nothing in all creation will ever be able to separate us from the love of God that is revealed in Christ Jesus our Lord.

God's Selection of Israel

9 With Christ as my witness, I speak with utter truthfulness. My conscience and the Holy Spirit confirm it. ²My heart is filled with bitter sorrow and unending grief ³for my people, my Jewish brothers and sisters.* I would be willing to be forever cursed—cut off from Christ!—if that would save them. ⁴They are the people of Israel, chosen to be God's adopted children.* God revealed his glory to them. He made covenants with them and gave them his law. He gave them the privilege of worshiping him and receiving his wonderful promises. ⁵Abraham, Isaac, and Jacob are their ancestors, and Christ himself was an Israelite as far as his human nature is concerned. And he is God, the one who rules over everything and is worthy of eternal praise! Amen.*

⁶Well then, has God failed to fulfill his promise to Israel? No, for not all who are born into the nation of Israel are truly members of God's people! ⁷Being descendants of Abraham doesn't make them truly Abraham's children. For the Scriptures say, "Isaac is the son through whom your descendants will be counted,"* though Abraham had other children, too. ⁸This means that Abraham's physical descendants are not necessarily children of God. Only the children of the promise are considered to be Abraham's children. ⁹For God had promised, "I will return about this time next year, and Sarah will have a son."*

¹⁰This son was our ancestor Isaac. When he married Rebekah, she gave birth to twins.* ¹¹But before they were born, before they had done anything good or bad, she received a message from God. (This message shows that God chooses people according to his own purposes; ¹²he calls people, but not according to their good or bad works.) She was told, "Your older son will serve your younger son."* ¹³In the words of the Scriptures, "I loved Jacob, but I rejected Esau."*

¹⁴Are we saying, then, that God was unfair? Of course not! ¹⁵For God said to Moses,

"I will show mercy to anyone I choose,
    and I will show compassion to anyone I
        choose."*

¹⁶So it is God who decides to show mercy. We can neither choose it nor work for it.

¹⁷For the Scriptures say that God told Pharaoh, "I have appointed you for the very purpose of displaying my power in you and to spread my fame throughout the earth."* ¹⁸So you see, God chooses to show mercy to some, and he chooses to harden the hearts of others so they refuse to listen.

¹⁹Well then, you might say, "Why does God blame people for not responding? Haven't they simply done what he makes them do?"

²⁰No, don't say that. Who are you, a mere human being, to argue with God? Should the thing that was created say to the one who created it, "Why have you made me like this?" ²¹When a potter makes jars out of clay, doesn't he have a right to use the same lump of clay to make one jar for decoration and another to throw garbage into? ²²In the same way, even though God has the right to show his anger and his power, he is

---

8:27 Greek *for God's holy people.* **8:28** Some manuscripts read *And we know that everything works together.* **8:29** Or *would be supreme.* **8:36** Ps 44:22. **8:38** Greek *nor rulers.* **9:3** Greek *my brothers.* **9:4** Greek *chosen for sonship.* **9:5** Or *May God, the one who rules over everything, be praised forever. Amen.* **9:7** Gen 21:12. **9:9** Gen 18:10, 14. **9:10** Greek *she conceived children through this one man.* **9:12** Gen 25:23. **9:13** Mal 1:2-3. **9:15** Exod 33:19. **9:17** Exod 9:16 (Greek version).

very patient with those on whom his anger falls, who are destined for destruction. [23]He does this to make the riches of his glory shine even brighter on those to whom he shows mercy, who were prepared in advance for glory. [24]And we are among those whom he selected, both from the Jews and from the Gentiles.

[25]Concerning the Gentiles, God says in the prophecy of Hosea,

> "Those who were not my people,
> I will now call my people.
> And I will love those
> whom I did not love before."*

[26]And,

> "Then, at the place where they were told,
> 'You are not my people,'
> there they will be called
> 'children of the living God.'"*

[27]And concerning Israel, Isaiah the prophet cried out,

> "Though the people of Israel are as
> numerous as the sand of the seashore,
> only a remnant will be saved.
> [28] For the LORD will carry out his sentence upon
> the earth
> quickly and with finality."*

[29]And Isaiah said the same thing in another place:

> "If the LORD of Heaven's Armies
> had not spared a few of our children,
> we would have been wiped out like Sodom,
> destroyed like Gomorrah."*

Israel's Unbelief

[30]What does all this mean? Even though the Gentiles were not trying to follow God's standards, they were made right with God. And it was by faith that this took place. [31]But the people of Israel, who tried so hard to get right with God by keeping the law, never succeeded. [32]Why not? Because they were trying to get right with God by keeping the law* instead of by trusting in him. They stumbled over the great rock in their path. [33]God warned them of this in the Scriptures when he said,

> "I am placing a stone in Jerusalem* that
> makes people stumble,
> a rock that makes them fall.
> But anyone who trusts in him
> will never be disgraced."*

10 Dear brothers and sisters,* the longing of my heart and my prayer to God is for the people of Israel to be saved. [2]I know what enthu-siasm they have for God, but it is misdirected zeal. [3]For they don't understand God's way of making people right with himself. Refusing to accept God's way, they cling to their own way of getting right with God by trying to keep the law. [4]For Christ has already accomplished the pur-pose for which the law was given.* As a result, all who believe in him are made right with God.

Salvation Is for Everyone

[5]For Moses writes that the law's way of making a person right with God requires obedience to all of its commands.* [6]But faith's way of getting right with God says, "Don't say in your heart, 'Who will go up to heaven?' (to bring Christ down to earth). [7]And don't say, 'Who will go down to the place of the dead?' (to bring Christ back to life again)." [8]In fact, it says,

> "The message is very close at hand;
> it is on your lips and in your heart."*

And that message is the very message about faith that we preach: [9]If you confess with your mouth that Jesus is Lord and believe in your heart that God raised him from the dead, you will be saved. [10]For it is by believing in your heart that you are made right with God, and it is by confessing with your mouth that you are saved. [11]As the Scrip-tures tell us, "Anyone who trusts in him will never be disgraced."* [12]Jew and Gentile* are the same in this respect. They have the same Lord, who gives generously to all who call on him. [13]For "Everyone who calls on the name of the LORD will be saved."*

[14]But how can they call on him to save them unless they believe in him? And how can they believe in him if they have never heard about him? And how can they hear about him unless someone tells them? [15]And how will anyone go and tell them without being sent? That is why the Scriptures say, "How beautiful are the feet of messengers who bring good news!"*

[16]But not everyone welcomes the Good News, for Isaiah the prophet said, "LORD, who has be-lieved our message?"* [17]So faith comes from hearing, that is, hearing the Good News about Christ. [18]But I ask, have the people of Israel actu-ally heard the message? Yes, they have:

> "The message has gone throughout the earth,
> and the words to all the world."*

[19]But I ask, did the people of Israel really under-stand? Yes, they did, for even in the time of Moses, God said,

> "I will rouse your jealousy through people
> who are not even a nation.
> I will provoke your anger through the
> foolish Gentiles."*

9:25 Hos 2:23. **9:26** Greek *sons of the living God.* Hos 1:10. **9:27-28** Isa 10:22-23 (Greek version). **9:29** Isa 1:9. **9:32** Greek *by works.* **9:33a** Greek *in Zion.* **9:33b** Isa 8:14; 28:16 (Greek version). **10:1** Greek *Brothers.* **10:4** Or *For Christ is the end of the law.* **10:5** See Lev 18:5. **10:6-8** Deut 30:12-14. **10:11** Isa 28:16 (Greek version). **10:12** Greek *and Greek.* **10:13** Joel 2:32. **10:15** Isa 52:7. **10:16** Isa 53:1. **10:18** Ps 19:4. **10:19** Deut 32:21.

²⁰And later Isaiah spoke boldly for God, saying,

"I was found by people who were not looking
for me.
I showed myself to those who were not
asking for me."*

²¹But regarding Israel, God said,

"All day long I opened my arms to them,
but they were disobedient and
rebellious."*

God's Mercy on Israel

11 I ask, then, has God rejected his own people, the nation of Israel? Of course not! I myself am an Israelite, a descendant of Abraham and a member of the tribe of Benjamin. ²No, God has not rejected his own people, whom he chose from the very beginning. Do you realize what the Scriptures say about this? Elijah the prophet complained to God about the people of Israel and said, ³"LORD, they have killed your prophets and torn down your altars. I am the only one left, and now they are trying to kill me, too."*

⁴And do you remember God's reply? He said, "No, I have 7,000 others who have never bowed down to Baal!"*

⁵It is the same today, for a few of the people of Israel* have remained faithful because of God's grace—his undeserved kindness in choosing them. ⁶And since it is through God's kindness, then it is not by their good works. For in that case, God's grace would not be what it really is—free and undeserved.

⁷So this is the situation: Most of the people of Israel have not found the favor of God they are looking for so earnestly. A few have—the ones God has chosen—but the hearts of the rest were hardened. ⁸As the Scriptures say,

"God has put them into a deep sleep.
To this day he has shut their eyes so they do
not see,
and closed their ears so they do not
hear."*

⁹Likewise, David said,

"Let their bountiful table become a snare,
a trap that makes them think all is well.
Let their blessings cause them to stumble,
and let them get what they deserve.
¹⁰ Let their eyes go blind so they cannot see,
and let their backs be bent forever."*

¹¹Did God's people stumble and fall beyond recovery? Of course not! They were disobedient, so God made salvation available to the Gentiles. But he wanted his own people to become jealous and claim it for themselves. ¹²Now if the Gentiles were enriched because the people of Israel turned down God's offer of salvation, think how much greater a blessing the world will share when they finally accept it.

¹³I am saying all this especially for you Gentiles. God has appointed me as the apostle to the Gentiles. I stress this, ¹⁴for I want somehow to make the people of Israel jealous of what you Gentiles have, so I might save some of them. ¹⁵For since their rejection meant that God offered salvation to the rest of the world, their acceptance will be even more wonderful. It will be life for those who were dead! ¹⁶And since Abraham and the other patriarchs were holy, their descendants will also be holy—just as the entire batch of dough is holy because the portion given as an offering is holy. For if the roots of the tree are holy, the branches will be, too.

¹⁷But some of these branches from Abraham's tree—some of the people of Israel—have been broken off. And you Gentiles, who were branches from a wild olive tree, have been grafted in. So now you also receive the blessing God has promised Abraham and his children, sharing in the rich nourishment from the root of God's special olive tree. ¹⁸But you must not brag about being grafted in to replace the branches that were broken off. You are just a branch, not the root.

¹⁹"Well," you may say, "those branches were broken off to make room for me." ²⁰Yes, but remember—those branches were broken off because they didn't believe in Christ, and you are there because you do believe. So don't think highly of yourself, but fear what could happen. ²¹For if God did not spare the original branches, he won't* spare you either.

²²Notice how God is both kind and severe. He is severe toward those who disobeyed, but kind to you if you continue to trust in his kindness. But if you stop trusting, you also will be cut off. ²³And if the people of Israel turn from their unbelief, they will be grafted in again, for God has the power to graft them back into the tree. ²⁴You, by nature, were a branch cut from a wild olive tree. So if God was willing to do something contrary to nature by grafting you into his cultivated tree, he will be far more eager to graft the original branches back into the tree where they belong.

God's Mercy Is for Everyone

²⁵I want you to understand this mystery, dear brothers and sisters,* so that you will not feel proud about yourselves. Some of the people of Israel have hard hearts, but this will last only until the full number of Gentiles comes to Christ. ²⁶And so all Israel will be saved. As the Scriptures say,

---

10:20 Isa 65:1 (Greek version).　**10:21** Isa 65:2 (Greek version).　**11:3** 1 Kgs 19:10, 14.　**11:4** 1 Kgs 19:18.　**11:5** Greek *for a remnant.*　**11:8** Isa 29:10; Deut 29:4.　**11:9-10** Ps 69:22-23 (Greek version).　**11:21** Some manuscripts read *perhaps he won't.* **11:25** Greek *brothers.*

"The one who rescues will come from
Jerusalem,*
and he will turn Israel* away from
ungodliness.
²⁷ And this is my covenant with them,
that I will take away their sins."*

²⁸Many of the people of Israel are now ene-mies of the Good News, and this benefits you Gentiles. Yet they are still the people he loves be-cause he chose their ancestors Abraham, Isaac, and Jacob. ²⁹For God's gifts and his call can never be withdrawn. ³⁰Once, you Gentiles were rebels against God, but when the people of Israel re-belled against him, God was merciful to you in-stead. ³¹Now they are the rebels, and God's mercy has come to you so that they, too, will share* in God's mercy. ³²For God has imprisoned everyone in disobedience so he could have mercy on everyone.

³³Oh, how great are God's riches and wisdom and knowledge! How impossible it is for us to understand his decisions and his ways!

³⁴ For who can know the Lord's thoughts?
Who knows enough to give him advice?*
³⁵ And who has given him so much
that he needs to pay it back?*

³⁶For everything comes from him and exists by his power and is intended for his glory. All glory to him forever! Amen.

A Living Sacrifice to God

12 And so, dear brothers and sisters,* I plead with you to give your bodies to God be-cause of all he has done for you. Let them be a living and holy sacrifice—the kind he will find acceptable. This is truly the way to worship him.* ²Don't copy the behavior and customs of this world, but let God transform you into a new person by changing the way you think. Then you will learn to know God's will for you, which is good and pleasing and perfect.

³Because of the privilege and authority* God has given me, I give each of you this warning: Don't think you are better than you really are. Be honest in your evaluation of yourselves, measur-ing yourselves by the faith God has given us.* ⁴Just as our bodies have many parts and each part has a special function, ⁵so it is with Christ's body. We are many parts of one body, and we all belong to each other.

⁶In his grace, God has given us different gifts for doing certain things well. So if God has given you the ability to prophesy, speak out with as much faith as God has given you. ⁷If your gift is serving others, serve them well. If you are a teacher, teach well. ⁸If your gift is to encourage

others, be encouraging. If it is giving, give gen-erously. If God has given you leadership ability, take the responsibility seriously. And if you have a gift for showing kindness to others, do it gladly.

⁹Don't just pretend to love others. Really love them. Hate what is wrong. Hold tightly to what is good. ¹⁰Love each other with genuine affec-tion,* and take delight in honoring each other. ¹¹Never be lazy, but work hard and serve the Lord enthusiastically.* ¹²Rejoice in our confi-dent hope. Be patient in trouble, and keep on praying. ¹³When God's people are in need, be ready to help them. Always be eager to practice hospitality.

¹⁴Bless those who persecute you. Don't curse them; pray that God will bless them. ¹⁵Be happy with those who are happy, and weep with those who weep. ¹⁶Live in harmony with each other. Don't be too proud to enjoy the company of ordi-nary people. And don't think you know it all!

¹⁷Never pay back evil with more evil. Do things in such a way that everyone can see you are honorable. ¹⁸Do all that you can to live in peace with everyone.

¹⁹Dear friends, never take revenge. Leave that to the righteous anger of God. For the Scriptures say,

"I will take revenge;
I will pay them back,"*
says the Lord.

²⁰Instead,

"If your enemies are hungry, feed them.
If they are thirsty, give them something
to drink.
In doing this, you will heap
burning coals of shame on their heads."*

²¹Don't let evil conquer you, but conquer evil by doing good.

Respect for Authority

13 Everyone must submit to governing au-thorities. For all authority comes from God, and those in positions of authority have been placed there by God. ²So anyone who re-bels against authority is rebelling against what God has instituted, and they will be punished. ³For the authorities do not strike fear in people who are doing right, but in those who are doing wrong. Would you like to live without fear of the authorities? Do what is right, and they will honor you. ⁴The authorities are God's servants, sent for your good. But if you are doing wrong, of course you should be afraid, for they have the power to punish you. They are God's servants,

11:26a Greek *from Zion.*   11:26b Greek *Jacob.*   11:26-27 Isa 59:20-21; 27:9 (Greek version).   11:31 Other manuscripts read *will now share;* still others read *will someday share.*   11:34 Isa 40:13 (Greek version).   12:1a Greek *brothers.*   12:1b Or *This is your spiritual worship;* or *This is your reasonable service.*   12:3a Or *Because of the grace;* compare 1:5.   12:3b Or *by the faith God has given you;* or *by the standard of our God-given faith.*   12:10 Greek *with brotherly love.*   12:11 Or *but serve the Lord with a zealous spirit;* or *but let the Spirit excite you as you serve the Lord.*   12:19 Deut 32:35.   12:20 Prov 25:21-22.

sent for the very purpose of punishing those who do what is wrong. ⁵So you must submit to them, not only to avoid punishment, but also to keep a clear conscience.

⁶Pay your taxes, too, for these same reasons. For government workers need to be paid. They are serving God in what they do. ⁷Give to everyone what you owe them: Pay your taxes and government fees to those who collect them, and give respect and honor to those who are in authority.

Love Fulfills God's Requirements

⁸Owe nothing to anyone—except for your obligation to love one another. If you love your neighbor, you will fulfill the requirements of God's law. ⁹For the commandments say, "You must not commit adultery. You must not murder. You must not steal. You must not covet."* These—and other such commandments—are summed up in this one commandment: "Love your neighbor as yourself."* ¹⁰Love does no wrong to others, so love fulfills the requirements of God's law.

¹¹This is all the more urgent, for you know how late it is; time is running out. Wake up, for our salvation is nearer now than when we first believed. ¹²The night is almost gone; the day of salvation will soon be here. So remove your dark deeds like dirty clothes, and put on the shining armor of right living. ¹³Because we belong to the day, we must live decent lives for all to see. Don't participate in the darkness of wild parties and drunkenness, or in sexual promiscuity and immoral living, or in quarreling and jealousy. ¹⁴Instead, clothe yourself with the presence of the Lord Jesus Christ. And don't let yourself think about ways to indulge your evil desires.

The Danger of Criticism

14 Accept other believers who are weak in faith, and don't argue with them about what they think is right or wrong. ²For instance, one person believes it's all right to eat anything. But another believer with a sensitive conscience will eat only vegetables. ³Those who feel free to eat anything must not look down on those who don't. And those who don't eat certain foods must not condemn those who do, for God has accepted them. ⁴Who are you to condemn someone else's servants? Their own master will judge whether they stand or fall. And with the Lord's help, they will stand and receive his approval.

⁵In the same way, some think one day is more holy than another day, while others think every day is alike. You should each be fully convinced that whichever day you choose is acceptable. ⁶Those who worship the Lord on a special day do it to honor him. Those who eat any kind of food do so to honor the Lord, since they give thanks to God before eating. And those who refuse to eat certain foods also want to please the Lord and give thanks to God. ⁷For we don't live for ourselves or die for ourselves. ⁸If we live, it's to honor the Lord. And if we die, it's to honor the Lord. So whether we live or die, we belong to the Lord. ⁹Christ died and rose again for this very purpose—to be Lord both of the living and of the dead.

¹⁰So why do you condemn another believer*? Why do you look down on another believer? Remember, we will all stand before the judgment seat of God. ¹¹For the Scriptures say,

"'As surely as I live,' says the LORD,
'every knee will bend to me,
    and every tongue will confess and give
        praise to God.*'"

¹²Yes, each of us will give a personal account to God. ¹³So let's stop condemning each other. Decide instead to live in such a way that you will not cause another believer to stumble and fall.

¹⁴I know and am convinced on the authority of the Lord Jesus that no food, in and of itself, is wrong to eat. But if someone believes it is wrong, then for that person it is wrong. ¹⁵And if another believer is distressed by what you eat, you are not acting in love if you eat it. Don't let your eating ruin someone for whom Christ died. ¹⁶Then you will not be criticized for doing something you believe is good. ¹⁷For the Kingdom of God is not a matter of what we eat or drink, but of living a life of goodness and peace and joy in the Holy Spirit. ¹⁸If you serve Christ with this attitude, you will please God, and others will approve of you, too. ¹⁹So then, let us aim for harmony in the church and try to build each other up.

²⁰Don't tear apart the work of God over what you eat. Remember, all foods are acceptable, but it is wrong to eat something if it makes another person stumble. ²¹It is better not to eat meat or drink wine or do anything else if it might cause another believer to stumble. ²²You may believe there's nothing wrong with what you are doing, but keep it between yourself and God. Blessed are those who don't feel guilty for doing something they have decided is right. ²³But if you have doubts about whether or not you should eat something, you are sinning if you go ahead and do it. For you are not following your convictions. If you do anything you believe is not right, you are sinning.

Living to Please Others

15 We who are strong must be considerate of those who are sensitive about things like this. We must not just please ourselves. ²We should help others do what is right and build

---

13:9a Exod 20:13-15, 17. **13:9b** Lev 19:18. **14:10** Greek *your brother;* also in 14:10b, 13, 15, 21. **14:11** Or *confess allegiance to God.* Isa 49:18; 45:23 (Greek version).

them up in the Lord. ³For even Christ didn't live to please himself. As the Scriptures say, "The insults of those who insult you, O God, have fallen on me."* ⁴Such things were written in the Scriptures long ago to teach us. And the Scriptures give us hope and encouragement as we wait patiently for God's promises to be fulfilled.

⁵May God, who gives this patience and encouragement, help you live in complete harmony with each other, as is fitting for followers of Christ Jesus. ⁶Then all of you can join together with one voice, giving praise and glory to God, the Father of our Lord Jesus Christ.

⁷Therefore, accept each other just as Christ has accepted you so that God will be given glory. ⁸Remember that Christ came as a servant to the Jews* to show that God is true to the promises he made to their ancestors. ⁹He also came so that the Gentiles might give glory to God for his mercies to them. That is what the psalmist meant when he wrote:

"For this, I will praise you among the
Gentiles;
I will sing praises to your name."*

¹⁰And in another place it is written,

"Rejoice with his people,
you Gentiles."*

¹¹And yet again,

"Praise the LORD, all you Gentiles.
Praise him, all you people of the earth."*

¹²And in another place Isaiah said,

"The heir to David's throne* will come,
and he will rule over the Gentiles.
They will place their hope on him."*

¹³I pray that God, the source of hope, will fill you completely with joy and peace because you trust in him. Then you will overflow with confident hope through the power of the Holy Spirit.

Paul's Reason for Writing

¹⁴I am fully convinced, my dear brothers and sisters,* that you are full of goodness. You know these things so well you can teach each other all about them. ¹⁵Even so, I have been bold enough to write about some of these points, knowing that all you need is this reminder. For by God's grace, ¹⁶I am a special messenger from Christ Jesus to you Gentiles. I bring you the Good News so that I might present you as an acceptable offering to God, made holy by the Holy Spirit. ¹⁷So I have reason to be enthusiastic about all Christ Jesus has done through me in my service to God.

¹⁸Yet I dare not boast about anything except what Christ has done through me, bringing the Gentiles to God by my message and by the way I worked among them. ¹⁹They were convinced by the power of miraculous signs and wonders and by the power of God's Spirit.* In this way, I have fully presented the Good News of Christ from Jerusalem all the way to Illyricum.*

²⁰My ambition has always been to preach the Good News where the name of Christ has never been heard, rather than where a church has already been started by someone else. ²¹I have been following the plan spoken of in the Scriptures, where it says,

"Those who have never been told about him
will see,
and those who have never heard of him
will understand."*

²²In fact, my visit to you has been delayed so long because I have been preaching in these places.

Paul's Travel Plans

²³But now I have finished my work in these regions, and after all these long years of waiting, I am eager to visit you. ²⁴I am planning to go to Spain, and when I do, I will stop off in Rome. And after I have enjoyed your fellowship for a little while, you can provide for my journey.

²⁵But before I come, I must go to Jerusalem to take a gift to the believers* there. ²⁶For you see, the believers in Macedonia and Achaia* have eagerly taken up an offering for the poor among the believers in Jerusalem. ²⁷They were glad to do this because they feel they owe a real debt to them. Since the Gentiles received the spiritual blessings of the Good News from the believers in Jerusalem, they feel the least they can do in return is to help them financially. ²⁸As soon as I have delivered this money and completed this good deed of theirs, I will come to see you on my way to Spain. ²⁹And I am sure that when I come, Christ will richly bless our time together.

³⁰Dear brothers and sisters, I urge you in the name of our Lord Jesus Christ to join in my struggle by praying to God for me. Do this because of your love for me, given to you by the Holy Spirit. ³¹Pray that I will be rescued from those in Judea who refuse to obey God. Pray also that the believers there will be willing to accept the donation* I am taking to Jerusalem. ³²Then, by the will of God, I will be able to come to you with a joyful heart, and we will be an encouragement to each other.

³³And now may God, who gives us his peace, be with you all. Amen.*

15:3 Greek *who insult you have fallen on me*. Ps 69:9.   **15:8** Greek *servant of circumcision*.   **15:9** Ps 18:49.   **15:10** Deut 32:43.   **15:11** Ps 117:1.   **15:12a** Greek *The root of Jesse*. David was the son of Jesse.   **15:12b** Isa 11:10 (Greek version).   **15:14** Greek *brothers*; also in 15:30.   **15:19a** Other manuscripts read *the Spirit*; still others read *the Holy Spirit*.   **15:19b** *Illyricum* was a region northeast of Italy.   **15:21** Isa 52:15 (Greek version).   **15:25** Greek *God's holy people*; also in 15:26, 31.   **15:26** *Macedonia* and *Achaia* were the northern and southern regions of Greece.   **15:31** Greek *the ministry*; other manuscripts read *the gift*.   **15:33** Some manuscripts do not include *Amen*. One very early manuscript places 16:25-27 here.

Paul Greets His Friends

16 I commend to you our sister Phoebe, who is a deacon in the church in Cenchrea. ²Welcome her in the Lord as one who is worthy of honor among God's people. Help her in whatever she needs, for she has been helpful to many, and especially to me.

³Give my greetings to Priscilla and Aquila, my co-workers in the ministry of Christ Jesus. ⁴In fact, they once risked their lives for me. I am thankful to them, and so are all the Gentile churches. ⁵Also give my greetings to the church that meets in their home.

Greet my dear friend Epenetus. He was the first person from the province of Asia to become a follower of Christ. ⁶Give my greetings to Mary, who has worked so hard for your benefit. ⁷Greet Andronicus and Junia,* my fellow Jews,* who were in prison with me. They are highly respected among the apostles and became followers of Christ before I did. ⁸Greet Ampliatus, my dear friend in the Lord. ⁹Greet Urbanus, our co-worker in Christ, and my dear friend Stachys.

¹⁰Greet Apelles, a good man whom Christ approves. And give my greetings to the believers from the household of Aristobulus. ¹¹Greet Herodion, my fellow Jew.* Greet the Lord's people from the household of Narcissus. ¹²Give my greetings to Tryphena and Tryphosa, the Lord's workers, and to dear Persis, who has worked so hard for the Lord. ¹³Greet Rufus, whom the Lord picked out to be his very own; and also his dear mother, who has been a mother to me.

¹⁴Give my greetings to Asyncritus, Phlegon, Hermes, Patrobas, Hermas, and the brothers and sisters* who meet with them. ¹⁵Give my greetings to Philologus, Julia, Nereus and his sister, and to Olympas and all the believers* who meet with them. ¹⁶Greet each other in Christian love.* All the churches of Christ send you their greetings.

Paul's Final Instructions

¹⁷And now I make one more appeal, my dear brothers and sisters. Watch out for people who cause divisions and upset people's faith by teaching things contrary to what you have been taught. Stay away from them. ¹⁸Such people are not serving Christ our Lord; they are serving their own personal interests. By smooth talk and glowing words they deceive innocent people. ¹⁹But everyone knows that you are obedient to the Lord. This makes me very happy. I want you to be wise in doing right and to stay innocent of any wrong. ²⁰The God of peace will soon crush Satan under your feet. May the grace of our Lord Jesus* be with you.

²¹Timothy, my fellow worker, sends you his greetings, as do Lucius, Jason, and Sosipater, my fellow Jews.

²²I, Tertius, the one writing this letter for Paul, send my greetings, too, as one of the Lord's followers.

²³Gaius says hello to you. He is my host and also serves as host to the whole church. Erastus, the city treasurer, sends you his greetings, and so does our brother Quartus.*

²⁵Now all glory to God, who is able to make you strong, just as my Good News says. This message about Jesus Christ has revealed his plan for you Gentiles, a plan kept secret from the beginning of time. ²⁶But now as the prophets* foretold and as the eternal God has commanded, this message is made known to all Gentiles everywhere, so that they too might believe and obey him. ²⁷All glory to the only wise God, through Jesus Christ, forever. Amen.

16:7a *Junia* is a feminine name. Some late manuscripts accent the word so it reads *Junias,* a masculine name; still others read *Julia* (feminine). **16:7b** Or *compatriots;* also in 16:21. **16:11** Or *compatriot.* **16:14** Greek *brothers;* also in 16:17. **16:15** Greek *all of God's holy people.* **16:16** Greek *with a sacred kiss.* **16:20** Some manuscripts read *Lord Jesus Christ.* **16:23** Some manuscripts add verse 24, *May the grace of our Lord Jesus Christ be with you all. Amen.* Still others add this sentence after verse 27. **16:26** Greek *the prophetic writings.*

GIGI MARVIN
Forward, Boston Blades/Team USA

I believe the Bible is the game plan for our lives. All teams have playbooks. We study these game plans to know what's expected. This is what the Bible does. It is the playbook for life with Christ containing plays for every situation: Struggle with judging others? Go to Matthew 7. How to escape temptation? Check 1 Corinthians 10:13. Consumed with worry? Exchange it for peace with Philippians 4:6-7. The more I immerse myself in the Bible, the stronger I grow in faith. It's simple: if I don't read the playbook, I will struggle mightily. However, if I internalize it, study, and continually refer back to it then I will be strong in Christ.

An example; at every USA Hockey camp, we do a variety of incredibly difficult testing that can wear us down. Many times the worry drags me into a spiral of despair. Thankfully the Lord directed my heart to Matthew 6:27: *"Who of you by worrying can add a single hour to his life?"* Instantly I recognized how pointless it is to worry. The Lord was telling me to exchange stress for peace. And God doesn't just fill one person up, he fills us so that we overflow onto others. By etching this verse on my heart, I shared it with other people and it created a tidal wave of hope. Players all around me were repeating this verse throughout the testing. Encouraging others and building people up in God's love; what an amazing effect! The Lord saved us from crippling fear and set us free to embrace the testing, encourage others, and extend His love.

"All teams have playbooks—the Bible . . . is the playbook for life with Christ."

I love Galatians 2:20, *"I have been crucified with Christ and I no longer live, but Christ lives in me,"* because it hammers home the point that "Gigi" can't do this life alone and needs Jesus. A friend shared that Gigi stands for *G*od & *I* *G*od & *I*. What an awesome reminder: I put God first, check my ego at the door, and allow Him to do His will.

I grew up in a strong Christian home where I always believed in God, but never truly knew what that meant. While at the University of Minnesota I attended a Training Camp put on by Athletes in Action where I completely devoted my life to Christ!

"Faith in God is my secret to success!"

One of my favorite verses is Deuteronomy 31:6: *"Be strong and courageous. Do not be afraid or terrified because of them, for the Lord your God goes with you; he will never leave you nor forsake you."* I love this verse because it not only provides comfort in the challenges life brings, but also in hockey when competing with and against the best athletes in my sport. Knowing that God is with me brings an indescribable sense of confidence on the ice as I can perform freely for the Lord who gave me this talent. I often use Ao1 (Audience of One) as a focal point during competition to remind me who I'm playing for and who got me to this point in my life. This perspective brings freedom and strength to not only my game of hockey, but to life!

Now, as a Christian hockey player, I am able to more easily enjoy the journey of a game I love to play! I get to see how God uses me in every game, practice, workout, and in the lives of my teammates. Christ is a constant reminder of how I should treat others; I am to serve them before serving myself.

There are too many self-serving and self-glorifying habits found in sport, so without the Lord's guidance and daily leading of the Holy Spirit, my career in hockey would not only be physically and mentally draining, but would probably not be as successful either. Faith in God is my secret to success!

WHITNEY NASLUND
Forward, Boston Blades, CWHL

Jesus Christ has changed my life both on and off the ice in very dramatic ways. My purpose in life is to follow where He leads me with my whole heart. When I am in total surrender, He gives me inexpressible joy that manifests itself in continuous motivation to work hard on my skills with a positive attitude. He also gives me the strength to face constructive criticism, tough officiating or disagreements with teammates or coaches.

There were times in my career when I would get easily angered about the game. Playing angry or using frustration to play harder actually restricted my ability to play. When I began to pray and trust the Lord, I discovered God's freedom. I learned that as I turned over my anxiety to God, He replaced it not only with peace but joy as well. The freedom to play with joy did not come from the removal of the trials, but from being allowed to play my game at my best without any worries of past mistakes.

As hockey players, we all create habits and are taught that perfect practice makes perfect. This concept translates over to my faith in God and the need to create good habits like getting into the Word, praying and meeting regularly with other believers.

> ## "Playing angry or using frustration to play harder actually restricted my ability to play."

My favorite promise comes from Philippians 4:6 and 7: Don't worry about anything. Tell God what you need, and thank Him for all he has done. If you do this, you will experience God's peace, which is far more wonderful than the human mind can understand. His peace will guard your hearts and minds as you live in Christ." Knowing that Christ is in control gives me comfort that I need not worry. God's peace is an overwhelming feeling that cannot be mistaken for anything else.

My purpose in life is to follow where He leads me with my whole heart.

LAURA HALLDORSON

Former Coach, University of Minnesota Golden Gophers/
AHCA Coach of the Year recipient

I grew up in a Christian home and attended Sunday school at an early age. My mother and grandmother were huge influences on me and they taught me about Jesus. When I was 13 years old, I accepted Christ and was baptized.

Years ago, I made a point of reading at least one chapter of the New Testament each morning. As I look back, I believe the Holy Spirit was changing me from the inside, without my even realizing it at the time. The New Testament informs us that: " . . . the word of God is living and active . . . " and getting it into my heart and mind certainly strengthened my faith.

"Knowing that the Lord is in control is so comforting."

One of my favorite passages is Isaiah 55:8,9: *"For My thoughts are not your thoughts, Neither are your ways My ways,"* declares the LORD. *"For as the heavens are higher than the earth, So are My ways higher than your ways and My thoughts than your thoughts."* These verses put everything into perspective for me. They remind me to be humble and to depend on God. They also encourage me to seek His will and His ways.

Knowing that the Lord is in control is so comforting. My tendency as a coach was to always want to control things: to fix things and to achieve more by working harder. As I grew in my faith, I learned that these were not the answers. There were actually very few things I could control or fix and working harder didn't always help.

I remember an exceptionally trying time when I was worried about the potential reactions to some of my decisions, but I wanted to stick with what I believed was the right thing to do. I ran across 1 Corinthians 16:13,14 which says: *"Be on guard. Stand true to what you believe. Be courageous. Be strong. And everything you do must be done with love."* That passage was perfect for the situation and it gave me the strength, confidence, and courage to do what needed to be done. It was a good lesson for me to stand up for my values as a coach and to lean on God to work out the consequences.

1 Corinthians

Greetings from Paul

1 This letter is from Paul, chosen by the will of God to be an apostle of Christ Jesus, and from our brother Sosthenes.

²I am writing to God's church in Corinth,* to you who have been called by God to be his own holy people. He made you holy by means of Christ Jesus,* just as he did for all people everywhere who call on the name of our Lord Jesus Christ, their Lord and ours.

³May God our Father and the Lord Jesus Christ give you grace and peace.

Paul Gives Thanks to God

⁴I always thank my God for you and for the gracious gifts he has given you, now that you belong to Christ Jesus. ⁵Through him, God has enriched your church in every way—with all of your eloquent words and all of your knowledge. ⁶This confirms that what I told you about Christ is true. ⁷Now you have every spiritual gift you need as you eagerly wait for the return of our Lord Jesus Christ. ⁸He will keep you strong to the end so that you will be free from all blame on the day when our Lord Jesus Christ returns. ⁹God will do this, for he is faithful to do what he says, and he has invited you into partnership with his Son, Jesus Christ our Lord.

Divisions in the Church

¹⁰I appeal to you, dear brothers and sisters,* by the authority of our Lord Jesus Christ, to live in harmony with each other. Let there be no divisions in the church. Rather, be of one mind, united in thought and purpose. ¹¹For some members of Chloe's household have told me about your quarrels, my dear brothers and sisters. ¹²Some of you are saying, "I am a follower of Paul." Others are saying, "I follow Apollos," or "I follow Peter,*" or "I follow only Christ."

¹³Has Christ been divided into factions? Was I, Paul, crucified for you? Were any of you baptized in the name of Paul? Of course not! ¹⁴I thank God that I did not baptize any of you except Crispus and Gaius, ¹⁵for now no one can say they were baptized in my name. ¹⁶(Oh yes, I also baptized the household of Stephanas, but I don't remember baptizing anyone else.) ¹⁷For Christ didn't send me to baptize, but to preach the Good News—and not with clever speech, for fear that the cross of Christ would lose its power.

The Wisdom of God

¹⁸The message of the cross is foolish to those who are headed for destruction! But we who are being saved know it is the very power of God. ¹⁹As the Scriptures say,

> "I will destroy the wisdom of the wise
> and discard the intelligence of the
> intelligent."*

²⁰So where does this leave the philosophers, the scholars, and the world's brilliant debaters? God has made the wisdom of this world look foolish. ²¹Since God in his wisdom saw to it that the world would never know him through human wisdom, he has used our foolish preaching to save those who believe. ²²It is foolish to the Jews, who ask for signs from heaven. And it is foolish to the Greeks, who seek human wisdom. ²³So when we preach that Christ was crucified, the Jews are offended and the Gentiles say it's all nonsense.

²⁴But to those called by God to salvation, both Jews and Gentiles,* Christ is the power of God and the wisdom of God. ²⁵This foolish plan of God is wiser than the wisest of human plans, and God's weakness is stronger than the greatest of human strength.

²⁶Remember, dear brothers and sisters, that few of you were wise in the world's eyes or powerful or wealthy* when God called you. ²⁷Instead, God chose things the world considers foolish in order to shame those who think they are wise. And he chose things that are powerless to shame those who are powerful. ²⁸God chose things despised by the world,* things counted as nothing at all, and used them to bring to nothing what the world considers important. ²⁹As a result, no one can ever boast in the presence of God.

³⁰God has united you with Christ Jesus. For our benefit God made him to be wisdom itself. Christ made us right with God; he made us pure

1:2a *Corinth* was the capital city of Achaia, the southern region of the Greek peninsula.   1:2b Or *because you belong to Christ Jesus.*
1:10 Greek *brothers;* also in 1:11, 26.   1:12 Greek *Cephas.*   1:19 Isa 29:14.   1:24 Greek *and Greeks.*   1:26 Or *high born.*
1:28 Or *God chose those who are low born.*

and holy, and he freed us from sin. ³¹Therefore, as the Scriptures say, "If you want to boast, boast only about the Lord."*

Paul's Message of Wisdom

2 When I first came to you, dear brothers and sisters,* I didn't use lofty words and impressive wisdom to tell you God's secret plan.* ²For I decided that while I was with you I would forget everything except Jesus Christ, the one who was crucified. ³I came to you in weakness—timid and trembling. ⁴And my message and my preaching were very plain. Rather than using clever and persuasive speeches, I relied only on the power of the Holy Spirit. ⁵I did this so you would trust not in human wisdom but in the power of God.

⁶Yet when I am among mature believers, I do speak with words of wisdom, but not the kind of wisdom that belongs to this world or to the rulers of this world, who are soon forgotten. ⁷No, the wisdom we speak of is the mystery of God*— his plan that was previously hidden, even though he made it for our ultimate glory before the world began. ⁸But the rulers of this world have not understood it; if they had, they would not have crucified our glorious Lord. ⁹That is what the Scriptures mean when they say,

"No eye has seen, no ear has heard,
  and no mind has imagined
what God has prepared
  for those who love him."*

¹⁰But* it was to us that God revealed these things by his Spirit. For his Spirit searches out everything and shows us God's deep secrets. ¹¹No one can know a person's thoughts except that person's own spirit, and no one can know God's thoughts except God's own Spirit. ¹²And we have received God's Spirit (not the world's spirit), so we can know the wonderful things God has freely given us.

¹³When we tell you these things, we do not use words that come from human wisdom. Instead, we speak words given to us by the Spirit, using the Spirit's words to explain spiritual truths.* ¹⁴But people who aren't spiritual* can't receive these truths from God's Spirit. It all sounds foolish to them and they can't understand it, for only those who are spiritual can understand what the Spirit means. ¹⁵Those who are spiritual can evaluate all things, but they themselves cannot be evaluated by others. ¹⁶For,

"Who can know the Lord's thoughts?
  Who knows enough to teach him?"*

But we understand these things, for we have the mind of Christ.

Paul and Apollos, Servants of Christ

3 Dear brothers and sisters,* when I was with you I couldn't talk to you as I would to spiritual people.* I had to talk as though you belonged to this world or as though you were infants in the Christian life.* ²I had to feed you with milk, not with solid food, because you weren't ready for anything stronger. And you still aren't ready, ³for you are still controlled by your sinful nature. You are jealous of one another and quarrel with each other. Doesn't that prove you are controlled by your sinful nature? Aren't you living like people of the world? ⁴When one of you says, "I am a follower of Paul," and another says, "I follow Apollos," aren't you acting just like people of the world?

⁵After all, who is Apollos? Who is Paul? We are only God's servants through whom you believed the Good News. Each of us did the work the Lord gave us. ⁶I planted the seed in your hearts, and Apollos watered it, but it was God who made it grow. ⁷It's not important who does the planting, or who does the watering. What's important is that God makes the seed grow. ⁸The one who plants and the one who waters work together with the same purpose. And both will be rewarded for their own hard work. ⁹For we are both God's workers. And you are God's field. You are God's building.

¹⁰Because of God's grace to me, I have laid the foundation like an expert builder. Now others are building on it. But whoever is building on this foundation must be very careful. ¹¹For no one can lay any foundation other than the one we already have—Jesus Christ.

¹²Anyone who builds on that foundation may use a variety of materials—gold, silver, jewels, wood, hay, or straw. ¹³But on the judgment day, fire will reveal what kind of work each builder has done. The fire will show if a person's work has any value. ¹⁴If the work survives, that builder will receive a reward. ¹⁵But if the work is burned up, the builder will suffer great loss. The builder will be saved, but like someone barely escaping through a wall of flames.

¹⁶Don't you realize that all of you together are the temple of God and that the Spirit of God lives in* you? ¹⁷God will destroy anyone who destroys this temple. For God's temple is holy, and you are that temple.

¹⁸Stop deceiving yourselves. If you think you are wise by this world's standards, you need to become a fool to be truly wise. ¹⁹For the wisdom of this world is foolishness to God. As the Scriptures say,

"He traps the wise
  in the snare of their own cleverness."*

1:31 Jer 9:24.   **2:1a** Greek *brothers.*   **2:1b** Greek *God's mystery;* other manuscripts read *God's testimony.*   **2:7** Greek *But we speak God's wisdom in a mystery.*   **2:9** Isa 64:4.   **2:10** Some manuscripts read *For.*   **2:13** Or *explaining spiritual truths in spiritual language,* or *explaining spiritual truths to spiritual people.*   **2:14** Or *who don't have the Spirit;* or *who have only physical life.* **2:16** Isa 40:13 (Greek version).   **3:1a** Greek *Brothers.*   **3:1b** Or *to people who have the Spirit.*   **3:1c** Greek *in Christ.* **3:16** Or *among.*   **3:19** Job 5:13.

²⁰And again,

> "The LORD knows the thoughts of the wise;
> he knows they are worthless."*

²¹So don't boast about following a particular human leader. For everything belongs to you—²²whether Paul or Apollos or Peter,* or the world, or life and death, or the present and the future. Everything belongs to you, ²³and you belong to Christ, and Christ belongs to God.

Paul's Relationship with the Corinthians

4 So look at Apollos and me as mere servants of Christ who have been put in charge of explaining God's mysteries. ²Now, a person who is put in charge as a manager must be faithful. ³As for me, it matters very little how I might be evaluated by you or by any human authority. I don't even trust my own judgment on this point. ⁴My conscience is clear, but that doesn't prove I'm right. It is the Lord himself who will examine me and decide.

⁵So don't make judgments about anyone ahead of time—before the Lord returns. For he will bring our darkest secrets to light and will reveal our private motives. Then God will give to each one whatever praise is due.

⁶Dear brothers and sisters,* I have used Apollos and myself to illustrate what I've been saying. If you pay attention to what I have quoted from the Scriptures,* you won't be proud of one of your leaders at the expense of another. ⁷For what gives you the right to make such a judgment? What do you have that God hasn't given you? And if everything you have is from God, why boast as though it were not a gift?

⁸You think you already have everything you need. You think you are already rich. You have begun to reign in God's kingdom without us! I wish you really were reigning already, for then we would be reigning with you. ⁹Instead, I sometimes think God has put us apostles on display, like prisoners of war at the end of a victor's parade, condemned to die. We have become a spectacle to the entire world—to people and angels alike.

¹⁰Our dedication to Christ makes us look like fools, but you claim to be so wise in Christ! We are weak, but you are so powerful! You are honored, but we are ridiculed. ¹¹Even now we go hungry and thirsty, and we don't have enough clothes to keep warm. We are often beaten and have no home. ¹²We work wearily with our own hands to earn our living. We bless those who curse us. We are patient with those who abuse us. ¹³We appeal gently when evil things are said about us. Yet we are treated like the world's garbage, like everybody's trash—right up to the present moment.

¹⁴I am not writing these things to shame you, but to warn you as my beloved children. ¹⁵For even if you had ten thousand others to teach you about Christ, you have only one spiritual father. For I became your father in Christ Jesus when I preached the Good News to you. ¹⁶So I urge you to imitate me.

¹⁷That's why I have sent Timothy, my beloved and faithful child in the Lord. He will remind you of how I follow Christ Jesus, just as I teach in all the churches wherever I go.

¹⁸Some of you have become arrogant, thinking I will not visit you again. ¹⁹But I will come—and soon—if the Lord lets me, and then I'll find out whether these arrogant people just give pretentious speeches or whether they really have God's power. ²⁰For the Kingdom of God is not just a lot of talk; it is living by God's power. ²¹Which do you choose? Should I come with a rod to punish you, or should I come with love and a gentle spirit?

Paul Condemns Spiritual Pride

5 I can hardly believe the report about the sexual immorality going on among you—something that even pagans don't do. I am told that a man in your church is living in sin with his stepmother.* ²You are so proud of yourselves, but you should be mourning in sorrow and shame. And you should remove this man from your fellowship.

³Even though I am not with you in person, I am with you in the Spirit.* And as though I were there, I have already passed judgment on this man ⁴in the name of the Lord Jesus. You must call a meeting of the church.* I will be present with you in spirit, and so will the power of our Lord Jesus. ⁵Then you must throw this man out and hand him over to Satan so that his sinful nature will be destroyed* and he himself* will be saved on the day the Lord* returns.

⁶Your boasting about this is terrible. Don't you realize that this sin is like a little yeast that spreads through the whole batch of dough? ⁷Get rid of the old "yeast" by removing this wicked person from among you. Then you will be a fresh batch of dough made without yeast, which is what you really are. Christ, our Passover Lamb, has been sacrificed for us.* ⁸So let us celebrate the festival, not with the old bread* of wickedness and evil, but with the new bread* of sincerity and truth.

⁹When I wrote to you before, I told you not to associate with people who indulge in sexual sin. ¹⁰But I wasn't talking about unbelievers who indulge in sexual sin, or are greedy, or cheat people, or worship idols. You would have to leave this world to avoid people like that. ¹¹I meant

---

3:20 Ps 94:11.   **3:22** Greek *Cephas.*   **4:6a** Greek *Brothers.*   **4:6b** Or *If you learn not to go beyond "what is written."*   **5:1** Greek *his father's wife.*   **5:3** Or *in spirit.*   **5:4** Or *In the name of the Lord Jesus, you must call a meeting of the church.*   **5:5a** Or *so that his body will be destroyed;* Greek reads *for the destruction of the flesh.*   **5:5b** Greek *and the spirit.*   **5:5c** Other manuscripts read *the Lord Jesus;* still others read *our Lord Jesus Christ.*   **5:7** Greek *has been sacrificed.*   **5:8a** Greek *not with old leaven.*   **5:8b** Greek *but with unleavened [bread].*

that you are not to associate with anyone who claims to be a believer* yet indulges in sexual sin, or is greedy, or worships idols, or is abusive, or is a drunkard, or cheats people. Don't even eat with such people.

¹²It isn't my responsibility to judge outsiders, but it certainly is your responsibility to judge those inside the church who are sinning. ¹³God will judge those on the outside; but as the Scriptures say, "You must remove the evil person from among you."*

Avoiding Lawsuits with Christians

6 When one of you has a dispute with another believer, how dare you file a lawsuit and ask a secular court to decide the matter instead of taking it to other believers*! ²Don't you realize that someday we believers will judge the world? And since you are going to judge the world, can't you decide even these little things among yourselves? ³Don't you realize that we will judge angels? So you should surely be able to resolve ordinary disputes in this life. ⁴If you have legal disputes about such matters, why go to outside judges who are not respected by the church? ⁵I am saying this to shame you. Isn't there anyone in all the church who is wise enough to decide these issues? ⁶But instead, one believer* sues another—right in front of unbelievers!

⁷Even to have such lawsuits with one another is a defeat for you. Why not just accept the injustice and leave it at that? Why not let yourselves be cheated? ⁸Instead, you yourselves are the ones who do wrong and cheat even your fellow believers.*

⁹Don't you realize that those who do wrong will not inherit the Kingdom of God? Don't fool yourselves. Those who indulge in sexual sin, or who worship idols, or commit adultery, or are male prostitutes, or practice homosexuality, ¹⁰or are thieves, or greedy people, or drunkards, or are abusive, or cheat people—none of these will inherit the Kingdom of God. ¹¹Some of you were once like that. But you were cleansed; you were made holy; you were made right with God by calling on the name of the Lord Jesus Christ and by the Spirit of our God.

Avoiding Sexual Sin

¹²You say, "I am allowed to do anything"—but not everything is good for you. And even though "I am allowed to do anything," I must not become a slave to anything. ¹³You say, "Food was made for the stomach, and the stomach for food." (This is true, though someday God will do away with both of them.) But you can't say that our bodies were made for sexual immorality. They were made for the Lord, and the Lord cares about our bodies. ¹⁴And God will raise us from the dead by his power, just as he raised our Lord from the dead.

¹⁵Don't you realize that your bodies are actually parts of Christ? Should a man take his body, which is part of Christ, and join it to a prostitute? Never! ¹⁶And don't you realize that if a man joins himself to a prostitute, he becomes one body with her? For the Scriptures say, "The two are united into one."* ¹⁷But the person who is joined to the Lord is one spirit with him.

¹⁸Run from sexual sin! No other sin so clearly affects the body as this one does. For sexual immorality is a sin against your own body. ¹⁹Don't you realize that your body is the temple of the Holy Spirit, who lives in you and was given to you by God? You do not belong to yourself, ²⁰for God bought you with a high price. So you must honor God with your body.

Instruction on Marriage

7 Now regarding the questions you asked in your letter. Yes, it is good to abstain from sexual relations.* ²But because there is so much sexual immorality, each man should have his own wife, and each woman should have her own husband.

³The husband should fulfill his wife's sexual needs, and the wife should fulfill her husband's needs. ⁴The wife gives authority over her body to her husband, and the husband gives authority over his body to his wife.

⁵Do not deprive each other of sexual relations, unless you both agree to refrain from sexual intimacy for a limited time so you can give yourselves more completely to prayer. Afterward, you should come together again so that Satan won't be able to tempt you because of your lack of self-control. ⁶I say this as a concession, not as a command. ⁷But I wish everyone were single, just as I am. Yet each person has a special gift from God, of one kind or another.

⁸So I say to those who aren't married and to widows—it's better to stay unmarried, just as I am. ⁹But if they can't control themselves, they should go ahead and marry. It's better to marry than to burn with lust.

¹⁰But for those who are married, I have a command that comes not from me, but from the Lord.* A wife must not leave her husband. ¹¹But if she does leave him, let her remain single or else be reconciled to him. And the husband must not leave his wife.

¹²Now, I will speak to the rest of you, though I do not have a direct command from the Lord. If a Christian man* has a wife who is not a believer and she is willing to continue living with him, he must not leave her. ¹³And if a Christian woman has a husband who is not a believer and he is willing to continue living with her, she must not leave him. ¹⁴For the Christian wife brings

---

5:11 Greek *a brother.*   **5:13** Deut 17:7.   **6:1** Greek *God's holy people;* also in 6:2.   **6:6** Greek *one brother.*   **6:8** Greek *even the brothers.*   **6:16** Gen 2:24.   **7:1** Or *to live a celibate life;* Greek reads *It is good for a man not to touch a woman.*   **7:10** See Matt 5:32; 19:9; Mark 10:11-12; Luke 16:18.   **7:12** Greek *a brother.*

holiness to her marriage, and the Christian husband* brings holiness to his marriage. Otherwise, your children would not be holy, but now they are holy. ¹⁵(But if the husband or wife who isn't a believer insists on leaving, let them go. In such cases the Christian husband or wife* is no longer bound to the other, for God has called you* to live in peace.) ¹⁶Don't you wives realize that your husbands might be saved because of you? And don't you husbands realize that your wives might be saved because of you?

¹⁷Each of you should continue to live in whatever situation the Lord has placed you, and remain as you were when God first called you. This is my rule for all the churches. ¹⁸For instance, a man who was circumcised before he became a believer should not try to reverse it. And the man who was uncircumcised when he became a believer should not be circumcised now. ¹⁹For it makes no difference whether or not a man has been circumcised. The important thing is to keep God's commandments.

²⁰Yes, each of you should remain as you were when God called you. ²¹Are you a slave? Don't let that worry you—but if you get a chance to be free, take it. ²²And remember, if you were a slave when the Lord called you, you are now free in the Lord. And if you were free when the Lord called you, you are now a slave of Christ. ²³God paid a high price for you, so don't be enslaved by the world.* ²⁴Each of you, dear brothers and sisters,* should remain as you were when God first called you.

²⁵Now regarding your question about the young women who are not yet married. I do not have a command from the Lord for them. But the Lord in his mercy has given me wisdom that can be trusted, and I will share it with you. ²⁶Because of the present crisis,* I think it is best to remain as you are. ²⁷If you have a wife, do not seek to end the marriage. If you do not have a wife, do not seek to get married. ²⁸But if you do get married, it is not a sin. And if a young woman gets married, it is not a sin. However, those who get married at this time will have troubles, and I am trying to spare you those problems.

²⁹But let me say this, dear brothers and sisters: The time that remains is very short. So from now on, those with wives should not focus only on their marriage. ³⁰Those who weep or who rejoice or who buy things should not be absorbed by their weeping or their joy or their possessions. ³¹Those who use the things of the world should not become attached to them. For this world as we know it will soon pass away.

³²I want you to be free from the concerns of this life. An unmarried man can spend his time doing the Lord's work and thinking how to please him. ³³But a married man has to think about his earthly responsibilities and how to please his wife. ³⁴His interests are divided. In the same way, a woman who is no longer married or has never been married can be devoted to the Lord and holy in body and in spirit. But a married woman has to think about her earthly responsibilities and how to please her husband. ³⁵I am saying this for your benefit, not to place restrictions on you. I want you to do whatever will help you serve the Lord best, with as few distractions as possible.

³⁶But if a man thinks that he's treating his fiancée improperly and will inevitably give in to his passion, let him marry her as he wishes. It is not a sin. ³⁷But if he has decided firmly not to marry and there is no urgency and he can control his passion, he does well not to marry. ³⁸So the person who marries his fiancée does well, and the person who doesn't marry does even better.

³⁹A wife is bound to her husband as long as he lives. If her husband dies, she is free to marry anyone she wishes, but only if he loves the Lord.* ⁴⁰But in my opinion it would be better for her to stay single, and I think I am giving you counsel from God's Spirit when I say this.

Food Sacrificed to Idols

8 Now regarding your question about food that has been offered to idols. Yes, we know that "we all have knowledge" about this issue. But while knowledge makes us feel important, it is love that strengthens the church. ²Anyone who claims to know all the answers doesn't really know very much. ³But the person who loves God is the one whom God recognizes.*

⁴So, what about eating meat that has been offered to idols? Well, we all know that an idol is not really a god and that there is only one God. ⁵There may be so-called gods both in heaven and on earth, and some people actually worship many gods and many lords. ⁶But we know that there is only one God, the Father, who created everything, and we live for him. And there is only one Lord, Jesus Christ, through whom God made everything and through whom we have been given life.

⁷However, not all believers know this. Some are accustomed to thinking of idols as being real, so when they eat food that has been offered to idols, they think of it as the worship of real gods, and their weak consciences are violated. ⁸It's true that we can't win God's approval by what we eat. We don't lose anything if we don't eat it, and we don't gain anything if we do.

⁹But you must be careful so that your freedom does not cause others with a weaker conscience to stumble. ¹⁰For if others see you—with your "superior knowledge"—eating in the temple of

7:14 Greek *the brother.* **7:15a** Greek *the brother or sister.* **7:15b** Some manuscripts read *us.* **7:23** Greek *don't become slaves of people.* **7:24** Greek *brothers;* also in 7:29. **7:26** Or *the pressures of life.* **7:39** Greek *but only in the Lord.* **8:3** Some manuscripts read *the person who loves has full knowledge.*

an idol, won't they be encouraged to violate their conscience by eating food that has been offered to an idol? 11So because of your superior knowledge, a weak believer* for whom Christ died will be destroyed. 12And when you sin against other believers* by encouraging them to do something they believe is wrong, you are sinning against Christ. 13So if what I eat causes another believer to sin, I will never eat meat again as long as I live—for I don't want to cause another believer to stumble.

Paul Gives Up His Rights

9 Am I not as free as anyone else? Am I not an apostle? Haven't I seen Jesus our Lord with my own eyes? Isn't it because of my work that you belong to the Lord? 2Even if others think I am not an apostle, I certainly am to you. You yourselves are proof that I am the Lord's apostle.

3This is my answer to those who question my authority.* 4Don't we have the right to live in your homes and share your meals? 5Don't we have the right to bring a Christian wife with us as the other apostles and the Lord's brothers do, and as Peter* does? 6Or is it only Barnabas and I who have to work to support ourselves?

7What soldier has to pay his own expenses? What farmer plants a vineyard and doesn't have the right to eat some of its fruit? What shepherd cares for a flock of sheep and isn't allowed to drink some of the milk? 8Am I expressing merely a human opinion, or does the law say the same thing? 9For the law of Moses says, "You must not muzzle an ox to keep it from eating as it treads out the grain."* Was God thinking only about oxen when he said this? 10Wasn't he actually speaking to us? Yes, it was written for us, so that the one who plows and the one who threshes the grain might both expect a share of the harvest.

11Since we have planted spiritual seed among you, aren't we entitled to a harvest of physical food and drink? 12If you support others who preach to you, shouldn't we have an even greater right to be supported? But we have never used this right. We would rather put up with anything than be an obstacle to the Good News about Christ.

13Don't you realize that those who work in the temple get their meals from the offerings brought to the temple? And those who serve at the altar get a share of the sacrificial offerings. 14In the same way, the Lord ordered that those who preach the Good News should be supported by those who benefit from it. 15Yet I have never used any of these rights. And I am not writing this to suggest that I want to start now. In fact, I would rather die than lose my right to boast about preaching without charge. 16Yet preaching the Good News is not something I can boast about. I am compelled by God to do it. How terrible for me if I didn't preach the Good News!

17If I were doing this on my own initiative, I would deserve payment. But I have no choice, for God has given me this sacred trust. 18What then is my pay? It is the opportunity to preach the Good News without charging anyone. That's why I never demand my rights when I preach the Good News.

19Even though I am a free man with no master, I have become a slave to all people to bring many to Christ. 20When I was with the Jews, I lived like a Jew to bring the Jews to Christ. When I was with those who follow the Jewish law, I too lived under that law. Even though I am not subject to the law, I did this so I could bring to Christ those who are under the law. 21When I am with the Gentiles who do not follow the Jewish law,* I too live apart from that law so I can bring them to Christ. But I do not ignore the law of God; I obey the law of Christ.

22When I am with those who are weak, I share their weakness, for I want to bring the weak to Christ. Yes, I try to find common ground with everyone, doing everything I can to save some. 23I do everything to spread the Good News and share in its blessings.

24Don't you realize that in a race everyone runs, but only one person gets the prize? So run to win! 25All athletes are disciplined in their training. They do it to win a prize that will fade away, but we do it for an eternal prize. 26So I run with purpose in every step. I am not just shadowboxing. 27I discipline my body like an athlete, training it to do what it should. Otherwise, I fear that after preaching to others I myself might be disqualified.

Lessons from Israel's Idolatry

10 I don't want you to forget, dear brothers and sisters,* about our ancestors in the wilderness long ago. All of them were guided by a cloud that moved ahead of them, and all of them walked through the sea on dry ground. 2In the cloud and in the sea, all of them were baptized as followers of Moses. 3All of them ate the same spiritual food, 4and all of them drank the same spiritual water. For they drank from the spiritual rock that traveled with them, and that rock was Christ. 5Yet God was not pleased with most of them, and their bodies were scattered in the wilderness.

6These things happened as a warning to us, so that we would not crave evil things as they did, 7or worship idols as some of them did. As the Scriptures say, "The people celebrated with feasting and drinking, and they indulged in pagan revelry."* 8And we must not engage in sexual immorality as some of them did, causing 23,000 of them to die in one day.

8:11 Greek *brother*; also in 8:13.   **8:12** Greek *brothers*.   **9:3** Greek *those who examine me*.   **9:5** Greek *Cephas*.   **9:9** Deut 25:4.
9:21 Greek *those without the law*.   **10:1** Greek *brothers*.   **10:7** Exod 32:6.

⁹Nor should we put Christ* to the test, as some of them did and then died from snakebites. ¹⁰And don't grumble as some of them did, and then were destroyed by the angel of death. ¹¹These things happened to them as examples for us. They were written down to warn us who live at the end of the age.

¹²If you think you are standing strong, be careful not to fall. ¹³The temptations in your life are no different from what others experience. And God is faithful. He will not allow the temptation to be more than you can stand. When you are tempted, he will show you a way out so that you can endure.

¹⁴So, my dear friends, flee from the worship of idols. ¹⁵You are reasonable people. Decide for yourselves if what I am saying is true. ¹⁶When we bless the cup at the Lord's Table, aren't we sharing in the blood of Christ? And when we break the bread, aren't we sharing in the body of Christ? ¹⁷And though we are many, we all eat from one loaf of bread, showing that we are one body. ¹⁸Think about the people of Israel. Weren't they united by eating the sacrifices at the altar?

¹⁹What am I trying to say? Am I saying that food offered to idols has some significance, or that idols are real gods? ²⁰No, not at all. I am saying that these sacrifices are offered to demons, not to God. And I don't want you to participate with demons. ²¹You cannot drink from the cup of the Lord and from the cup of demons, too. You cannot eat at the Lord's Table and at the table of demons, too. ²²What? Do we dare to rouse the Lord's jealousy? Do you think we are stronger than he is?

²³You say, "I am allowed to do anything"*—but not everything is good for you. You say, "I am allowed to do anything"—but not everything is beneficial. ²⁴Don't be concerned for your own good but for the good of others.

²⁵So you may eat any meat that is sold in the marketplace without raising questions of conscience. ²⁶For "the earth is the Lord's, and everything in it."*

²⁷If someone who isn't a believer asks you home for dinner, accept the invitation if you want to. Eat whatever is offered to you without raising questions of conscience. ²⁸(But suppose someone tells you, "This meat was offered to an idol." Don't eat it, out of consideration for the conscience of the one who told you. ²⁹It might not be a matter of conscience for you, but it is for the other person.) For why should my freedom be limited by what someone else thinks? ³⁰If I can thank God for the food and enjoy it, why should I be condemned for eating it?

³¹So whether you eat or drink, or whatever you do, do it all for the glory of God. ³²Don't give offense to Jews or Gentiles* or the church of God. ³³I, too, try to please everyone in everything I do. I don't just do what is best for me; I do what is best for others so that many may be saved. ¹¹:¹And you should imitate me, just as I imitate Christ.

Instructions for Public Worship

11 ²I am so glad that you always keep me in your thoughts, and that you are following the teachings I passed on to you. ³But there is one thing I want you to know: The head of every man is Christ, the head of woman is man, and the head of Christ is God.* ⁴A man dishonors his head* if he covers his head while praying or prophesying. ⁵But a woman dishonors her head* if she prays or prophesies without a covering on her head, for this is the same as shaving her head. ⁶Yes, if she refuses to wear a head covering, she should cut off all her hair! But since it is shameful for a woman to have her hair cut or her head shaved, she should wear a covering.*

⁷A man should not wear anything on his head when worshiping, for man is made in God's image and reflects God's glory. And woman reflects man's glory. ⁸For the first man didn't come from woman, but the first woman came from man. ⁹And man was not made for woman, but woman was made for man. ¹⁰For this reason, and because the angels are watching, a woman should wear a covering on her head to show she is under authority.*

¹¹But among the Lord's people, women are not independent of men, and men are not independent of women. ¹²For although the first woman came from man, every other man was born from a woman, and everything comes from God.

¹³Judge for yourselves. Is it right for a woman to pray to God in public without covering her head? ¹⁴Isn't it obvious that it's disgraceful for a man to have long hair? ¹⁵And isn't long hair a woman's pride and joy? For it has been given to her as a covering. ¹⁶But if anyone wants to argue about this, I simply say that we have no other custom than this, and neither do God's other churches.

Order at the Lord's Supper

¹⁷But in the following instructions, I cannot praise you. For it sounds as if more harm than good is done when you meet together. ¹⁸First, I hear that there are divisions among you when you meet as a church, and to some extent I believe it. ¹⁹But, of course, there must be divisions among you so that you who have God's approval will be recognized! ²⁰When you meet together, you are not really interested in the Lord's Supper. ²¹For some of you hurry to eat your own meal without sharing

---

10:9 Some manuscripts read *the Lord*. **10:23** Greek *All things are lawful*; also in 10:23b. **10:26** Ps 24:1. **10:32** Greek *or Greeks*. **11:3** Or *to know: The source of every man is Christ, the source of woman is man, and the source of Christ is God.* Or *to know: Every man is responsible to Christ, a woman is responsible to her husband, and Christ is responsible to God.* **11:4** Or *dishonors Christ.* **11:5** Or *dishonors her husband.* **11:6** Or *should have long hair.* **11:10** Greek *should have an authority on her head.*

with others. As a result, some go hungry while others get drunk. ²²What? Don't you have your own homes for eating and drinking? Or do you really want to disgrace God's church and shame the poor? What am I supposed to say? Do you want me to praise you? Well, I certainly will not praise you for this!

²³For I pass on to you what I received from the Lord himself. On the night when he was betrayed, the Lord Jesus took some bread ²⁴and gave thanks to God for it. Then he broke it in pieces and said, "This is my body, which is given for you.* Do this to remember me." ²⁵In the same way, he took the cup of wine after supper, saying, "This cup is the new covenant between God and his people—an agreement confirmed with my blood. Do this to remember me as often as you drink it." ²⁶For every time you eat this bread and drink this cup, you are announcing the Lord's death until he comes again.

²⁷So anyone who eats this bread or drinks this cup of the Lord unworthily is guilty of sinning against* the body and blood of the Lord. ²⁸That is why you should examine yourself before eating the bread and drinking the cup. ²⁹For if you eat the bread or drink the cup without honoring the body of Christ,* you are eating and drinking God's judgment upon yourself. ³⁰That is why many of you are weak and sick and some have even died.

³¹But if we would examine ourselves, we would not be judged by God in this way. ³²Yet when we are judged by the Lord, we are being disciplined so that we will not be condemned along with the world.

³³So, my dear brothers and sisters,* when you gather for the Lord's Supper, wait for each other. ³⁴If you are really hungry, eat at home so you won't bring judgment upon yourselves when you meet together. I'll give you instructions about the other matters after I arrive.

Spiritual Gifts

12 Now, dear brothers and sisters,* regarding your question about the special abilities the Spirit gives us. I don't want you to misunderstand this. ²You know that when you were still pagans, you were led astray and swept along in worshiping speechless idols. ³So I want you to know that no one speaking by the Spirit of God will curse Jesus, and no one can say Jesus is Lord, except by the Holy Spirit.

⁴There are different kinds of spiritual gifts, but the same Spirit is the source of them all. ⁵There are different kinds of service, but we serve the same Lord. ⁶God works in different ways, but it is the same God who does the work in all of us.

⁷A spiritual gift is given to each of us so we can help each other. ⁸To one person the Spirit gives the ability to give wise advice*; to another the same Spirit gives a message of special knowledge.* ⁹The same Spirit gives great faith to another, and to someone else the one Spirit gives the gift of healing. ¹⁰He gives one person the power to perform miracles, and another the ability to prophesy. He gives someone else the ability to discern whether a message is from the Spirit of God or from another spirit. Still another person is given the ability to speak in unknown languages,* while another is given the ability to interpret what is being said. ¹¹It is the one and only Spirit who distributes all these gifts. He alone decides which gift each person should have.

One Body with Many Parts

¹²The human body has many parts, but the many parts make up one whole body. So it is with the body of Christ. ¹³Some of us are Jews, some are Gentiles,* some are slaves, and some are free. But we have all been baptized into one body by one Spirit, and we all share the same Spirit.*

¹⁴Yes, the body has many different parts, not just one part. ¹⁵If the foot says, "I am not a part of the body because I am not a hand," that does not make it any less a part of the body. ¹⁶And if the ear says, "I am not part of the body because I am not an eye," would that make it any less a part of the body? ¹⁷If the whole body were an eye, how would you hear? Or if your whole body were an ear, how would you smell anything?

¹⁸But our bodies have many parts, and God has put each part just where he wants it. ¹⁹How strange a body would be if it had only one part! ²⁰Yes, there are many parts, but only one body. ²¹The eye can never say to the hand, "I don't need you." The head can't say to the feet, "I don't need you."

²²In fact, some parts of the body that seem weakest and least important are actually the most necessary. ²³And the parts we regard as less honorable are those we clothe with the greatest care. So we carefully protect those parts that should not be seen, ²⁴while the more honorable parts do not require this special care. So God has put the body together such that extra honor and care are given to those parts that have less dignity. ²⁵This makes for harmony among the members, so that all the members care for each other. ²⁶If one part suffers, all the parts suffer with it, and if one part is honored, all the parts are glad.

²⁷All of you together are Christ's body, and each of you is a part of it. ²⁸Here are some of the parts God has appointed for the church:

first are apostles,
second are prophets,

11:24 Greek *which is for you;* other manuscripts read *which is broken for you.*   **11:27** Or *is responsible for.*   **11:29** Greek *the body;* other manuscripts read *the Lord's body.*   **11:33** Greek *brothers.*   **12:1** Greek *brothers.*   **12:8a** Or *gives a word of wisdom.* **12:8b** Or *gives a word of knowledge.*   **12:10** Or *in various tongues;* also in 12:28, 30.   **12:13a** Greek *some are Greeks.* **12:13b** Greek *we were all given one Spirit to drink.*

third are teachers,
then those who do miracles,
those who have the gift of healing,
those who can help others,
those who have the gift of leadership,
those who speak in unknown languages.

²⁹Are we all apostles? Are we all prophets? Are we all teachers? Do we all have the power to do miracles? ³⁰Do we all have the gift of healing? Do we all have the ability to speak in unknown languages? Do we all have the ability to interpret unknown languages? Of course not! ³¹So you should earnestly desire the most helpful gifts.

But now let me show you a way of life that is best of all.

Love Is the Greatest

13 If I could speak all the languages of earth and of angels, but didn't love others, I would only be a noisy gong or a clanging cymbal. ²If I had the gift of prophecy, and if I understood all of God's secret plans and possessed all knowledge, and if I had such faith that I could move mountains, but didn't love others, I would be nothing. ³If I gave everything I have to the poor and even sacrificed my body, I could boast about it;* but if I didn't love others, I would have gained nothing.

⁴Love is patient and kind. Love is not jealous or boastful or proud ⁵or rude. It does not demand its own way. It is not irritable, and it keeps no record of being wronged. ⁶It does not rejoice about injustice but rejoices whenever the truth wins out. ⁷Love never gives up, never loses faith, is always hopeful, and endures through every circumstance.

⁸Prophecy and speaking in unknown languages* and special knowledge will become useless. But love will last forever! ⁹Now our knowledge is partial and incomplete, and even the gift of prophecy reveals only part of the whole picture! ¹⁰But when the time of perfection comes, these partial things will become useless.

¹¹When I was a child, I spoke and thought and reasoned as a child. But when I grew up, I put away childish things. ¹²Now we see things imperfectly, like puzzling reflections in a mirror, but then we will see everything with perfect clarity.* All that I know now is partial and incomplete, but then I will know everything completely, just as God now knows me completely.

¹³Three things will last forever—faith, hope, and love—and the greatest of these is love.

Tongues and Prophecy

14 Let love be your highest goal! But you should also desire the special abilities the Spirit gives—especially the ability to proph-

esy. ²For if you have the ability to speak in tongues,* you will be talking only to God, since people won't be able to understand you. You will be speaking by the power of the Spirit,* but it will all be mysterious. ³But one who prophesies strengthens others, encourages them, and comforts them. ⁴A person who speaks in tongues is strengthened personally, but one who speaks a word of prophecy strengthens the entire church.

⁵I wish you could all speak in tongues, but even more I wish you could all prophesy. For prophecy is greater than speaking in tongues, unless someone interprets what you are saying so that the whole church will be strengthened.

⁶Dear brothers and sisters,* if I should come to you speaking in an unknown language,* how would that help you? But if I bring you a revelation or some special knowledge or prophecy or teaching, that will be helpful. ⁷Even lifeless instruments like the flute or the harp must play the notes clearly, or no one will recognize the melody. ⁸And if the bugler doesn't sound a clear call, how will the soldiers know they are being called to battle?

⁹It's the same for you. If you speak to people in words they don't understand, how will they know what you are saying? You might as well be talking into empty space.

¹⁰There are many different languages in the world, and every language has meaning. ¹¹But if I don't understand a language, I will be a foreigner to someone who speaks it, and the one who speaks it will be a foreigner to me. ¹²And the same is true for you. Since you are so eager to have the special abilities the Spirit gives, seek those that will strengthen the whole church.

¹³So anyone who speaks in tongues should pray also for the ability to interpret what has been said. ¹⁴For if I pray in tongues, my spirit is praying, but I don't understand what I am saying.

¹⁵Well then, what shall I do? I will pray in the spirit,* and I will also pray in words I understand. I will sing in the spirit, and I will also sing in words I understand. ¹⁶For if you praise God only in the spirit, how can those who don't understand you praise God along with you? How can they join you in giving thanks when they don't understand what you are saying? ¹⁷You will be giving thanks very well, but it won't strengthen the people who hear you.

¹⁸I thank God that I speak in tongues more than any of you. ¹⁹But in a church meeting I would rather speak five understandable words to help others than ten thousand words in an unknown language.

²⁰Dear brothers and sisters, don't be childish in your understanding of these things. Be innocent as babies when it comes to evil, but be ma-

---

13:3 Some manuscripts read *sacrificed my body to be burned.* **13:8** Or *in tongues.* **13:12** Greek *see face to face.* **14:2a** Or *in unknown languages; also in* 14:4, 5, 13, 14, 18, 22, 26, 27, 28, 39. **14:2b** Or *speaking in your spirit.* **14:6a** Greek *brothers; also in* 14:20, 26, 39. **14:6b** Or *in tongues; also in* 14:19, 23. **14:15** Or *in the Spirit; also in* 14:15b, 16.

ture in understanding matters of this kind. [21]It is written in the Scriptures:*

"I will speak to my own people
through strange languages
and through the lips of foreigners.
But even then, they will not listen to me,"*
says the LORD.

[22]So you see that speaking in tongues is a sign, not for believers, but for unbelievers. Prophecy, however, is for the benefit of believers, not unbelievers. [23]Even so, if unbelievers or people who don't understand these things come into your church meeting and hear everyone speaking in an unknown language, they will think you are crazy. [24]But if all of you are prophesying, and unbelievers or people who don't understand these things come into your meeting, they will be convicted of sin and judged by what you say. [25]As they listen, their secret thoughts will be exposed, and they will fall to their knees and worship God, declaring, "God is truly here among you."

A Call to Orderly Worship

[26]Well, my brothers and sisters, let's summarize. When you meet together, one will sing, another will teach, another will tell some special revelation God has given, one will speak in tongues, and another will interpret what is said. But everything that is done must strengthen all of you.

[27]No more than two or three should speak in tongues. They must speak one at a time, and someone must interpret what they say. [28]But if no one is present who can interpret, they must be silent in your church meeting and speak in tongues to God privately.

[29]Let two or three people prophesy, and let the others evaluate what is said. [30]But if someone is prophesying and another person receives a revelation from the Lord, the one who is speaking must stop. [31]In this way, all who prophesy will have a turn to speak, one after the other, so that everyone will learn and be encouraged. [32]Remember that people who prophesy are in control of their spirit and can take turns. [33]For God is not a God of disorder but of peace, as in all the meetings of God's holy people.*

[34]Women should be silent during the church meetings. It is not proper for them to speak. They should be submissive, just as the law says. [35]If they have any questions, they should ask their husbands at home, for it is improper for women to speak in church meetings.*

[36]Or do you think God's word originated with you Corinthians? Are you the only ones to whom it was given? [37]If you claim to be a prophet or think you are spiritual, you should recognize that what I am saying is a command from the Lord himself. [38]But if you do not recognize this, you yourself will not be recognized.*

[39]So, my dear brothers and sisters, be eager to prophesy, and don't forbid speaking in tongues. [40]But be sure that everything is done properly and in order.

The Resurrection of Christ

15 Let me now remind you, dear brothers and sisters,* of the Good News I preached to you before. You welcomed it then, and you still stand firm in it. [2]It is this Good News that saves you if you continue to believe the message I told you—unless, of course, you believed something that was never true in the first place.*

[3]I passed on to you what was most important and what had also been passed on to me. Christ died for our sins, just as the Scriptures said. [4]He was buried, and he was raised from the dead on the third day, just as the Scriptures said. [5]He was seen by Peter* and then by the Twelve. [6]After that, he was seen by more than 500 of his followers* at one time, most of whom are still alive, though some have died. [7]Then he was seen by James and later by all the apostles. [8]Last of all, as though I had been born at the wrong time, I also saw him. [9]For I am the least of all the apostles. In fact, I'm not even worthy to be called an apostle after the way I persecuted God's church.

[10]But whatever I am now, it is all because God poured out his special favor on me—and not without results. For I have worked harder than any of the other apostles; yet it was not I but God who was working through me by his grace. [11]So it makes no difference whether I preach or they preach, for we all preach the same message you have already believed.

The Resurrection of the Dead

[12]But tell me this—since we preach that Christ rose from the dead, why are some of you saying there will be no resurrection of the dead? [13]For if there is no resurrection of the dead, then Christ has not been raised either. [14]And if Christ has not been raised, then all our preaching is useless, and your faith is useless. [15]And we apostles would all be lying about God—for we have said that God raised Christ from the grave. But that can't be true if there is no resurrection of the dead. [16]And if there is no resurrection of the dead, then Christ has not been raised. [17]And if Christ has not been raised, then your faith is useless and you are still guilty of your sins. [18]In that case, all who have died believing in Christ are lost! [19]And if our hope in Christ is only for this life, we are more to be pitied than anyone in the world.

14:21a Greek *in the law.* **14:21b** Isa 28:11-12. **14:33** The phrase *as in all the meetings of God's holy people* could instead be joined to the beginning of 14:34. **14:35** Some manuscripts place verses 34-35 after 14:40. **14:38** Some manuscripts read *If you are ignorant of this, stay in your ignorance.* **15:1** Greek *brothers;* also in 15:31, 50, 58. **15:2** Or *unless you never believed it in the first place.* **15:5** Greek *Cephas.* **15:6** Greek *the brothers.*

²⁰But in fact, Christ has been raised from the dead. He is the first of a great harvest of all who have died.

²¹So you see, just as death came into the world through a man, now the resurrection from the dead has begun through another man. ²²Just as everyone dies because we all belong to Adam, everyone who belongs to Christ will be given new life. ²³But there is an order to this resurrection: Christ was raised as the first of the harvest; then all who belong to Christ will be raised when he comes back.

²⁴After that the end will come, when he will turn the Kingdom over to God the Father, having destroyed every ruler and authority and power. ²⁵For Christ must reign until he humbles all his enemies beneath his feet. ²⁶And the last enemy to be destroyed is death. ²⁷For the Scriptures say, "God has put all things under his authority."* (Of course, when it says "all things are under his authority," that does not include God himself, who gave Christ his authority.) ²⁸Then, when all things are under his authority, the Son will put himself under God's authority, so that God, who gave his Son authority over all things, will be utterly supreme over everything everywhere.

²⁹If the dead will not be raised, what point is there in people being baptized for those who are dead? Why do it unless the dead will someday rise again?

³⁰And why should we ourselves risk our lives hour by hour? ³¹For I swear, dear brothers and sisters, that I face death daily. This is as certain as my pride in what Christ Jesus our Lord has done in you. ³²And what value was there in fighting wild beasts—those people of Ephesus*—if there will be no resurrection from the dead? And if there is no resurrection, "Let's feast and drink, for tomorrow we die!"* ³³Don't be fooled by those who say such things, for "bad company corrupts good character." ³⁴Think carefully about what is right, and stop sinning. For to your shame I say that some of you don't know God at all.

The Resurrection Body

³⁵But someone may ask, "How will the dead be raised? What kind of bodies will they have?" ³⁶What a foolish question! When you put a seed into the ground, it doesn't grow into a plant unless it dies first. ³⁷And what you put in the ground is not the plant that will grow, but only a bare seed of wheat or whatever you are planting. ³⁸Then God gives it the new body he wants it to have. A different plant grows from each kind of seed. ³⁹Similarly there are different kinds of flesh—one kind for humans, another for animals, another for birds, and another for fish.

⁴⁰There are also bodies in the heavens and bodies on the earth. The glory of the heavenly bodies is different from the glory of the earthly bodies. ⁴¹The sun has one kind of glory, while the moon and stars each have another kind. And even the stars differ from each other in their glory.

⁴²It is the same way with the resurrection of the dead. Our earthly bodies are planted in the ground when we die, but they will be raised to live forever. ⁴³Our bodies are buried in brokenness, but they will be raised in glory. They are buried in weakness, but they will be raised in strength. ⁴⁴They are buried as natural human bodies, but they will be raised as spiritual bodies. For just as there are natural bodies, there are also spiritual bodies.

⁴⁵The Scriptures tell us, "The first man, Adam, became a living person."* But the last Adam—that is, Christ—is a life-giving Spirit. ⁴⁶What comes first is the natural body, then the spiritual body comes later. ⁴⁷Adam, the first man, was made from the dust of the earth, while Christ, the second man, came from heaven. ⁴⁸Earthly people are like the earthly man, and heavenly people are like the heavenly man. ⁴⁹Just as we are now like the earthly man, we will someday be like* the heavenly man.

⁵⁰What I am saying, dear brothers and sisters, is that our physical bodies cannot inherit the Kingdom of God. These dying bodies cannot inherit what will last forever.

⁵¹But let me reveal to you a wonderful secret. We will not all die, but we will all be transformed! ⁵²It will happen in a moment, in the blink of an eye, when the last trumpet is blown. For when the trumpet sounds, those who have died will be raised to live forever. And we who are living will also be transformed. ⁵³For our dying bodies must be transformed into bodies that will never die; our mortal bodies must be transformed into immortal bodies.

⁵⁴Then, when our dying bodies have been transformed into bodies that will never die,* this Scripture will be fulfilled:

"Death is swallowed up in victory.*
⁵⁵ O death, where is your victory?
    O death, where is your sting?*"

⁵⁶For sin is the sting that results in death, and the law gives sin its power. ⁵⁷But thank God! He gives us victory over sin and death through our Lord Jesus Christ.

⁵⁸So, my dear brothers and sisters, be strong and immovable. Always work enthusiastically for the Lord, for you know that nothing you do for the Lord is ever useless.

The Collection for Jerusalem

16 Now regarding your question about the money being collected for God's people in Jerusalem. You should follow the same proce-

---

15:27 Ps 8:6.   **15:32a** Greek *fighting wild beasts in Ephesus.*   **15:32b** Isa 22:13.   **15:45** Gen 2:7.   **15:49** Some manuscripts read *let us be like.*   **15:54a** Some manuscripts add *and our mortal bodies have been transformed into immortal bodies.*   **15:54b** Isa 25:8.
15:55 Hos 13:14 (Greek version).

dure I gave to the churches in Galatia. ²On the first day of each week, you should each put aside a portion of the money you have earned. Don't wait until I get there and then try to collect it all at once. ³When I come, I will write letters of recommendation for the messengers you choose to deliver your gift to Jerusalem. ⁴And if it seems appropriate for me to go along, they can travel with me.

Paul's Final Instructions

⁵I am coming to visit you after I have been to Macedonia,* for I am planning to travel through Macedonia. ⁶Perhaps I will stay awhile with you, possibly all winter, and then you can send me on my way to my next destination. ⁷This time I don't want to make just a short visit and then go right on. I want to come and stay awhile, if the Lord will let me. ⁸In the meantime, I will be staying here at Ephesus until the Festival of Pentecost. ⁹There is a wide-open door for a great work here, although many oppose me.

¹⁰When Timothy comes, don't intimidate him. He is doing the Lord's work, just as I am. ¹¹Don't let anyone treat him with contempt. Send him on his way with your blessing when he returns to me. I expect him to come with the other believers.*

¹²Now about our brother Apollos—I urged him to visit you with the other believers, but he was not willing to go right now. He will see you later when he has the opportunity.

¹³Be on guard. Stand firm in the faith. Be courageous.* Be strong. ¹⁴And do everything with love.

¹⁵You know that Stephanas and his household were the first of the harvest of believers in Greece,* and they are spending their lives in service to God's people. I urge you, dear brothers and sisters,* ¹⁶to submit to them and others like them who serve with such devotion. ¹⁷I am very glad that Stephanas, Fortunatus, and Achaicus have come here. They have been providing the help you weren't here to give me. ¹⁸They have been a wonderful encouragement to me, as they have been to you. You must show your appreciation to all who serve so well.

Paul's Final Greetings

¹⁹The churches here in the province of Asia* send greetings in the Lord, as do Aquila and Priscilla* and all the others who gather in their home for church meetings. ²⁰All the brothers and sisters here send greetings to you. Greet each other with Christian love.*

²¹HERE IS MY GREETING IN MY OWN HANDWRITING—PAUL.

²²If anyone does not love the Lord, that person is cursed. Our Lord, come!*

²³May the grace of the Lord Jesus be with you. ²⁴My love to all of you in Christ Jesus.*

16:5 *Macedonia* was in the northern region of Greece.   **16:11** Greek *with the brothers;* also in 16:12.   **16:13** Greek *Be men.*
16:15a Greek *in Achaia,* the southern region of the Greek peninsula.   **16:15b** Greek *brothers;* also in 16:20.   **16:19a** *Asia* was a
Roman province in what is now western Turkey.   **16:19b** Greek *Prisca.*   **16:20** Greek *with a sacred kiss.*   **16:22** From Aramaic,
Marana tha. Some manuscripts read *Maran atha, "Our Lord has come."*   **16:24** Some manuscripts add *Amen.*

2 Corinthians

Greetings from Paul

1 This letter is from Paul, chosen by the will of God to be an apostle of Christ Jesus, and from our brother Timothy.

I am writing to God's church in Corinth and to all of his holy people throughout Greece.*

²May God our Father and the Lord Jesus Christ give you grace and peace.

God Offers Comfort to All

³All praise to God, the Father of our Lord Jesus Christ. God is our merciful Father and the source of all comfort. ⁴He comforts us in all our troubles so that we can comfort others. When they are troubled, we will be able to give them the same comfort God has given us. ⁵For the more we suffer for Christ, the more God will shower us with his comfort through Christ. ⁶Even when we are weighed down with troubles, it is for your comfort and salvation! For when we ourselves are comforted, we will certainly comfort you. Then you can patiently endure the same things we suffer. ⁷We are confident that as you share in our sufferings, you will also share in the comfort God gives us.

⁸We think you ought to know, dear brothers and sisters,* about the trouble we went through in the province of Asia. We were crushed and overwhelmed beyond our ability to endure, and we thought we would never live through it. ⁹In fact, we expected to die. But as a result, we stopped relying on ourselves and learned to rely only on God, who raises the dead. ¹⁰And he did rescue us from mortal danger, and he will rescue us again. We have placed our confidence in him, and he will continue to rescue us. ¹¹And you are helping us by praying for us. Then many people will give thanks because God has graciously answered so many prayers for our safety.

Paul's Change of Plans

¹²We can say with confidence and a clear conscience that we have lived with a God-given holiness* and sincerity in all our dealings. We have depended on God's grace, not on our own human wisdom. That is how we have conducted ourselves before the world, and especially toward you. ¹³Our letters have been straightforward, and there is nothing written between the lines and nothing you can't understand. I hope someday you will fully understand us, ¹⁴even if you don't understand us now. Then on the day when the Lord Jesus* returns, you will be proud of us in the same way we are proud of you.

¹⁵Since I was so sure of your understanding and trust, I wanted to give you a double blessing by visiting you twice—¹⁶first on my way to Macedonia and again when I returned from Macedonia.* Then you could send me on my way to Judea.

¹⁷You may be asking why I changed my plan. Do you think I make my plans carelessly? Do you think I am like people of the world who say "Yes" when they really mean "No"? ¹⁸As surely as God is faithful, our word to you does not waver between "Yes" and "No." ¹⁹For Jesus Christ, the Son of God, does not waver between "Yes" and "No." He is the one whom Silas,* Timothy, and I preached to you, and as God's ultimate "Yes," he always does what he says. ²⁰For all of God's promises have been fulfilled in Christ with a resounding "Yes!" And through Christ, our "Amen" (which means "Yes") ascends to God for his glory.

²¹It is God who enables us, along with you, to stand firm for Christ. He has commissioned us, ²²and he has identified us as his own by placing the Holy Spirit in our hearts as the first installment that guarantees everything he has promised us.

²³Now I call upon God as my witness that I am telling the truth. The reason I didn't return to Corinth was to spare you from a severe rebuke. ²⁴But that does not mean we want to dominate you by telling you how to put your faith into practice. We want to work together with you so you will be full of joy, for it is by your own faith that you stand firm.

2 So I decided that I would not bring you grief with another painful visit. ²For if I cause you grief, who will make me glad? Certainly not someone I have grieved. ³That is why I wrote to you as I did, so that when I do come, I won't be grieved by the very ones who ought to give me the greatest joy. Surely you all know that my joy comes from your being joyful. ⁴I wrote that letter in great anguish, with a troubled heart and many

1:1 Greek *Achaia*, the southern region of the Greek peninsula. **1:8** Greek *brothers*. **1:12** Some manuscripts read *honesty*. **1:14** Some manuscripts read *our Lord Jesus*. **1:16** *Macedonia* was in the northern region of Greece. **1:19** Greek *Silvanus*.

tears. I didn't want to grieve you, but I wanted to let you know how much love I have for you.

Forgiveness for the Sinner

[5]I am not overstating it when I say that the man who caused all the trouble hurt all of you more than he hurt me. [6]Most of you opposed him, and that was punishment enough. [7]Now, however, it is time to forgive and comfort him. Otherwise he may be overcome by discouragement. [8]So I urge you now to reaffirm your love for him.

[9]I wrote to you as I did to test you and see if you would fully comply with my instructions. [10]When you forgive this man, I forgive him, too. And when I forgive whatever needs to be forgiven, I do so with Christ's authority for your benefit, [11]so that Satan will not outsmart us. For we are familiar with his evil schemes.

[12]When I came to the city of Troas to preach the Good News of Christ, the Lord opened a door of opportunity for me. [13]But I had no peace of mind because my dear brother Titus hadn't yet arrived with a report from you. So I said goodbye and went on to Macedonia to find him.

Ministers of the New Covenant

[14]But thank God! He has made us his captives and continues to lead us along in Christ's triumphal procession. Now he uses us to spread the knowledge of Christ everywhere, like a sweet perfume. [15]Our lives are a Christ-like fragrance rising up to God. But this fragrance is perceived differently by those who are being saved and by those who are perishing. [16]To those who are perishing, we are a dreadful smell of death and doom. But to those who are being saved, we are a life-giving perfume. And who is adequate for such a task as this?

[17]You see, we are not like the many hucksters* who preach for personal profit. We preach the word of God with sincerity and with Christ's authority, knowing that God is watching us.

3 Are we beginning to praise ourselves again? Are we like others, who need to bring you letters of recommendation, or who ask you to write such letters on their behalf? Surely not! [2]The only letter of recommendation we need is you yourselves. Your lives are a letter written in our* hearts; everyone can read it and recognize our good work among you. [3]Clearly, you are a letter from Christ showing the result of our ministry among you. This "letter" is written not with pen and ink, but with the Spirit of the living God. It is carved not on tablets of stone, but on human hearts.

[4]We are confident of all this because of our great trust in God through Christ. [5]It is not that we think we are qualified to do anything on our own. Our qualification comes from God. [6]He has enabled us to be ministers of his new covenant. This is a covenant not of written laws, but of the Spirit. The old written covenant ends in death; but under the new covenant, the Spirit gives life.

The Glory of the New Covenant

[7]The old way,* with laws etched in stone, led to death, though it began with such glory that the people of Israel could not bear to look at Moses' face. For his face shone with the glory of God, even though the brightness was already fading away. [8]Shouldn't we expect far greater glory under the new way, now that the Holy Spirit is giving life? [9]If the old way, which brings condemnation, was glorious, how much more glorious is the new way, which makes us right with God! [10]In fact, that first glory was not glorious at all compared with the overwhelming glory of the new way. [11]So if the old way, which has been replaced, was glorious, how much more glorious is the new, which remains forever!

[12]Since this new way gives us such confidence, we can be very bold. [13]We are not like Moses, who put a veil over his face so the people of Israel would not see the glory, even though it was destined to fade away. [14]But the people's minds were hardened, and to this day whenever the old covenant is being read, the same veil covers their minds so they cannot understand the truth. And this veil can be removed only by believing in Christ. [15]Yes, even today when they read Moses' writings, their hearts are covered with that veil, and they do not understand.

[16]But whenever someone turns to the Lord, the veil is taken away. [17]For the Lord is the Spirit, and wherever the Spirit of the Lord is, there is freedom. [18]So all of us who have had that veil removed can see and reflect the glory of the Lord. And the Lord—who is the Spirit—makes us more and more like him as we are changed into his glorious image.

Treasure in Fragile Clay Jars

4 Therefore, since God in his mercy has given us this new way,* we never give up. [2]We reject all shameful deeds and underhanded methods. We don't try to trick anyone or distort the word of God. We tell the truth before God, and all who are honest know this.

[3]If the Good News we preach is hidden behind a veil, it is hidden only from people who are perishing. [4]Satan, who is the god of this world, has blinded the minds of those who don't believe. They are unable to see the glorious light of the Good News. They don't understand this message about the glory of Christ, who is the exact likeness of God.

[5]You see, we don't go around preaching about

2:17 Some manuscripts read *the rest of the hucksters.*   **3:2** Some manuscripts read *your.*   **3:7** Or *ministry;* also in 3:8, 9, 10, 11, 12. **4:1** Or *ministry.*

ourselves. We preach that Jesus Christ is Lord, and we ourselves are your servants for Jesus' sake. 6For God, who said, "Let there be light in the darkness," has made this light shine in our hearts so we could know the glory of God that is seen in the face of Jesus Christ.

7We now have this light shining in our hearts, but we ourselves are like fragile clay jars containing this great treasure.* This makes it clear that our great power is from God, not from ourselves.

8We are pressed on every side by troubles, but we are not crushed. We are perplexed, but not driven to despair. 9We are hunted down, but never abandoned by God. We get knocked down, but we are not destroyed. 10Through suffering, our bodies continue to share in the death of Jesus so that the life of Jesus may also be seen in our bodies.

11Yes, we live under constant danger of death because we serve Jesus, so that the life of Jesus will be evident in our dying bodies. 12So we live in the face of death, but this has resulted in eternal life for you.

13But we continue to preach because we have the same kind of faith the psalmist had when he said, "I believed in God, so I spoke."* 14We know that God, who raised the Lord Jesus,* will also raise us with Jesus and present us to himself together with you. 15All of this is for your benefit. And as God's grace reaches more and more people, there will be great thanksgiving, and God will receive more and more glory.

16That is why we never give up. Though our bodies are dying, our spirits are* being renewed every day. 17For our present troubles are small and won't last very long. Yet they produce for us a glory that vastly outweighs them and will last forever! 18So we don't look at the troubles we can see now; rather, we fix our gaze on things that cannot be seen. For the things we see now will soon be gone, but the things we cannot see will last forever.

New Bodies

5 For we know that when this earthly tent we live in is taken down (that is, when we die and leave this earthly body), we will have a house in heaven, an eternal body made for us by God himself and not by human hands. 2We grow weary in our present bodies, and we long to put on our heavenly bodies like new clothing. 3For we will put on heavenly bodies; we will not be spirits without bodies.* 4While we live in these earthly bodies, we groan and sigh, but it's not that we want to die and get rid of these bodies that clothe us. Rather, we want to put on our new bodies so that these dying bodies will be swallowed up by life. 5God himself has prepared us

for this, and as a guarantee he has given us his Holy Spirit.

6So we are always confident, even though we know that as long as we live in these bodies we are not at home with the Lord. 7For we live by believing and not by seeing. 8Yes, we are fully confident, and we would rather be away from these earthly bodies, for then we will be at home with the Lord. 9So whether we are here in this body or away from this body, our goal is to please him. 10For we must all stand before Christ to be judged. We will each receive whatever we deserve for the good or evil we have done in this earthly body.

We Are God's Ambassadors

11Because we understand our fearful responsibility to the Lord, we work hard to persuade others. God knows we are sincere, and I hope you know this, too. 12Are we commending ourselves to you again? No, we are giving you a reason to be proud of us,* so you can answer those who brag about having a spectacular ministry rather than having a sincere heart. 13If it seems we are crazy, it is to bring glory to God. And if we are in our right minds, it is for your benefit. 14Either way, Christ's love controls us.* Since we believe that Christ died for all, we also believe that we have all died to our old life.* 15He died for everyone so that those who receive his new life will no longer live for themselves. Instead, they will live for Christ, who died and was raised for them.

16So we have stopped evaluating others from a human point of view. At one time we thought of Christ merely from a human point of view. How differently we know him now! 17This means that anyone who belongs to Christ has become a new person. The old life is gone; a new life has begun!

18And all of this is a gift from God, who brought us back to himself through Christ. And God has given us this task of reconciling people to him. 19For God was in Christ, reconciling the world to himself, no longer counting people's sins against them. And he gave us this wonderful message of reconciliation. 20So we are Christ's ambassadors; God is making his appeal through us. We speak for Christ when we plead, "Come back to God!" 21For God made Christ, who never sinned, to be the offering for our sin,* so that we could be made right with God through Christ.

6 As God's partners,* we beg you not to accept this marvelous gift of God's kindness and then ignore it. 2For God says,

"At just the right time, I heard you.
    On the day of salvation, I helped you."*

4:7 Greek *We now have this treasure in clay jars.*   4:13 Ps 116:10.   4:14 Some manuscripts read *who raised Jesus.*   4:16 Greek *our inner being is.*   5:3 Greek *we will not be naked.*   5:12 Some manuscripts read *proud of yourselves.*   5:14a Or *urges us on.*   5:14b Greek *Since one died for all, then all died.*   5:21 Or *to become sin itself.*   6:1 Or *As we work together.*   6:2 Isa 49:8 (Greek version).

Indeed, the "right time" is now. Today is the day of salvation.

Paul's Hardships

³We live in such a way that no one will stumble because of us, and no one will find fault with our ministry. ⁴In everything we do, we show that we are true ministers of God. We patiently endure troubles and hardships and calamities of every kind. ⁵We have been beaten, been put in prison, faced angry mobs, worked to exhaustion, endured sleepless nights, and gone without food. ⁶We prove ourselves by our purity, our understanding, our patience, our kindness, by the Holy Spirit within us,* and by our sincere love. ⁷We faithfully preach the truth. God's power is working in us. We use the weapons of righteousness in the right hand for attack and the left hand for defense. ⁸We serve God whether people honor us or despise us, whether they slander us or praise us. We are honest, but they call us impostors. ⁹We are ignored, even though we are well known. We live close to death, but we are still alive. We have been beaten, but we have not been killed. ¹⁰Our hearts ache, but we always have joy. We are poor, but we give spiritual riches to others. We own nothing, and yet we have everything.

¹¹Oh, dear Corinthian friends! We have spoken honestly with you, and our hearts are open to you. ¹²There is no lack of love on our part, but you have withheld your love from us. ¹³I am asking you to respond as if you were my own children. Open your hearts to us!

The Temple of the Living God

¹⁴Don't team up with those who are unbelievers. How can righteousness be a partner with wickedness? How can light live with darkness? ¹⁵What harmony can there be between Christ and the devil*? How can a believer be a partner with an unbeliever? ¹⁶And what union can there be between God's temple and idols? For we are the temple of the living God. As God said:

"I will live in them
  and walk among them.
I will be their God,
  and they will be my people.*
¹⁷ Therefore, come out from among
    unbelievers,
  and separate yourselves from them, says
    the Lord.
Don't touch their filthy things,
  and I will welcome you.*
¹⁸ And I will be your Father,
    and you will be my sons and daughters,
  says the Lord Almighty.*"

7 Because we have these promises, dear friends, let us cleanse ourselves from everything that can defile our body or spirit. And let us work toward complete holiness because we fear God.

²Please open your hearts to us. We have not done wrong to anyone, nor led anyone astray, nor taken advantage of anyone. ³I'm not saying this to condemn you. I said before that you are in our hearts, and we live or die together with you. ⁴I have the highest confidence in you, and I take great pride in you. You have greatly encouraged me and made me happy despite all our troubles.

Paul's Joy at the Church's Repentance

⁵When we arrived in Macedonia, there was no rest for us. We faced conflict from every direction, with battles on the outside and fear on the inside. ⁶But God, who encourages those who are discouraged, encouraged us by the arrival of Titus. ⁷His presence was a joy, but so was the news he brought of the encouragement he received from you. When he told us how much you long to see me, and how sorry you are for what happened, and how loyal you are to me, I was filled with joy!

⁸I am not sorry that I sent that severe letter to you, though I was sorry at first, for I know it was painful to you for a little while. ⁹Now I am glad I sent it, not because it hurt you, but because the pain caused you to repent and change your ways. It was the kind of sorrow God wants his people to have, so you were not harmed by us in any way. ¹⁰For the kind of sorrow God wants us to experience leads us away from sin and results in salvation. There's no regret for that kind of sorrow. But worldly sorrow, which lacks repentance, results in spiritual death.

¹¹Just see what this godly sorrow produced in you! Such earnestness, such concern to clear yourselves, such indignation, such alarm, such longing to see me, such zeal, and such a readiness to punish wrong. You showed that you have done everything necessary to make things right. ¹²My purpose, then, was not to write about who did the wrong or who was wronged. I wrote to you so that in the sight of God you could see for yourselves how loyal you are to us. ¹³We have been greatly encouraged by this.

In addition to our own encouragement, we were especially delighted to see how happy Titus was about the way all of you welcomed him and set his mind* at ease. ¹⁴I had told him how proud I was of you—and you didn't disappoint me. I have always told you the truth, and now my boasting to Titus has also proved true! ¹⁵Now he cares for you more than ever when he remembers the way all of you obeyed him and welcomed him with such fear and deep respect. ¹⁶I am very happy now because I have complete confidence in you.

6:6 Or *by our holiness of spirit.*   **6:15** Greek *Beliar;* various other manuscripts render this proper name of the devil as *Belian, Beliab,* or *Belial.*   **6:16** Lev 26:12; Ezek 37:27.   **6:17** Isa 52:11; Ezek 20:34 (Greek version).   **6:18** 2 Sam 7:14.   **7:13** Greek *his spirit.*

A Call to Generous Giving

8 Now I want you to know, dear brothers and sisters,* what God in his kindness has done through the churches in Macedonia. ²They are being tested by many troubles, and they are very poor. But they are also filled with abundant joy, which has overflowed in rich generosity.

³For I can testify that they gave not only what they could afford, but far more. And they did it of their own free will. ⁴They begged us again and again for the privilege of sharing in the gift for the believers in Jerusalem.* ⁵They even did more than we had hoped, for their first action was to give themselves to the Lord and to us, just as God wanted them to do.

⁶So we have urged Titus, who encouraged your giving in the first place, to return to you and encourage you to finish this ministry of giving. ⁷Since you excel in so many ways—in your faith, your gifted speakers, your knowledge, your enthusiasm, and your love from us*—I want you to excel also in this gracious act of giving.

⁸I am not commanding you to do this. But I am testing how genuine your love is by comparing it with the eagerness of the other churches. ⁹You know the generous grace of our Lord Jesus Christ. Though he was rich, yet for your sakes he became poor, so that by his poverty he could make you rich.

¹⁰Here is my advice: It would be good for you to finish what you started a year ago. Last year you were the first who wanted to give, and you were the first to begin doing it. ¹¹Now you should finish what you started. Let the eagerness you showed in the beginning be matched now by your giving. Give in proportion to what you have. ¹²Whatever you give is acceptable if you give it eagerly. And give according to what you have, not what you don't have. ¹³Of course, I don't mean your giving should make life easy for others and hard for yourselves. I only mean that there should be some equality. ¹⁴Right now you have plenty and can help those who are in need. Later, they will have plenty and can share with you when you need it. In this way, things will be equal. ¹⁵As the Scriptures say,

> "Those who gathered a lot had nothing left
> over,
> and those who gathered only a little had
> enough."*

Titus and His Companions

¹⁶But thank God! He has given Titus the same enthusiasm for you that I have. ¹⁷Titus welcomed our request that he visit you again. In fact, he himself was very eager to go and see you. ¹⁸We are also sending another brother with Titus. All the churches praise him as a preacher of the Good News. ¹⁹He was appointed by the churches to accompany us as we take the offering to Jerusalem*—a service that glorifies the Lord and shows our eagerness to help.

²⁰We are traveling together to guard against any criticism for the way we are handling this generous gift. ²¹We are careful to be honorable before the Lord, but we also want everyone else to see that we are honorable.

²²We are also sending with them another of our brothers who has proven himself many times and has shown on many occasions how eager he is. He is now even more enthusiastic because of his great confidence in you. ²³If anyone asks about Titus, say that he is my partner who works with me to help you. And the brothers with him have been sent by the churches,* and they bring honor to Christ. ²⁴So show them your love, and prove to all the churches that our boasting about you is justified.

The Collection for Christians in Jerusalem

9 I really don't need to write to you about this ministry of giving for the believers in Jerusalem.* ²For I know how eager you are to help, and I have been boasting to the churches in Macedonia that you in Greece* were ready to send an offering a year ago. In fact, it was your enthusiasm that stirred up many of the Macedonian believers to begin giving.

³But I am sending these brothers to be sure you really are ready, as I have been telling them, and that your money is all collected. I don't want to be wrong in my boasting about you. ⁴We would be embarrassed—not to mention your own embarrassment—if some Macedonian believers came with me and found that you weren't ready after all I had told them! ⁵So I thought I should send these brothers ahead of me to make sure the gift you promised is ready. But I want it to be a willing gift, not one given grudgingly.

⁶Remember this—a farmer who plants only a few seeds will get a small crop. But the one who plants generously will get a generous crop. ⁷You must each decide in your heart how much to give. And don't give reluctantly or in response to pressure. "For God loves a person who gives cheerfully."* ⁸And God will generously provide all you need. Then you will always have everything you need and plenty left over to share with others. ⁹As the Scriptures say,

> "They share freely and give generously to the
> poor.
> Their good deeds will be remembered
> forever."*

¹⁰For God is the one who provides seed for the farmer and then bread to eat. In the same way, he will provide and increase your resources and then produce a great harvest of generosity* in you.

8:1 Greek *brothers.*   **8:4** Greek *for God's holy people.*   **8:7** Some manuscripts read *your love for us.*   **8:15** Exod 16:18.   **8:19** See 1 Cor 16:3-4.   **8:23** Greek *are apostles of the churches.*   **9:1** Greek *about the offering for God's holy people.*   **9:2** Greek *in Achaia,* the southern region of the Greek peninsula. *Macedonia* was in the northern region of Greece.   **9:7** See footnote on Prov 22:8. **9:9** Ps 112:9.   **9:10** Greek *righteousness.*

¹¹Yes, you will be enriched in every way so that you can always be generous. And when we take your gifts to those who need them, they will thank God. ¹²So two good things will result from this ministry of giving—the needs of the believers in Jerusalem* will be met, and they will joyfully express their thanks to God.

¹³As a result of your ministry, they will give glory to God. For your generosity to them and to all believers will prove that you are obedient to the Good News of Christ. ¹⁴And they will pray for you with deep affection because of the overflowing grace God has given to you. ¹⁵Thank God for this gift* too wonderful for words!

Paul Defends His Authority

10 Now I, Paul, appeal to you with the gentleness and kindness of Christ—though I realize you think I am timid in person and bold only when I write from far away. ²Well, I am begging you now so that when I come I won't have to be bold with those who think we act from human motives.

³We are human, but we don't wage war as humans do. ⁴*We use God's mighty weapons, not worldly weapons, to knock down the strongholds of human reasoning and to destroy false arguments. ⁵We destroy every proud obstacle that keeps people from knowing God. We capture their rebellious thoughts and teach them to obey Christ. ⁶And after you have become fully obedient, we will punish everyone who remains disobedient.

⁷Look at the obvious facts.* Those who say they belong to Christ must recognize that we belong to Christ as much as they do. ⁸I may seem to be boasting too much about the authority given to us by the Lord. But our authority builds you up; it doesn't tear you down. So I will not be ashamed of using my authority.

⁹I'm not trying to frighten you by my letters. ¹⁰For some say, "Paul's letters are demanding and forceful, but in person he is weak, and his speeches are worthless!" ¹¹Those people should realize that our actions when we arrive in person will be as forceful as what we say in our letters from far away.

¹²Oh, don't worry; we wouldn't dare say that we are as wonderful as these other men who tell you how important they are! But they are only comparing themselves with each other, using themselves as the standard of measurement. How ignorant!

¹³We will not boast about things done outside our area of authority. We will boast only about what has happened within the boundaries of the work God has given us, which includes our working with you. ¹⁴We are not reaching beyond these boundaries when we claim authority over you, as if we had never visited you. For we were the first to travel all the way to Corinth with the Good News of Christ.

¹⁵Nor do we boast and claim credit for the work someone else has done. Instead, we hope that your faith will grow so that the boundaries of our work among you will be extended. ¹⁶Then we will be able to go and preach the Good News in other places far beyond you, where no one else is working. Then there will be no question of our boasting about work done in someone else's territory. ¹⁷As the Scriptures say, "If you want to boast, boast only about the LORD."*

¹⁸When people commend themselves, it doesn't count for much. The important thing is for the Lord to commend them.

Paul and the False Apostles

11 I hope you will put up with a little more of my foolishness. Please bear with me. ²For I am jealous for you with the jealousy of God himself. I promised you as a pure bride* to one husband—Christ. ³But I fear that somehow your pure and undivided devotion to Christ will be corrupted, just as Eve was deceived by the cunning ways of the serpent. ⁴You happily put up with whatever anyone tells you, even if they preach a different Jesus than the one we preach, or a different kind of Spirit than the one you received, or a different kind of gospel than the one you believed.

⁵But I don't consider myself inferior in any way to these "super apostles" who teach such things. ⁶I may be unskilled as a speaker, but I'm not lacking in knowledge. We have made this clear to you in every possible way.

⁷Was I wrong when I humbled myself and honored you by preaching God's Good News to you without expecting anything in return? ⁸I "robbed" other churches by accepting their contributions so I could serve you at no cost. ⁹And when I was with you and didn't have enough to live on, I did not become a financial burden to anyone. For the brothers who came from Macedonia brought me all that I needed. I have never been a burden to you, and I never will be. ¹⁰As surely as the truth of Christ is in me, no one in all of Greece* will ever stop me from boasting about this. ¹¹Why? Because I don't love you? God knows that I do.

¹²But I will continue doing what I have always done. This will undercut those who are looking for an opportunity to boast that their work is just like ours. ¹³These people are false apostles. They are deceitful workers who disguise themselves as apostles of Christ. ¹⁴But I am not surprised! Even Satan disguises himself as an angel of light. ¹⁵So it is no wonder that his servants also disguise themselves as servants of righteousness. In the end they will get the punishment their wicked deeds deserve.

Paul's Many Trials

¹⁶Again I say, don't think that I am a fool to talk like this. But even if you do, listen to me, as you would to a foolish person, while I also boast a little. ¹⁷Such boasting is not from the Lord, but I am acting like a fool. ¹⁸And since others boast about their human achievements, I will, too. ¹⁹After all, you think you are so wise, but you enjoy putting up with fools! ²⁰You put up with it when someone enslaves you, takes everything you have, takes advantage of you, takes control of everything, and slaps you in the face. ²¹I'm ashamed to say that we've been too "weak" to do that!

But whatever they dare to boast about—I'm talking like a fool again—I dare to boast about it, too. ²²Are they Hebrews? So am I. Are they Israelites? So am I. Are they descendants of Abraham? So am I. ²³Are they servants of Christ? I know I sound like a madman, but I have served him far more! I have worked harder, been put in prison more often, been whipped times without number, and faced death again and again. ²⁴Five different times the Jewish leaders gave me thirty-nine lashes. ²⁵Three times I was beaten with rods. Once I was stoned. Three times I was shipwrecked. Once I spent a whole night and a day adrift at sea. ²⁶I have traveled on many long journeys. I have faced danger from rivers and from robbers. I have faced danger from my own people, the Jews, as well as from the Gentiles. I have faced danger in the cities, in the deserts, and on the seas. And I have faced danger from men who claim to be believers but are not.* ²⁷I have worked hard and long, enduring many sleepless nights. I have been hungry and thirsty and have often gone without food. I have shivered in the cold, without enough clothing to keep me warm.

²⁸Then, besides all this, I have the daily burden of my concern for all the churches. ²⁹Who is weak without my feeling that weakness? Who is led astray, and I do not burn with anger?

³⁰If I must boast, I would rather boast about the things that show how weak I am. ³¹God, the Father of our Lord Jesus, who is worthy of eternal praise, knows I am not lying. ³²When I was in Damascus, the governor under King Aretas kept guards at the city gates to catch me. ³³I had to be lowered in a basket through a window in the city wall to escape from him.

Paul's Vision and His Thorn in the Flesh

12 This boasting will do no good, but I must go on. I will reluctantly tell about visions and revelations from the Lord. ²I* was caught up to the third heaven fourteen years ago. Whether I was in my body or out of my body, I don't know—only God knows. ³Yes, only God knows whether I was in my body or outside my body. But I do know ⁴that I was caught up* to paradise

and heard things so astounding that they cannot be expressed in words, things no human is allowed to tell.

⁵That experience is worth boasting about, but I'm not going to do it. I will boast only about my weaknesses. ⁶If I wanted to boast, I would be no fool in doing so, because I would be telling the truth. But I won't do it, because I don't want anyone to give me credit beyond what they can see in my life or hear in my message, ⁷even though I have received such wonderful revelations from God. So to keep me from becoming proud, I was given a thorn in my flesh, a messenger from Satan to torment me and keep me from becoming proud.

⁸Three different times I begged the Lord to take it away. ⁹Each time he said, "My grace is all you need. My power works best in weakness." So now I am glad to boast about my weaknesses, so that the power of Christ can work through me. ¹⁰That's why I take pleasure in my weaknesses, and in the insults, hardships, persecutions, and troubles that I suffer for Christ. For when I am weak, then I am strong.

Paul's Concern for the Corinthians

¹¹You have made me act like a fool—boasting like this.* You ought to be writing commendations for me, for I am not at all inferior to these "super apostles," even though I am nothing at all. ¹²When I was with you, I certainly gave you proof that I am an apostle. For I patiently did many signs and wonders and miracles among you. ¹³The only thing I failed to do, which I do in the other churches, was to become a financial burden to you. Please forgive me for this wrong!

¹⁴Now I am coming to you for the third time, and I will not be a burden to you. I don't want what you have—I want you. After all, children don't provide for their parents. Rather, parents provide for their children. ¹⁵I will gladly spend myself and all I have for you, even though it seems that the more I love you, the less you love me.

¹⁶Some of you admit I was not a burden to you. But others still think I was sneaky and took advantage of you by trickery. ¹⁷But how? Did any of the men I sent to you take advantage of you? ¹⁸When I urged Titus to visit you and sent our other brother with him, did Titus take advantage of you? No! For we have the same spirit and walk in each other's steps, doing things the same way.

¹⁹Perhaps you think we're saying these things just to defend ourselves. No, we tell you this as Christ's servants, and with God as our witness. Everything we do, dear friends, is to strengthen you. ²⁰For I am afraid that when I come I won't like what I find, and you won't like my response. I am afraid that I will find quarreling, jealousy,

11:26 Greek *from false brothers.*   **12:2** Greek *I know a man in Christ who.*   **12:3-4** Greek *But I know such a man, 'that he was caught up.*   **12:11** Some manuscripts do not include *boasting like this.*

anger, selfishness, slander, gossip, arrogance, and disorderly behavior. 21Yes, I am afraid that when I come again, God will humble me in your presence. And I will be grieved because many of you have not given up your old sins. You have not repented of your impurity, sexual immorality, and eagerness for lustful pleasure.

Paul's Final Advice

13 This is the third time I am coming to visit you (and as the Scriptures say, "The facts of every case must be established by the testimony of two or three witnesses"*). 2I have already warned those who had been sinning when I was there on my second visit. Now I again warn them and all others, just as I did before, that next time I will not spare them.

3I will give you all the proof you want that Christ speaks through me. Christ is not weak when he deals with you; he is powerful among you. 4Although he was crucified in weakness, he now lives by the power of God. We, too, are weak, just as Christ was, but when we deal with you we will be alive with him and will have God's power.

5Examine yourselves to see if your faith is genuine. Test yourselves. Surely you know that Jesus Christ is among you*; if not, you have failed the test of genuine faith. 6As you test yourselves, I hope you will recognize that we have not failed the test of apostolic authority.

7We pray to God that you will not do what is wrong by refusing our correction. I hope we won't need to demonstrate our authority when we arrive. Do the right thing before we come— even if that makes it look like we have failed to demonstrate our authority. 8For we cannot oppose the truth, but must always stand for the truth. 9We are glad to seem weak if it helps show that you are actually strong. We pray that you will become mature.

10I am writing this to you before I come, hoping that I won't need to deal severely with you when I do come. For I want to use the authority the Lord has given me to strengthen you, not to tear you down.

Paul's Final Greetings

11Dear brothers and sisters,* I close my letter with these last words: Be joyful. Grow to maturity. Encourage each other. Live in harmony and peace. Then the God of love and peace will be with you.

12Greet each other with Christian love.* 13All of God's people here send you their greetings.

14*May the grace of the Lord Jesus Christ, the love of God, and the fellowship of the Holy Spirit be with you all.

13:1 Deut 19:15.   **13:5** Or *in you.*   **13:11** Greek *Brothers.*   **13:12** Greek *with a sacred kiss.*   **13:14** Some English translations include verse 13 as part of verse 12, and then verse 14 becomes verse 13.

Galatians

Greetings from Paul

1 This letter is from Paul, an apostle. I was not appointed by any group of people or any human authority, but by Jesus Christ himself and by God the Father, who raised Jesus from the dead.

²All the brothers and sisters* here join me in sending this letter to the churches of Galatia.

³May God our Father and the Lord Jesus Christ* give you grace and peace. ⁴Jesus gave his life for our sins, just as God our Father planned, in order to rescue us from this evil world in which we live. ⁵All glory to God forever and ever! Amen.

There Is Only One Good News

⁶I am shocked that you are turning away so soon from God, who called you to himself through the loving mercy of Christ.* You are following a different way that pretends to be the Good News ⁷but is not the Good News at all. You are being fooled by those who deliberately twist the truth concerning Christ.

⁸Let God's curse fall on anyone, including us or even an angel from heaven, who preaches a different kind of Good News than the one we preached to you. ⁹I say again what we have said before: If anyone preaches any other Good News than the one you welcomed, let that person be cursed.

¹⁰Obviously, I'm not trying to win the approval of people, but of God. If pleasing people were my goal, I would not be Christ's servant.

Paul's Message Comes from Christ

¹¹Dear brothers and sisters, I want you to understand that the gospel message I preach is not based on mere human reasoning. ¹²I received my message from no human source, and no one taught me. Instead, I received it by direct revelation from Jesus Christ.*

¹³You know what I was like when I followed the Jewish religion—how I violently persecuted God's church. I did my best to destroy it. ¹⁴I was far ahead of my fellow Jews in my zeal for the traditions of my ancestors.

¹⁵But even before I was born, God chose me and called me by his marvelous grace. Then it pleased him ¹⁶to reveal his Son to me* so that I would proclaim the Good News about Jesus to the Gentiles.

When this happened, I did not rush out to consult with any human being.* ¹⁷Nor did I go up to Jerusalem to consult with those who were apostles before I was. Instead, I went away into Arabia, and later I returned to the city of Damascus.

¹⁸Then three years later I went to Jerusalem to get to know Peter,* and I stayed with him for fifteen days. ¹⁹The only other apostle I met at that time was James, the Lord's brother. ²⁰I declare before God that what I am writing to you is not a lie.

²¹After that visit I went north into the provinces of Syria and Cilicia. ²²And still the Christians in the churches in Judea didn't know me personally. ²³All they knew was that people were saying, "The one who used to persecute us is now preaching the very faith he tried to destroy!" ²⁴And they praised God because of me.

The Apostles Accept Paul

2 Then fourteen years later I went back to Jerusalem again, this time with Barnabas; and Titus came along, too. ²I went there because God revealed to me that I should go. While I was there I met privately with those considered to be leaders of the church and shared with them the message I had been preaching to the Gentiles. I wanted to make sure that we were in agreement, for fear that all my efforts had been wasted and I was running the race for nothing. ³And they supported me and did not even demand that my companion Titus be circumcised, though he was a Gentile.*

⁴Even that question came up only because of some so-called Christians there—false ones, really*—who were secretly brought in. They sneaked in to spy on us and take away the freedom we have in Christ Jesus. They wanted to enslave us and force us to follow their Jewish regulations. ⁵But we refused to give in to them for a single moment. We wanted to preserve the truth of the gospel message for you.

⁶And the leaders of the church had nothing to add to what I was preaching. (By the way, their reputation as great leaders made no difference to me, for God has no favorites.) ⁷Instead, they

1:2 Greek *brothers;* also in 1:11.   **1:3** Some manuscripts read *God the Father and our Lord Jesus Christ.*   **1:6** Some manuscripts read *through loving mercy.*   **1:12** Or *by the revelation of Jesus Christ.*   **1:16a** Or *in me.*   **1:16b** Greek *with flesh and blood.* **1:18** Greek *Cephas.*   **2:3** Greek *a Greek.*   **2:4** Greek *some false brothers.*

saw that God had given me the responsibility of preaching the gospel to the Gentiles, just as he had given Peter the responsibility of preaching to the Jews. **8**For the same God who worked through Peter as the apostle to the Jews also worked through me as the apostle to the Gentiles.

9In fact, James, Peter,* and John, who were known as pillars of the church, recognized the gift God had given me, and they accepted Barnabas and me as their co-workers. They encouraged us to keep preaching to the Gentiles, while they continued their work with the Jews. **10**Their only suggestion was that we keep on helping the poor, which I have always been eager to do.

Paul Confronts Peter

11But when Peter came to Antioch, I had to oppose him to his face, for what he did was very wrong. **12**When he first arrived, he ate with the Gentile Christians, who were not circumcised. But afterward, when some friends of James came, Peter wouldn't eat with the Gentiles anymore. He was afraid of criticism from these people who insisted on the necessity of circumcision. **13**As a result, other Jewish Christians followed Peter's hypocrisy, and even Barnabas was led astray by their hypocrisy.

14When I saw that they were not following the truth of the gospel message, I said to Peter in front of all the others, "Since you, a Jew by birth, have discarded the Jewish laws and are living like a Gentile, why are you now trying to make these Gentiles follow the Jewish traditions?

15"You and I are Jews by birth, not 'sinners' like the Gentiles. **16**Yet we know that a person is made right with God by faith in Jesus Christ, not by obeying the law. And we have believed in Christ Jesus, so that we might be made right with God because of our faith in Christ, not because we have obeyed the law. For no one will ever be made right with God by obeying the law."*

17But suppose we seek to be made right with God through faith in Christ and then we are found guilty because we have abandoned the law. Would that mean Christ has led us into sin? Absolutely not! **18**Rather, I am a sinner if I rebuild the old system of law I already tore down. **19**For when I tried to keep the law, it condemned me. So I died to the law—I stopped trying to meet all its requirements—so that I might live for God. **20**My old self has been crucified with Christ.* It is no longer I who live, but Christ lives in me. So I live in this earthly body by trusting in the Son of God, who loved me and gave himself for me. **21**I do not treat the grace of God as meaningless. For if keeping the law could make us right with God, then there was no need for Christ to die.

The Law and Faith in Christ

3 Oh, foolish Galatians! Who has cast an evil spell on you? For the meaning of Jesus Christ's death was made as clear to you as if you had seen a picture of his death on the cross. **2**Let me ask you this one question: Did you receive the Holy Spirit by obeying the law of Moses? Of course not! You received the Spirit because you believed the message you heard about Christ. **3**How foolish can you be? After starting your Christian lives in the Spirit, why are you now trying to become perfect by your own human effort? **4**Have you experienced* so much for nothing? Surely it was not in vain, was it?

5I ask you again, does God give you the Holy Spirit and work miracles among you because you obey the law? Of course not! It is because you believe the message you heard about Christ.

6In the same way, "Abraham believed God, and God counted him as righteous because of his faith."* **7**The real children of Abraham, then, are those who put their faith in God.

8What's more, the Scriptures looked forward to this time when God would declare the Gentiles to be righteous because of their faith. God proclaimed this good news to Abraham long ago when he said, "All nations will be blessed through you."* **9**So all who put their faith in Christ share the same blessing Abraham received because of his faith.

10But those who depend on the law to make them right with God are under his curse, for the Scriptures say, "Cursed is everyone who does not observe and obey all the commands that are written in God's Book of the Law."* **11**So it is clear that no one can be made right with God by trying to keep the law. For the Scriptures say, "It is through faith that a righteous person has life."* **12**This way of faith is very different from the way of law, which says, "It is through obeying the law that a person has life."*

13But Christ has rescued us from the curse pronounced by the law. When he was hung on the cross, he took upon himself the curse for our wrongdoing. For it is written in the Scriptures, "Cursed is everyone who is hung on a tree."* **14**Through Christ Jesus, God has blessed the Gentiles with the same blessing he promised to Abraham, so that we who are believers might receive the promised* Holy Spirit through faith.

The Law and God's Promise

15Dear brothers and sisters,* here's an example from everyday life. Just as no one can set aside or amend an irrevocable agreement, so it is in this case. **16**God gave the promises to Abraham and his child.* And notice that the Scripture doesn't say "to his children,*" as if it meant

---

2:9 Greek *Cephas;* also in 2:11, 14.   **2:16** Some translators hold that the quotation extends through verse 14; others through verse 16; and still others through verse 21.   **2:20** Some English translations put this sentence in verse 19.   **3:4** Or *Have you suffered.* **3:6** Gen 15:6.   **3:8** Gen 12:3; 18:18; 22:18.   **3:10** Deut 27:26.   **3:11** Hab 2:4.   **3:12** Lev 18:5.   **3:13** Deut 21:23 (Greek version). **3:14** Some manuscripts read *the blessing of the.*   **3:15** Greek *Brothers.*   **3:16a** Greek *seed;* also in 3:16c, 19. See notes on Gen 12:7 and 13:15.   **3:16b** Greek *seeds.*

many descendants. Rather, it says "to his child"—and that, of course, means Christ. 17This is what I am trying to say: The agreement God made with Abraham could not be canceled 430 years later when God gave the law to Moses. God would be breaking his promise. 18For if the inheritance could be received by keeping the law, then it would not be the result of accepting God's promise. But God graciously gave it to Abraham as a promise.

19Why, then, was the law given? It was given alongside the promise to show people their sins. But the law was designed to last only until the coming of the child who was promised. God gave his law through angels to Moses, who was the mediator between God and the people. 20Now a mediator is helpful if more than one party must reach an agreement. But God, who is one, did not use a mediator when he gave his promise to Abraham.

21Is there a conflict, then, between God's law and God's promises?* Absolutely not! If the law could give us new life, we could be made right with God by obeying it. 22But the Scriptures declare that we are all prisoners of sin, so we receive God's promise of freedom only by believing in Jesus Christ.

God's Children through Faith

23Before the way of faith in Christ was available to us, we were placed under guard by the law. We were kept in protective custody, so to speak, until the way of faith was revealed.

24Let me put it another way. The law was our guardian until Christ came; it protected us until we could be made right with God through faith. 25And now that the way of faith has come, we no longer need the law as our guardian.

26For you are all children* of God through faith in Christ Jesus. 27And all who have been united with Christ in baptism have put on Christ, like putting on new clothes.* 28There is no longer Jew or Gentile,* slave or free, male and female. For you are all one in Christ Jesus. 29And now that you belong to Christ, you are the true children* of Abraham. You are his heirs, and God's promise to Abraham belongs to you.

4 Think of it this way. If a father dies and leaves an inheritance for his young children, those children are not much better off than slaves until they grow up, even though they actually own everything their father had. 2They have to obey their guardians until they reach whatever age their father set. 3And that's the way it was with us before Christ came. We were like children; we were slaves to the basic spiritual principles* of this world.

4But when the right time came, God sent his Son, born of a woman, subject to the law. 5God sent him to buy freedom for us who were slaves to the law, so that he could adopt us as his very own children.* 6And because we* are his children, God has sent the Spirit of his Son into our hearts, prompting us to call out, "Abba, Father."* 7Now you are no longer a slave but God's own child.* And since you are his child, God has made you his heir.

Paul's Concern for the Galatians

8Before you Gentiles knew God, you were slaves to so-called gods that do not even exist. 9So now that you know God (or should I say, now that God knows you), why do you want to go back again and become slaves once more to the weak and useless spiritual principles of this world? 10You are trying to earn favor with God by observing certain days or months or seasons or years. 11I fear for you. Perhaps all my hard work with you was for nothing. 12Dear brothers and sisters,* I plead with you to live as I do in freedom from these things, for I have become like you Gentiles—free from those laws.

You did not mistreat me when I first preached to you. 13Surely you remember that I was sick when I first brought you the Good News. 14But even though my condition tempted you to reject me, you did not despise me or turn me away. No, you took me in and cared for me as though I were an angel from God or even Christ Jesus himself. 15Where is that joyful and grateful spirit you felt then? I am sure you would have taken out your own eyes and given them to me if it had been possible. 16Have I now become your enemy because I am telling you the truth?

17Those false teachers are so eager to win your favor, but their intentions are not good. They are trying to shut you off from me so that you will pay attention only to them. 18If someone is eager to do good things for you, that's all right; but let them do it all the time, not just when I'm with you.

19Oh, my dear children! I feel as if I'm going through labor pains for you again, and they will continue until Christ is fully developed in your lives. 20I wish I were with you right now so I could change my tone. But at this distance I don't know how else to help you.

Abraham's Two Children

21Tell me, you who want to live under the law, do you know what the law actually says? 22The Scriptures say that Abraham had two sons, one from his slave wife and one from his freeborn wife.* 23The son of the slave wife was born in a human attempt to bring about the fulfillment of God's

---

3:21 Some manuscripts read *and the promises?*   3:26 Greek *sons.*   3:27 Greek *have put on Christ.*   3:28 Greek *Jew or Greek.* 3:29 Greek *seed.*   4:3 Or *powers;* also in 4:9.   4:5 Greek *sons;* also in 4:6.   4:6a Greek *you.*   4:6b *Abba* is an Aramaic term for "father."   4:7 Greek *son;* also in 4:7b.   4:12 Greek *brothers;* also in 4:28, 31.   4:22 See Gen 16:15; 21:2-3.

promise. But the son of the freeborn wife was born as God's own fulfillment of his promise.

²⁴These two women serve as an illustration of God's two covenants. The first woman, Hagar, represents Mount Sinai where people received the law that enslaved them. ²⁵And now Jerusalem is just like Mount Sinai in Arabia,* because she and her children live in slavery to the law. ²⁶But the other woman, Sarah, represents the heavenly Jerusalem. She is the free woman, and she is our mother. ²⁷As Isaiah said,

"Rejoice, O childless woman,
 you who have never given birth!
Break into a joyful shout,
 you who have never been in labor!
For the desolate woman now has more
  children
 than the woman who lives with her
   husband!"*

²⁸And you, dear brothers and sisters, are children of the promise, just like Isaac. ²⁹But you are now being persecuted by those who want you to keep the law, just as Ishmael, the child born by human effort, persecuted Isaac, the child born by the power of the Spirit.

³⁰But what do the Scriptures say about that? "Get rid of the slave and her son, for the son of the slave woman will not share the inheritance with the free woman's son."* ³¹So, dear brothers and sisters, we are not children of the slave woman; we are children of the free woman.

Freedom in Christ

5 So Christ has truly set us free. Now make sure that you stay free, and don't get tied up again in slavery to the law.

²Listen! I, Paul, tell you this: If you are counting on circumcision to make you right with God, then Christ will be of no benefit to you. ³I'll say it again. If you are trying to find favor with God by being circumcised, you must obey every regulation in the whole law of Moses. ⁴For if you are trying to make yourselves right with God by keeping the law, you have been cut off from Christ! You have fallen away from God's grace.

⁵But we who live by the Spirit eagerly wait to receive by faith the righteousness God has promised to us. ⁶For when we place our faith in Christ Jesus, there is no benefit in being circumcised or being uncircumcised. What is important is faith expressing itself in love.

⁷You were running the race so well. Who has held you back from following the truth? ⁸It certainly isn't God, for he is the one who called you to freedom. ⁹This false teaching is like a little yeast that spreads through the whole batch of dough! ¹⁰I am trusting the Lord to keep you

from believing false teachings. God will judge that person, whoever he is, who has been confusing you.

¹¹Dear brothers and sisters,* if I were still preaching that you must be circumcised—as some say I do—why am I still being persecuted? If I were no longer preaching salvation through the cross of Christ, no one would be offended. ¹²I just wish that those troublemakers who want to mutilate you by circumcision would mutilate themselves.*

¹³For you have been called to live in freedom, my brothers and sisters. But don't use your freedom to satisfy your sinful nature. Instead, use your freedom to serve one another in love. ¹⁴For the whole law can be summed up in this one command: "Love your neighbor as yourself."* ¹⁵But if you are always biting and devouring one another, watch out! Beware of destroying one another.

Living by the Spirit's Power

¹⁶So I say, let the Holy Spirit guide your lives. Then you won't be doing what your sinful nature craves. ¹⁷The sinful nature wants to do evil, which is just the opposite of what the Spirit wants. And the Spirit gives us desires that are the opposite of what the sinful nature desires. These two forces are constantly fighting each other, so you are not free to carry out your good intentions. ¹⁸But when you are directed by the Spirit, you are not under obligation to the law of Moses.

¹⁹When you follow the desires of your sinful nature, the results are very clear: sexual immorality, impurity, lustful pleasures, ²⁰idolatry, sorcery, hostility, quarreling, jealousy, outbursts of anger, selfish ambition, dissension, division, ²¹envy, drunkenness, wild parties, and other sins like these. Let me tell you again, as I have before, that anyone living that sort of life will not inherit the Kingdom of God.

²²But the Holy Spirit produces this kind of fruit in our lives: love, joy, peace, patience, kindness, goodness, faithfulness, ²³gentleness, and self-control. There is no law against these things!

²⁴Those who belong to Christ Jesus have nailed the passions and desires of their sinful nature to his cross and crucified them there. ²⁵Since we are living by the Spirit, let us follow the Spirit's leading in every part of our lives. ²⁶Let us not become conceited, or provoke one another, or be jealous of one another.

We Harvest What We Plant

6 Dear brothers and sisters, if another believer* is overcome by some sin, you who are godly* should gently and humbly help that

---

4:25 Greek *And Hagar, which is Mount Sinai in Arabia, is now like Jerusalem;* other manuscripts read *And Mount Sinai in Arabia is now like Jerusalem.* **4:27** Isa 54:1. **4:30** Gen 21:10. **5:11** Greek *Brothers;* similarly in 5:13. **5:12** Or *castrate themselves, or cut themselves off from you;* Greek reads *cut themselves off.* **5:14** Lev 19:18. **6:1a** Greek *Brothers, if a man.* **6:1b** Greek *spiritual.*

person back onto the right path. And be careful not to fall into the same temptation yourself. ²Share each other's burdens, and in this way obey the law of Christ. ³If you think you are too important to help someone, you are only fooling yourself. You are not that important.

⁴Pay careful attention to your own work, for then you will get the satisfaction of a job well done, and you won't need to compare yourself to anyone else. ⁵For we are each responsible for our own conduct.

⁶Those who are taught the word of God should provide for their teachers, sharing all good things with them.

⁷Don't be misled—you cannot mock the justice of God. You will always harvest what you plant. ⁸Those who live only to satisfy their own sinful nature will harvest decay and death from that sinful nature. But those who live to please the Spirit will harvest everlasting life from the Spirit. ⁹So let's not get tired of doing what is good. At just the right time we will reap a harvest of blessing if we don't give up. ¹⁰Therefore, whenever we have the opportunity, we should do good to everyone—especially to those in the family of faith.

Paul's Final Advice

¹¹Notice what large letters I use as I write these closing words in my own handwriting.

¹²Those who are trying to force you to be circumcised want to look good to others. They don't want to be persecuted for teaching that the cross of Christ alone can save. ¹³And even those who advocate circumcision don't keep the whole law themselves. They only want you to be circumcised so they can boast about it and claim you as their disciples.

¹⁴As for me, may I never boast about anything except the cross of our Lord Jesus Christ. Because of that cross,* my interest in this world has been crucified, and the world's interest in me has also died. ¹⁵It doesn't matter whether we have been circumcised or not. What counts is whether we have been transformed into a new creation. ¹⁶May God's peace and mercy be upon all who live by this principle; they are the new people of God.*

¹⁷From now on, don't let anyone trouble me with these things. For I bear on my body the scars that show I belong to Jesus.

¹⁸Dear brothers and sisters,* may the grace of our Lord Jesus Christ be with your spirit. Amen.

6:14 Or *Because of him.*   **6:16** Greek *this principle, and upon the Israel of God.*   **6:18** Greek *Brothers.*

Ephesians

Greetings from Paul

1 This letter is from Paul, chosen by the will of God to be an apostle of Christ Jesus.

I am writing to God's holy people in Ephesus,* who are faithful followers of Christ Jesus.

²May God our Father and the Lord Jesus Christ give you grace and peace.

Spiritual Blessings

³All praise to God, the Father of our Lord Jesus Christ, who has blessed us with every spiritual blessing in the heavenly realms because we are united with Christ. ⁴Even before he made the world, God loved us and chose us in Christ to be holy and without fault in his eyes. ⁵God decided in advance to adopt us into his own family by bringing us to himself through Jesus Christ. This is what he wanted to do, and it gave him great pleasure. ⁶So we praise God for the glorious grace he has poured out on us who belong to his dear Son.* ⁷He is so rich in kindness and grace that he purchased our freedom with the blood of his Son and forgave our sins. ⁸He has showered his kindness on us, along with all wisdom and understanding.

⁹God has now revealed to us his mysterious plan regarding Christ, a plan to fulfill his own good pleasure. ¹⁰And this is the plan: At the right time he will bring everything together under the authority of Christ—everything in heaven and on earth. ¹¹Furthermore, because we are united with Christ, we have received an inheritance from God,* for he chose us in advance, and he makes everything work out according to his plan.

¹²God's purpose was that we Jews who were the first to trust in Christ would bring praise and glory to God. ¹³And now you Gentiles have also heard the truth, the Good News that God saves you. And when you believed in Christ, he identified you as his own* by giving you the Holy Spirit, whom he promised long ago. ¹⁴The Spirit is God's guarantee that he will give us the inheritance he promised and that he has purchased us to be his own people. He did this so we would praise and glorify him.

Paul's Prayer for Spiritual Wisdom

¹⁵Ever since I first heard of your strong faith in the Lord Jesus and your love for God's people everywhere,* ¹⁶I have not stopped thanking God for you. I pray for you constantly, ¹⁷asking God, the glorious Father of our Lord Jesus Christ, to give you spiritual wisdom* and insight so that you might grow in your knowledge of God. ¹⁸I pray that your hearts will be flooded with light so that you can understand the confident hope he has given to those he called—his holy people who are his rich and glorious inheritance.*

¹⁹I also pray that you will understand the incredible greatness of God's power for us who believe him. This is the same mighty power ²⁰that raised Christ from the dead and seated him in the place of honor at God's right hand in the heavenly realms. ²¹Now he is far above any ruler or authority or power or leader or anything else—not only in this world but also in the world to come. ²²God has put all things under the authority of Christ and has made him head over all things for the benefit of the church. ²³And the church is his body; it is made full and complete by Christ, who fills all things everywhere with himself.

Made Alive with Christ

2 Once you were dead because of your disobedience and your many sins. ²You used to live in sin, just like the rest of the world, obeying the devil—the commander of the powers in the unseen world.* He is the spirit at work in the hearts of those who refuse to obey God. ³All of us used to live that way, following the passionate desires and inclinations of our sinful nature. By our very nature we were subject to God's anger, just like everyone else.

⁴But God is so rich in mercy, and he loved us so much, ⁵that even though we were dead because of our sins, he gave us life when he raised Christ from the dead. (It is only by God's grace that you have been saved!) ⁶For he raised us from the dead along with Christ and seated us with him in the heavenly realms because we are united with Christ Jesus. ⁷So God can point to us in all future ages as examples of the incredible

1:1 The most ancient manuscripts do not include *in Ephesus.* **1:6** Greek *to us in the beloved.* **1:11** Or *we have become God's inheritance.* **1:13** Or *he put his seal on you.* **1:15** Some manuscripts read *your faithfulness to the Lord Jesus and to God's people everywhere.* **1:17** Or *to give you the Spirit of wisdom.* **1:18** Or *called, and the rich and glorious inheritance he has given to his holy people.* **2:2** Greek *obeying the commander of the power of the air.*

wealth of his grace and kindness toward us, as shown in all he has done for us who are united with Christ Jesus.

⁸God saved you by his grace when you believed. And you can't take credit for this; it is a gift from God. ⁹Salvation is not a reward for the good things we have done, so none of us can boast about it. ¹⁰For we are God's masterpiece. He has created us anew in Christ Jesus, so we can do the good things he planned for us long ago.

Oneness and Peace in Christ

¹¹Don't forget that you Gentiles used to be outsiders. You were called "uncircumcised heathens" by the Jews, who were proud of their circumcision, even though it affected only their bodies and not their hearts. ¹²In those days you were living apart from Christ. You were excluded from citizenship among the people of Israel, and you did not know the covenant promises God had made to them. You lived in this world without God and without hope. ¹³But now you have been united with Christ Jesus. Once you were far away from God, but now you have been brought near to him through the blood of Christ.

¹⁴For Christ himself has brought peace to us. He united Jews and Gentiles into one people when, in his own body on the cross, he broke down the wall of hostility that separated us. ¹⁵He did this by ending the system of law with its commandments and regulations. He made peace between Jews and Gentiles by creating in himself one new people from the two groups. ¹⁶Together as one body, Christ reconciled both groups to God by means of his death on the cross, and our hostility toward each other was put to death.

¹⁷He brought this Good News of peace to you Gentiles who were far away from him, and peace to the Jews who were near. ¹⁸Now all of us can come to the Father through the same Holy Spirit because of what Christ has done for us.

A Temple for the Lord

¹⁹So now you Gentiles are no longer strangers and foreigners. You are citizens along with all of God's holy people. You are members of God's family. ²⁰Together, we are his house, built on the foundation of the apostles and the prophets. And the cornerstone is Christ Jesus himself. ²¹We are carefully joined together in him, becoming a holy temple for the Lord. ²²Through him you Gentiles are also being made part of this dwelling where God lives by his Spirit.

God's Mysterious Plan Revealed

3 When I think of all this, I, Paul, a prisoner of Christ Jesus for the benefit of you Gentiles* . . . ²assuming, by the way, that you know God gave me the special responsibility of ex-

tending his grace to you Gentiles. ³As I briefly wrote earlier, God himself revealed his mysterious plan to me. ⁴As you read what I have written, you will understand my insight into this plan regarding Christ. ⁵God did not reveal it to previous generations, but now by his Spirit he has revealed it to his holy apostles and prophets.

⁶And this is God's plan: Both Gentiles and Jews who believe the Good News share equally in the riches inherited by God's children. Both are part of the same body, and both enjoy the promise of blessings because they belong to Christ Jesus.* ⁷By God's grace and mighty power, I have been given the privilege of serving him by spreading this Good News.

⁸Though I am the least deserving of all God's people, he graciously gave me the privilege of telling the Gentiles about the endless treasures available to them in Christ. ⁹I was chosen to explain to everyone* this mysterious plan that God, the Creator of all things, had kept secret from the beginning.

¹⁰God's purpose in all this was to use the church to display his wisdom in its rich variety to all the unseen rulers and authorities in the heavenly places. ¹¹This was his eternal plan, which he carried out through Christ Jesus our Lord.

¹²Because of Christ and our faith in him,* we can now come boldly and confidently into God's presence. ¹³So please don't lose heart because of my trials here. I am suffering for you, so you should feel honored.

Paul's Prayer for Spiritual Growth

¹⁴When I think of all this, I fall to my knees and pray to the Father,* ¹⁵the Creator of everything in heaven and on earth.* ¹⁶I pray that from his glorious, unlimited resources he will empower you with inner strength through his Spirit. ¹⁷Then Christ will make his home in your hearts as you trust in him. Your roots will grow down into God's love and keep you strong. ¹⁸And may you have the power to understand, as all God's people should, how wide, how long, how high, and how deep his love is. ¹⁹May you experience the love of Christ, though it is too great to understand fully. Then you will be made complete with all the fullness of life and power that comes from God.

²⁰Now all glory to God, who is able, through his mighty power at work within us, to accomplish infinitely more than we might ask or think. ²¹Glory to him in the church and in Christ Jesus through all generations forever and ever! Amen.

Unity in the Body

4 Therefore I, a prisoner for serving the Lord, beg you to lead a life worthy of your calling, for you have been called by God. ²Always be humble and gentle. Be patient with each other, mak-

---

3:1 Paul resumes this thought in verse 14: "When I think of all this, I fall to my knees and pray to the Father." **3:6** Or *because they are united with Christ Jesus.* **3:9** Some manuscripts do not include *to everyone.* **3:12** Or *Because of Christ's faithfulness.* **3:14** Some manuscripts read *the Father of our Lord Jesus Christ.* **3:15** Or *from whom every family in heaven and on earth takes its name.*

ing allowance for each other's faults because of your love. ³Make every effort to keep yourselves united in the Spirit, binding yourselves together with peace. ⁴For there is one body and one Spirit, just as you have been called to one glorious hope for the future. ⁵There is one Lord, one faith, one baptism, ⁶and one God and Father, who is over all and in all and living through all.

⁷However, he has given each one of us a special gift* through the generosity of Christ. ⁸That is why the Scriptures say,

"When he ascended to the heights,
he led a crowd of captives
and gave gifts to his people."*

⁹Notice that it says "he ascended." This clearly means that Christ also descended to our lowly world.* ¹⁰And the same one who descended is the one who ascended higher than all the heavens, so that he might fill the entire universe with himself.

¹¹Now these are the gifts Christ gave to the church: the apostles, the prophets, the evangelists, and the pastors and teachers. ¹²Their responsibility is to equip God's people to do his work and build up the church, the body of Christ. ¹³This will continue until we all come to such unity in our faith and knowledge of God's Son that we will be mature in the Lord, measuring up to the full and complete standard of Christ.

¹⁴Then we will no longer be immature like children. We won't be tossed and blown about by every wind of new teaching. We will not be influenced when people try to trick us with lies so clever they sound like the truth. ¹⁵Instead, we will speak the truth in love, growing in every way more and more like Christ, who is the head of his body, the church. ¹⁶He makes the whole body fit together perfectly. As each part does its own special work, it helps the other parts grow, so that the whole body is healthy and growing and full of love.

Living as Children of Light

¹⁷With the Lord's authority I say this: Live no longer as the Gentiles do, for they are hopelessly confused. ¹⁸Their minds are full of darkness; they wander far from the life God gives because they have closed their minds and hardened their hearts against him. ¹⁹They have no sense of shame. They live for lustful pleasure and eagerly practice every kind of impurity.

²⁰But that isn't what you learned about Christ. ²¹Since you have heard about Jesus and have learned the truth that comes from him, ²²throw off your old sinful nature and your former way of life, which is corrupted by lust and deception. ²³Instead, let the Spirit renew your thoughts and attitudes. ²⁴Put on your new nature, created to be like God—truly righteous and holy.

²⁵So stop telling lies. Let us tell our neighbors the truth, for we are all parts of the same body. ²⁶And "don't sin by letting anger control you."* Don't let the sun go down while you are still angry, ²⁷for anger gives a foothold to the devil.

²⁸If you are a thief, quit stealing. Instead, use your hands for good hard work, and then give generously to others in need. ²⁹Don't use foul or abusive language. Let everything you say be good and helpful, so that your words will be an encouragement to those who hear them.

³⁰And do not bring sorrow to God's Holy Spirit by the way you live. Remember, he has identified you as his own,* guaranteeing that you will be saved on the day of redemption.

³¹Get rid of all bitterness, rage, anger, harsh words, and slander, as well as all types of evil behavior. ³²Instead, be kind to each other, tenderhearted, forgiving one another, just as God through Christ has forgiven you.

Living in the Light

5 Imitate God, therefore, in everything you do, because you are his dear children. ²Live a life filled with love, following the example of Christ. He loved us* and offered himself as a sacrifice for us, a pleasing aroma to God.

³Let there be no sexual immorality, impurity, or greed among you. Such sins have no place among God's people. ⁴Obscene stories, foolish talk, and coarse jokes—these are not for you. Instead, let there be thankfulness to God. ⁵You can be sure that no immoral, impure, or greedy person will inherit the Kingdom of Christ and of God. For a greedy person is an idolater, worshiping the things of this world.

⁶Don't be fooled by those who try to excuse these sins, for the anger of God will fall on all who disobey him. ⁷Don't participate in the things these people do. ⁸For once you were full of darkness, but now you have light from the Lord. So live as people of light! ⁹For this light within you produces only what is good and right and true.

¹⁰Carefully determine what pleases the Lord. ¹¹Take no part in the worthless deeds of evil and darkness; instead, expose them. ¹²It is shameful even to talk about the things that ungodly people do in secret. ¹³But their evil intentions will be exposed when the light shines on them, ¹⁴for the light makes everything visible. This is why it is said,

"Awake, O sleeper,
rise up from the dead,
and Christ will give you light."

Living by the Spirit's Power

¹⁵So be careful how you live. Don't live like fools, but like those who are wise. ¹⁶Make the most of

4:7 Greek *a grace.*   **4:8** Ps 68:18.   **4:9** Or *to the lowest parts of the earth.*   **4:26** Ps 4:4.   **4:30** Or *has put his seal on you.*
5:2 Some manuscripts read *loved you.*

every opportunity in these evil days. [17]Don't act thoughtlessly, but understand what the Lord wants you to do. [18]Don't be drunk with wine, because that will ruin your life. Instead, be filled with the Holy Spirit, [19]singing psalms and hymns and spiritual songs among yourselves, and making music to the Lord in your hearts. [20]And give thanks for everything to God the Father in the name of our Lord Jesus Christ.

Spirit-Guided Relationships: Wives and Husbands

[21]And further, submit to one another out of reverence for Christ.

[22]For wives, this means submit to your husbands as to the Lord. [23]For a husband is the head of his wife as Christ is the head of the church. He is the Savior of his body, the church. [24]As the church submits to Christ, so you wives should submit to your husbands in everything.

[25]For husbands, this means love your wives, just as Christ loved the church. He gave up his life for her [26]to make her holy and clean, washed by the cleansing of God's word.* [27]He did this to present her to himself as a glorious church without a spot or wrinkle or any other blemish. Instead, she will be holy and without fault. [28]In the same way, husbands ought to love their wives as they love their own bodies. For a man who loves his wife actually shows love for himself. [29]No one hates his own body but feeds and cares for it, just as Christ cares for the church. [30]And we are members of his body.

[31]As the Scriptures say, "A man leaves his father and mother and is joined to his wife, and the two are united into one."* [32]This is a great mystery, but it is an illustration of the way Christ and the church are one. [33]So again I say, each man must love his wife as he loves himself, and the wife must respect her husband.

Children and Parents

6 Children, obey your parents because you belong to the Lord,* for this is the right thing to do. [2]"Honor your father and mother." This is the first commandment with a promise: [3]If you honor your father and mother, "things will go well for you, and you will have a long life on the earth."*

[4]Fathers, do not provoke your children to anger by the way you treat them. Rather, bring them up with the discipline and instruction that comes from the Lord.

Slaves and Masters

[5]Slaves, obey your earthly masters with deep respect and fear. Serve them sincerely as you would serve Christ. [6]Try to please them all the time, not just when they are watching you. As slaves of Christ, do the will of God with all your heart. [7]Work with enthusiasm, as though you were working for the Lord rather than for people. [8]Remember that the Lord will reward each one of us for the good we do, whether we are slaves or free.

[9]Masters, treat your slaves in the same way. Don't threaten them; remember, you both have the same Master in heaven, and he has no favorites.

The Whole Armor of God

[10]A final word: Be strong in the Lord and in his mighty power. [11]Put on all of God's armor so that you will be able to stand firm against all strategies of the devil. [12]For we* are not fighting against flesh-and-blood enemies, but against evil rulers and authorities of the unseen world, against mighty powers in this dark world, and against evil spirits in the heavenly places.

[13]Therefore, put on every piece of God's armor so you will be able to resist the enemy in the time of evil. Then after the battle you will still be standing firm. [14]Stand your ground, putting on the belt of truth and the body armor of God's righteousness. [15]For shoes, put on the peace that comes from the Good News so that you will be fully prepared.* [16]In addition to all of these, hold up the shield of faith to stop the fiery arrows of the devil.* [17]Put on salvation as your helmet, and take the sword of the Spirit, which is the word of God.

[18]Pray in the Spirit at all times and on every occasion. Stay alert and be persistent in your prayers for all believers everywhere.*

[19]And pray for me, too. Ask God to give me the right words so I can boldly explain God's mysterious plan that the Good News is for Jews and Gentiles alike.* [20]I am in chains now, still preaching this message as God's ambassador. So pray that I will keep on speaking boldly for him, as I should.

Final Greetings

[21]To bring you up to date, Tychicus will give you a full report about what I am doing and how I am getting along. He is a beloved brother and faithful helper in the Lord's work. [22]I have sent him to you for this very purpose—to let you know how we are doing and to encourage you.

[23]Peace be with you, dear brothers and sisters,* and may God the Father and the Lord Jesus Christ give you love with faithfulness. [24]May God's grace be eternally upon all who love our Lord Jesus Christ.

5:26 Greek *washed by water with the word.* **5:31** Gen 2:24. **6:1** Or *Children, obey your parents who belong to the Lord;* some manuscripts read simply *Children, obey your parents.* **6:2-3** Exod 20:12; Deut 5:16. **6:12** Some manuscripts read *you.* **6:15** Or *For shoes, put on the readiness to preach the Good News of peace with God.* **6:16** Greek *the evil one.* **6:18** Greek *all of God's holy people.* **6:19** Greek *explain the mystery of the Good News;* some manuscripts read simply *explain the mystery.* **6:23** Greek *brothers.*

Philippians

Greetings from Paul

1 This letter is from Paul and Timothy, slaves of Christ Jesus.

I am writing to all of God's holy people in Philippi who belong to Christ Jesus, including the elders* and deacons.

²May God our Father and the Lord Jesus Christ give you grace and peace.

Paul's Thanksgiving and Prayer

³Every time I think of you, I give thanks to my God. ⁴Whenever I pray, I make my requests for all of you with joy, ⁵for you have been my partners in spreading the Good News about Christ from the time you first heard it until now. ⁶And I am certain that God, who began the good work within you, will continue his work until it is finally finished on the day when Christ Jesus returns.

⁷So it is right that I should feel as I do about all of you, for you have a special place in my heart. You share with me the special favor of God, both in my imprisonment and in defending and confirming the truth of the Good News. ⁸God knows how much I love you and long for you with the tender compassion of Christ Jesus.

⁹I pray that your love will overflow more and more, and that you will keep on growing in knowledge and understanding. ¹⁰For I want you to understand what really matters, so that you may live pure and blameless lives until the day of Christ's return. ¹¹May you always be filled with the fruit of your salvation—the righteous character produced in your life by Jesus Christ*—for this will bring much glory and praise to God.

Paul's Joy That Christ Is Preached

¹²And I want you to know, my dear brothers and sisters,* that everything that has happened to me here has helped to spread the Good News. ¹³For everyone here, including the whole palace guard,* knows that I am in chains because of Christ. ¹⁴And because of my imprisonment, most of the believers* here have gained confidence and boldly speak God's message* without fear.

¹⁵It's true that some are preaching out of jealousy and rivalry. But others preach about Christ with pure motives. ¹⁶They preach because they love me, for they know I have been appointed to defend the Good News. ¹⁷Those others do not have pure motives as they preach about Christ. They preach with selfish ambition, not sincerely, intending to make my chains more painful to me. ¹⁸But that doesn't matter. Whether their motives are false or genuine, the message about Christ is being preached either way, so I rejoice. And I will continue to rejoice. ¹⁹For I know that as you pray for me and the Spirit of Jesus Christ helps me, this will lead to my deliverance.

Paul's Life for Christ

²⁰For I fully expect and hope that I will never be ashamed, but that I will continue to be bold for Christ, as I have been in the past. And I trust that my life will bring honor to Christ, whether I live or die. ²¹For to me, living means living for Christ, and dying is even better. ²²But if I live, I can do more fruitful work for Christ. So I really don't know which is better. ²³I'm torn between two desires: I long to go and be with Christ, which would be far better for me. ²⁴But for your sakes, it is better that I continue to live.

²⁵Knowing this, I am convinced that I will remain alive so I can continue to help all of you grow and experience the joy of your faith. ²⁶And when I come to you again, you will have even more reason to take pride in Christ Jesus because of what he is doing through me.

Live as Citizens of Heaven

²⁷Above all, you must live as citizens of heaven, conducting yourselves in a manner worthy of the Good News about Christ. Then, whether I come and see you again or only hear about you, I will know that you are standing together with one spirit and one purpose, fighting together for the faith, which is the Good News. ²⁸Don't be intimidated in any way by your enemies. This will be a sign to them that they are going to be destroyed, but that you are going to be saved, even by God himself. ²⁹For you have been given not only the privilege of trusting in Christ but also the privilege of suffering for him. ³⁰We are in this struggle together. You have seen my struggle in the past, and you know that I am still in the midst of it.

1:1 Or *overseers;* or *bishops.* **1:11** Greek *with the fruit of righteousness through Jesus Christ.* **1:12** Greek *brothers.* **1:13** Greek *including all the Praetorium.* **1:14a** Greek *brothers in the Lord.* **1:14b** Some manuscripts read *speak the message.*

Have the Attitude of Christ

2 Is there any encouragement from belonging to Christ? Any comfort from his love? Any fellowship together in the Spirit? Are your hearts tender and compassionate? ²Then make me truly happy by agreeing wholeheartedly with each other, loving one another, and working together with one mind and purpose.

³Don't be selfish; don't try to impress others. Be humble, thinking of others as better than yourselves. ⁴Don't look out only for your own interests, but take an interest in others, too.

⁵You must have the same attitude that Christ Jesus had.

⁶ Though he was God,*
   he did not think of equality with God
   as something to cling to.
⁷ Instead, he gave up his divine privileges*;
   he took the humble position of a slave*
   and was born as a human being.
   When he appeared in human form,*
⁸   he humbled himself in obedience
      to God
   and died a criminal's death on a cross.

⁹ Therefore, God elevated him to the place
   of highest honor
   and gave him the name above all other
      names,
¹⁰ that at the name of Jesus every knee
      should bow,
   in heaven and on earth and under
      the earth,
¹¹ and every tongue confess that Jesus Christ
      is Lord,
   to the glory of God the Father.

Shine Brightly for Christ

¹²Dear friends, you always followed my instructions when I was with you. And now that I am away, it is even more important. Work hard to show the results of your salvation, obeying God with deep reverence and fear. ¹³For God is working in you, giving you the desire and the power to do what pleases him.

¹⁴Do everything without complaining and arguing, ¹⁵so that no one can criticize you. Live clean, innocent lives as children of God, shining like bright lights in a world full of crooked and perverse people. ¹⁶Hold firmly to the word of life; then, on the day of Christ's return, I will be proud that I did not run the race in vain and that my work was not useless. ¹⁷But I will rejoice even if I lose my life, pouring it out like a liquid offering to God,* just like your faithful service is an offering to God. And I want all of you to share that joy. ¹⁸Yes, you should rejoice, and I will share your joy.

Paul Commends Timothy

¹⁹If the Lord Jesus is willing, I hope to send Timothy to you soon for a visit. Then he can cheer me up by telling me how you are getting along. ²⁰I have no one else like Timothy, who genuinely cares about your welfare. ²¹All the others care only for themselves and not for what matters to Jesus Christ. ²²But you know how Timothy has proved himself. Like a son with his father, he has served with me in preaching the Good News. ²³I hope to send him to you just as soon as I find out what is going to happen to me here. ²⁴And I have confidence from the Lord that I myself will come to see you soon.

Paul Commends Epaphroditus

²⁵Meanwhile, I thought I should send Epaphroditus back to you. He is a true brother, co-worker, and fellow soldier. And he was your messenger to help me in my need. ²⁶I am sending him because he has been longing to see you, and he was very distressed that you heard he was ill. ²⁷And he certainly was ill; in fact, he almost died. But God had mercy on him—and also on me, so that I would not have one sorrow after another.

²⁸So I am all the more anxious to send him back to you, for I know you will be glad to see him, and then I will not be so worried about you. ²⁹Welcome him with Christian love* and with great joy, and give him the honor that people like him deserve. ³⁰For he risked his life for the work of Christ, and he was at the point of death while doing for me what you couldn't do from far away.

The Priceless Value of Knowing Christ

3 Whatever happens, my dear brothers and sisters,* rejoice in the Lord. I never get tired of telling you these things, and I do it to safeguard your faith.

²Watch out for those dogs, those people who do evil, those mutilators who say you must be circumcised to be saved. ³For we who worship by the Spirit of God* are the ones who are truly circumcised. We rely on what Christ Jesus has done for us. We put no confidence in human effort, ⁴though I could have confidence in my own effort if anyone could. Indeed, if others have reason for confidence in their own efforts, I have even more!

⁵I was circumcised when I was eight days old. I am a pure-blooded citizen of Israel and a member of the tribe of Benjamin—a real Hebrew if there ever was one! I was a member of the Pharisees, who demand the strictest obedience to the Jewish law. ⁶I was so zealous that I harshly persecuted the church. And as for righteousness, I obeyed the law without fault.

⁷I once thought these things were valuable,

2:6 Or *Being in the form of God.* **2:7a** Greek *he emptied himself.* **2:7b** Or *the form of a slave.* **2:7c** Some English translations put this phrase in verse 8. **2:17** Greek *I will rejoice even if I am to be poured out as a liquid offering.* **2:29** Greek *in the Lord.* **3:1** Greek *brothers;* also in 3:13, 17. **3:3** Some manuscripts read *worship God in spirit;* one early manuscript reads *worship in spirit.*

but now I consider them worthless because of what Christ has done. [8]Yes, everything else is worthless when compared with the infinite value of knowing Christ Jesus my Lord. For his sake I have discarded everything else, counting it all as garbage, so that I could gain Christ [9]and become one with him. I no longer count on my own righteousness through obeying the law; rather, I become righteous through faith in Christ.* For God's way of making us right with himself depends on faith. [10]I want to know Christ and experience the mighty power that raised him from the dead. I want to suffer with him, sharing in his death, [11]so that one way or another I will experience the resurrection from the dead!

Pressing toward the Goal

[12]I don't mean to say that I have already achieved these things or that I have already reached perfection. But I press on to possess that perfection for which Christ Jesus first possessed me. [13]No, dear brothers and sisters, I have not achieved it,* but I focus on this one thing: Forgetting the past and looking forward to what lies ahead, [14]I press on to reach the end of the race and receive the heavenly prize for which God, through Christ Jesus, is calling us.

[15]Let all who are spiritually mature agree on these things. If you disagree on some point, I believe God will make it plain to you. [16]But we must hold on to the progress we have already made.

[17]Dear brothers and sisters, pattern your lives after mine, and learn from those who follow our example. [18]For I have told you often before, and I say it again with tears in my eyes, that there are many whose conduct shows they are really enemies of the cross of Christ. [19]They are headed for destruction. Their god is their appetite, they brag about shameful things, and they think only about this life here on earth. [20]But we are citizens of heaven, where the Lord Jesus Christ lives. And we are eagerly waiting for him to return as our Savior. [21]He will take our weak mortal bodies and change them into glorious bodies like his own, using the same power with which he will bring everything under his control.

4 Therefore, my dear brothers and sisters,* stay true to the Lord. I love you and long to see you, dear friends, for you are my joy and the crown I receive for my work.

Words of Encouragement

[2]Now I appeal to Euodia and Syntyche. Please, because you belong to the Lord, settle your disagreement. [3]And I ask you, my true partner,* to help these two women, for they worked hard with me in telling others the Good News. They worked along with Clement and the rest of my co-workers, whose names are written in the Book of Life.

[4]Always be full of joy in the Lord. I say it again—rejoice! [5]Let everyone see that you are considerate in all you do. Remember, the Lord is coming soon.

[6]Don't worry about anything; instead, pray about everything. Tell God what you need, and thank him for all he has done. [7]Then you will experience God's peace, which exceeds anything we can understand. His peace will guard your hearts and minds as you live in Christ Jesus.

[8]And now, dear brothers and sisters, one final thing. Fix your thoughts on what is true, and honorable, and right, and pure, and lovely, and admirable. Think about things that are excellent and worthy of praise. [9]Keep putting into practice all you learned and received from me—everything you heard from me and saw me doing. Then the God of peace will be with you.

Paul's Thanks for Their Gifts

[10]How I praise the Lord that you are concerned about me again. I know you have always been concerned for me, but you didn't have the chance to help me. [11]Not that I was ever in need, for I have learned how to be content with whatever I have. [12]I know how to live on almost nothing or with everything. I have learned the secret of living in every situation, whether it is with a full stomach or empty, with plenty or little. [13]For I can do everything through Christ,* who gives me strength. [14]Even so, you have done well to share with me in my present difficulty.

[15]As you know, you Philippians were the only ones who gave me financial help when I first brought you the Good News and then traveled on from Macedonia. No other church did this. [16]Even when I was in Thessalonica you sent help more than once. [17]I don't say this because I want a gift from you. Rather, I want you to receive a reward for your kindness. [18]At the moment I have all I need—and more! I am generously supplied with the gifts you sent me with Epaphroditus. They are a sweet-smelling sacrifice that is acceptable and pleasing to God. [19]And this same God who takes care of me will supply all your needs from his glorious riches, which have been given to us in Christ Jesus.

[20]Now all glory to God our Father forever and ever! Amen.

Paul's Final Greetings

[21]Give my greetings to each of God's holy people—all who belong to Christ Jesus. The brothers who are with me send you their greetings. [22]And all the rest of God's people send you greetings, too, especially those in Caesar's household.

[23]May the grace of the Lord Jesus Christ be with your spirit.

3:9 Or *through the faithfulness of Christ.*   **3:13** Some manuscripts read *not yet achieved it.*   **4:1** Greek *brothers;* also in 4:8.
4:3 Or *loyal Syzygus.*   **4:13** Greek *through the one.*

Colossians

Greetings from Paul

1 This letter is from Paul, chosen by the will of God to be an apostle of Christ Jesus, and from our brother Timothy.

²We are writing to God's holy people in the city of Colosse, who are faithful brothers and sisters* in Christ.

May God our Father give you grace and peace.

Paul's Thanksgiving and Prayer

³We always pray for you, and we give thanks to God, the Father of our Lord Jesus Christ. ⁴For we have heard of your faith in Christ Jesus and your love for all of God's people, ⁵which come from your confident hope of what God has reserved for you in heaven. You have had this expectation ever since you first heard the truth of the Good News.

⁶This same Good News that came to you is going out all over the world. It is bearing fruit everywhere by changing lives, just as it changed your lives from the day you first heard and understood the truth about God's wonderful grace.

⁷You learned about the Good News from Epaphras, our beloved co-worker. He is Christ's faithful servant, and he is helping us on your behalf.* ⁸He has told us about the love for others that the Holy Spirit has given you.

⁹So we have not stopped praying for you since we first heard about you. We ask God to give you complete knowledge of his will and to give you spiritual wisdom and understanding. ¹⁰Then the way you live will always honor and please the Lord, and your lives will produce every kind of good fruit. All the while, you will grow as you learn to know God better and better.

¹¹We also pray that you will be strengthened with all his glorious power so you will have all the endurance and patience you need. May you be filled with joy,* ¹²always thanking the Father. He has enabled you to share in the inheritance that belongs to his people, who live in the light. ¹³For he has rescued us from the kingdom of darkness and transferred us into the Kingdom of his dear Son, ¹⁴who purchased our freedom* and forgave our sins.

Christ Is Supreme

¹⁵ Christ is the visible image of the invisible God.
> He existed before anything was created
> and is supreme over all creation,*
¹⁶ for through him God created everything
> in the heavenly realms and on earth.
> He made the things we can see
> and the things we can't see—
> such as thrones, kingdoms, rulers, and
> authorities in the unseen world.
> Everything was created through him and
> for him.
¹⁷ He existed before anything else,
> and he holds all creation together.
¹⁸ Christ is also the head of the church,
> which is his body.
> He is the beginning,
> supreme over all who rise from the dead.*
> So he is first in everything.
¹⁹ For God in all his fullness
> was pleased to live in Christ,
²⁰ and through him God reconciled
> everything to himself.
> He made peace with everything in heaven
> and on earth
> by means of Christ's blood on
> the cross.

²¹This includes you who were once far away from God. You were his enemies, separated from him by your evil thoughts and actions. ²²Yet now he has reconciled you to himself through the death of Christ in his physical body. As a result, he has brought you into his own presence, and you are holy and blameless as you stand before him without a single fault.

²³But you must continue to believe this truth and stand firmly in it. Don't drift away from the assurance you received when you heard the Good News. The Good News has been preached all over the world, and I, Paul, have been appointed as God's servant to proclaim it.

Paul's Work for the Church

²⁴I am glad when I suffer for you in my body, for I am participating in the sufferings of Christ

1:2 Greek *faithful brothers.*   **1:7** Or *he is ministering on your behalf;* some manuscripts read *he is ministering on our behalf.*   **1:11** Or *all the patience and endurance you need with joy.*   **1:14** Some manuscripts add *with his blood.*   **1:15** Or *He is the firstborn of all creation.*   **1:18** Or *the firstborn from the dead.*

that continue for his body, the church. 25God has given me the responsibility of serving his church by proclaiming his entire message to you. 26This message was kept secret for centuries and generations past, but now it has been revealed to God's people. 27For God wanted them to know that the riches and glory of Christ are for you Gentiles, too. And this is the secret: Christ lives in you. This gives you assurance of sharing his glory.

28So we tell others about Christ, warning everyone and teaching everyone with all the wisdom God has given us. We want to present them to God, perfect* in their relationship to Christ. 29That's why I work and struggle so hard, depending on Christ's mighty power that works within me.

2 I want you to know how much I have agonized for you and for the church at Laodicea, and for many other believers who have never met me personally. 2I want them to be encouraged and knit together by strong ties of love. I want them to have complete confidence that they understand God's mysterious plan, which is Christ himself. 3In him lie hidden all the treasures of wisdom and knowledge.

4I am telling you this so no one will deceive you with well-crafted arguments. 5For though I am far away from you, my heart is with you. And I rejoice that you are living as you should and that your faith in Christ is strong.

Freedom from Rules and New Life in Christ

6And now, just as you accepted Christ Jesus as your Lord, you must continue to follow him. 7Let your roots grow down into him, and let your lives be built on him. Then your faith will grow strong in the truth you were taught, and you will overflow with thankfulness.

8Don't let anyone capture you with empty philosophies and high-sounding nonsense that come from human thinking and from the spiritual powers* of this world, rather than from Christ. 9For in Christ lives all the fullness of God in a human body.* 10So you also are complete through your union with Christ, who is the head over every ruler and authority.

11When you came to Christ, you were "circumcised," but not by a physical procedure. Christ performed a spiritual circumcision—the cutting away of your sinful nature.* 12For you were buried with Christ when you were baptized. And with him you were raised to new life because you trusted the mighty power of God, who raised Christ from the dead.

13You were dead because of your sins and because your sinful nature was not yet cut away. Then God made you alive with Christ, for he for-

gave all our sins. 14He canceled the record of the charges against us and took it away by nailing it to the cross. 15In this way, he disarmed* the spiritual rulers and authorities. He shamed them publicly by his victory over them on the cross.

16So don't let anyone condemn you for what you eat or drink, or for not celebrating certain holy days or new moon ceremonies or Sabbaths. 17For these rules are only shadows of the reality yet to come. And Christ himself is that reality. 18Don't let anyone condemn you by insisting on pious self-denial or the worship of angels,* saying they have had visions about these things. Their sinful minds have made them proud, 19and they are not connected to Christ, the head of the body. For he holds the whole body together with its joints and ligaments, and it grows as God nourishes it.

20You have died with Christ, and he has set you free from the spiritual powers of this world. So why do you keep on following the rules of the world, such as, 21"Don't handle! Don't taste! Don't touch!"? 22Such rules are mere human teachings about things that deteriorate as we use them. 23These rules may seem wise because they require strong devotion, pious self-denial, and severe bodily discipline. But they provide no help in conquering a person's evil desires.

Living the New Life

3 Since you have been raised to new life with Christ, set your sights on the realities of heaven, where Christ sits in the place of honor at God's right hand. 2Think about the things of heaven, not the things of earth. 3For you died to this life, and your real life is hidden with Christ in God. 4And when Christ, who is your* life, is revealed to the whole world, you will share in all his glory.

5So put to death the sinful, earthly things lurking within you. Have nothing to do with sexual immorality, impurity, lust, and evil desires. Don't be greedy, for a greedy person is an idolater, worshiping the things of this world. 6Because of these sins, the anger of God is coming.* 7You used to do these things when your life was still part of this world. 8But now is the time to get rid of anger, rage, malicious behavior, slander, and dirty language. 9Don't lie to each other, for you have stripped off your old sinful nature and all its wicked deeds. 10Put on your new nature, and be renewed as you learn to know your Creator and become like him. 11In this new life, it doesn't matter if you are a Jew or a Gentile,* circumcised or uncircumcised, barbaric, uncivilized,* slave, or free. Christ is all that matters, and he lives in all of us.

12Since God chose you to be the holy people

1:28 Or *mature.*   **2:8** Or *the spiritual principles;* also in 2:20.   **2:9** Or *in him dwells all the completeness of the Godhead bodily.* **2:11** Greek *the cutting away of the body of the flesh.*   **2:15** Or *he stripped off.*   **2:18** Or *or worshiping with angels.*   **3:4** Some manuscripts read *our.*   **3:6** Some manuscripts read *is coming on all who disobey him.*   **3:11a** Greek *a Greek.*   **3:11b** Greek *Barbarian, Scythian.*

he loves, you must clothe yourselves with tenderhearted mercy, kindness, humility, gentleness, and patience. [13]Make allowance for each other's faults, and forgive anyone who offends you. Remember, the Lord forgave you, so you must forgive others. [14]Above all, clothe yourselves with love, which binds us all together in perfect harmony. [15]And let the peace that comes from Christ rule in your hearts. For as members of one body you are called to live in peace. And always be thankful.

[16]Let the message about Christ, in all its richness, fill your lives. Teach and counsel each other with all the wisdom he gives. Sing psalms and hymns and spiritual songs to God with thankful hearts. [17]And whatever you do or say, do it as a representative of the Lord Jesus, giving thanks through him to God the Father.

Instructions for Christian Households

[18]Wives, submit to your husbands, as is fitting for those who belong to the Lord.

[19]Husbands, love your wives and never treat them harshly.

[20]Children, always obey your parents, for this pleases the Lord. [21]Fathers, do not aggravate your children, or they will become discouraged.

[22]Slaves, obey your earthly masters in everything you do. Try to please them all the time, not just when they are watching you. Serve them sincerely because of your reverent fear of the Lord. [23]Work willingly at whatever you do, as though you were working for the Lord rather than for people. [24]Remember that the Lord will give you an inheritance as your reward, and that the Master you are serving is Christ.* [25]But if you do what is wrong, you will be paid back for the wrong you have done. For God has no favorites.

4 Masters, be just and fair to your slaves. Remember that you also have a Master—in heaven.

An Encouragement for Prayer

[2]Devote yourselves to prayer with an alert mind and a thankful heart. [3]Pray for us, too, that God will give us many opportunities to speak about his mysterious plan concerning Christ. That is why I am here in chains. [4]Pray that I will proclaim this message as clearly as I should.

[5]Live wisely among those who are not believers, and make the most of every opportunity. [6]Let your conversation be gracious and attractive* so that you will have the right response for everyone.

Paul's Final Instructions and Greetings

[7]Tychicus will give you a full report about how I am getting along. He is a beloved brother and faithful helper who serves with me in the Lord's work. [8]I have sent him to you for this very purpose—to let you know how we are doing and to encourage you. [9]I am also sending Onesimus, a faithful and beloved brother, one of your own people. He and Tychicus will tell you everything that's happening here.

[10]Aristarchus, who is in prison with me, sends you his greetings, and so does Mark, Barnabas's cousin. As you were instructed before, make Mark welcome if he comes your way. [11]Jesus (the one we call Justus) also sends his greetings. These are the only Jewish believers among my co-workers; they are working with me here for the Kingdom of God. And what a comfort they have been!

[12]Epaphras, a member of your own fellowship and a servant of Christ Jesus, sends you his greetings. He always prays earnestly for you, asking God to make you strong and perfect, fully confident that you are following the whole will of God. [13]I can assure you that he prays hard for you and also for the believers in Laodicea and Hierapolis.

[14]Luke, the beloved doctor, sends his greetings, and so does Demas. [15]Please give my greetings to our brothers and sisters* at Laodicea, and to Nympha and the church that meets in her house.

[16]After you have read this letter, pass it on to the church at Laodicea so they can read it, too. And you should read the letter I wrote to them.

[17]And say to Archippus, "Be sure to carry out the ministry the Lord gave you."

[18]HERE IS MY GREETING IN MY OWN HANDWRITING—PAUL.

Remember my chains.

May God's grace be with you.

3:24 Or *and serve Christ as your Master.*   **4:6** Greek *and seasoned with salt.*   **4:15** Greek *brothers.*

1 Thessalonians

Greetings from Paul

1 This letter is from Paul, Silas,* and Timothy.
We are writing to the church in Thessalonica, to you who belong to God the Father and the Lord Jesus Christ.

May God give you grace and peace.

The Faith of the Thessalonian Believers

²We always thank God for all of you and pray for you constantly. ³As we pray to our God and Father about you, we think of your faithful work, your loving deeds, and the enduring hope you have because of our Lord Jesus Christ.

⁴We know, dear brothers and sisters,* that God loves you and has chosen you to be his own people. ⁵For when we brought you the Good News, it was not only with words but also with power, for the Holy Spirit gave you full assurance* that what we said was true. And you know of our concern for you from the way we lived when we were with you. ⁶So you received the message with joy from the Holy Spirit in spite of the severe suffering it brought you. In this way, you imitated both us and the Lord. ⁷As a result, you have become an example to all the believers in Greece—throughout both Macedonia and Achaia.*

⁸And now the word of the Lord is ringing out from you to people everywhere, even beyond Macedonia and Achaia, for wherever we go we find people telling us about your faith in God. We don't need to tell them about it, ⁹for they keep talking about the wonderful welcome you gave us and how you turned away from idols to serve the living and true God. ¹⁰And they speak of how you are looking forward to the coming of God's Son from heaven—Jesus, whom God raised from the dead. He is the one who has rescued us from the terrors of the coming judgment.

Paul Remembers His Visit

2 You yourselves know, dear brothers and sisters,* that our visit to you was not a failure. ²You know how badly we had been treated at Philippi just before we came to you and how much we suffered there. Yet our God gave us the courage to declare his Good News to you boldly, in spite of great opposition. ³So you can see we were not preaching with any deceit or impure motives or trickery.

⁴For we speak as messengers approved by God to be entrusted with the Good News. Our purpose is to please God, not people. He alone examines the motives of our hearts. ⁵Never once did we try to win you with flattery, as you well know. And God is our witness that we were not pretending to be your friends just to get your money! ⁶As for human praise, we have never sought it from you or anyone else.

⁷As apostles of Christ we certainly had a right to make some demands of you, but instead we were like children* among you. Or we were like a mother feeding and caring for her own children. ⁸We loved you so much that we shared with you not only God's Good News but our own lives, too.

⁹Don't you remember, dear brothers and sisters, how hard we worked among you? Night and day we toiled to earn a living so that we would not be a burden to any of you as we preached God's Good News to you. ¹⁰You yourselves are our witnesses—and so is God—that we were devout and honest and faultless toward all of you believers. ¹¹And you know that we treated each of you as a father treats his own children. ¹²We pleaded with you, encouraged you, and urged you to live your lives in a way that God would consider worthy. For he called you to share in his Kingdom and glory.

¹³Therefore, we never stop thanking God that when you received his message from us, you didn't think of our words as mere human ideas. You accepted what we said as the very word of God—which, of course, it is. And this word continues to work in you who believe.

¹⁴And then, dear brothers and sisters, you suffered persecution from your own countrymen. In this way, you imitated the believers in God's churches in Judea who, because of their belief in Christ Jesus, suffered from their own people, the Jews. ¹⁵For some of the Jews killed the prophets, and some even killed the Lord Jesus. Now they have persecuted us, too. They fail to please God

1:1 Greek *Silvanus*, the Greek form of the name.   1:4 Greek *brothers*.   1:5 Or *with the power of the Holy Spirit, so you can have full assurance*.   1:7 *Macedonia* and *Achaia* were the northern and southern regions of Greece.   2:1 Greek *brothers*; also in 2:9, 14, 17.
2:7 Some manuscripts read *we were gentle*.

and work against all humanity [16]as they try to keep us from preaching the Good News of salvation to the Gentiles. By doing this, they continue to pile up their sins. But the anger of God has caught up with them at last.

Timothy's Good Report about the Church

[17]Dear brothers and sisters, after we were separated from you for a little while (though our hearts never left you), we tried very hard to come back because of our intense longing to see you again. [18]We wanted very much to come to you, and I, Paul, tried again and again, but Satan prevented us. [19]After all, what gives us hope and joy, and what will be our proud reward and crown as we stand before our Lord Jesus when he returns? It is you! [20]Yes, you are our pride and joy.

3 Finally, when we could stand it no longer, we decided to stay alone in Athens, [2]and we sent Timothy to visit you. He is our brother and God's co-worker* in proclaiming the Good News of Christ. We sent him to strengthen you, to encourage you in your faith, [3]and to keep you from being shaken by the troubles you were going through. But you know that we are destined for such troubles. [4]Even while we were with you, we warned you that troubles would soon come—and they did, as you well know. [5]That is why, when I could bear it no longer, I sent Timothy to find out whether your faith was still strong. I was afraid that the tempter had gotten the best of you and that our work had been useless.

[6]But now Timothy has just returned, bringing us good news about your faith and love. He reports that you always remember our visit with joy and that you want to see us as much as we want to see you. [7]So we have been greatly encouraged in the midst of our troubles and suffering, dear brothers and sisters,* because you have remained strong in your faith. [8]It gives us new life to know that you are standing firm in the Lord.

[9]How we thank God for you! Because of you we have great joy as we enter God's presence. [10]Night and day we pray earnestly for you, asking God to let us see you again to fill the gaps in your faith.

[11]May God our Father and our Lord Jesus bring us to you very soon. [12]And may the Lord make your love for one another and for all people grow and overflow, just as our love for you overflows. [13]May he, as a result, make your hearts strong, blameless, and holy as you stand before God our Father when our Lord Jesus comes again with all his holy people. Amen.

Live to Please God

4 Finally, dear brothers and sisters,* we urge you in the name of the Lord Jesus to live in a way that pleases God, as we have taught you. You live this way already, and we encourage you to do so even more. [2]For you remember what we taught you by the authority of the Lord Jesus.

[3]God's will is for you to be holy, so stay away from all sexual sin. [4]Then each of you will control his own body* and live in holiness and honor— [5]not in lustful passion like the pagans who do not know God and his ways. [6]Never harm or cheat a Christian brother in this matter by violating his wife,* for the Lord avenges all such sins, as we have solemnly warned you before. [7]God has called us to live holy lives, not impure lives. [8]Therefore, anyone who refuses to live by these rules is not disobeying human teaching but is rejecting God, who gives his Holy Spirit to you.

[9]But we don't need to write to you about the importance of loving each other,* for God himself has taught you to love one another. [10]Indeed, you already show your love for all the believers* throughout Macedonia. Even so, dear brothers and sisters, we urge you to love them even more.

[11]Make it your goal to live a quiet life, minding your own business and working with your hands, just as we instructed you before. [12]Then people who are not Christians will respect the way you live, and you will not need to depend on others.

The Hope of the Resurrection

[13]And now, dear brothers and sisters, we want you to know what will happen to the believers who have died* so you will not grieve like people who have no hope. [14]For since we believe that Jesus died and was raised to life again, we also believe that when Jesus returns, God will bring back with him the believers who have died.

[15]We tell you this directly from the Lord: We who are still living when the Lord returns will not meet him ahead of those who have died.* [16]For the Lord himself will come down from heaven with a commanding shout, with the voice of the archangel, and with the trumpet call of God. First, the Christians who have died* will rise from their graves. [17]Then, together with them, we who are still alive and remain on the earth will be caught up in the clouds to meet the Lord in the air. Then we will be with the Lord forever. [18]So encourage each other with these words.

5 Now concerning how and when all this will happen, dear brothers and sisters,* we don't really need to write to you. [2]For you know quite

3:2 Other manuscripts read *and God's servant;* still others read *and a co-worker,* or *and a servant and co-worker for God,* or *and God's servant and our co-worker.* **3:7** Greek *brothers.* **4:1** Greek *brothers;* also in 4:10, 13. **4:4** Or *will know how to take a wife for himself;* or *will learn to live with his own wife;* Greek reads *will know how to possess his own vessel.* **4:6** Greek *Never harm or cheat a brother in this matter.* **4:9** Greek *about brotherly love.* **4:10** Greek *the brothers.* **4:13** Greek *those who have fallen asleep;* also in 4:14. **4:15** Greek *those who have fallen asleep.* **4:16** Greek *the dead in Christ.* **5:1** Greek *brothers;* also in 5:4, 12, 14, 25, 26, 27.

well that the day of the Lord's return will come unexpectedly, like a thief in the night. ³When people are saying, "Everything is peaceful and secure," then disaster will fall on them as suddenly as a pregnant woman's labor pains begin. And there will be no escape.

⁴But you aren't in the dark about these things, dear brothers and sisters, and you won't be surprised when the day of the Lord comes like a thief.* ⁵For you are all children of the light and of the day; we don't belong to darkness and night. ⁶So be on your guard, not asleep like the others. Stay alert and be clearheaded. ⁷Night is the time when people sleep and drinkers get drunk. ⁸But let us who live in the light be clearheaded, protected by the armor of faith and love, and wearing as our helmet the confidence of our salvation.

⁹For God chose to save us through our Lord Jesus Christ, not to pour out his anger on us. ¹⁰Christ died for us so that, whether we are dead or alive when he returns, we can live with him forever. ¹¹So encourage each other and build each other up, just as you are already doing.

Paul's Final Advice

¹²Dear brothers and sisters, honor those who are your leaders in the Lord's work. They work hard among you and give you spiritual guidance. ¹³Show them great respect and wholehearted love because of their work. And live peacefully with each other.

¹⁴Brothers and sisters, we urge you to warn those who are lazy. Encourage those who are timid. Take tender care of those who are weak. Be patient with everyone.

¹⁵See that no one pays back evil for evil, but always try to do good to each other and to all people.

¹⁶Always be joyful. ¹⁷Never stop praying. ¹⁸Be thankful in all circumstances, for this is God's will for you who belong to Christ Jesus.

¹⁹Do not stifle the Holy Spirit. ²⁰Do not scoff at prophecies, ²¹but test everything that is said. Hold on to what is good. ²²Stay away from every kind of evil.

Paul's Final Greetings

²³Now may the God of peace make you holy in every way, and may your whole spirit and soul and body be kept blameless until our Lord Jesus Christ comes again. ²⁴God will make this happen, for he who calls you is faithful.

²⁵Dear brothers and sisters, pray for us.

²⁶Greet all the brothers and sisters with Christian love.*

²⁷I command you in the name of the Lord to read this letter to all the brothers and sisters.

²⁸May the grace of our Lord Jesus Christ be with you.

5:4 Some manuscripts read *comes upon you as if you were thieves.*   **5:26** Greek *with a holy kiss.*

I have gone through hard times, whether being cut from teams, healthy scratched or injured. But I know that Jesus has overcome the world and so my joy, hope and peace are in Him.

I was raised in a Christian family, and in my late teens I made the decision to make my family's faith my own and I chose to follow Christ. I knew I believed in God, but I had to dig deeper into the Bible to actually find out what it means to be a true follower of Jesus.

It was amazing to discover that God, the Maker of this entire world, wanted to have a personal relationship with me! He made us not only to have a relationship with Him but also with others, so that we can teach and encourage and straighten each other out from time to time.

When I read God's teachings in the Bible, I discovered they weren't there to take fun away from us, but rather to protect us! God knows what is best for people He created. He gives us purpose for this life, and hope for eternal life with Him!

I know God has gifted me with the talent to play hockey. Every chance I get to play I want to work hard, play fair and be a good teammate. In everything I do I want to bring glory to God.

I want to care for my teammates just as God does. That means encouraging, serving, forgiving or asking for forgiveness and sharing the truth about Jesus with those who don't know Him!

"I believed in God but had to dig deeper into the Bible."

The Bible is God's spoken word to us. It defines my faith. In Matthew 22:37-39, Jesus tells us, " 'You must love the LORD your God with all your heart, all your soul, and all your mind.' This is the first and greatest commandment. A second is equally important: 'Love your neighbor as yourself.' " This sums up how I strive to live my life for Jesus.

I've always been a person who likes to be in control. It took me a while to come to the realization that I can't control everything. I have to work my hardest and trust in God. I can be a stubborn person. But trusting that He has a plan for me and knowing that I just have to work my hardest at living it out helps me to stay more even-keeled through all of life's ups and downs.

I've experienced some different circumstances this last year: enduring the NHL lockout, getting traded, and having another child. Any of these would be difficult by itself; but combined, these things would have been overwhelming if not for my faith and being able to put everything in God's hands. Getting traded is always a little bit of a surprise, but not knowing where you're going with a baby coming, and getting everything prepared and being exhausted can be worrisome. We just tried to take it one week at a time and take it off our minds by giving it to the Lord.

"He has a plan for me."

I constantly go back to Philippians 4:13: *"I can do everything through him who gives me strength."* I think every person doubts himself, and this verse gives me confidence that if He puts me in a situation, I can succeed at it. I have to work hard, but I can always lean on this promise.

Daily, I have to remind myself to trust God. I have to practice it day in and day out, in big things as well as little things. I'm always working on trying to put things in God's hands, making the most of every situation and enjoying what He has for me. That's one area where I know I can become stronger. When you have a relationship with Jesus Christ, you can have faith that He has everything under His control. You have to put your best foot forward, work hard at what you can do, and trust in Him that His plan will always be the best.

RYAN SMYTH
Left Wing, Edmonton Oilers, NHL

"One man's dream come true . . . but there is more . . ."

I grew up in a home where we went to church, so as a child I knew a little about God and I was taught right from wrong.

I left home when I was 15 to pursue a career in hockey and I played junior hockey in Moose Jaw for 3 years. It was there that I met my wonderful wife Stacey, for whom I thank God every day. My life's dream at that early age was to play hockey in the NHL and nothing was going to stop me. I didn't drink or do drugs and I was a very determined young man. With time I was drafted by the Edmonton Oilers, my favorite childhood team. I played $11^1/_2$ years in Edmonton, 3 months in New York with the Islanders, 2 years with the Colorado Avalanche, 2 years with the Los Angeles Kings, and now I've come full-circle to play for the Oilers once again.

This brief biography no doubt sounds a lot like one man's dream come true. But there is much more to the story! Through these years my career and my life outside of hockey saw me through peaks and valleys that exposed me to Satan and almost destroyed me. Thankfully God had a different plan. He put people in my life, especially my wife Stacey, to help carry me through the tough times. Without God I don't know if I would be here today and I am thankful for the lessons I have learned along the way. Most importantly I have learned that as vital as life's dreams and goals are to all of us, more vital still is that we put God in our lives first so that He can guide us through life's journey.

I will leave you with one of my favorite verses, Ephesians 6:13— *"Therefore, put on every piece of God's armor so you will be able to resist the enemy in the time of evil. Then after the battle you will still be standing firm."*

KEVIN COMPTON
Former Owner, San Jose Sharks, NHL

I have learned God's purpose and the desires of our hearts are typically in line as His love for us allows us to pursue our passions while serving Him.

I love looking forward to new things. In sports, there is always a new season with new players, new challenges and new opportunities. Each year, like each season in life, starts with so much hope and opportunity. We must be prepared if we are to be our best.

" . . . the value of helping others . . . is one of the most rewarding things in my life."

Being on the business side of the sport, I am constantly balancing tough leadership decisions with my faith-based compassion. While I have never felt the two were conflicting in their fundamentals, there are times when doing the right thing for the organization certainly felt less than compassionate. I try to remember that every situation is in God's hands and I gain perspective from Isaiah 43:19: *"For I am about to do something new. See, I have already begun! Do you not see it? I will make a pathway through the wilderness. I will create rivers in the dry wasteland."* In my role, I am constantly reminded I am dealing with people, not pucks. Having the teachings and presence of Jesus guiding my decisions reminds me of the value of treating people the way I would want to be treated, as guided by Matthew 7:12: *"So in everything, do to others what you would have them do to you, for this sums up the Law and the Prophets."*

I feel the comfort and strength of Jesus every time I need it. I have so often been thankful for the accountability and responsibilities living a life for Jesus has brought. I know He has kept me out of countless bad situations simply by staying away from elements of life that tend to bring about unhappy endings.

For almost 20 years I taught an adult Bible Study at our church. Each week, I found a key point of support from the Bible verses, or someone from the class would report how a particular Scripture helped them. I soon learned the value of helping others in their life's journey was one of the most rewarding things in my life.

I have been married to a wonderful woman, Gayla, for over 30 years. We have a great friendship and share a deep faith in Jesus. We have complete trust in each other through our faith in each other and our faith in Jesus.

JOE VITALE
Center, Pittsburgh Penguins, NHL

I was brought to Christ from a very young age through my parents. Since that time God has always been the center of my life, including my life in hockey. In surrendering my life to Jesus, I have found my purpose here on earth. God has given me a job and goals, and he has gifted me to see those goals through.

The courage, confidence, and peace I receive from Him get me through each day. I keep God close during the rigors of a season by making the choice to do so. It can be hard at times with all the distractions, but making that choice to read the Bible and talk to God in prayer has made all the difference. It's all about having that desire to get to know Jesus more, and when I do that, I feel so much strength.

My wife is my biggest supporter and challenger all at the same time. Her unconditional love and support have made all the difference for me. My relationship with God has strengthened every aspect of my life including my relationship with my wife and children.

In chapter 14 in Matthew's Gospel, Jesus walks on the water and so does Peter. This has been the most important passage for me. Every day I am faced with new challenges that scare me. But I am forced to do what Peter did, and that is to put my full trust in Jesus and do what seems impossible.

"I keep God close during the rigors of a season."

Jesus challenged us: "love each other as I have loved you." The best way to show my teammates the love of Christ is by encouraging them, picking someone up after a bad game, taking a teammate out to lunch, helping someone with a skill they're struggling with, just being there for the guy next to me.

I think there is a common misconception that being a Christian hockey player means you are weak and nerdy. In reality, being a Christian is awesome! It makes you strong and courageous.

My purpose in life is to follow where He leads me with my whole heart.

DREW MACINTYRE
Goaltender, Toronto Marlies, AHL

I have become more and more amazed as I discover all the ways God loves us. I have tried to live by Philippians 4:13 for quite a while now, which says, *"I can do all things through Christ who strengthens me."* It is awesome to realize not only how much He loves us, but how He loves us enough to teach us lessons in the most surprising and seemingly impossible moments of our lives.

With the help of many great people from Hockey Ministries International, my wife and I have been able to feel God's hand teaching, guiding and loving us in so many different ways. In hockey we have recently found ourselves in situations where we were really excited for an opportunity only to see it not go the way we wanted. I can honestly say He has taught us the most in the midst of those times.

Learning through life's challenges

Each day brings something new and the lessons are ongoing—but it's an amazing feeling to know that no matter how many times we mess up or make mistakes, God always loves us enough to teach us and to guide us.

2 Thessalonians

Greetings from Paul

1 This letter is from Paul, Silas,* and Timothy.
We are writing to the church in Thessalonica, to you who belong to God our Father and the Lord Jesus Christ.

2May God our Father* and the Lord Jesus Christ give you grace and peace.

Encouragement during Persecution

3Dear brothers and sisters,* we can't help but thank God for you, because your faith is flourishing and your love for one another is growing. 4We proudly tell God's other churches about your endurance and faithfulness in all the persecutions and hardships you are suffering. 5And God will use this persecution to show his justice and to make you worthy of his Kingdom, for which you are suffering. 6In his justice he will pay back those who persecute you.

7And God will provide rest for you who are being persecuted and also for us when the Lord Jesus appears from heaven. He will come with his mighty angels, 8in flaming fire, bringing judgment on those who don't know God and on those who refuse to obey the Good News of our Lord Jesus. 9They will be punished with eternal destruction, forever separated from the Lord and from his glorious power. 10When he comes on that day, he will receive glory from his holy people—praise from all who believe. And this includes you, for you believed what we told you about him.

11So we keep on praying for you, asking our God to enable you to live a life worthy of his call. May he give you the power to accomplish all the good things your faith prompts you to do. 12Then the name of our Lord Jesus will be honored because of the way you live, and you will be honored along with him. This is all made possible because of the grace of our God and Lord, Jesus Christ.*

Events prior to the Lord's Second Coming

2 Now, dear brothers and sisters,* let us clarify some things about the coming of our Lord Jesus Christ and how we will be gathered to meet him. 2Don't be so easily shaken or alarmed by those who say that the day of the Lord has already begun. Don't believe them, even if they claim to have had a spiritual vision, a revelation, or a letter supposedly from us. 3Don't be fooled by what they say. For that day will not come until there is a great rebellion against God and the man of lawlessness* is revealed—the one who brings destruction.* 4He will exalt himself and defy everything that people call god and every object of worship. He will even sit in the temple of God, claiming that he himself is God.

5Don't you remember that I told you about all this when I was with you? 6And you know what is holding him back, for he can be revealed only when his time comes. 7For this lawlessness is already at work secretly, and it will remain secret until the one who is holding it back steps out of the way. 8Then the man of lawlessness will be revealed, but the Lord Jesus will kill him with the breath of his mouth and destroy him by the splendor of his coming.

9This man will come to do the work of Satan with counterfeit power and signs and miracles. 10He will use every kind of evil deception to fool those on their way to destruction, because they refuse to love and accept the truth that would save them. 11So God will cause them to be greatly deceived, and they will believe these lies. 12Then they will be condemned for enjoying evil rather than believing the truth.

Believers Should Stand Firm

13As for us, we can't help but thank God for you, dear brothers and sisters loved by the Lord. We are always thankful that God chose you to be among the first* to experience salvation—a salvation that came through the Spirit who makes you holy and through your belief in the truth. 14He called you to salvation when we told you the Good News; now you can share in the glory of our Lord Jesus Christ.

15With all these things in mind, dear brothers and sisters, stand firm and keep a strong grip on the teaching we passed on to you both in person and by letter.

16Now may our Lord Jesus Christ himself and God our Father, who loved us and by his grace gave us eternal comfort and a wonderful hope, 17comfort you and strengthen you in every good thing you do and say.

1:1 Greek *Silvanus*, the Greek form of the name.   **1:2** Some manuscripts read *God the Father.*   **1:3** Greek *Brothers.*   **1:12** Or *of our God and our Lord Jesus Christ.*   **2:1** Greek *brothers;* also in 2:13, 15.   **2:3a** Some manuscripts read *the man of sin.*   **2:3b** Greek *the son of destruction.*   **2:13** Some manuscripts read *chose you from the very beginning.*

Paul's Request for Prayer

3 Finally, dear brothers and sisters,* we ask you to pray for us. Pray that the Lord's message will spread rapidly and be honored wherever it goes, just as when it came to you. ²Pray, too, that we will be rescued from wicked and evil people, for not everyone is a believer. ³But the Lord is faithful; he will strengthen you and guard you from the evil one.* ⁴And we are confident in the Lord that you are doing and will continue to do the things we commanded you. ⁵May the Lord lead your hearts into a full understanding and expression of the love of God and the patient endurance that comes from Christ.

An Exhortation to Proper Living

⁶And now, dear brothers and sisters, we give you this command in the name of our Lord Jesus Christ: Stay away from all believers* who live idle lives and don't follow the tradition they received* from us. ⁷For you know that you ought to imitate us. We were not idle when we were with you. ⁸We never accepted food from anyone without paying for it. We worked hard day and night so we would not be a burden to any of you. ⁹We certainly had the right to ask you to feed us, but we wanted to give you an example to follow. ¹⁰Even while we were with you, we gave you this command: "Those unwilling to work will not get to eat."

¹¹Yet we hear that some of you are living idle lives, refusing to work and meddling in other people's business. ¹²We command such people and urge them in the name of the Lord Jesus Christ to settle down and work to earn their own living. ¹³As for the rest of you, dear brothers and sisters, never get tired of doing good.

¹⁴Take note of those who refuse to obey what we say in this letter. Stay away from them so they will be ashamed. ¹⁵Don't think of them as enemies, but warn them as you would a brother or sister.*

Paul's Final Greetings

¹⁶Now may the Lord of peace himself give you his peace at all times and in every situation. The Lord be with you all.

¹⁷HERE IS MY GREETING IN MY OWN HANDWRITING—PAUL. I DO THIS IN ALL MY LETTERS TO PROVE THEY ARE FROM ME.

¹⁸May the grace of our Lord Jesus Christ be with you all.

3:1 Greek *brothers;* also in 3:6, 13.   **3:3** Or *from evil.*   **3:6a** Greek *from every brother.*   **3:6b** Some manuscripts read *you received.*
3:15 Greek *as a brother.*

1 Timothy

Greetings from Paul

1 This letter is from Paul, an apostle of Christ Jesus, appointed by the command of God our Savior and Christ Jesus, who gives us hope.

²I am writing to Timothy, my true son in the faith.

May God the Father and Christ Jesus our Lord give you grace, mercy, and peace.

Warnings against False Teachings

³When I left for Macedonia, I urged you to stay there in Ephesus and stop those whose teaching is contrary to the truth. ⁴Don't let them waste their time in endless discussion of myths and spiritual pedigrees. These things only lead to meaningless speculations,* which don't help people live a life of faith in God.*

⁵The purpose of my instruction is that all believers would be filled with love that comes from a pure heart, a clear conscience, and genuine faith. ⁶But some people have missed this whole point. They have turned away from these things and spend their time in meaningless discussions. ⁷They want to be known as teachers of the law of Moses, but they don't know what they are talking about, even though they speak so confidently.

⁸We know that the law is good when used correctly. ⁹For the law was not intended for people who do what is right. It is for people who are lawless and rebellious, who are ungodly and sinful, who consider nothing sacred and defile what is holy, who kill their father or mother or commit other murders. ¹⁰The law is for people who are sexually immoral, or who practice homosexuality, or are slave traders,* liars, promise breakers, or who do anything else that contradicts the wholesome teaching ¹¹that comes from the glorious Good News entrusted to me by our blessed God.

Paul's Gratitude for God's Mercy

¹²I thank Christ Jesus our Lord, who has given me strength to do his work. He considered me trustworthy and appointed me to serve him, ¹³even though I used to blaspheme the name of Christ. In my insolence, I persecuted his people. But God had mercy on me because I did it in ig-

norance and unbelief. ¹⁴Oh, how generous and gracious our Lord was! He filled me with the faith and love that come from Christ Jesus.

¹⁵This is a trustworthy saying, and everyone should accept it: "Christ Jesus came into the world to save sinners"—and I am the worst of them all. ¹⁶But God had mercy on me so that Christ Jesus could use me as a prime example of his great patience with even the worst sinners. Then others will realize that they, too, can believe in him and receive eternal life. ¹⁷All honor and glory to God forever and ever! He is the eternal King, the unseen one who never dies; he alone is God. Amen.

Timothy's Responsibility

¹⁸Timothy, my son, here are my instructions for you, based on the prophetic words spoken about you earlier. May they help you fight well in the Lord's battles. ¹⁹Cling to your faith in Christ, and keep your conscience clear. For some people have deliberately violated their consciences; as a result, their faith has been shipwrecked. ²⁰Hymenaeus and Alexander are two examples. I threw them out and handed them over to Satan so they might learn not to blaspheme God.

Instructions about Worship

2 I urge you, first of all, to pray for all people. Ask God to help them; intercede on their behalf, and give thanks for them. ²Pray this way for kings and all who are in authority so that we can live peaceful and quiet lives marked by godliness and dignity. ³This is good and pleases God our Savior, ⁴who wants everyone to be saved and to understand the truth. ⁵For there is only one God and one Mediator who can reconcile God and humanity—the man Christ Jesus. ⁶He gave his life to purchase freedom for everyone. This is the message God gave to the world at just the right time. ⁷And I have been chosen as a preacher and apostle to teach the Gentiles this message about faith and truth. I'm not exaggerating—just telling the truth.

⁸In every place of worship, I want men to pray with holy hands lifted up to God, free from anger and controversy.

⁹And I want women to be modest in their appearance.* They should wear decent and appro-

1:4a Greek *in myths and endless genealogies, which cause speculation.* 1:4b Greek *a stewardship of God in faith.* 1:10 Or *kidnappers.* 2:9 Or *to pray in modest apparel.*

priate clothing and not draw attention to themselves by the way they fix their hair or by wearing gold or pearls or expensive clothes. [10]For women who claim to be devoted to God should make themselves attractive by the good things they do.

[11]Women should learn quietly and submissively. [12]I do not let women teach men or have authority over them.* Let them listen quietly. [13]For God made Adam first, and afterward he made Eve. [14]And it was not Adam who was deceived by Satan. The woman was deceived, and sin was the result. [15]But women will be saved through childbearing,* assuming they continue to live in faith, love, holiness, and modesty.

Leaders in the Church

3 This is a trustworthy saying: "If someone aspires to be an elder,* he desires an honorable position." [2]So an elder must be a man whose life is above reproach. He must be faithful to his wife.* He must exercise self-control, live wisely, and have a good reputation. He must enjoy having guests in his home, and he must be able to teach. [3]He must not be a heavy drinker* or be violent. He must be gentle, not quarrelsome, and not love money. [4]He must manage his own family well, having children who respect and obey him. [5]For if a man cannot manage his own household, how can he take care of God's church?

[6]An elder must not be a new believer, because he might become proud, and the devil would cause him to fall.* [7]Also, people outside the church must speak well of him so that he will not be disgraced and fall into the devil's trap.

[8]In the same way, deacons must be well respected and have integrity. They must not be heavy drinkers or dishonest with money. [9]They must be committed to the mystery of the faith now revealed and must live with a clear conscience. [10]Before they are appointed as deacons, let them be closely examined. If they pass the test, then let them serve as deacons.

[11]In the same way, their wives* must be respected and must not slander others. They must exercise self-control and be faithful in everything they do.

[12]A deacon must be faithful to his wife, and he must manage his children and household well. [13]Those who do well as deacons will be rewarded with respect from others and will have increased confidence in their faith in Christ Jesus.

The Truths of Our Faith

[14]I am writing these things to you now, even though I hope to be with you soon, [15]so that if I am delayed, you will know how people must conduct themselves in the household of God. This is the church of the living God, which is the pillar and foundation of the truth.

[16]Without question, this is the great mystery of our faith*:

Christ* was revealed in a human body
and vindicated by the Spirit.*
He was seen by angels
and announced to the nations.
He was believed in throughout the world
and taken to heaven in glory.

Warnings against False Teachers

4 Now the Holy Spirit tells us clearly that in the last times some will turn away from the true faith; they will follow deceptive spirits and teachings that come from demons. [2]These people are hypocrites and liars, and their consciences are dead.*

[3]They will say it is wrong to be married and wrong to eat certain foods. But God created those foods to be eaten with thanks by faithful people who know the truth. [4]Since everything God created is good, we should not reject any of it but receive it with thanks. [5]For we know it is made acceptable* by the word of God and prayer.

A Good Servant of Christ Jesus

[6]If you explain these things to the brothers and sisters,* Timothy, you will be a worthy servant of Christ Jesus, one who is nourished by the message of faith and the good teaching you have followed. [7]Do not waste time arguing over godless ideas and old wives' tales. Instead, train yourself to be godly. [8]"Physical training is good, but training for godliness is much better, promising benefits in this life and in the life to come." [9]This is a trustworthy saying, and everyone should accept it. [10]This is why we work hard and continue to struggle,* for our hope is in the living God, who is the Savior of all people and particularly of all believers.

[11]Teach these things and insist that everyone learn them. [12]Don't let anyone think less of you because you are young. Be an example to all believers in what you say, in the way you live, in your love, your faith, and your purity. [13]Until I get there, focus on reading the Scriptures to the church, encouraging the believers, and teaching them.

[14]Do not neglect the spiritual gift you received through the prophecy spoken over you when the elders of the church laid their hands on you. [15]Give your complete attention to these matters. Throw yourself into your tasks so that everyone

2:12 Or *teach men or usurp their authority.* **2:15** Or *will be saved by accepting their role as mothers,* or *will be saved by the birth of the Child.* **3:1** Or *an overseer,* or *a bishop;* also in 3:2, 6. **3:2** Or *must have only one wife,* or *must be married only once;* Greek reads *must be the husband of one wife;* also in 3:12. **3:3** Greek *must not drink too much wine;* similarly in 3:8. **3:6** Or *he might fall into the same judgment as the devil.* **3:11** Or *the women deacons.* The Greek word can be translated *women* or *wives.* **3:16a** Or *of godliness.* **3:16b** Greek *He who;* other manuscripts read *God.* **3:16c** Or *in his spirit.* **4:2** Greek *are seared.* **4:5** Or *made holy.* **4:6** Greek *brothers.* **4:10** Some manuscripts read *continue to suffer.*

will see your progress. [16]Keep a close watch on how you live and on your teaching. Stay true to what is right for the sake of your own salvation and the salvation of those who hear you.

Advice about Widows, Elders, and Slaves

5 Never speak harshly to an older man,* but appeal to him respectfully as you would to your own father. Talk to younger men as you would to your own brothers. [2]Treat older women as you would your mother, and treat younger women with all purity as you would your own sisters.

[3]Take care of* any widow who has no one else to care for her. [4]But if she has children or grandchildren, their first responsibility is to show godliness at home and repay their parents by taking care of them. This is something that pleases God.

[5]Now a true widow, a woman who is truly alone in this world, has placed her hope in God. She prays night and day, asking God for his help. [6]But the widow who lives only for pleasure is spiritually dead even while she lives. [7]Give these instructions to the church so that no one will be open to criticism.

[8]But those who won't care for their relatives, especially those in their own household, have denied the true faith. Such people are worse than unbelievers.

[9]A widow who is put on the list for support must be a woman who is at least sixty years old and was faithful to her husband.* [10]She must be well respected by everyone because of the good she has done. Has she brought up her children well? Has she been kind to strangers and served other believers humbly?* Has she helped those who are in trouble? Has she always been ready to do good?

[11]The younger widows should not be on the list, because their physical desires will overpower their devotion to Christ and they will want to remarry. [12]Then they would be guilty of breaking their previous pledge. [13]And if they are on the list, they will learn to be lazy and will spend their time gossiping from house to house, meddling in other people's business and talking about things they shouldn't. [14]So I advise these younger widows to marry again, have children, and take care of their own homes. Then the enemy will not be able to say anything against them. [15]For I am afraid that some of them have already gone astray and now follow Satan.

[16]If a woman who is a believer has relatives who are widows, she must take care of them and not put the responsibility on the church. Then the church can care for the widows who are truly alone.

[17]Elders who do their work well should be respected and paid well,* especially those who work hard at both preaching and teaching. [18]For the Scripture says, "You must not muzzle an ox to keep it from eating as it treads out the grain." And in another place, "Those who work deserve their pay!"*

[19]Do not listen to an accusation against an elder unless it is confirmed by two or three witnesses. [20]Those who sin should be reprimanded in front of the whole church; this will serve as a strong warning to others.

[21]I solemnly command you in the presence of God and Christ Jesus and the highest angels to obey these instructions without taking sides or showing favoritism to anyone.

[22]Never be in a hurry about appointing a church leader.* Do not share in the sins of others. Keep yourself pure.

[23]Don't drink only water. You ought to drink a little wine for the sake of your stomach because you are sick so often.

[24]Remember, the sins of some people are obvious, leading them to certain judgment. But there are others whose sins will not be revealed until later. [25]In the same way, the good deeds of some people are obvious. And the good deeds done in secret will someday come to light.

6 All slaves should show full respect for their masters so they will not bring shame on the name of God and his teaching. [2]If the masters are believers, that is no excuse for being disrespectful. Those slaves should work all the harder because their efforts are helping other believers* who are well loved.

False Teaching and True Riches

Teach these things, Timothy, and encourage everyone to obey them. [3]Some people may contradict our teaching, but these are the wholesome teachings of the Lord Jesus Christ. These teachings promote a godly life. [4]Anyone who teaches something different is arrogant and lacks understanding. Such a person has an unhealthy desire to quibble over the meaning of words. This stirs up arguments ending in jealousy, division, slander, and evil suspicions. [5]These people always cause trouble. Their minds are corrupt, and they have turned their backs on the truth. To them, a show of godliness is just a way to become wealthy.

[6]Yet true godliness with contentment is itself great wealth. [7]After all, we brought nothing with us when we came into the world, and we can't take anything with us when we leave it. [8]So if we have enough food and clothing, let us be content.

[9]But people who long to be rich fall into temptation and are trapped by many foolish and harmful desires that plunge them into ruin and

5:1 Or *an elder.* **5:3** Or *Honor.* **5:9** Greek *was the wife of one husband.* **5:10** Greek *and washed the feet of God's holy people?* **5:17** Greek *should be worthy of double honor.* **5:18** Deut 25:4; Luke 10:7. **5:22** Greek *about the laying on of hands.* **6:2** Greek *brothers.*

destruction. [10]For the love of money is the root of all kinds of evil. And some people, craving money, have wandered from the true faith and pierced themselves with many sorrows.

Paul's Final Instructions

[11]But you, Timothy, are a man of God; so run from all these evil things. Pursue righteousness and a godly life, along with faith, love, perseverance, and gentleness. [12]Fight the good fight for the true faith. Hold tightly to the eternal life to which God has called you, which you have confessed so well before many witnesses. [13]And I charge you before God, who gives life to all, and before Christ Jesus, who gave a good testimony before Pontius Pilate, [14]that you obey this command without wavering. Then no one can find fault with you from now until our Lord Jesus Christ comes again. [15]For at just the right time Christ will be revealed from heaven by the blessed and only almighty God, the King of all kings and Lord of all lords. [16]He alone can never die, and he lives in light so brilliant that no human can approach him. No human eye has ever seen him, nor ever will. All honor and power to him forever! Amen.

[17]Teach those who are rich in this world not to be proud and not to trust in their money, which is so unreliable. Their trust should be in God, who richly gives us all we need for our enjoyment. [18]Tell them to use their money to do good. They should be rich in good works and generous to those in need, always being ready to share with others. [19]By doing this they will be storing up their treasure as a good foundation for the future so that they may experience true life.

[20]Timothy, guard what God has entrusted to you. Avoid godless, foolish discussions with those who oppose you with their so-called knowledge. [21]Some people have wandered from the faith by following such foolishness.

May God's grace be with you all.

2 Timothy

Greetings from Paul

1 This letter is from Paul, chosen by the will of God to be an apostle of Christ Jesus. I have been sent out to tell others about the life he has promised through faith in Christ Jesus.

²I am writing to Timothy, my dear son.

May God the Father and Christ Jesus our Lord give you grace, mercy, and peace.

Encouragement to Be Faithful

³Timothy, I thank God for you—the God I serve with a clear conscience, just as my ancestors did. Night and day I constantly remember you in my prayers. ⁴I long to see you again, for I remember your tears as we parted. And I will be filled with joy when we are together again.

⁵I remember your genuine faith, for you share the faith that first filled your grandmother Lois and your mother, Eunice. And I know that same faith continues strong in you. ⁶This is why I remind you to fan into flames the spiritual gift God gave you when I laid my hands on you. ⁷For God has not given us a spirit of fear and timidity, but of power, love, and self-discipline.

⁸So never be ashamed to tell others about our Lord. And don't be ashamed of me, either, even though I'm in prison for him. With the strength God gives you, be ready to suffer with me for the sake of the Good News. ⁹For God saved us and called us to live a holy life. He did this, not because we deserved it, but because that was his plan from before the beginning of time—to show us his grace through Christ Jesus. ¹⁰And now he has made all of this plain to us by the appearing of Christ Jesus, our Savior. He broke the power of death and illuminated the way to life and immortality through the Good News. ¹¹And God chose me to be a preacher, an apostle, and a teacher of this Good News.

¹²That is why I am suffering here in prison. But I am not ashamed of it, for I know the one in whom I trust, and I am sure that he is able to guard what I have entrusted to him* until the day of his return.

¹³Hold on to the pattern of wholesome teaching you learned from me—a pattern shaped by the faith and love that you have in Christ Jesus. ¹⁴Through the power of the Holy Spirit who lives within us, carefully guard the precious truth that has been entrusted to you.

¹⁵As you know, everyone from the province of Asia has deserted me—even Phygelus and Hermogenes.

¹⁶May the Lord show special kindness to Onesiphorus and all his family because he often visited and encouraged me. He was never ashamed of me because I was in chains. ¹⁷When he came to Rome, he searched everywhere until he found me. ¹⁸May the Lord show him special kindness on the day of Christ's return. And you know very well how helpful he was in Ephesus.

A Good Soldier of Christ Jesus

2 Timothy, my dear son, be strong through the grace that God gives you in Christ Jesus. ²You have heard me teach things that have been confirmed by many reliable witnesses. Now teach these truths to other trustworthy people who will be able to pass them on to others.

³Endure suffering along with me, as a good soldier of Christ Jesus. ⁴Soldiers don't get tied up in the affairs of civilian life, for then they cannot please the officer who enlisted them. ⁵And athletes cannot win the prize unless they follow the rules. ⁶And hardworking farmers should be the first to enjoy the fruit of their labor. ⁷Think about what I am saying. The Lord will help you understand all these things.

⁸Always remember that Jesus Christ, a descendant of King David, was raised from the dead. This is the Good News I preach. ⁹And because I preach this Good News, I am suffering and have been chained like a criminal. But the word of God cannot be chained. ¹⁰So I am willing to endure anything if it will bring salvation and eternal glory in Christ Jesus to those God has chosen.

¹¹This is a trustworthy saying:

If we die with him,
    we will also live with him.
¹² If we endure hardship,
    we will reign with him.
If we deny him,
    he will deny us.
¹³ If we are unfaithful,
    he remains faithful,
    for he cannot deny who he is.

1:12 Or *what has been entrusted to me.*

[14]Remind everyone about these things, and command them in God's presence to stop fighting over words. Such arguments are useless, and they can ruin those who hear them.

An Approved Worker

[15]Work hard so you can present yourself to God and receive his approval. Be a good worker, one who does not need to be ashamed and who correctly explains the word of truth. [16]Avoid worthless, foolish talk that only leads to more godless behavior. [17]This kind of talk spreads like cancer,* as in the case of Hymenaeus and Philetus. [18]They have left the path of truth, claiming that the resurrection of the dead has already occurred; in this way, they have turned some people away from the faith.

[19]But God's truth stands firm like a foundation stone with this inscription: "The LORD knows those who are his,"* and "All who belong to the LORD must turn away from evil."*

[20]In a wealthy home some utensils are made of gold and silver, and some are made of wood and clay. The expensive utensils are used for special occasions, and the cheap ones are for everyday use. [21]If you keep yourself pure, you will be a special utensil for honorable use. Your life will be clean, and you will be ready for the Master to use you for every good work.

[22]Run from anything that stimulates youthful lusts. Instead, pursue righteous living, faithfulness, love, and peace. Enjoy the companionship of those who call on the Lord with pure hearts.

[23]Again I say, don't get involved in foolish, ignorant arguments that only start fights. [24]A servant of the Lord must not quarrel but must be kind to everyone, be able to teach, and be patient with difficult people. [25]Gently instruct those who oppose the truth. Perhaps God will change those people's hearts, and they will learn the truth. [26]Then they will come to their senses and escape from the devil's trap. For they have been held captive by him to do whatever he wants.

The Dangers of the Last Days

3 You should know this, Timothy, that in the last days there will be very difficult times. [2]For people will love only themselves and their money. They will be boastful and proud, scoffing at God, disobedient to their parents, and ungrateful. They will consider nothing sacred. [3]They will be unloving and unforgiving; they will slander others and have no self-control. They will be cruel and hate what is good. [4]They will betray their friends, be reckless, be puffed up with pride, and love pleasure rather than God. [5]They will act religious, but they will reject the power that could make them godly. Stay away from people like that!

[6]They are the kind who work their way into people's homes and win the confidence of* vulnerable women who are burdened with the guilt of sin and controlled by various desires. [7](Such women are forever following new teachings, but they are never able to understand the truth.) [8]These teachers oppose the truth just as Jannes and Jambres opposed Moses. They have depraved minds and a counterfeit faith. [9]But they won't get away with this for long. Someday everyone will recognize what fools they are, just as with Jannes and Jambres.

Paul's Charge to Timothy

[10]But you, Timothy, certainly know what I teach, and how I live, and what my purpose in life is. You know my faith, my patience, my love, and my endurance. [11]You know how much persecution and suffering I have endured. You know all about how I was persecuted in Antioch, Iconium, and Lystra—but the Lord rescued me from all of it. [12]Yes, and everyone who wants to live a godly life in Christ Jesus will suffer persecution. [13]But evil people and impostors will flourish. They will deceive others and will themselves be deceived.

[14]But you must remain faithful to the things you have been taught. You know they are true, for you know you can trust those who taught you. [15]You have been taught the holy Scriptures from childhood, and they have given you the wisdom to receive the salvation that comes by trusting in Christ Jesus. [16]All Scripture is inspired by God and is useful to teach us what is true and to make us realize what is wrong in our lives. It corrects us when we are wrong and teaches us to do what is right. [17]God uses it to prepare and equip his people to do every good work.

4 I solemnly urge you in the presence of God and Christ Jesus, who will someday judge the living and the dead when he appears to set up his Kingdom: [2]Preach the word of God. Be prepared, whether the time is favorable or not. Patiently correct, rebuke, and encourage your people with good teaching.

[3]For a time is coming when people will no longer listen to sound and wholesome teaching. They will follow their own desires and will look for teachers who will tell them whatever their itching ears want to hear. [4]They will reject the truth and chase after myths.

[5]But you should keep a clear mind in every situation. Don't be afraid of suffering for the Lord. Work at telling others the Good News, and fully carry out the ministry God has given you.

[6]As for me, my life has already been poured out as an offering to God. The time of my death is near. [7]I have fought the good fight, I have finished the race, and I have remained faithful. [8]And now the prize awaits me—the crown of righteousness, which the Lord, the righteous

2:17 Greek *gangrene.*   2:19a Num 16:5.   2:19b See Isa 52:11.   3:6 Greek *and take captive.*

Judge, will give me on the day of his return. And the prize is not just for me but for all who eagerly look forward to his appearing.

Paul's Final Words

[9]Timothy, please come as soon as you can. [10]Demas has deserted me because he loves the things of this life and has gone to Thessalonica. Crescens has gone to Galatia, and Titus has gone to Dalmatia. [11]Only Luke is with me. Bring Mark with you when you come, for he will be helpful to me in my ministry. [12]I sent Tychicus to Ephesus. [13]When you come, be sure to bring the coat I left with Carpus at Troas. Also bring my books, and especially my papers.*

[14]Alexander the coppersmith did me much harm, but the Lord will judge him for what he has done. [15]Be careful of him, for he fought against everything we said.

[16]The first time I was brought before the judge, no one came with me. Everyone abandoned me. May it not be counted against them. [17]But the Lord stood with me and gave me strength so that I might preach the Good News in its entirety for all the Gentiles to hear. And he rescued me from certain death.* [18]Yes, and the Lord will deliver me from every evil attack and will bring me safely into his heavenly Kingdom. All glory to God forever and ever! Amen.

Paul's Final Greetings

[19]Give my greetings to Priscilla and Aquila and those living in the household of Onesiphorus. [20]Erastus stayed at Corinth, and I left Trophimus sick at Miletus.

[21]Do your best to get here before winter. Eubulus sends you greetings, and so do Pudens, Linus, Claudia, and all the brothers and sisters.*

[22]May the Lord be with your spirit. And may his grace be with all of you.

4:13 Greek *especially the parchments.*   4:17 Greek *from the mouth of a lion.*   4:21 Greek *brothers.*

Titus

Greetings from Paul

1 This letter is from Paul, a slave of God and an apostle of Jesus Christ. I have been sent to proclaim faith to* those God has chosen and to teach them to know the truth that shows them how to live godly lives. [2]This truth gives them confidence that they have eternal life, which God—who does not lie—promised them before the world began. [3]And now at just the right time he has revealed this message, which we announce to everyone. It is by the command of God our Savior that I have been entrusted with this work for him.

[4]I am writing to Titus, my true son in the faith that we share.

May God the Father and Christ Jesus our Savior give you grace and peace.

Titus's Work in Crete

[5]I left you on the island of Crete so you could complete our work there and appoint elders in each town as I instructed you. [6]An elder must live a blameless life. He must be faithful to his wife,* and his children must be believers who don't have a reputation for being wild or rebellious. [7]An elder* is a manager of God's household, so he must live a blameless life. He must not be arrogant or quick-tempered; he must not be a heavy drinker,* violent, or dishonest with money.

[8]Rather, he must enjoy having guests in his home, and he must love what is good. He must live wisely and be just. He must live a devout and disciplined life. [9]He must have a strong belief in the trustworthy message he was taught; then he will be able to encourage others with wholesome teaching and show those who oppose it where they are wrong.

[10]For there are many rebellious people who engage in useless talk and deceive others. This is especially true of those who insist on circumcision for salvation. [11]They must be silenced, because they are turning whole families away from the truth by their false teaching. And they do it only for money. [12]Even one of their own men, a prophet from Crete, has said about them, "The people of Crete are all liars, cruel animals, lazy gluttons."* [13]This is true. So reprimand them sternly to make them strong in the faith. [14]They must stop listening to Jewish myths and the commands of people who have turned away from the truth.

[15]Everything is pure to those whose hearts are pure. But nothing is pure to those who are corrupt and unbelieving, because their minds and consciences are corrupted. [16]Such people claim they know God, but they deny him by the way they live. They are detestable and disobedient, worthless for doing anything good.

Promote Right Teaching

2 As for you, Titus, promote the kind of living that reflects wholesome teaching. [2]Teach the older men to exercise self-control, to be worthy of respect, and to live wisely. They must have sound faith and be filled with love and patience.

[3]Similarly, teach the older women to live in a way that honors God. They must not slander others or be heavy drinkers.* Instead, they should teach others what is good. [4]These older women must train the younger women to love their husbands and their children, [5]to live wisely and be pure, to work in their homes,* to do good, and to be submissive to their husbands. Then they will not bring shame on the word of God.

[6]In the same way, encourage the young men to live wisely. [7]And you yourself must be an example to them by doing good works of every kind. Let everything you do reflect the integrity and seriousness of your teaching. [8]Teach the truth so that your teaching can't be criticized. Then those who oppose us will be ashamed and have nothing bad to say about us.

[9]Slaves must always obey their masters and do their best to please them. They must not talk back [10]or steal, but must show themselves to be entirely trustworthy and good. Then they will make the teaching about God our Savior attractive in every way.

[11]For the grace of God has been revealed, bringing salvation to all people. [12]And we are instructed to turn from godless living and sinful pleasures. We should live in this evil world with wisdom, righteousness, and devotion to God, [13]while we look forward with hope to that

---

1:1 Or *to strengthen the faith of.*   **1:6** Or *must have only one wife,* or *must be married only once;* Greek reads *must be the husband of one wife.*   **1:7a** Or *An overseer,* or *A bishop.*   **1:7b** Greek *must not drink too much wine.*   **1:12** This quotation is from Epimenides of Knossos.   **2:3** Greek *be enslaved to much wine.*   **2:5** Some manuscripts read *to care for their homes.*

wonderful day when the glory of our great God and Savior, Jesus Christ, will be revealed. [14]He gave his life to free us from every kind of sin, to cleanse us, and to make us his very own people, totally committed to doing good deeds.

[15]You must teach these things and encourage the believers to do them. You have the authority to correct them when necessary, so don't let anyone disregard what you say.

Do What Is Good

3 Remind the believers to submit to the government and its officers. They should be obedient, always ready to do what is good. [2]They must not slander anyone and must avoid quarreling. Instead, they should be gentle and show true humility to everyone.

[3]Once we, too, were foolish and disobedient. We were misled and became slaves to many lusts and pleasures. Our lives were full of evil and envy, and we hated each other. [4]But—"When God our Savior revealed his kindness and love, [5]he saved us, not because of the righteous things we had done, but because of his mercy. He washed away our sins, giving us a new birth and new life through the Holy Spirit.* [6]He generously poured out the Spirit upon us through Jesus Christ our Savior. [7]Because of his grace he declared us righteous and gave us confidence that we will inherit eternal life." [8]This is a trustworthy saying, and I want you to insist on these teachings so that all who trust in God will devote themselves to doing good. These teachings are good and beneficial for everyone.

[9]Do not get involved in foolish discussions about spiritual pedigrees* or in quarrels and fights about obedience to Jewish laws. These things are useless and a waste of time. [10]If people are causing divisions among you, give a first and second warning. After that, have nothing more to do with them. [11]For people like that have turned away from the truth, and their own sins condemn them.

Paul's Final Remarks and Greetings

[12]I am planning to send either Artemas or Tychicus to you. As soon as one of them arrives, do your best to meet me at Nicopolis, for I have decided to stay there for the winter. [13]Do everything you can to help Zenas the lawyer and Apollos with their trip. See that they are given everything they need. [14]Our people must learn to do good by meeting the urgent needs of others; then they will not be unproductive.

[15]Everybody here sends greetings. Please give my greetings to the believers—all who love us.

May God's grace be with you all.

3:5 Greek *He saved us through the washing of regeneration and renewing of the Holy Spirit.*   3:9 Or *spiritual genealogies.*

Philemon

Greetings from Paul

This letter is from Paul, a prisoner for preaching the Good News about Christ Jesus, and from our brother Timothy.

I am writing to Philemon, our beloved co-worker, [2]and to our sister Apphia, and to our fellow soldier Archippus, and to the church that meets in your* house.

[3]May God our Father and the Lord Jesus Christ give you grace and peace.

Paul's Thanksgiving and Prayer

[4]I always thank my God when I pray for you, Philemon, [5]because I keep hearing about your faith in the Lord Jesus and your love for all of God's people. [6]And I am praying that you will put into action the generosity that comes from your faith as you understand and experience all the good things we have in Christ. [7]Your love has given me much joy and comfort, my brother, for your kindness has often refreshed the hearts of God's people.

Paul's Appeal for Onesimus

[8]That is why I am boldly asking a favor of you. I could demand it in the name of Christ because it is the right thing for you to do. [9]But because of our love, I prefer simply to ask you. Consider this as a request from me—Paul, an old man and now also a prisoner for the sake of Christ Jesus.*

[10]I appeal to you to show kindness to my child, Onesimus. I became his father in the faith while here in prison. [11]Onesimus* hasn't been of much use to you in the past, but now he is very useful to both of us. [12]I am sending him back to you, and with him comes my own heart.

[13]I wanted to keep him here with me while I am in these chains for preaching the Good News, and he would have helped me on your behalf. [14]But I didn't want to do anything without your consent. I wanted you to help because you were willing, not because you were forced. [15]It seems you lost Onesimus for a little while so that you could have him back forever. [16]He is no longer like a slave to you. He is more than a slave, for he is a beloved brother, especially to me. Now he will mean much more to you, both as a man and as a brother in the Lord.

[17]So if you consider me your partner, welcome him as you would welcome me. [18]If he has wronged you in any way or owes you anything, charge it to me. [19]I, PAUL, WRITE THIS WITH MY OWN HAND: I WILL REPAY IT. AND I WON'T MENTION THAT YOU OWE ME YOUR VERY SOUL!

[20]Yes, my brother, please do me this favor* for the Lord's sake. Give me this encouragement in Christ.

[21]I am confident as I write this letter that you will do what I ask and even more! [22]One more thing—please prepare a guest room for me, for I am hoping that God will answer your prayers and let me return to you soon.

Paul's Final Greetings

[23]Epaphras, my fellow prisoner in Christ Jesus, sends you his greetings. [24]So do Mark, Aristarchus, Demas, and Luke, my co-workers.

[25]May the grace of the Lord Jesus Christ be with your spirit.

2 Throughout this letter, *you* and *your* are singular except in verses 3, 22, and 25.   **9** Or *a prisoner of Christ Jesus.*   **11** *Onesimus* means "useful."   **20** Greek *onaimen*, a play on the name Onesimus.

Hebrews

Jesus Christ Is God's Son

1 Long ago God spoke many times and in many ways to our ancestors through the prophets. ²And now in these final days, he has spoken to us through his Son. God promised everything to the Son as an inheritance, and through the Son he created the universe. ³The Son radiates God's own glory and expresses the very character of God, and he sustains everything by the mighty power of his command. When he had cleansed us from our sins, he sat down in the place of honor at the right hand of the majestic God in heaven. ⁴This shows that the Son is far greater than the angels, just as the name God gave him is greater than their names.

The Son Is Greater Than the Angels

⁵For God never said to any angel what he said to Jesus:

"You are my Son.
Today I have become your Father.*"

God also said,

"I will be his Father,
and he will be my Son."*

⁶And when he brought his supreme* Son into the world, God said,*

"Let all of God's angels worship him."*

⁷Regarding the angels, he says,

"He sends his angels like the winds,
his servants like flames of fire."*

⁸But to the Son he says,

"Your throne, O God, endures forever and ever.
You rule with a scepter of justice.
⁹ You love justice and hate evil.
Therefore, O God, your God has anointed you,
pouring out the oil of joy on you more than on anyone else."*

¹⁰He also says to the Son,

"In the beginning, Lord, you laid the foundation of the earth
and made the heavens with your hands.
¹¹ They will perish, but you remain forever.
They will wear out like old clothing.
¹² You will fold them up like a cloak
and discard them like old clothing.
But you are always the same;
you will live forever."*

¹³And God never said to any of the angels,

"Sit in the place of honor at my right hand
until I humble your enemies,
making them a footstool under your feet."*

¹⁴Therefore, angels are only servants—spirits sent to care for people who will inherit salvation.

A Warning against Drifting Away

2 So we must listen very carefully to the truth we have heard, or we may drift away from it. ²For the message God delivered through angels has always stood firm, and every violation of the law and every act of disobedience was punished. ³So what makes us think we can escape if we ignore this great salvation that was first announced by the Lord Jesus himself and then delivered to us by those who heard him speak? ⁴And God confirmed the message by giving signs and wonders and various miracles and gifts of the Holy Spirit whenever he chose.

Jesus, the Man

⁵And furthermore, it is not angels who will control the future world we are talking about. ⁶For in one place the Scriptures say,

"What are mere mortals that you should think about them,
or a son of man* that you should care for him?
⁷ Yet you made them only a little lower than the angels
and crowned them with glory and honor.*
⁸ You gave them authority over all things."*

Now when it says "all things," it means nothing is left out. But we have not yet seen all things put under their authority. ⁹What we do see is Jesus,

1:5a Or *Today I reveal you as my Son.* Ps 2:7.   **1:5b** 2 Sam 7:14.   **1:6a** Or *firstborn.*   **1:6b** Or *when he again brings his supreme Son [or firstborn Son] into the world, God will say.*   **1:6c** Deut 32:43.   **1:7** Ps 104:4 (Greek version).   **1:8-9** Ps 45:6-7.   **1:10-12** Ps 102:25-27.   **1:13** Ps 110:1.   **2:6** Or *the Son of Man.*   **2:7** Some manuscripts add *You gave them charge of everything you made.*   **2:6-8** Ps 8:4-6 (Greek version).

who was given a position "a little lower than the angels"; and because he suffered death for us, he is now "crowned with glory and honor." Yes, by God's grace, Jesus tasted death for everyone. [10]God, for whom and through whom everything was made, chose to bring many children into glory. And it was only right that he should make Jesus, through his suffering, a perfect leader, fit to bring them into their salvation.

[11]So now Jesus and the ones he makes holy have the same Father. That is why Jesus is not ashamed to call them his brothers and sisters.* [12]For he said to God,

"I will proclaim your name to my brothers
        and sisters.
    I will praise you among your assembled
        people."*

[13]He also said,

"I will put my trust in him,"
    that is, "I and the children God has given
        me."*

[14]Because God's children are human beings—made of flesh and blood—the Son also became flesh and blood. For only as a human being could he die, and only by dying could he break the power of the devil, who had* the power of death. [15]Only in this way could he set free all who have lived their lives as slaves to the fear of dying.

[16]We also know that the Son did not come to help angels; he came to help the descendants of Abraham. [17]Therefore, it was necessary for him to be made in every respect like us, his brothers and sisters,* so that he could be our merciful and faithful High Priest before God. Then he could offer a sacrifice that would take away the sins of the people. [18]Since he himself has gone through suffering and testing, he is able to help us when we are being tested.

Jesus Is Greater Than Moses

3 And so, dear brothers and sisters who belong to God and* are partners with those called to heaven, think carefully about this Jesus whom we declare to be God's messenger* and High Priest. [2]For he was faithful to God, who appointed him, just as Moses served faithfully when he was entrusted with God's entire* house.

[3]But Jesus deserves far more glory than Moses, just as a person who builds a house deserves more praise than the house itself. [4]For every house has a builder, but the one who built everything is God.

[5]Moses was certainly faithful in God's house as a servant. His work was an illustration of the truths God would reveal later. [6]But Christ, as the Son, is in charge of God's entire house. And we are God's house, if we keep our courage and remain confident in our hope in Christ.*

[7]That is why the Holy Spirit says,

"Today when you hear his voice,
[8]   don't harden your hearts
    as Israel did when they rebelled,
        when they tested me in the wilderness.
[9] There your ancestors tested and tried my
        patience,
        even though they saw my miracles for
            forty years.
[10] So I was angry with them, and I said,
    'Their hearts always turn away from me.
        They refuse to do what I tell them.'
[11] So in my anger I took an oath:
    'They will never enter my place of rest.'"*

[12]Be careful then, dear brothers and sisters.* Make sure that your own hearts are not evil and unbelieving, turning you away from the living God. [13]You must warn each other every day, while it is still "today," so that none of you will be deceived by sin and hardened against God. [14]For if we are faithful to the end, trusting God just as firmly as when we first believed, we will share in all that belongs to Christ. [15]Remember what it says:

"Today when you hear his voice,
    don't harden your hearts
    as Israel did when they rebelled."*

[16]And who was it who rebelled against God, even though they heard his voice? Wasn't it the people Moses led out of Egypt? [17]And who made God angry for forty years? Wasn't it the people who sinned, whose corpses lay in the wilderness? [18]And to whom was God speaking when he took an oath that they would never enter his rest? Wasn't it the people who disobeyed him? [19]So we see that because of their unbelief they were not able to enter his rest.

Promised Rest for God's People

4 God's promise of entering his rest still stands, so we ought to tremble with fear that some of you might fail to experience it. [2]For this good news—that God has prepared this rest—has been announced to us just as it was to them. But it did them no good because they didn't share the faith of those who listened to God.* [3]For only we who believe can enter his rest. As for the others, God said,

"In my anger I took an oath:
    'They will never enter my place of rest,'"*

even though this rest has been ready since he made the world. [4]We know it is ready because of the place in the Scriptures where it mentions the seventh day: "On the seventh day God rested from all his work."* ⁵But in the other passage God said, "They will never enter my place of rest."*

⁶So God's rest is there for people to enter, but those who first heard this good news failed to enter because they disobeyed God. ⁷So God set another time for entering his rest, and that time is today. God announced this through David much later in the words already quoted:

"Today when you hear his voice,
    don't harden your hearts."*

⁸Now if Joshua had succeeded in giving them this rest, God would not have spoken about another day of rest still to come. ⁹So there is a special rest* still waiting for the people of God. ¹⁰For all who have entered into God's rest have rested from their labors, just as God did after creating the world. ¹¹So let us do our best to enter that rest. But if we disobey God, as the people of Israel did, we will fall.

¹²For the word of God is alive and powerful. It is sharper than the sharpest two-edged sword, cutting between soul and spirit, between joint and marrow. It exposes our innermost thoughts and desires. ¹³Nothing in all creation is hidden from God. Everything is naked and exposed before his eyes, and he is the one to whom we are accountable.

Christ Is Our High Priest

¹⁴So then, since we have a great High Priest who has entered heaven, Jesus the Son of God, let us hold firmly to what we believe. ¹⁵This High Priest of ours understands our weaknesses, for he faced all of the same testings we do, yet he did not sin. ¹⁶So let us come boldly to the throne of our gracious God. There we will receive his mercy, and we will find grace to help us when we need it most.

5 Every high priest is a man chosen to represent other people in their dealings with God. He presents their gifts to God and offers sacrifices for their sins. ²And he is able to deal gently with ignorant and wayward people because he himself is subject to the same weaknesses. ³That is why he must offer sacrifices for his own sins as well as theirs.

⁴And no one can become a high priest simply because he wants such an honor. He must be called by God for this work, just as Aaron was. ⁵That is why Christ did not honor himself by assuming he could become High Priest. No, he was chosen by God, who said to him,

"You are my Son.
    Today I have become your Father.*"

⁶And in another passage God said to him,

"You are a priest forever in the order of
    Melchizedek."*

⁷While Jesus was here on earth, he offered prayers and pleadings, with a loud cry and tears, to the one who could rescue him from death. And God heard his prayers because of his deep reverence for God. ⁸Even though Jesus was God's Son, he learned obedience from the things he suffered. ⁹In this way, God qualified him as a perfect High Priest, and he became the source of eternal salvation for all those who obey him. ¹⁰And God designated him to be a High Priest in the order of Melchizedek.

A Call to Spiritual Growth

¹¹There is much more we would like to say about this, but it is difficult to explain, especially since you are spiritually dull and don't seem to listen. ¹²You have been believers so long now that you ought to be teaching others. Instead, you need someone to teach you again the basic things about God's word.* You are like babies who need milk and cannot eat solid food. ¹³For someone who lives on milk is still an infant and doesn't know how to do what is right. ¹⁴Solid food is for those who are mature, who through training have the skill to recognize the difference between right and wrong.

6 So let us stop going over the basic teachings about Christ again and again. Let us go on instead and become mature in our understanding. Surely we don't need to start again with the fundamental importance of repenting from evil deeds* and placing our faith in God. ²You don't need further instruction about baptisms, the laying on of hands, the resurrection of the dead, and eternal judgment. ³And so, God willing, we will move forward to further understanding.

⁴For it is impossible to bring back to repentance those who were once enlightened—those who have experienced the good things of heaven and shared in the Holy Spirit, ⁵who have tasted the goodness of the word of God and the power of the age to come—⁶and who then turn away from God. It is impossible to bring such people back to repentance; by rejecting the Son of God, they themselves are nailing him to the cross once again and holding him up to public shame.

⁷When the ground soaks up the falling rain and bears a good crop for the farmer, it has God's blessing. ⁸But if a field bears thorns and thistles, it is useless. The farmer will soon condemn that field and burn it.

⁹Dear friends, even though we are talking this way, we really don't believe it applies to you. We are confident that you are meant for better things, things that come with salvation. ¹⁰For

4:4 Gen 2:2. 4:5 Ps 95:11. 4:7 Ps 95:7-8. 4:9 Or *a Sabbath rest.* 5:5 Or *Today I reveal you as my Son.* Ps 2:7. 5:6 Ps 110:4.
5:12 Or *about the oracles of God.* 6:1 Greek *from dead works.*

God is not unjust. He will not forget how hard you have worked for him and how you have shown your love to him by caring for other believers,* as you still do. [11]Our great desire is that you will keep on loving others as long as life lasts, in order to make certain that what you hope for will come true. [12]Then you will not become spiritually dull and indifferent. Instead, you will follow the example of those who are going to inherit God's promises because of their faith and endurance.

God's Promises Bring Hope

[13]For example, there was God's promise to Abraham. Since there was no one greater to swear by, God took an oath in his own name, saying:

[14] "I will certainly bless you,
and I will multiply your descendants
beyond number."*

[15]Then Abraham waited patiently, and he received what God had promised.

[16]Now when people take an oath, they call on someone greater than themselves to hold them to it. And without any question that oath is binding. [17]God also bound himself with an oath, so that those who received the promise could be perfectly sure that he would never change his mind. [18]So God has given both his promise and his oath. These two things are unchangeable because it is impossible for God to lie. Therefore, we who have fled to him for refuge can have great confidence as we hold to the hope that lies before us. [19]This hope is a strong and trustworthy anchor for our souls. It leads us through the curtain into God's inner sanctuary. [20]Jesus has already gone in there for us. He has become our eternal High Priest in the order of Melchizedek.

Melchizedek Is Greater Than Abraham

7 This Melchizedek was king of the city of Salem and also a priest of God Most High. When Abraham was returning home after winning a great battle against the kings, Melchizedek met him and blessed him. [2]Then Abraham took a tenth of all he had captured in battle and gave it to Melchizedek. The name Melchizedek means "king of justice," and king of Salem means "king of peace." [3]There is no record of his father or mother or any of his ancestors—no beginning or end to his life. He remains a priest forever, resembling the Son of God.

[4]Consider then how great this Melchizedek was. Even Abraham, the great patriarch of Israel, recognized this by giving him a tenth of what he had taken in battle. [5]Now the law of Moses required that the priests, who are descendants of Levi, must collect a tithe from the rest of the people of Israel,* who are also descendants of Abraham. [6]But Melchizedek, who was not a descendant of Levi, collected a tenth from Abraham. And Melchizedek placed a blessing upon Abraham, the one who had already received the promises of God. [7]And without question, the person who has the power to give a blessing is greater than the one who is blessed.

[8]The priests who collect tithes are men who die, so Melchizedek is greater than they are, because we are told that he lives on. [9]In addition, we might even say that these Levites—the ones who collect the tithe—paid a tithe to Melchizedek when their ancestor Abraham paid a tithe to him. [10]For although Levi wasn't born yet, the seed from which he came was in Abraham's body when Melchizedek collected the tithe from him.

[11]So if the priesthood of Levi, on which the law was based, could have achieved the perfection God intended, why did God need to establish a different priesthood, with a priest in the order of Melchizedek instead of the order of Levi and Aaron?*

[12]And if the priesthood is changed, the law must also be changed to permit it. [13]For the priest we are talking about belongs to a different tribe, whose members have never served at the altar as priests. [14]What I mean is, our Lord came from the tribe of Judah, and Moses never mentioned priests coming from that tribe.

Jesus Is like Melchizedek

[15]This change has been made very clear since a different priest, who is like Melchizedek, has appeared. [16]Jesus became a priest, not by meeting the physical requirement of belonging to the tribe of Levi, but by the power of a life that cannot be destroyed. [17]And the psalmist pointed this out when he prophesied,

"You are a priest forever in the order of
Melchizedek."*

[18]Yes, the old requirement about the priesthood was set aside because it was weak and useless. [19]For the law never made anything perfect. But now we have confidence in a better hope, through which we draw near to God.

[20]This new system was established with a solemn oath. Aaron's descendants became priests without such an oath, [21]but there was an oath regarding Jesus. For God said to him,

"The LORD has taken an oath and will not
break his vow:
'You are a priest forever.'"*

[22]Because of this oath, Jesus is the one who guarantees this better covenant with God.

[23]There were many priests under the old system, for death prevented them from remaining in office. [24]But because Jesus lives forever, his priesthood lasts forever. [25]Therefore he is able,

---

6:10 Greek *for God's holy people.* **6:14** Gen 22:17. **7:5** Greek *from their brothers.* **7:11** Greek *the order of Aaron?* **7:17** Ps 110:4. **7:21** Ps 110:4.

once and forever, to save* those who come to God through him. He lives forever to intercede with God on their behalf.

²⁶He is the kind of high priest we need because he is holy and blameless, unstained by sin. He has been set apart from sinners and has been given the highest place of honor in heaven.* ²⁷Unlike those other high priests, he does not need to offer sacrifices every day. They did this for their own sins first and then for the sins of the people. But Jesus did this once for all when he offered himself as the sacrifice for the people's sins. ²⁸The law appointed high priests who were limited by human weakness. But after the law was given, God appointed his Son with an oath, and his Son has been made the perfect High Priest forever.

Christ Is Our High Priest

8 Here is the main point: We have a High Priest who sat down in the place of honor beside the throne of the majestic God in heaven. ²There he ministers in the heavenly Tabernacle,* the true place of worship that was built by the Lord and not by human hands.

³And since every high priest is required to offer gifts and sacrifices, our High Priest must make an offering, too. ⁴If he were here on earth, he would not even be a priest, since there already are priests who offer the gifts required by the law. ⁵They serve in a system of worship that is only a copy, a shadow of the real one in heaven. For when Moses was getting ready to build the Tabernacle, God gave him this warning: "Be sure that you make everything according to the pattern I have shown you here on the mountain."*

⁶But now Jesus, our High Priest, has been given a ministry that is far superior to the old priesthood, for he is the one who mediates for us a far better covenant with God, based on better promises.

⁷If the first covenant had been faultless, there would have been no need for a second covenant to replace it. ⁸But when God found fault with the people, he said:

"The day is coming, says the Lord,
when I will make a new covenant
with the people of Israel and Judah.
⁹ This covenant will not be like the one
I made with their ancestors
when I took them by the hand
and led them out of the land of Egypt.
They did not remain faithful to my
covenant,
so I turned my back on them, says the
Lord.
¹⁰ But this is the new covenant I will make
with the people of Israel on that day,* says
the Lord:
I will put my laws in their minds,
and I will write them on their hearts.
I will be their God,
and they will be my people.
¹¹ And they will not need to teach their
neighbors,
nor will they need to teach their
relatives,*
saying, 'You should know the Lord.'
For everyone, from the least to the greatest,
will know me already.
¹² And I will forgive their wickedness,
and I will never again remember their
sins."*

¹³When God speaks of a "new" covenant, it means he has made the first one obsolete. It is now out of date and will soon disappear.

Old Rules about Worship

9 That first covenant between God and Israel had regulations for worship and a place of worship here on earth. ²There were two rooms in that Tabernacle.* In the first room were a lampstand, a table, and sacred loaves of bread on the table. This room was called the Holy Place. ³Then there was a curtain, and behind the curtain was the second room* called the Most Holy Place. ⁴In that room were a gold incense altar and a wooden chest called the Ark of the Covenant, which was covered with gold on all sides. Inside the Ark were a gold jar containing manna, Aaron's staff that sprouted leaves, and the stone tablets of the covenant. ⁵Above the Ark were the cherubim of divine glory, whose wings stretched out over the Ark's cover, the place of atonement. But we cannot explain these things in detail now.

⁶When these things were all in place, the priests regularly entered the first room* as they performed their religious duties. ⁷But only the high priest ever entered the Most Holy Place, and only once a year. And he always offered blood for his own sins and for the sins the people had committed in ignorance. ⁸By these regulations the Holy Spirit revealed that the entrance to the Most Holy Place was not freely open as long as the Tabernacle* and the system it represented were still in use.

⁹This is an illustration pointing to the present time. For the gifts and sacrifices that the priests offer are not able to cleanse the consciences of the people who bring them. ¹⁰For that old system deals only with food and drink and various cleansing ceremonies—physical regulations that were in effect only until a better system could be established.

7:25 Or *is able to save completely.* **7:26** Or *has been exalted higher than the heavens.* **8:2** Or *tent;* also in 8:5. **8:5** Exod 25:40; 26:30. **8:10** Greek *after those days.* **8:11** Greek *their brother.* **8:8-12** Jer 31:31-34. **9:2** Or *tent;* also in 9:11, 21. **9:3** Greek *second tent.* **9:6** Greek *first tent.* **9:8** Or *the first room;* Greek reads *the first tent.*

Christ Is the Perfect Sacrifice

¹¹So Christ has now become the High Priest over all the good things that have come.* He has entered that greater, more perfect Tabernacle in heaven, which was not made by human hands and is not part of this created world. ¹²With his own blood—not the blood of goats and calves—he entered the Most Holy Place once for all time and secured our redemption forever.

¹³Under the old system, the blood of goats and bulls and the ashes of a young cow could cleanse people's bodies from ceremonial impurity. ¹⁴Just think how much more the blood of Christ will purify our consciences from sinful deeds* so that we can worship the living God. For by the power of the eternal Spirit, Christ offered himself to God as a perfect sacrifice for our sins. ¹⁵That is why he is the one who mediates a new covenant between God and people, so that all who are called can receive the eternal inheritance God has promised them. For Christ died to set them free from the penalty of the sins they had committed under that first covenant.

¹⁶Now when someone leaves a will,* it is necessary to prove that the person who made it is dead.* ¹⁷The will goes into effect only after the person's death. While the person who made it is still alive, the will cannot be put into effect. ¹⁸That is why even the first covenant was put into effect with the blood of an animal. ¹⁹For after Moses had read each of God's commandments to all the people, he took the blood of calves and goats,* along with water, and sprinkled both the book of God's law and all the people, using hyssop branches and scarlet wool. ²⁰Then he said, "This blood confirms the covenant God has made with you."* ²¹And in the same way, he sprinkled blood on the Tabernacle and on everything used for worship. ²²In fact, according to the law of Moses, nearly everything was purified with blood. For without the shedding of blood, there is no forgiveness.

²³That is why the Tabernacle and everything in it, which were copies of things in heaven, had to be purified by the blood of animals. But the real things in heaven had to be purified with far better sacrifices than the blood of animals.

²⁴For Christ did not enter into a holy place made with human hands, which was only a copy of the true one in heaven. He entered into heaven itself to appear now before God on our behalf. ²⁵And he did not enter heaven to offer himself again and again, like the high priest here on earth who enters the Most Holy Place year after year with the blood of an animal. ²⁶If that had been necessary, Christ would have had to die again and again, ever since the world began. But now, once for all time, he has appeared at the end of the age* to remove sin by his own death as a sacrifice.

²⁷And just as each person is destined to die once and after that comes judgment, ²⁸so also Christ died once for all time as a sacrifice to take away the sins of many people. He will come again, not to deal with our sins, but to bring salvation to all who are eagerly waiting for him.

Christ's Sacrifice Once for All

10 The old system under the law of Moses was only a shadow, a dim preview of the good things to come, not the good things themselves. The sacrifices under that system were repeated again and again, year after year, but they were never able to provide perfect cleansing for those who came to worship. ²If they could have provided perfect cleansing, the sacrifices would have stopped, for the worshipers would have been purified once for all time, and their feelings of guilt would have disappeared.

³But instead, those sacrifices actually reminded them of their sins year after year. ⁴For it is not possible for the blood of bulls and goats to take away sins. ⁵That is why, when Christ* came into the world, he said to God,

"You did not want animal sacrifices or sin
  offerings.
    But you have given me a body to offer.
⁶ You were not pleased with burnt
    offerings
    or other offerings for sin.
⁷ Then I said, 'Look, I have come to do your
    will, O God—
    as is written about me in the Scriptures.'"*

⁸First, Christ said, "You did not want animal sacrifices or sin offerings or burnt offerings or other offerings for sin, nor were you pleased with them" (though they are required by the law of Moses). ⁹Then he said, "Look, I have come to do your will." He cancels the first covenant in order to put the second into effect. ¹⁰For God's will was for us to be made holy by the sacrifice of the body of Jesus Christ, once for all time.

¹¹Under the old covenant, the priest stands and ministers before the altar day after day, offering the same sacrifices again and again, which can never take away sins. ¹²But our High Priest offered himself to God as a single sacrifice for sins, good for all time. Then he sat down in the place of honor at God's right hand. ¹³There he waits until his enemies are humbled and made a footstool under his feet. ¹⁴For by that one offering he forever made perfect those who are being made holy.

¹⁵And the Holy Spirit also testifies that this is so. For he says,

---

9:11 Some manuscripts read *that are about to come.* **9:14** Greek *from dead works.* **9:16a** Or *covenant;* also in 9:17. **9:16b** Or *Now when someone makes a covenant, it is necessary to ratify it with the death of a sacrifice.* **9:19** Some manuscripts do not include *and goats.* **9:20** Exod 24:8. **9:26** Greek *the ages.* **10:5** Greek *he;* also in 10:8. **10:5-7** Ps 40:6-8 (Greek version).

¹⁶ "This is the new covenant I will make
with my people on that day,* says the
Lord:
I will put my laws in their hearts,
and I will write them on their minds."*

¹⁷Then he says,

"I will never again remember
their sins and lawless deeds."*

¹⁸And when sins have been forgiven, there is no
need to offer any more sacrifices.

A Call to Persevere

¹⁹And so, dear brothers and sisters,* we can
boldly enter heaven's Most Holy Place because
of the blood of Jesus. ²⁰By his death,* Jesus
opened a new and life-giving way through the
curtain into the Most Holy Place. ²¹And since we
have a great High Priest who rules over God's
house, ²²let us go right into the presence of God
with sincere hearts fully trusting him. For our
guilty consciences have been sprinkled with
Christ's blood to make us clean, and our bodies
have been washed with pure water.

²³Let us hold tightly without wavering to the
hope we affirm, for God can be trusted to keep
his promise. ²⁴Let us think of ways to motivate
one another to acts of love and good works.
²⁵And let us not neglect our meeting together, as
some people do, but encourage one another, especially now that the day of his return is draw-
ing near.

²⁶Dear friends, if we deliberately continue sin-
ning after we have received knowledge of the
truth, there is no longer any sacrifice that will
cover these sins. ²⁷There is only the terrible expectation of God's judgment and the raging fire
that will consume his enemies. ²⁸For anyone who
refused to obey the law of Moses was put to
death without mercy on the testimony of two or
three witnesses. ²⁹Just think how much worse
the punishment will be for those who have trampled on the Son of God, and have treated the
blood of the covenant, which made us holy, as if it
were common and unholy, and have insulted and
disdained the Holy Spirit who brings God's
mercy to us. ³⁰For we know the one who said,

"I will take revenge.
I will pay them back."*

He also said,

"The Lord will judge his own people."*

³¹It is a terrible thing to fall into the hands of the
living God.

³²Think back on those early days when you
first learned about Christ.* Remember how you
remained faithful even though it meant terrible

suffering. ³³Sometimes you were exposed to
public ridicule and were beaten, and sometimes
you helped others who were suffering the same
things. ³⁴You suffered along with those who
were thrown into jail, and when all you owned
was taken from you, you accepted it with joy. You
knew there were better things waiting for you
that will last forever.

³⁵So do not throw away this confident trust in
the Lord. Remember the great reward it brings
you! ³⁶Patient endurance is what you need now,
so that you will continue to do God's will. Then
you will receive all that he has promised.

³⁷ "For in just a little while,
the Coming One will come and not delay.
³⁸ And my righteous ones will live by faith.*
But I will take no pleasure in anyone who
turns away."*

³⁹But we are not like those who turn away from
God to their own destruction. We are the faithful
ones, whose souls will be saved.

Great Examples of Faith

11 Faith is the confidence that what we hope
for will actually happen; it gives us assurance about things we cannot see. ²Through their
faith, the people in days of old earned a good
reputation.

³By faith we understand that the entire uni-
verse was formed at God's command, that what
we now see did not come from anything that can
be seen.

⁴It was by faith that Abel brought a more ac-
ceptable offering to God than Cain did. Abel's
offering gave evidence that he was a righteous
man, and God showed his approval of his gifts.
Although Abel is long dead, he still speaks to us
by his example of faith.

⁵It was by faith that Enoch was taken up to
heaven without dying—"he disappeared, because God took him."* For before he was taken
up, he was known as a person who pleased God.
⁶And it is impossible to please God without faith.
Anyone who wants to come to him must believe
that God exists and that he rewards those who
sincerely seek him.

⁷It was by faith that Noah built a large boat to
save his family from the flood. He obeyed God,
who warned him about things that had never
happened before. By his faith Noah condemned
the rest of the world, and he received the righteousness that comes by faith.

⁸It was by faith that Abraham obeyed when God
called him to leave home and go to another land
that God would give him as his inheritance. He
went without knowing where he was going. ⁹And
even when he reached the land God promised
him, he lived there by faith—for he was like a for-

10:16a Greek *after those days.*   **10:16b** Jer 31:33a.   **10:17** Jer 31:34b.   **10:19** Greek *brothers.*   **10:20** Greek *Through his flesh.*
10:30a Deut 32:35.   **10:30b** Deut 32:36.   **10:32** Greek *when you were first enlightened.*   **10:38** Or *my righteous ones will live
by their faithfulness;* Greek reads *my righteous one will live by faith.*   **10:37-38** Hab 2:3-4.   **11:5** Gen 5:24.

eigner, living in tents. And so did Isaac and Jacob, who inherited the same promise. ¹⁰Abraham was confidently looking forward to a city with eternal foundations, a city designed and built by God.

¹¹It was by faith that even Sarah was able to have a child, though she was barren and was too old. She believed* that God would keep his promise. ¹²And so a whole nation came from this one man who was as good as dead—a nation with so many people that, like the stars in the sky and the sand on the seashore, there is no way to count them.

¹³All these people died still believing what God had promised them. They did not receive what was promised, but they saw it all from a distance and welcomed it. They agreed that they were foreigners and nomads here on earth. ¹⁴Obviously people who say such things are looking forward to a country they can call their own. ¹⁵If they had longed for the country they came from, they could have gone back. ¹⁶But they were looking for a better place, a heavenly homeland. That is why God is not ashamed to be called their God, for he has prepared a city for them.

¹⁷It was by faith that Abraham offered Isaac as a sacrifice when God was testing him. Abraham, who had received God's promises, was ready to sacrifice his only son, Isaac, ¹⁸even though God had told him, "Isaac is the son through whom your descendants will be counted."* ¹⁹Abraham reasoned that if Isaac died, God was able to bring him back to life again. And in a sense, Abraham did receive his son back from the dead.

²⁰It was by faith that Isaac promised blessings for the future to his sons, Jacob and Esau.

²¹It was by faith that Jacob, when he was old and dying, blessed each of Joseph's sons and bowed in worship as he leaned on his staff.

²²It was by faith that Joseph, when he was about to die, said confidently that the people of Israel would leave Egypt. He even commanded them to take his bones with them when they left.

²³It was by faith that Moses' parents hid him for three months when he was born. They saw that God had given them an unusual child, and they were not afraid to disobey the king's command.

²⁴It was by faith that Moses, when he grew up, refused to be called the son of Pharaoh's daughter. ²⁵He chose to share the oppression of God's people instead of enjoying the fleeting pleasures of sin. ²⁶He thought it was better to suffer for the sake of Christ than to own the treasures of Egypt, for he was looking ahead to his great reward. ²⁷It was by faith that Moses left the land of Egypt, not fearing the king's anger. He kept right on going because he kept his eyes on the one who is invisible. ²⁸It was by faith that Moses

commanded the people of Israel to keep the Passover and to sprinkle blood on the doorposts so that the angel of death would not kill their firstborn sons.

²⁹It was by faith that the people of Israel went right through the Red Sea as though they were on dry ground. But when the Egyptians tried to follow, they were all drowned.

³⁰It was by faith that the people of Israel marched around Jericho for seven days, and the walls came crashing down.

³¹It was by faith that Rahab the prostitute was not destroyed with the people in her city who refused to obey God. For she had given a friendly welcome to the spies.

³²How much more do I need to say? It would take too long to recount the stories of the faith of Gideon, Barak, Samson, Jephthah, David, Samuel, and all the prophets. ³³By faith these people overthrew kingdoms, ruled with justice, and received what God had promised them. They shut the mouths of lions, ³⁴quenched the flames of fire, and escaped death by the edge of the sword. Their weakness was turned to strength. They became strong in battle and put whole armies to flight. ³⁵Women received their loved ones back again from death.

But others were tortured, refusing to turn from God in order to be set free. They placed their hope in a better life after the resurrection. ³⁶Some were jeered at, and their backs were cut open with whips. Others were chained in prisons. ³⁷Some died by stoning, some were sawed in half,* and others were killed with the sword. Some went about wearing skins of sheep and goats, destitute and oppressed and mistreated. ³⁸They were too good for this world, wandering over deserts and mountains, hiding in caves and holes in the ground.

³⁹All these people earned a good reputation because of their faith, yet none of them received all that God had promised. ⁴⁰For God had something better in mind for us, so that they would not reach perfection without us.

God's Discipline Proves His Love

12 Therefore, since we are surrounded by such a huge crowd of witnesses to the life of faith, let us strip off every weight that slows us down, especially the sin that so easily trips us up. And let us run with endurance the race God has set before us. ²We do this by keeping our eyes on Jesus, the champion who initiates and perfects our faith.* Because of the joy* awaiting him, he endured the cross, disregarding its shame. Now he is seated in the place of honor beside God's throne. ³Think of all the hostility he endured from sinful people;* then you won't become weary and give up. ⁴After all, you have

---

11:11 Or *It was by faith that he [Abraham] was able to have a child, even though Sarah was barren and he was too old. He believed.*
11:18 Gen 21:12.   11:37 Some manuscripts add *some were tested.*   12:2a Or *Jesus, the originator and perfecter of our faith.*
12:2b Or *Instead of the joy.*   12:3 Some manuscripts read *Think of how people hurt themselves by opposing him.*

not yet given your lives in your struggle against sin.

⁵And have you forgotten the encouraging words God spoke to you as his children?* He said,

> "My child,* don't make light of the LORD's discipline,
> and don't give up when he corrects you.
> ⁶ For the LORD disciplines those he loves,
> and he punishes each one he accepts as his child."*

⁷As you endure this divine discipline, remember that God is treating you as his own children. Who ever heard of a child who is never disciplined by its father? ⁸If God doesn't discipline you as he does all of his children, it means that you are illegitimate and are not really his children at all. ⁹Since we respected our earthly fathers who disciplined us, shouldn't we submit even more to the discipline of the Father of our spirits, and live forever?*

¹⁰For our earthly fathers disciplined us for a few years, doing the best they knew how. But God's discipline is always good for us, so that we might share in his holiness. ¹¹No discipline is enjoyable while it is happening—it's painful! But afterward there will be a peaceful harvest of right living for those who are trained in this way.

¹²So take a new grip with your tired hands and strengthen your weak knees. ¹³Mark out a straight path for your feet so that those who are weak and lame will not fall but become strong.

A Call to Listen to God

¹⁴Work at living in peace with everyone, and work at living a holy life, for those who are not holy will not see the Lord. ¹⁵Look after each other so that none of you fails to receive the grace of God. Watch out that no poisonous root of bitterness grows up to trouble you, corrupting many. ¹⁶Make sure that no one is immoral or godless like Esau, who traded his birthright as the firstborn son for a single meal. ¹⁷You know that afterward, when he wanted his father's blessing, he was rejected. It was too late for repentance, even though he begged with bitter tears.

¹⁸You have not come to a physical mountain,* to a place of flaming fire, darkness, gloom, and whirlwind, as the Israelites did at Mount Sinai. ¹⁹For they heard an awesome trumpet blast and a voice so terrible that they begged God to stop speaking. ²⁰They staggered back under God's command: "If even an animal touches the mountain, it must be stoned to death."* ²¹Moses himself was so frightened at the sight that he said, "I am terrified and trembling."*

²²No, you have come to Mount Zion, to the city of the living God, the heavenly Jerusalem, and to countless thousands of angels in a joyful gathering. ²³You have come to the assembly of God's firstborn children, whose names are written in heaven. You have come to God himself, who is the judge over all things. You have come to the spirits of the righteous ones in heaven who have now been made perfect. ²⁴You have come to Jesus, the one who mediates the new covenant between God and people, and to the sprinkled blood, which speaks of forgiveness instead of crying out for vengeance like the blood of Abel.

²⁵Be careful that you do not refuse to listen to the One who is speaking. For if the people of Israel did not escape when they refused to listen to Moses, the earthly messenger, we will certainly not escape if we reject the One who speaks to us from heaven! ²⁶When God spoke from Mount Sinai his voice shook the earth, but now he makes another promise: "Once again I will shake not only the earth but the heavens also."* ²⁷This means that all of creation will be shaken and removed, so that only unshakable things will remain.

²⁸Since we are receiving a Kingdom that is unshakable, let us be thankful and please God by worshiping him with holy fear and awe. ²⁹For our God is a devouring fire.

Concluding Words

13 Keep on loving each other as brothers and sisters.* ²Don't forget to show hospitality to strangers, for some who have done this have entertained angels without realizing it! ³Remember those in prison, as if you were there yourself. Remember also those being mistreated, as if you felt their pain in your own bodies.

⁴Give honor to marriage, and remain faithful to one another in marriage. God will surely judge people who are immoral and those who commit adultery.

⁵Don't love money; be satisfied with what you have. For God has said,

> "I will never fail you.
> I will never abandon you."*

⁶So we can say with confidence,

> "The LORD is my helper,
> so I will have no fear.
> What can mere people do to me?"*

⁷Remember your leaders who taught you the word of God. Think of all the good that has come from their lives, and follow the example of their faith.

⁸Jesus Christ is the same yesterday, today, and

12:5a Greek *sons;* also in 12:7, 8.   **12:5b** Greek *son;* also in 12:6, 7.   **12:5-6** Prov 3:11-12 (Greek version).   **12:9** Or *and really live?*
12:18 Greek *to something that can be touched.*   **12:20** Exod 19:13.   **12:21** Deut 9:19.   **12:26** Hag 2:6.   **13:1** Greek *Continue in brotherly love.*   **13:5** Deut 31:6, 8.   **13:6** Ps 118:6.

forever. ⁹So do not be attracted by strange, new ideas. Your strength comes from God's grace, not from rules about food, which don't help those who follow them.

¹⁰We have an altar from which the priests in the Tabernacle* have no right to eat. ¹¹Under the old system, the high priest brought the blood of animals into the Holy Place as a sacrifice for sin, and the bodies of the animals were burned outside the camp. ¹²So also Jesus suffered and died outside the city gates to make his people holy by means of his own blood. ¹³So let us go out to him, outside the camp, and bear the disgrace he bore. ¹⁴For this world is not our permanent home; we are looking forward to a home yet to come.

¹⁵Therefore, let us offer through Jesus a continual sacrifice of praise to God, proclaiming our allegiance to his name. ¹⁶And don't forget to do good and to share with those in need. These are the sacrifices that please God.

¹⁷Obey your spiritual leaders, and do what they say. Their work is to watch over your souls, and they are accountable to God. Give them reason to do this with joy and not with sorrow. That would certainly not be for your benefit.

¹⁸Pray for us, for our conscience is clear and we want to live honorably in everything we do. ¹⁹And especially pray that I will be able to come back to you soon.

²⁰ Now may the God of peace—
who brought up from the dead our
Lord Jesus,
the great Shepherd of the sheep,
and ratified an eternal covenant with
his blood—
²¹ may he equip you with all you need
for doing his will.
May he produce in you,*
through the power of Jesus Christ,
every good thing that is pleasing to him.
All glory to him forever and ever! Amen.

²²I urge you, dear brothers and sisters,* to pay attention to what I have written in this brief exhortation.

²³I want you to know that our brother Timothy has been released from jail. If he comes here soon, I will bring him with me to see you.

²⁴Greet all your leaders and all the believers there.* The believers from Italy send you their greetings.

²⁵May God's grace be with you all.

13:10 Or *tent.*   **13:21** Some manuscripts read *in us.*   **13:22** Greek *brothers.*   **13:24** Greek *all of God's holy people.*

James

Greetings from James

1 This letter is from James, a slave of God and of the Lord Jesus Christ.

I am writing to the "twelve tribes"—Jewish believers scattered abroad.

Greetings!

Faith and Endurance

²Dear brothers and sisters,* when troubles come your way, consider it an opportunity for great joy. ³For you know that when your faith is tested, your endurance has a chance to grow. ⁴So let it grow, for when your endurance is fully developed, you will be perfect and complete, needing nothing.

⁵If you need wisdom, ask our generous God, and he will give it to you. He will not rebuke you for asking. ⁶But when you ask him, be sure that your faith is in God alone. Do not waver, for a person with divided loyalty is as unsettled as a wave of the sea that is blown and tossed by the wind. ⁷Such people should not expect to receive anything from the Lord. ⁸Their loyalty is divided between God and the world, and they are unstable in everything they do.

⁹Believers who are* poor have something to boast about, for God has honored them. ¹⁰And those who are rich should boast that God has humbled them. They will fade away like a little flower in the field. ¹¹The hot sun rises and the grass withers; the little flower droops and falls, and its beauty fades away. In the same way, the rich will fade away with all of their achievements.

¹²God blesses those who patiently endure testing and temptation. Afterward they will receive the crown of life that God has promised to those who love him. ¹³And remember, when you are being tempted, do not say, "God is tempting me." God is never tempted to do wrong,* and he never tempts anyone else. ¹⁴Temptation comes from our own desires, which entice us and drag us away. ¹⁵These desires give birth to sinful actions. And when sin is allowed to grow, it gives birth to death.

¹⁶So don't be misled, my dear brothers and sisters. ¹⁷Whatever is good and perfect comes down to us from God our Father, who created all the lights in the heavens.* He never changes or casts a shifting shadow.* ¹⁸He chose to give birth to us by giving us his true word. And we, out of all creation, became his prized possession.*

Listening and Doing

¹⁹Understand this, my dear brothers and sisters: You must all be quick to listen, slow to speak, and slow to get angry. ²⁰Human anger* does not produce the righteousness* God desires. ²¹So get rid of all the filth and evil in your lives, and humbly accept the word God has planted in your hearts, for it has the power to save your souls.

²²But don't just listen to God's word. You must do what it says. Otherwise, you are only fooling yourselves. ²³For if you listen to the word and don't obey, it is like glancing at your face in a mirror. ²⁴You see yourself, walk away, and forget what you look like. ²⁵But if you look carefully into the perfect law that sets you free, and if you do what it says and don't forget what you heard, then God will bless you for doing it.

²⁶If you claim to be religious but don't control your tongue, you are fooling yourself, and your religion is worthless. ²⁷Pure and genuine religion in the sight of God the Father means caring for orphans and widows in their distress and refusing to let the world corrupt you.

A Warning against Prejudice

2 My dear brothers and sisters,* how can you claim to have faith in our glorious Lord Jesus Christ if you favor some people over others?

²For example, suppose someone comes into your meeting* dressed in fancy clothes and expensive jewelry, and another comes in who is poor and dressed in dirty clothes. ³If you give special attention and a good seat to the rich person, but you say to the poor one, "You can stand over there, or else sit on the floor"—well, ⁴doesn't this discrimination show that your judgments are guided by evil motives?

1:2 Greek *brothers;* also in 1:16, 19. **1:9** Greek *The brother who is.* **1:13** Or *God should not be put to a test by evil people.* **1:17a** Greek *from above, from the Father of lights.* **1:17b** Some manuscripts read *He never changes, as a shifting shadow does.* **1:18** Greek *we became a kind of firstfruit of his creatures.* **1:20a** Greek *A man's anger.* **1:20b** Or *the justice.* **2:1** Greek *brothers;* also in 2:5, 14. **2:2** Greek *your synagogue.*

[5]Listen to me, dear brothers and sisters. Hasn't God chosen the poor in this world to be rich in faith? Aren't they the ones who will inherit the Kingdom he promised to those who love him? [6]But you dishonor the poor! Isn't it the rich who oppress you and drag you into court? [7]Aren't they the ones who slander Jesus Christ, whose noble name* you bear?

[8]Yes indeed, it is good when you obey the royal law as found in the Scriptures: "Love your neighbor as yourself."* [9]But if you favor some people over others, you are committing a sin. You are guilty of breaking the law.

[10]For the person who keeps all of the laws except one is as guilty as a person who has broken all of God's laws. [11]For the same God who said, "You must not commit adultery," also said, "You must not murder."* So if you murder someone but do not commit adultery, you have still broken the law.

[12]So whatever you say or whatever you do, remember that you will be judged by the law that sets you free. [13]There will be no mercy for those who have not shown mercy to others. But if you have been merciful, God will be merciful when he judges you.

Faith without Good Deeds Is Dead

[14]What good is it, dear brothers and sisters, if you say you have faith but don't show it by your actions? Can that kind of faith save anyone? [15]Suppose you see a brother or sister who has no food or clothing, [16]and you say, "Good-bye and have a good day; stay warm and eat well"—but then you don't give that person any food or clothing. What good does that do?

[17]So you see, faith by itself isn't enough. Unless it produces good deeds, it is dead and useless.

[18]Now someone may argue, "Some people have faith; others have good deeds." But I say, "How can you show me your faith if you don't have good deeds? I will show you my faith by my good deeds."

[19]You say you have faith, for you believe that there is one God.* Good for you! Even the demons believe this, and they tremble in terror. [20]How foolish! Can't you see that faith without good deeds is useless?

[21]Don't you remember that our ancestor Abraham was shown to be right with God by his actions when he offered his son Isaac on the altar? [22]You see, his faith and his actions worked together. His actions made his faith complete. [23]And so it happened just as the Scriptures say: "Abraham believed God, and God counted him as righteous because of his faith."* He was even called the friend of God.* [24]So you see, we are shown to be right with God by what we do, not by faith alone.

[25]Rahab the prostitute is another example. She was shown to be right with God by her actions when she hid those messengers and sent them safely away by a different road. [26]Just as the body is dead without breath,* so also faith is dead without good works.

Controlling the Tongue

3 Dear brothers and sisters,* not many of you should become teachers in the church, for we who teach will be judged more strictly. [2]Indeed, we all make many mistakes. For if we could control our tongues, we would be perfect and could also control ourselves in every other way.

[3]We can make a large horse go wherever we want by means of a small bit in its mouth. [4]And a small rudder makes a huge ship turn wherever the pilot chooses to go, even though the winds are strong. [5]In the same way, the tongue is a small thing that makes grand speeches.

But a tiny spark can set a great forest on fire. [6]And the tongue is a flame of fire. It is a whole world of wickedness, corrupting your entire body. It can set your whole life on fire, for it is set on fire by hell itself.*

[7]People can tame all kinds of animals, birds, reptiles, and fish, [8]but no one can tame the tongue. It is restless and evil, full of deadly poison. [9]Sometimes it praises our Lord and Father, and sometimes it curses those who have been made in the image of God. [10]And so blessing and cursing come pouring out of the same mouth. Surely, my brothers and sisters, this is not right! [11]Does a spring of water bubble out with both fresh water and bitter water? [12]Does a fig tree produce olives, or a grapevine produce figs? No, and you can't draw fresh water from a salty spring.*

True Wisdom Comes from God

[13]If you are wise and understand God's ways, prove it by living an honorable life, doing good works with the humility that comes from wisdom. [14]But if you are bitterly jealous and there is selfish ambition in your heart, don't cover up the truth with boasting and lying. [15]For jealousy and selfishness are not God's kind of wisdom. Such things are earthly, unspiritual, and demonic. [16]For wherever there is jealousy and selfish ambition, there you will find disorder and evil of every kind.

[17]But the wisdom from above is first of all pure. It is also peace loving, gentle at all times, and willing to yield to others. It is full of mercy and good deeds. It shows no favoritism and is always sincere. [18]And those who are peacemakers will plant seeds of peace and reap a harvest of righteousness.*

2:7 Greek *slander the noble name.* **2:8** Lev 19:18. **2:11** Exod 20:13-14; Deut 5:17-18. **2:19** Some manuscripts read *that God is one;* see Deut 6:4. **2:23a** Gen 15:6. **2:23b** See Isa 41:8. **2:26** Or *without spirit.* **3:1** Greek *brothers;* also in 3:10. **3:6** Or *for it will burn in hell* (Greek *Gehenna*). **3:12** Greek *from salt.* **3:18** Or *of good things,* or *of justice.*

Drawing Close to God

4 What is causing the quarrels and fights among you? Don't they come from the evil desires at war within you? ²You want what you don't have, so you scheme and kill to get it. You are jealous of what others have, but you can't get it, so you fight and wage war to take it away from them. Yet you don't have what you want because you don't ask God for it. ³And even when you ask, you don't get it because your motives are all wrong—you want only what will give you pleasure.

⁴You adulterers!* Don't you realize that friendship with the world makes you an enemy of God? I say it again: If you want to be a friend of the world, you make yourself an enemy of God. ⁵What do you think the Scriptures mean when they say that the spirit God has placed within us is filled with envy?* ⁶But he gives us even more grace to stand against such evil desires. As the Scriptures say,

"God opposes the proud
but favors the humble."*

⁷So humble yourselves before God. Resist the devil, and he will flee from you. ⁸Come close to God, and God will come close to you. Wash your hands, you sinners; purify your hearts, for your loyalty is divided between God and the world. ⁹Let there be tears for what you have done. Let there be sorrow and deep grief. Let there be sadness instead of laughter, and gloom instead of joy. ¹⁰Humble yourselves before the Lord, and he will lift you up in honor.

Warning against Judging Others

¹¹Don't speak evil against each other, dear brothers and sisters.* If you criticize and judge each other, then you are criticizing and judging God's law. But your job is to obey the law, not to judge whether it applies to you. ¹²God alone, who gave the law, is the Judge. He alone has the power to save or to destroy. So what right do you have to judge your neighbor?

Warning about Self-Confidence

¹³Look here, you who say, "Today or tomorrow we are going to a certain town and will stay there a year. We will do business there and make a profit." ¹⁴How do you know what your life will be like tomorrow? Your life is like the morning fog—it's here a little while, then it's gone. ¹⁵What you ought to say is, "If the Lord wants us to, we will live and do this or that." ¹⁶Otherwise you are boasting about your own plans, and all such boasting is evil.

¹⁷Remember, it is sin to know what you ought to do and then not do it.

Warning to the Rich

5 Look here, you rich people: Weep and groan with anguish because of all the terrible troubles ahead of you. ²Your wealth is rotting away, and your fine clothes are moth-eaten rags. ³Your gold and silver have become worthless. The very wealth you were counting on will eat away your flesh like fire. This treasure you have accumulated will stand as evidence against you on the day of judgment. ⁴For listen! Hear the cries of the field workers whom you have cheated of their pay. The wages you held back cry out against you. The cries of those who harvest your fields have reached the ears of the LORD of Heaven's Armies.

⁵You have spent your years on earth in luxury, satisfying your every desire. You have fattened yourselves for the day of slaughter. ⁶You have condemned and killed innocent people,* who do not resist you.*

Patience and Endurance

⁷Dear brothers and sisters,* be patient as you wait for the Lord's return. Consider the farmers who patiently wait for the rains in the fall and in the spring. They eagerly look for the valuable harvest to ripen. ⁸You, too, must be patient. Take courage, for the coming of the Lord is near.

⁹Don't grumble about each other, brothers and sisters, or you will be judged. For look—the Judge is standing at the door!

¹⁰For examples of patience in suffering, dear brothers and sisters, look at the prophets who spoke in the name of the Lord. ¹¹We give great honor to those who endure under suffering. For instance, you know about Job, a man of great endurance. You can see how the Lord was kind to him at the end, for the Lord is full of tenderness and mercy.

¹²But most of all, my brothers and sisters, never take an oath, by heaven or earth or anything else. Just say a simple yes or no, so that you will not sin and be condemned.

The Power of Prayer

¹³Are any of you suffering hardships? You should pray. Are any of you happy? You should sing praises. ¹⁴Are any of you sick? You should call for the elders of the church to come and pray over you, anointing you with oil in the name of the Lord. ¹⁵Such a prayer offered in faith will heal the sick, and the Lord will make you well. And if you have committed any sins, you will be forgiven.

¹⁶Confess your sins to each other and pray for each other so that you may be healed. The earnest prayer of a righteous person has great

---

4:4 Greek *You adulteresses!* 4:5 Or *that God longs jealously for the human spirit he has placed within us?* or *that the Holy Spirit, whom God has placed within us, opposes our envy?* 4:6 Prov 3:34 (Greek version). 4:11 Greek *brothers.* 5:6a Or *killed the Righteous One.* 5:6b Or *Don't they resist you?* or *Doesn't God oppose you?* or *Aren't they now accusing you before God?* 5:7 Greek *brothers;* also in 5:9, 10, 12, 19.

power and produces wonderful results. [17]Elijah was as human as we are, and yet when he prayed earnestly that no rain would fall, none fell for three and a half years! [18]Then, when he prayed again, the sky sent down rain and the earth began to yield its crops.

Restore Wandering Believers

[19]My dear brothers and sisters, if someone among you wanders away from the truth and is brought back, [20]you can be sure that whoever brings the sinner back will save that person from death and bring about the forgiveness of many sins.

1 Peter

Greetings from Peter

1 This letter is from Peter, an apostle of Jesus Christ.

I am writing to God's chosen people who are living as foreigners in the provinces of Pontus, Galatia, Cappadocia, Asia, and Bithynia.* ²God the Father knew you and chose you long ago, and his Spirit has made you holy. As a result, you have obeyed him and have been cleansed by the blood of Jesus Christ.

May God give you more and more grace and peace.

The Hope of Eternal Life

³All praise to God, the Father of our Lord Jesus Christ. It is by his great mercy that we have been born again, because God raised Jesus Christ from the dead. Now we live with great expectation, ⁴and we have a priceless inheritance—an inheritance that is kept in heaven for you, pure and undefiled, beyond the reach of change and decay. ⁵And through your faith, God is protecting you by his power until you receive this salvation, which is ready to be revealed on the last day for all to see.

⁶So be truly glad.* There is wonderful joy ahead, even though you have to endure many trials for a little while. ⁷These trials will show that your faith is genuine. It is being tested as fire tests and purifies gold—though your faith is far more precious than mere gold. So when your faith remains strong through many trials, it will bring you much praise and glory and honor on the day when Jesus Christ is revealed to the whole world.

⁸You love him even though you have never seen him. Though you do not see him now, you trust him; and you rejoice with a glorious, inexpressible joy. ⁹The reward for trusting him will be the salvation of your souls.

¹⁰This salvation was something even the prophets wanted to know more about when they prophesied about this gracious salvation prepared for you. ¹¹They wondered what time or situation the Spirit of Christ within them was talking about when he told them in advance about Christ's suffering and his great glory afterward.

¹²They were told that their messages were not for themselves, but for you. And now this Good News has been announced to you by those who preached in the power of the Holy Spirit sent from heaven. It is all so wonderful that even the angels are eagerly watching these things happen.

A Call to Holy Living

¹³So think clearly and exercise self-control. Look forward to the gracious salvation that will come to you when Jesus Christ is revealed to the world. ¹⁴So you must live as God's obedient children. Don't slip back into your old ways of living to satisfy your own desires. You didn't know any better then. ¹⁵But now you must be holy in everything you do, just as God who chose you is holy. ¹⁶For the Scriptures say, "You must be holy because I am holy."*

¹⁷And remember that the heavenly Father to whom you pray has no favorites. He will judge or reward you according to what you do. So you must live in reverent fear of him during your time as "foreigners in the land." ¹⁸For you know that God paid a ransom to save you from the empty life you inherited from your ancestors. And the ransom he paid was not mere gold or silver. ¹⁹It was the precious blood of Christ, the sinless, spotless Lamb of God. ²⁰God chose him as your ransom long before the world began, but he has now revealed him to you in these last days.

²¹Through Christ you have come to trust in God. And you have placed your faith and hope in God because he raised Christ from the dead and gave him great glory.

²²You were cleansed from your sins when you obeyed the truth, so now you must show sincere love to each other as brothers and sisters.* Love each other deeply with all your heart.*

²³For you have been born again, but not to a life that will quickly end. Your new life will last forever because it comes from the eternal, living word of God. ²⁴As the Scriptures say,

> "People are like grass;
>   their beauty is like a flower in the field.
> The grass withers and the flower fades.
> ²⁵   But the word of the Lord remains
>   forever."*

1:1 *Pontus, Galatia, Cappadocia, Asia,* and *Bithynia* were Roman provinces in what is now Turkey.   **1:6** Or *So you are truly glad.*
1:16 Lev 11:44-45; 19:2; 20:7.   **1:22a** Greek *must have brotherly love.*   **1:22b** Some manuscripts read *with a pure heart.*
1:24-25 Isa 40:6-8.

And that word is the Good News that was preached to you.

2 So get rid of all evil behavior. Be done with all deceit, hypocrisy, jealousy, and all unkind speech. ²Like newborn babies, you must crave pure spiritual milk so that you will grow into a full experience of salvation. Cry out for this nourishment, ³now that you have had a taste of the Lord's kindness.

Living Stones for God's House

⁴You are coming to Christ, who is the living cornerstone of God's temple. He was rejected by people, but he was chosen by God for great honor.

⁵And you are living stones that God is building into his spiritual temple. What's more, you are his holy priests.* Through the mediation of Jesus Christ, you offer spiritual sacrifices that please God. ⁶As the Scriptures say,

> "I am placing a cornerstone in
> Jerusalem,*
> chosen for great honor,
> and anyone who trusts in him
> will never be disgraced."*

⁷Yes, you who trust him recognize the honor God has given him. But for those who reject him,

> "The stone that the builders rejected
> has now become the cornerstone."*

⁸And,

> "He is the stone that makes people stumble,
> the rock that makes them fall."*

They stumble because they do not obey God's word, and so they meet the fate that was planned for them.

⁹But you are not like that, for you are a chosen people. You are royal priests,* a holy nation, God's very own possession. As a result, you can show others the goodness of God, for he called you out of the darkness into his wonderful light.

¹⁰ "Once you had no identity as a people;
> now you are God's people.
> Once you received no mercy;
> now you have received God's mercy."*

¹¹Dear friends, I warn you as "temporary residents and foreigners" to keep away from worldy desires that wage war against your very souls. ¹²Be careful to live properly among your unbelieving neighbors. Then even if they accuse you of doing wrong, they will see your honorable behavior, and they will give honor to God when he judges the world.*

Respecting People in Authority

¹³For the Lord's sake, respect all human authority—whether the king as head of state, ¹⁴or the officials he has appointed. For the king has sent them to punish those who do wrong and to honor those who do right.

¹⁵It is God's will that your honorable lives should silence those ignorant people who make foolish accusations against you. ¹⁶For you are free, yet you are God's slaves, so don't use your freedom as an excuse to do evil. ¹⁷Respect everyone, and love your Christian brothers and sisters.* Fear God, and respect the king.

Slaves

¹⁸You who are slaves must accept the authority of your masters with all respect.* Do what they tell you—not only if they are kind and reasonable, but even if they are cruel. ¹⁹For God is pleased with you when you do what you know is right and patiently endure unfair treatment. ²⁰Of course, you get no credit for being patient if you are beaten for doing wrong. But if you suffer for doing good and endure it patiently, God is pleased with you.

²¹For God called you to do good, even if it means suffering, just as Christ suffered* for you. He is your example, and you must follow in his steps.

²² He never sinned,
> nor ever deceived anyone.*
²³ He did not retaliate when he was insulted,
> nor threaten revenge when he suffered.
> He left his case in the hands of God,
> who always judges fairly.
²⁴ He personally carried our sins
> in his body on the cross
> so that we can be dead to sin
> and live for what is right.
> By his wounds
> you are healed.
²⁵ Once you were like sheep
> who wandered away.
> But now you have turned to your Shepherd,
> the Guardian of your souls.

Wives

3 In the same way, you wives must accept the authority of your husbands. Then, even if some refuse to obey the Good News, your godly lives will speak to them without any words. They will be won over ²by observing your pure and reverent lives.

³Don't be concerned about the outward beauty of fancy hairstyles, expensive jewelry, or beautiful clothes. ⁴You should clothe yourselves instead with the beauty that comes from within, the unfading beauty of a gentle and quiet spirit,

---

2:5 Greek *holy priesthood.* **2:6a** Greek *in Zion.* **2:6b** Isa 28:16 (Greek version). **2:7** Ps 118:22. **2:8** Isa 8:14. **2:9** Greek *a royal priesthood.* **2:10** Hos 1:6, 9; 2:23. **2:12** Or *on the day of visitation.* **2:17** Greek *love the brotherhood.* **2:18** Or *because you fear God.* **2:21** Some manuscripts read *died.* **2:22** Isa 53:9.

which is so precious to God. ⁵This is how the holy women of old made themselves beautiful. They trusted God and accepted the authority of their husbands. ⁶For instance, Sarah obeyed her husband, Abraham, and called him her master. You are her daughters when you do what is right without fear of what your husbands might do.

Husbands

⁷In the same way, you husbands must give honor to your wives. Treat your wife with understanding as you live together. She may be weaker than you are, but she is your equal partner in God's gift of new life. Treat her as you should so your prayers will not be hindered.

All Christians

⁸Finally, all of you should be of one mind. Sympathize with each other. Love each other as brothers and sisters.* Be tenderhearted, and keep a humble attitude. ⁹Don't repay evil for evil. Don't retaliate with insults when people insult you. Instead, pay them back with a blessing. That is what God has called you to do, and he will bless you for it. ¹⁰For the Scriptures say,

"If you want to enjoy life
  and see many happy days,
keep your tongue from speaking evil
  and your lips from telling lies.
¹¹ Turn away from evil and do good.
  Search for peace, and work to maintain it.
¹² The eyes of the Lord watch over those who
    do right,
  and his ears are open to their prayers.
But the Lord turns his face
  against those who do evil."*

Suffering for Doing Good

¹³Now, who will want to harm you if you are eager to do good? ¹⁴But even if you suffer for doing what is right, God will reward you for it. So don't worry or be afraid of their threats. ¹⁵Instead, you must worship Christ as Lord of your life. And if someone asks about your Christian hope, always be ready to explain it. ¹⁶But do this in a gentle and respectful way.* Keep your conscience clear. Then if people speak against you, they will be ashamed when they see what a good life you live because you belong to Christ. ¹⁷Remember, it is better to suffer for doing good, if that is what God wants, than to suffer for doing wrong!

¹⁸Christ suffered* for our sins once for all time. He never sinned, but he died for sinners to bring you safely home to God. He suffered physical death, but he was raised to life in the Spirit.*

¹⁹So he went and preached to the spirits in prison—²⁰those who disobeyed God long ago when God waited patiently while Noah was building his boat. Only eight people were saved from drowning in that terrible flood.* ²¹And that water is a picture of baptism, which now saves you, not by removing dirt from your body, but as a response to God from* a clean conscience. It is effective because of the resurrection of Jesus Christ.

²²Now Christ has gone to heaven. He is seated in the place of honor next to God, and all the angels and authorities and powers accept his authority.

Living for God

4 So then, since Christ suffered physical pain, you must arm yourselves with the same attitude he had, and be ready to suffer, too. For if you have suffered physically for Christ, you have finished with sin.* ²You won't spend the rest of your lives chasing your own desires, but you will be anxious to do the will of God. ³You have had enough in the past of the evil things that godless people enjoy—their immorality and lust, their feasting and drunkenness and wild parties, and their terrible worship of idols.

⁴Of course, your former friends are surprised when you no longer plunge into the flood of wild and destructive things they do. So they slander you. ⁵But remember that they will have to face God, who will judge everyone, both the living and the dead. ⁶That is why the Good News was preached to those who are now dead*—so although they were destined to die like all people,* they now live forever with God in the Spirit.*

⁷The end of the world is coming soon. Therefore, be earnest and disciplined in your prayers. ⁸Most important of all, continue to show deep love for each other, for love covers a multitude of sins. ⁹Cheerfully share your home with those who need a meal or a place to stay.

¹⁰God has given each of you a gift from his great variety of spiritual gifts. Use them well to serve one another. ¹¹Do you have the gift of speaking? Then speak as though God himself were speaking through you. Do you have the gift of helping others? Do it with all the strength and energy that God supplies. Then everything you do will bring glory to God through Jesus Christ. All glory and power to him forever and ever! Amen.

Suffering for Being a Christian

¹²Dear friends, don't be surprised at the fiery trials you are going through, as if something strange were happening to you. ¹³Instead, be very glad—for these trials make you partners with Christ in his suffering, so that you will have the wonderful joy of seeing his glory when it is revealed to all the world.

3:8 Greek *Show brotherly love.* **3:10-12** Ps 34:12-16. **3:16** Some English translations put this sentence in verse 15. **3:18a** Some manuscripts read *died.* **3:18b** Or *in spirit.* **3:20** Greek *saved through water.* **3:21** Or *as an appeal to God for.* **4:1** Or *For the one [or One] who has suffered physically has finished with sin.* **4:6a** Greek *preached even to the dead.* **4:6b** Or *so although people had judged them worthy of death.* **4:6c** Or *in spirit.*

[14]So be happy when you are insulted for being a Christian,* for then the glorious Spirit of God* rests upon you.* [15]If you suffer, however, it must not be for murder, stealing, making trouble, or prying into other people's affairs. [16]But it is no shame to suffer for being a Christian. Praise God for the privilege of being called by his name! [17]For the time has come for judgment, and it must begin with God's household. And if judgment begins with us, what terrible fate awaits those who have never obeyed God's Good News? [18]And also,

"If the righteous are barely saved,
what will happen to godless sinners?"*

[19]So if you are suffering in a manner that pleases God, keep on doing what is right, and trust your lives to the God who created you, for he will never fail you.

Advice for Elders and Young Men

5 And now, a word to you who are elders in the churches. I, too, am an elder and a witness to the sufferings of Christ. And I, too, will share in his glory when he is revealed to the whole world. As a fellow elder, I appeal to you: [2]Care for the flock that God has entrusted to you. Watch over it willingly, not grudgingly—not for what you will get out of it, but because you are eager to serve God. [3]Don't lord it over the people assigned to your care, but lead them by your own good example. [4]And when the Great Shepherd appears, you will receive a crown of never-ending glory and honor.

[5]In the same way, you younger men must ac-cept the authority of the elders. And all of you, serve each other in humility, for

"God opposes the proud
but favors the humble."*

[6]So humble yourselves under the mighty power of God, and at the right time he will lift you up in honor. [7]Give all your worries and cares to God, for he cares about you.

[8]Stay alert! Watch out for your great enemy, the devil. He prowls around like a roaring lion, looking for someone to devour. [9]Stand firm against him, and be strong in your faith. Remember that your Christian brothers and sisters* all over the world are going through the same kind of suffering you are.

[10]In his kindness God called you to share in his eternal glory by means of Christ Jesus. So after you have suffered a little while, he will restore, support, and strengthen you, and he will place you on a firm foundation. [11]All power to him forever! Amen.

Peter's Final Greetings

[12]I have written and sent this short letter to you with the help of Silas,* whom I commend to you as a faithful brother. My purpose in writing is to encourage you and assure you that what you are experiencing is truly part of God's grace for you. Stand firm in this grace.

[13]Your sister church here in Babylon* sends you greetings, and so does my son Mark. [14]Greet each other with Christian love.*

Peace be with all of you who are in Christ.

4:14a Greek *for the name of Christ.* **4:14b** Or *for the glory of God, which is his Spirit.* **4:14c** Some manuscripts add *On their part he is blasphemed, but on your part he is glorified.* **4:18** Prov 11:31 (Greek version). **5:5** Prov 3:34 (Greek version). **5:9** Greek *your brothers.* **5:12** Greek *Silvanus.* **5:13** Greek *The elect one in Babylon.* Babylon was probably symbolic for Rome. **5:14** Greek *with a kiss of love.*

2 Peter

Greetings from Peter

1 This letter is from Simon* Peter, a slave and apostle of Jesus Christ.

I am writing to you who share the same precious faith we have. This faith was given to you because of the justice and fairness* of Jesus Christ, our God and Savior.

²May God give you more and more grace and peace as you grow in your knowledge of God and Jesus our Lord.

Growing in Faith

³By his divine power, God has given us everything we need for living a godly life. We have received all of this by coming to know him, the one who called us to himself by means of his marvelous glory and excellence. ⁴And because of his glory and excellence, he has given us great and precious promises. These are the promises that enable you to share his divine nature and escape the world's corruption caused by human desires.

⁵In view of all this, make every effort to respond to God's promises. Supplement your faith with a generous provision of moral excellence, and moral excellence with knowledge, ⁶and knowledge with self-control, and self-control with patient endurance, and patient endurance with godliness, ⁷and godliness with brotherly affection, and brotherly affection with love for everyone.

⁸The more you grow like this, the more productive and useful you will be in your knowledge of our Lord Jesus Christ. ⁹But those who fail to develop in this way are shortsighted or blind, forgetting that they have been cleansed from their old sins.

¹⁰So, dear brothers and sisters,* work hard to prove that you really are among those God has called and chosen. Do these things, and you will never fall away. ¹¹Then God will give you a grand entrance into the eternal Kingdom of our Lord and Savior Jesus Christ.

Paying Attention to Scripture

¹²Therefore, I will always remind you about these things—even though you already know them and are standing firm in the truth you have

been taught. ¹³And it is only right that I should keep on reminding you as long as I live.* ¹⁴For our Lord Jesus Christ has shown me that I must soon leave this earthly life,* ¹⁵so I will work hard to make sure you always remember these things after I am gone.

¹⁶For we were not making up clever stories when we told you about the powerful coming of our Lord Jesus Christ. We saw his majestic splendor with our own eyes ¹⁷when he received honor and glory from God the Father. The voice from the majestic glory of God said to him, "This is my dearly loved Son, who brings me great joy."* ¹⁸We ourselves heard that voice from heaven when we were with him on the holy mountain.

¹⁹Because of that experience, we have even greater confidence in the message proclaimed by the prophets. You must pay close attention to what they wrote, for their words are like a lamp shining in a dark place—until the Day dawns, and Christ the Morning Star shines* in your hearts. ²⁰Above all, you must realize that no prophecy in Scripture ever came from the prophet's own understanding,* ²¹or from human initiative. No, those prophets were moved by the Holy Spirit, and they spoke from God.

The Danger of False Teachers

2 But there were also false prophets in Israel, just as there will be false teachers among you. They will cleverly teach destructive heresies and even deny the Master who bought them. In this way, they will bring sudden destruction on themselves. ²Many will follow their evil teaching and shameful immorality. And because of these teachers, the way of truth will be slandered. ³In their greed they will make up clever lies to get hold of your money. But God condemned them long ago, and their destruction will not be delayed.

⁴For God did not spare even the angels who sinned. He threw them into hell,* in gloomy pits of darkness,* where they are being held until the day of judgment. ⁵And God did not spare the ancient world—except for Noah and the seven others in his family. Noah warned the world of God's righteous judgment. So God protected

Noah when he destroyed the world of ungodly people with a vast flood. 6Later, God condemned the cities of Sodom and Gomorrah and turned them into heaps of ashes. He made them an example of what will happen to ungodly people. 7But God also rescued Lot out of Sodom because he was a righteous man who was sick of the shameful immorality of the wicked people around him. 8Yes, Lot was a righteous man who was tormented in his soul by the wickedness he saw and heard day after day. 9So you see, the Lord knows how to rescue godly people from their trials, even while keeping the wicked under punishment until the day of final judgment. 10He is especially hard on those who follow their own twisted sexual desire, and who despise authority.

These people are proud and arrogant, daring even to scoff at supernatural beings* without so much as trembling. 11But the angels, who are far greater in power and strength, do not dare to bring from the Lord* a charge of blasphemy against those supernatural beings.

12These false teachers are like unthinking animals, creatures of instinct, born to be caught and destroyed. They scoff at things they do not understand, and like animals, they will be destroyed. 13Their destruction is their reward for the harm they have done. They love to indulge in evil pleasures in broad daylight. They are a disgrace and a stain among you. They delight in deception* even as they eat with you in your fellowship meals. 14They commit adultery with their eyes, and their desire for sin is never satisfied. They lure unstable people into sin, and they are well trained in greed. They live under God's curse. 15They have wandered off the right road and followed the footsteps of Balaam son of Beor,* who loved to earn money by doing wrong. 16But Balaam was stopped from his mad course when his donkey rebuked him with a human voice.

17These people are as useless as dried-up springs or as mist blown away by the wind. They are doomed to blackest darkness. 18They brag about themselves with empty, foolish boasting. With an appeal to twisted sexual desires, they lure back into sin those who have barely escaped from a lifestyle of deception. 19They promise freedom, but they themselves are slaves of sin and corruption. For you are a slave to whatever controls you. 20And when people escape from the wickedness of the world by knowing our Lord and Savior Jesus Christ and then get tangled up and enslaved by sin again, they are worse off than before. 21It would be better if they had never known the way to righteousness than to know it and then reject the command they were given to live a holy life. 22They prove the truth of this proverb: "A dog

returns to its vomit."* And another says, "A washed pig returns to the mud."

The Day of the Lord Is Coming

3 This is my second letter to you, dear friends, and in both of them I have tried to stimulate your wholesome thinking and refresh your memory. 2I want you to remember what the holy prophets said long ago and what our Lord and Savior commanded through your apostles.

3Most importantly, I want to remind you that in the last days scoffers will come, mocking the truth and following their own desires. 4They will say, "What happened to the promise that Jesus is coming again? From before the times of our ancestors, everything has remained the same since the world was first created."

5They deliberately forget that God made the heavens by the word of his command, and he brought the earth out from the water and surrounded it with water. 6Then he used the water to destroy the ancient world with a mighty flood. 7And by the same word, the present heavens and earth have been stored up for fire. They are being kept for the day of judgment, when ungodly people will be destroyed.

8But you must not forget this one thing, dear friends: A day is like a thousand years to the Lord, and a thousand years is like a day. 9The Lord isn't really being slow about his promise, as some people think. No, he is being patient for your sake. He does not want anyone to be destroyed, but wants everyone to repent. 10But the day of the Lord will come as unexpectedly as a thief. Then the heavens will pass away with a terrible noise, and the very elements themselves will disappear in fire, and the earth and everything on it will be found to deserve judgment.*

11Since everything around us is going to be destroyed like this, what holy and godly lives you should live, 12looking forward to the day of God and hurrying it along. On that day, he will set the heavens on fire, and the elements will melt away in the flames. 13But we are looking forward to the new heavens and new earth he has promised, a world filled with God's righteousness.

14And so, dear friends, while you are waiting for these things to happen, make every effort to be found living peaceful lives that are pure and blameless in his sight.

15And remember, our Lord's patience gives people time to be saved. This is what our beloved brother Paul also wrote to you with the wisdom God gave him—16speaking of these things in all of his letters. Some of his comments are hard to understand, and those who are ignorant and unstable have twisted his letters to mean something quite different, just as they do

---

2:10 Greek *at glorious ones,* which are probably evil angels.   **2:11** Other manuscripts read *to the Lord;* still others do not include this phrase at all.   **2:13** Some manuscripts read *in fellowship meals.*   **2:15** Some manuscripts read *Bosor.*   **2:22** Prov 26:11.
3:10 Other manuscripts read *will be burned up;* still others read *will be found destroyed.*

with other parts of Scripture. And this will result in their destruction.

Peter's Final Words

¹⁷I am warning you ahead of time, dear friends. Be on guard so that you will not be carried away by the errors of these wicked people and lose your own secure footing. ¹⁸Rather, you must grow in the grace and knowledge of our Lord and Savior Jesus Christ.

All glory to him, both now and forever! Amen.

1 John

Introduction

1 We proclaim to you the one who existed from the beginning,* whom we have heard and seen. We saw him with our own eyes and touched him with our own hands. He is the Word of life. ²This one who is life itself was revealed to us, and we have seen him. And now we testify and proclaim to you that he is the one who is eternal life. He was with the Father, and then he was revealed to us. ³We proclaim to you what we ourselves have actually seen and heard so that you may have fellowship with us. And our fellowship is with the Father and with his Son, Jesus Christ. ⁴We are writing these things so that you may fully share our joy.*

Living in the Light

⁵This is the message we heard from Jesus* and now declare to you: God is light, and there is no darkness in him at all. ⁶So we are lying if we say we have fellowship with God but go on living in spiritual darkness; we are not practicing the truth. ⁷But if we are living in the light, as God is in the light, then we have fellowship with each other, and the blood of Jesus, his Son, cleanses us from all sin.

⁸If we claim we have no sin, we are only fooling ourselves and not living in the truth. ⁹But if we confess our sins to him, he is faithful and just to forgive us our sins and to cleanse us from all wickedness. ¹⁰If we claim we have not sinned, we are calling God a liar and showing that his word has no place in our hearts.

2 My dear children, I am writing this to you so that you will not sin. But if anyone does sin, we have an advocate who pleads our case before the Father. He is Jesus Christ, the one who is truly righteous. ²He himself is the sacrifice that atones for our sins—and not only our sins but the sins of all the world.

³And we can be sure that we know him if we obey his commandments. ⁴If someone claims, "I know God," but doesn't obey God's commandments, that person is a liar and is not living in the truth. ⁵But those who obey God's word truly show how completely they love him.

That is how we know we are living in him. ⁶Those who say they live in God should live their lives as Jesus did.

A New Commandment

⁷Dear friends, I am not writing a new commandment for you; rather it is an old one you have had from the very beginning. This old commandment—to love one another—is the same message you heard before. ⁸Yet it is also new. Jesus lived the truth of this commandment, and you also are living it. For the darkness is disappearing, and the true light is already shining.

⁹If anyone claims, "I am living in the light," but hates a Christian brother or sister,* that person is still living in darkness. ¹⁰Anyone who loves another brother or sister* is living in the light and does not cause others to stumble. ¹¹But anyone who hates another brother or sister is still living and walking in darkness. Such a person does not know the way to go, having been blinded by the darkness.

¹² I am writing to you who are God's children
> because your sins have been forgiven
> through Jesus.*

¹³ I am writing to you who are mature in
> the faith*
>> because you know Christ, who existed
>> from the beginning.
> I am writing to you who are young in
> the faith
>> because you have won your battle with the
>> evil one.

¹⁴ I have written to you who are God's children
> because you know the Father.
> I have written to you who are mature in
> the faith
>> because you know Christ, who existed
>> from the beginning.
> I have written to you who are young in
> the faith
>> because you are strong.
> God's word lives in your hearts,
>> and you have won your battle with the
>> evil one.

Do Not Love This World

15Do not love this world nor the things it offers you, for when you love the world, you do not have the love of the Father in you. 16For the world offers only a craving for physical pleasure, a craving for everything we see, and pride in our achievements and possessions. These are not from the Father, but are from this world. 17And this world is fading away, along with everything that people crave. But anyone who does what pleases God will live forever.

Warning about Antichrists

18Dear children, the last hour is here. You have heard that the Antichrist is coming, and already many such antichrists have appeared. From this we know that the last hour has come. 19These people left our churches, but they never really belonged with us; otherwise they would have stayed with us. When they left, it proved that they did not belong with us.

20But you are not like that, for the Holy One has given you his Spirit,* and all of you know the truth. 21So I am writing to you not because you don't know the truth but because you know the difference between truth and lies. 22And who is a liar? Anyone who says that Jesus is not the Christ.* Anyone who denies the Father and the Son is an antichrist.* 23Anyone who denies the Son doesn't have the Father, either. But anyone who acknowledges the Son has the Father also.

24So you must remain faithful to what you have been taught from the beginning. If you do, you will remain in fellowship with the Son and with the Father. 25And in this fellowship we enjoy the eternal life he promised us.

26I am writing these things to warn you about those who want to lead you astray. 27But you have received the Holy Spirit,* and he lives within you, so you don't need anyone to teach you what is true. For the Spirit* teaches you everything you need to know, and what he teaches is true—it is not a lie. So just as he has taught you, remain in fellowship with Christ.

Living as Children of God

28And now, dear children, remain in fellowship with Christ so that when he returns, you will be full of courage and not shrink back from him in shame.

29Since we know that Christ is righteous, we also know that all who do what is right are God's children.

3 See how very much our Father loves us, for he calls us his children, and that is what we are! But the people who belong to this world don't recognize that we are God's children be-

cause they don't know him. 2Dear friends, we are already God's children, but he has not yet shown us what we will be like when Christ appears. But we do know that we will be like him, for we will see him as he really is. 3And all who have this eager expectation will keep themselves pure, just as he is pure.

4Everyone who sins is breaking God's law, for all sin is contrary to the law of God. 5And you know that Jesus came to take away our sins, and there is no sin in him. 6Anyone who continues to live in him will not sin. But anyone who keeps on sinning does not know him or understand who he is.

7Dear children, don't let anyone deceive you about this: When people do what is right, it shows that they are righteous, even as Christ is righteous. 8But when people keep on sinning, it shows that they belong to the devil, who has been sinning since the beginning. But the Son of God came to destroy the works of the devil. 9Those who have been born into God's family do not make a practice of sinning, because God's life* is in them. So they can't keep on sinning, because they are children of God. 10So now we can tell who are children of God and who are children of the devil. Anyone who does not live righteously and does not love other believers* does not belong to God.

Love One Another

11This is the message you have heard from the beginning: We should love one another. 12We must not be like Cain, who belonged to the evil one and killed his brother. And why did he kill him? Because Cain had been doing what was evil, and his brother had been doing what was righteous. 13So don't be surprised, dear brothers and sisters,* if the world hates you.

14If we love our Christian brothers and sisters,* it proves that we have passed from death to life. But a person who has no love is still dead. 15Anyone who hates another brother or sister* is really a murderer at heart. And you know that murderers don't have eternal life within them.

16We know what real love is because Jesus gave up his life for us. So we also ought to give up our lives for our brothers and sisters. 17If someone has enough money to live well and sees a brother or sister* in need but shows no compassion—how can God's love be in that person?

18Dear children, let's not merely say that we love each other; let us show the truth by our actions. 19Our actions will show that we belong to the truth, so we will be confident when we stand before God. 20Even if we feel guilty, God is greater than our feelings, and he knows everything.

21Dear friends, if we don't feel guilty, we can come to God with bold confidence. 22And we

---

2:20 Greek *But you have an anointing from the Holy One.*   **2:22a** Or *not the Messiah.*   **2:22b** Or *the antichrist.*   **2:27a** Greek *the anointing from him.*   **2:27b** Greek *the anointing.*   **3:9** Greek *because his seed.*   **3:10** Greek *does not love his brother.*   **3:13** Greek *brothers.*   **3:14** Greek *the brothers;* similarly in 3:16.   **3:15** Greek *hates his brother.*   **3:17** Greek *sees his brother.*

will receive from him whatever we ask because we obey him and do the things that please him.

²³And this is his commandment: We must believe in the name of his Son, Jesus Christ, and love one another, just as he commanded us. ²⁴Those who obey God's commandments remain in fellowship with him, and he with them. And we know he lives in us because the Spirit he gave us lives in us.

Discerning False Prophets

4 Dear friends, do not believe everyone who claims to speak by the Spirit. You must test them to see if the spirit they have comes from God. For there are many false prophets in the world. ²This is how we know if they have the Spirit of God: If a person claiming to be a prophet* acknowledges that Jesus Christ came in a real body, that person has the Spirit of God. ³But if someone claims to be a prophet and does not acknowledge the truth about Jesus, that person is not from God. Such a person has the spirit of the Antichrist, which you heard is coming into the world and indeed is already here.

⁴But you belong to God, my dear children. You have already won a victory over those people, because the Spirit who lives in you is greater than the spirit who lives in the world. ⁵Those people belong to this world, so they speak from the world's viewpoint, and the world listens to them. ⁶But we belong to God, and those who know God listen to us. If they do not belong to God, they do not listen to us. That is how we know if someone has the Spirit of truth or the spirit of deception.

Loving One Another

⁷Dear friends, let us continue to love one another, for love comes from God. Anyone who loves is a child of God and knows God. ⁸But anyone who does not love does not know God, for God is love.

⁹God showed how much he loved us by sending his one and only Son into the world so that we might have eternal life through him. ¹⁰This is real love—not that we loved God, but that he loved us and sent his Son as a sacrifice to take away our sins.

¹¹Dear friends, since God loved us that much, we surely ought to love each other. ¹²No one has ever seen God. But if we love each other, God lives in us, and his love is brought to full expression in us.

¹³And God has given us his Spirit as proof that we live in him and he in us. ¹⁴Furthermore, we have seen with our own eyes and now testify that the Father sent his Son to be the Savior of the world. ¹⁵All who confess that Jesus is the Son of

God have God living in them, and they live in God. ¹⁶We know how much God loves us, and we have put our trust in his love.

God is love, and all who live in love live in God, and God lives in them. ¹⁷And as we live in God, our love grows more perfect. So we will not be afraid on the day of judgment, but we can face him with confidence because we live like Jesus here in this world.

¹⁸Such love has no fear, because perfect love expels all fear. If we are afraid, it is for fear of punishment, and this shows that we have not fully experienced his perfect love. ¹⁹We love each other* because he loved us first.

²⁰If someone says, "I love God," but hates a Christian brother or sister,* that person is a liar; for if we don't love people we can see, how can we love God, whom we cannot see? ²¹And he has given us this command: Those who love God must also love their Christian brothers and sisters.*

Faith in the Son of God

5 Everyone who believes that Jesus is the Christ* has become a child of God. And everyone who loves the Father loves his children, too. ²We know we love God's children if we love God and obey his commandments. ³Loving God means keeping his commandments, and his commandments are not burdensome. ⁴For every child of God defeats this evil world, and we achieve this victory through our faith. ⁵And who can win this battle against the world? Only those who believe that Jesus is the Son of God.

⁶And Jesus Christ was revealed as God's Son by his baptism in water and by shedding his blood on the cross*—not by water only, but by water and blood. And the Spirit, who is truth, confirms it with his testimony. ⁷So we have these three witnesses*—⁸the Spirit, the water, and the blood—and all three agree. ⁹Since we believe human testimony, surely we can believe the greater testimony that comes from God. And God has testified about his Son. ¹⁰All who believe in the Son of God know in their hearts that this testimony is true. Those who don't believe this are actually calling God a liar because they don't believe what God has testified about his Son.

¹¹And this is what God has testified: He has given us eternal life, and this life is in his Son. ¹²Whoever has the Son has life; whoever does not have God's Son does not have life.

Conclusion

¹³I have written this to you who believe in the name of the Son of God, so that you may know you have eternal life. ¹⁴And we are confident that he hears us whenever we ask for anything

4:2 Greek *If a spirit;* similarly in 4:3. **4:19** Greek *We love.* Other manuscripts read *We love God;* still others read *We love him.*
4:20 Greek *hates his brother.* **4:21** Greek *The one who loves God must also love his brother.* **5:1** Or *the Messiah.* **5:6** Greek *This is he who came by water and blood.* **5:7** A few very late manuscripts add *in heaven—the Father, the Word, and the Holy Spirit, and these three are one. And we have three witnesses on earth.*

that pleases him. [15]And since we know he hears us when we make our requests, we also know that he will give us what we ask for.

[16]If you see a Christian brother or sister* sinning in a way that does not lead to death, you should pray, and God will give that person life. But there is a sin that leads to death, and I am not saying you should pray for those who commit it. [17]All wicked actions are sin, but not every sin leads to death.

[18]We know that God's children do not make a practice of sinning, for God's Son holds them securely, and the evil one cannot touch them. [19]We know that we are children of God and that the world around us is under the control of the evil one.

[20]And we know that the Son of God has come, and he has given us understanding so that we can know the true God.* And now we live in fellowship with the true God because we live in fellowship with his Son, Jesus Christ. He is the only true God, and he is eternal life.

[21]Dear children, keep away from anything that might take God's place in your hearts.*

5:16 Greek *a brother.*   **5:20** Greek *the one who is true.*   **5:21** Greek *keep yourselves from idols.*

2 John

Greetings

This letter is from John, the elder.*

I am writing to the chosen lady and to her children,* whom I love in the truth—as does everyone else who knows the truth—²because the truth lives in us and will be with us forever.

³Grace, mercy, and peace, which come from God the Father and from Jesus Christ—the Son of the Father—will continue to be with us who live in truth and love.

Live in the Truth

⁴How happy I was to meet some of your children and find them living according to the truth, just as the Father commanded.

⁵I am writing to remind you, dear friends,* that we should love one another. This is not a new commandment, but one we have had from the beginning. ⁶Love means doing what God has commanded us, and he has commanded us to love one another, just as you heard from the beginning.

⁷I say this because many deceivers have gone out into the world. They deny that Jesus Christ came* in a real body. Such a person is a deceiver and an antichrist. ⁸Watch out that you do not lose what we* have worked so hard to achieve. Be diligent so that you receive your full reward. ⁹Anyone who wanders away from this teaching has no relationship with God. But anyone who remains in the teaching of Christ has a relationship with both the Father and the Son.

¹⁰If anyone comes to your meeting and does not teach the truth about Christ, don't invite that person into your home or give any kind of encouragement. ¹¹Anyone who encourages such people becomes a partner in their evil work.

Conclusion

¹²I have much more to say to you, but I don't want to do it with paper and ink. For I hope to visit you soon and talk with you face to face. Then our joy will be complete.

¹³Greetings from the children of your sister,* chosen by God.

1a Greek *From the elder.*   1b Or *the church God has chosen and its members.*   5 Greek *I urge you, lady.*   7 Or *will come.*
8 Some manuscripts read *you.*   13 Or *from the members of your sister church.*

3 John

Greetings

This letter is from John, the elder.*

I am writing to Gaius, my dear friend, whom I love in the truth.

²Dear friend, I hope all is well with you and that you are as healthy in body as you are strong in spirit. ³Some of the traveling teachers* recently returned and made me very happy by telling me about your faithfulness and that you are living according to the truth. ⁴I could have no greater joy than to hear that my children are following the truth.

Caring for the Lord's Workers

⁵Dear friend, you are being faithful to God when you care for the traveling teachers who pass through, even though they are strangers to you. ⁶They have told the church here of your loving friendship. Please continue providing for such teachers in a manner that pleases God. ⁷For they are traveling for the Lord,* and they accept nothing from people who are not believers.* ⁸So we ourselves should support them so that we can be their partners as they teach the truth.

⁹I wrote to the church about this, but Diotrephes, who loves to be the leader, refuses to have anything to do with us. ¹⁰When I come, I will report some of the things he is doing and the evil accusations he is making against us. Not only does he refuse to welcome the traveling teachers, he also tells others not to help them. And when they do help, he puts them out of the church.

¹¹Dear friend, don't let this bad example influence you. Follow only what is good. Remember that those who do good prove that they are God's children, and those who do evil prove that they do not know God.*

¹²Everyone speaks highly of Demetrius, as does the truth itself. We ourselves can say the same for him, and you know we speak the truth.

Conclusion

¹³I have much more to say to you, but I don't want to write it with pen and ink. ¹⁴For I hope to see you soon, and then we will talk face to face.

¹⁵*Peace be with you.

Your friends here send you their greetings. Please give my personal greetings to each of our friends there.

---

1 Greek *From the elder.*   **3** Greek *the brothers;* also in verses 5 and 10.   **7a** Greek *They went out on behalf of the Name.*   **7b** Greek *from Gentiles.*   **11** Greek *they have not seen God.*   **15** Some English translations combine verses 14 and 15 into verse 14.

Jude

Greetings from Jude

This letter is from Jude, a slave of Jesus Christ and a brother of James.

I am writing to all who have been called by God the Father, who loves you and keeps you safe in the care of Jesus Christ.*

²May God give you more and more mercy, peace, and love.

The Danger of False Teachers

³Dear friends, I had been eagerly planning to write to you about the salvation we all share. But now I find that I must write about something else, urging you to defend the faith that God has entrusted once for all time to his holy people. ⁴I say this because some ungodly people have wormed their way into your churches, saying that God's marvelous grace allows us to live immoral lives. The condemnation of such people was recorded long ago, for they have denied our only Master and Lord, Jesus Christ.

⁵So I want to remind you, though you already know these things, that Jesus* first rescued the nation of Israel from Egypt, but later he destroyed those who did not remain faithful. ⁶And I remind you of the angels who did not stay within the limits of authority God gave them but left the place where they belonged. God has kept them securely chained in prisons of darkness, waiting for the great day of judgment. ⁷And don't forget Sodom and Gomorrah and their neighboring towns, which were filled with immorality and every kind of sexual perversion. Those cities were destroyed by fire and serve as a warning of the eternal fire of God's judgment.

⁸In the same way, these people—who claim authority from their dreams—live immoral lives, defy authority, and scoff at supernatural beings.* ⁹But even Michael, one of the mightiest of the angels,* did not dare accuse the devil of blasphemy, but simply said, "The Lord rebuke you!" (This took place when Michael was arguing with the devil about Moses' body.) ¹⁰But these people scoff at things they do not understand. Like unthinking animals, they do whatever their instincts tell them, and so they bring about their own destruction. ¹¹What sorrow awaits them! For they follow in the footsteps of Cain, who killed his brother. Like Balaam, they deceive people for money. And like Korah, they perish in their rebellion.

¹²When these people eat with you in your fellowship meals commemorating the Lord's love, they are like dangerous reefs that can shipwreck you.* They are like shameless shepherds who care only for themselves. They are like clouds blowing over the land without giving any rain. They are like trees in autumn that are doubly dead, for they bear no fruit and have been pulled up by the roots. ¹³They are like wild waves of the sea, churning up the foam of their shameful deeds. They are like wandering stars, doomed forever to blackest darkness.

¹⁴Enoch, who lived in the seventh generation after Adam, prophesied about these people. He said, "Listen! The Lord is coming with countless thousands of his holy ones ¹⁵to execute judgment on the people of the world. He will convict every person of all the ungodly things they have done and for all the insults that ungodly sinners have spoken against him."*

¹⁶These people are grumblers and complainers, living only to satisfy their desires. They brag loudly about themselves, and they flatter others to get what they want.

A Call to Remain Faithful

¹⁷But you, my dear friends, must remember what the apostles of our Lord Jesus Christ said. ¹⁸They told you that in the last times there would be scoffers whose purpose in life is to satisfy their ungodly desires. ¹⁹These people are the ones who are creating divisions among you. They follow their natural instincts because they do not have God's Spirit in them.

²⁰But you, dear friends, must build each other up in your most holy faith, pray in the power of the Holy Spirit,* ²¹and await the mercy of our Lord Jesus Christ, who will bring you eternal life.

In this way, you will keep yourselves safe in God's love.

²²And you must show mercy to* those whose faith is wavering. ²³Rescue others by snatching them from the flames of judgment. Show mercy to still others,* but do so with great caution, hating the sins that contaminate their lives.*

A Prayer of Praise

²⁴Now all glory to God, who is able to keep you from falling away and will bring you with great joy into his glorious presence without a single fault. ²⁵All glory to him who alone is God, our Savior through Jesus Christ our Lord. All glory, majesty, power, and authority are his before all time, and in the present, and beyond all time! Amen.

22 Some manuscripts read *must reprove.*   **22-23a** Some manuscripts have only two categories of people: (1) those whose faith is wavering and therefore need to be snatched from the flames of judgment, and (2) those who need to be shown mercy.   **23b** Greek *with fear, hating even the clothing stained by the flesh.*

Revelation

Prologue

1 This is a revelation from* Jesus Christ, which God gave him to show his servants the events that must soon* take place. He sent an angel to present this revelation to his servant John, ²who faithfully reported everything he saw. This is his report of the word of God and the testimony of Jesus Christ.

³God blesses the one who reads the words of this prophecy to the church, and he blesses all who listen to its message and obey what it says, for the time is near.

John's Greeting to the Seven Churches

⁴This letter is from John to the seven churches in the province of Asia.*

Grace and peace to you from the one who is, who always was, and who is still to come; from the sevenfold Spirit* before his throne; ⁵and from Jesus Christ. He is the faithful witness to these things, the first to rise from the dead, and the ruler of all the kings of the world.

All glory to him who loves us and has freed us from our sins by shedding his blood for us. ⁶He has made us a Kingdom of priests for God his Father. All glory and power to him forever and ever! Amen.

⁷ Look! He comes with the clouds of heaven.
　　And everyone will see him—
　　　even those who pierced him.
　And all the nations of the world
　　will mourn for him.
Yes! Amen!

⁸"I am the Alpha and the Omega—the beginning and the end,"* says the Lord God. "I am the one who is, who always was, and who is still to come—the Almighty One."

Vision of the Son of Man

⁹I, John, am your brother and your partner in suffering and in God's Kingdom and in the patient endurance to which Jesus calls us. I was exiled to the island of Patmos for preaching the word of God and for my testimony about Jesus.

¹⁰It was the Lord's Day, and I was worshiping in the Spirit.* Suddenly, I heard behind me a loud voice like a trumpet blast. ¹¹It said, "Write in a book* everything you see, and send it to the seven churches in the cities of Ephesus, Smyrna, Pergamum, Thyatira, Sardis, Philadelphia, and Laodicea."

¹²When I turned to see who was speaking to me, I saw seven gold lampstands. ¹³And standing in the middle of the lampstands was someone like the Son of Man.* He was wearing a long robe with a gold sash across his chest. ¹⁴His head and his hair were white like wool, as white as snow. And his eyes were like flames of fire. ¹⁵His feet were like polished bronze refined in a furnace, and his voice thundered like mighty ocean waves. ¹⁶He held seven stars in his right hand, and a sharp two-edged sword came from his mouth. And his face was like the sun in all its brilliance.

¹⁷When I saw him, I fell at his feet as if I were dead. But he laid his right hand on me and said, "Don't be afraid! I am the First and the Last. ¹⁸I am the living one. I died, but look—I am alive forever and ever! And I hold the keys of death and the grave.*

¹⁹"Write down what you have seen—both the things that are now happening and the things that will happen.* ²⁰This is the meaning of the mystery of the seven stars you saw in my right hand and the seven gold lampstands: The seven stars are the angels* of the seven churches, and the seven lampstands are the seven churches.

The Message to the Church in Ephesus

2 "Write this letter to the angel* of the church in Ephesus. This is the message from the one who holds the seven stars in his right hand, the one who walks among the seven gold lampstands:

²"I know all the things you do. I have seen your hard work and your patient endurance. I know you don't tolerate evil people. You have examined the claims of those who say they are apostles but are not. You have

---

1:1a Or *of.*　**1:1b** Or *suddenly,* or *quickly.*　**1:4a** *Asia* was a Roman province in what is now western Turkey.　**1:4b** Greek *the seven spirits.*　**1:8** Greek *I am the Alpha and the Omega,* referring to the first and last letters of the Greek alphabet.　**1:10** Or *in spirit.*　**1:11** Or *on a scroll.*　**1:13** Or *like a son of man.* See Dan 7:13. "Son of Man" is a title Jesus used for himself.　**1:18** Greek *and Hades.*　**1:19** Or *what you have seen and what they mean—the things that have already begun to happen.*　**1:20** Or *the messengers.*　**2:1** Or *the messenger;* also in 2:8, 12, 18.

discovered they are liars. ³You have patiently suffered for me without quitting.

⁴"But I have this complaint against you. You don't love me or each other as you did at first!* ⁵Look how far you have fallen! Turn back to me and do the works you did at first. If you don't repent, I will come and remove your lampstand from its place among the churches. ⁶But this is in your favor: You hate the evil deeds of the Nicolaitans, just as I do.

⁷"Anyone with ears to hear must listen to the Spirit and understand what he is saying to the churches. To everyone who is victorious I will give fruit from the tree of life in the paradise of God.

The Message to the Church in Smyrna

⁸"Write this letter to the angel of the church in Smyrna. This is the message from the one who is the First and the Last, who was dead but is now alive:

⁹"I know about your suffering and your poverty—but you are rich! I know the blasphemy of those opposing you. They say they are Jews, but they are not, because their synagogue belongs to Satan. ¹⁰Don't be afraid of what you are about to suffer. The devil will throw some of you into prison to test you. You will suffer for ten days. But if you remain faithful even when facing death, I will give you the crown of life.

¹¹"Anyone with ears to hear must listen to the Spirit and understand what he is saying to the churches. Whoever is victorious will not be harmed by the second death.

The Message to the Church in Pergamum

¹²"Write this letter to the angel of the church in Pergamum. This is the message from the one with the sharp two-edged sword:

¹³"I know that you live in the city where Satan has his throne, yet you have remained loyal to me. You refused to deny me even when Antipas, my faithful witness, was martyred among you there in Satan's city.

¹⁴"But I have a few complaints against you. You tolerate some among you whose teaching is like that of Balaam, who showed Balak how to trip up the people of Israel. He taught them to sin by eating food offered to idols and by committing sexual sin. ¹⁵In a similar way, you have some Nicolaitans among you who follow the same teaching. ¹⁶Repent of your sin, or I will come to you suddenly and fight against them with the sword of my mouth.

¹⁷"Anyone with ears to hear must listen to the Spirit and understand what he is saying to the churches. To everyone who is victorious I will give some of the manna that has been hidden away in heaven. And I will give to each one a white stone, and on the stone will be engraved a new name that no one understands except the one who receives it.

The Message to the Church in Thyatira

¹⁸"Write this letter to the angel of the church in Thyatira. This is the message from the Son of God, whose eyes are like flames of fire, whose feet are like polished bronze:

¹⁹"I know all the things you do. I have seen your love, your faith, your service, and your patient endurance. And I can see your constant improvement in all these things.

²⁰"But I have this complaint against you. You are permitting that woman—that Jezebel who calls herself a prophet—to lead my servants astray. She teaches them to commit sexual sin and to eat food offered to idols. ²¹I gave her time to repent, but she does not want to turn away from her immorality.

²²"Therefore, I will throw her on a bed of suffering,* and those who commit adultery with her will suffer greatly unless they repent and turn away from her evil deeds. ²³I will strike her children dead. Then all the churches will know that I am the one who searches out the thoughts and intentions of every person. And I will give to each of you whatever you deserve.

²⁴"But I also have a message for the rest of you in Thyatira who have not followed this false teaching ('deeper truths,' as they call them—depths of Satan, actually). I will ask nothing more of you ²⁵except that you hold tightly to what you have until I come. ²⁶To all who are victorious, who obey me to the very end,

To them I will give authority over all the nations.
²⁷ They will rule the nations with an iron rod and smash them like clay pots.*

²⁸They will have the same authority I received from my Father, and I will also give them the morning star! ²⁹"Anyone with ears to hear must listen to the Spirit and understand what he is saying to the churches.

The Message to the Church in Sardis

3 "Write this letter to the angel* of the church in Sardis. This is the message from the one who has the sevenfold Spirit* of God and the seven stars:

"I know all the things you do, and that you have a reputation for being alive—but you are dead. ²Wake up! Strengthen what little

---

2:4 Greek *You have lost your first love.*   **2:22** Greek *a bed.*   **2:26-27** Ps 2:8-9 (Greek Version).   **3:1a** Or *the messenger;* also in 3:7, 14.   **3:1b** Greek *the seven spirits.*

remains, for even what is left is almost dead. I find that your actions do not meet the requirements of my God. ³Go back to what you heard and believed at first; hold to it firmly. Repent and turn to me again. If you don't wake up, I will come to you suddenly, as unexpected as a thief.

⁴"Yet there are some in the church in Sardis who have not soiled their clothes with evil. They will walk with me in white, for they are worthy. ⁵All who are victorious will be clothed in white. I will never erase their names from the Book of Life, but I will announce before my Father and his angels that they are mine.

⁶"Anyone with ears to hear must listen to the Spirit and understand what he is saying to the churches.

The Message to the Church in Philadelphia

⁷"Write this letter to the angel of the church in Philadelphia.

This is the message from the one who is holy and true,
the one who has the key of David.
What he opens, no one can close;
and what he closes, no one can open:*

⁸"I know all the things you do, and I have opened a door for you that no one can close. You have little strength, yet you obeyed my word and did not deny me. ⁹Look, I will force those who belong to Satan's synagogue— those liars who say they are Jews but are not— to come and bow down at your feet. They will acknowledge that you are the ones I love.

¹⁰"Because you have obeyed my command to persevere, I will protect you from the great time of testing that will come upon the whole world to test those who belong to this world. ¹¹I am coming soon.* Hold on to what you have, so that no one will take away your crown. ¹²All who are victorious will become pillars in the Temple of my God, and they will never have to leave it. And I will write on them the name of my God, and they will be citizens in the city of my God—the new Jerusalem that comes down from heaven from my God. And I will also write on them my new name.

¹³"Anyone with ears to hear must listen to the Spirit and understand what he is saying to the churches.

The Message to the Church in Laodicea

¹⁴"Write this letter to the angel of the church in Laodicea. This is the message from the one who is the Amen—the faithful and true witness, the beginning* of God's new creation:

¹⁵"I know all the things you do, that you are neither hot nor cold. I wish that you were one or the other! ¹⁶But since you are like lukewarm water, neither hot nor cold, I will spit you out of my mouth! ¹⁷You say, 'I am rich. I have everything I want. I don't need a thing!' And you don't realize that you are wretched and miserable and poor and blind and naked. ¹⁸So I advise you to buy gold from me—gold that has been purified by fire. Then you will be rich. Also buy white garments from me so you will not be shamed by your nakedness, and ointment for your eyes so you will be able to see. ¹⁹I correct and discipline everyone I love. So be diligent and turn from your indifference.

²⁰"Look! I stand at the door and knock. If you hear my voice and open the door, I will come in, and we will share a meal together as friends. ²¹Those who are victorious will sit with me on my throne, just as I was victorious and sat with my Father on his throne.

²²"Anyone with ears to hear must listen to the Spirit and understand what he is saying to the churches."

Worship in Heaven

4 Then as I looked, I saw a door standing open in heaven, and the same voice I had heard before spoke to me like a trumpet blast. The voice said, "Come up here, and I will show you what must happen after this." ²And instantly I was in the Spirit,* and I saw a throne in heaven and someone sitting on it. ³The one sitting on the throne was as brilliant as gemstones—like jasper and carnelian. And the glow of an emerald circled his throne like a rainbow. ⁴Twenty-four thrones surrounded him, and twenty-four elders sat on them. They were all clothed in white and had gold crowns on their heads. ⁵From the throne came flashes of lightning and the rumble of thunder. And in front of the throne were seven torches with burning flames. This is the sevenfold Spirit* of God. ⁶In front of the throne was a shiny sea of glass, sparkling like crystal.

In the center and around the throne were four living beings, each covered with eyes, front and back. ⁷The first of these living beings was like a lion; the second was like an ox; the third had a human face; and the fourth was like an eagle in flight. ⁸Each of these living beings had six wings, and their wings were covered all over with eyes, inside and out. Day after day and night after night they keep on saying,

"Holy, holy, holy is the Lord God, the Almighty—
the one who always was, who is, and who is still to come."

3:7 Isa 22:22. **3:11** Or *suddenly,* or *quickly.* **3:14** Or *the ruler,* or *the source.* **4:2** Or *in spirit.* **4:5** Greek *They are the seven spirits.*

⁹Whenever the living beings give glory and honor and thanks to the one sitting on the throne (the one who lives forever and ever), ¹⁰the twenty-four elders fall down and worship the one sitting on the throne (the one who lives forever and ever). And they lay their crowns before the throne and say,

¹¹ "You are worthy, O Lord our God,
to receive glory and honor and power.
For you created all things,
and they exist because you created what
you pleased."

The Lamb Opens the Scroll

5 Then I saw a scroll* in the right hand of the one who was sitting on the throne. There was writing on the inside and the outside of the scroll, and it was sealed with seven seals. ²And I saw a strong angel, who shouted with a loud voice: "Who is worthy to break the seals on this scroll and open it?" ³But no one in heaven or on earth or under the earth was able to open the scroll and read it.

⁴Then I began to weep bitterly because no one was found worthy to open the scroll and read it. ⁵But one of the twenty-four elders said to me, "Stop weeping! Look, the Lion of the tribe of Judah, the heir to David's throne,* has won the victory. He is worthy to open the scroll and its seven seals."

⁶Then I saw a Lamb that looked as if it had been slaughtered, but it was now standing between the throne and the four living beings and among the twenty-four elders. He had seven horns and seven eyes, which represent the sevenfold Spirit* of God that is sent out into every part of the earth. ⁷He stepped forward and took the scroll from the right hand of the one sitting on the throne. ⁸And when he took the scroll, the four living beings and the twenty-four elders fell down before the Lamb. Each one had a harp, and they held gold bowls filled with incense, which are the prayers of God's people. ⁹And they sang a new song with these words:

"You are worthy to take the scroll
and break its seals and open it.
For you were slaughtered, and your blood has
ransomed people for God
from every tribe and language and people
and nation.
¹⁰ And you have caused them to become
a Kingdom of priests for our God.
And they will reign* on the earth."

¹¹Then I looked again, and I heard the voices of thousands and millions of angels around the throne and of the living beings and the elders. ¹²And they sang in a mighty chorus:

"Worthy is the Lamb who was slaughtered—
to receive power and riches
and wisdom and strength
and honor and glory and blessing."

¹³And then I heard every creature in heaven and on earth and under the earth and in the sea. They sang:

"Blessing and honor and glory and power
belong to the one sitting on the throne
and to the Lamb forever and ever."

¹⁴And the four living beings said, "Amen!" And the twenty-four elders fell down and worshiped the Lamb.

The Lamb Breaks the First Six Seals

6 As I watched, the Lamb broke the first of the seven seals on the scroll.* Then I heard one of the four living beings say with a voice like thunder, "Come!" ²I looked up and saw a white horse standing there. Its rider carried a bow, and a crown was placed on his head. He rode out to win many battles and gain the victory.

³When the Lamb broke the second seal, I heard the second living being say, "Come!" ⁴Then another horse appeared, a red one. Its rider was given a mighty sword and the authority to take peace from the earth. And there was war and slaughter everywhere.

⁵When the Lamb broke the third seal, I heard the third living being say, "Come!" I looked up and saw a black horse, and its rider was holding a pair of scales in his hand. ⁶And I heard a voice from among the four living beings say, "A loaf of wheat bread or three loaves of barley will cost a day's pay.* And don't waste* the olive oil and wine."

⁷When the Lamb broke the fourth seal, I heard the fourth living being say, "Come!" ⁸I looked up and saw a horse whose color was pale green. Its rider was named Death, and his companion was the Grave.* These two were given authority over one-fourth of the earth, to kill with the sword and famine and disease* and wild animals.

⁹When the Lamb broke the fifth seal, I saw under the altar the souls of all who had been martyred for the word of God and for being faithful in their testimony. ¹⁰They shouted to the Lord and said, "O Sovereign Lord, holy and true, how long before you judge the people who belong to this world and avenge our blood for what they have done to us?" ¹¹Then a white robe was given to each of them. And they were told to rest a little longer until the full number of their brothers and sisters*—their fellow servants of Jesus who were to be martyred—had joined them.

5:1 Or *book;* also in 5:2, 3, 4, 5, 7, 8, 9.　**5:5** Greek *the root of David.* See Isa 11:10.　**5:6** Greek *which are the seven spirits.*
5:10 Some manuscripts read *they are reigning.*　**6:1** Or *book.*　**6:6a** Greek *A choinix* [1 quart or 1 liter] *of wheat for a denarius, and 3 choinix of barley for a denarius.* A denarius was equivalent to a laborer's full day's wage.　**6:6b** Or *harm.*　**6:8a** Greek *was Hades.*
6:8b Greek *death.*　**6:11** Greek *their brothers.*

¹²I watched as the Lamb broke the sixth seal, and there was a great earthquake. The sun became as dark as black cloth, and the moon became as red as blood. ¹³Then the stars of the sky fell to the earth like green figs falling from a tree shaken by a strong wind. ¹⁴The sky was rolled up like a scroll, and all of the mountains and islands were moved from their places.

¹⁵Then everyone—the kings of the earth, the rulers, the generals, the wealthy, the powerful, and every slave and free person—all hid themselves in the caves and among the rocks of the mountains. ¹⁶And they cried to the mountains and the rocks, "Fall on us and hide us from the face of the one who sits on the throne and from the wrath of the Lamb. ¹⁷For the great day of their wrath has come, and who is able to survive?"

God's People Will Be Preserved

7 Then I saw four angels standing at the four corners of the earth, holding back the four winds so they did not blow on the earth or the sea, or even on any tree. ²And I saw another angel coming up from the east, carrying the seal of the living God. And he shouted to those four angels, who had been given power to harm land and sea, ³"Wait! Don't harm the land or the sea or the trees until we have placed the seal of God on the foreheads of his servants."

⁴And I heard how many were marked with the seal of God—144,000 were sealed from all the tribes of Israel:

⁵	from Judah	12,000
	from Reuben	12,000
	from Gad	12,000
⁶	from Asher	12,000
	from Naphtali	12,000
	from Manasseh	12,000
⁷	from Simeon	12,000
	from Levi	12,000
	from Issachar	12,000
⁸	from Zebulun	12,000
	from Joseph	12,000
	from Benjamin	12,000

Praise from the Great Crowd

⁹After this I saw a vast crowd, too great to count, from every nation and tribe and people and language, standing in front of the throne and before the Lamb. They were clothed in white robes and held palm branches in their hands. ¹⁰And they were shouting with a great roar,

"Salvation comes from our God who sits on
the throne
and from the Lamb!"

¹¹And all the angels were standing around the throne and around the elders and the four living beings. And they fell before the throne with their faces to the ground and worshiped God. ¹²They sang,

"Amen! Blessing and glory and wisdom
and thanksgiving and honor
and power and strength belong to our God
forever and ever! Amen."

¹³Then one of the twenty-four elders asked me, "Who are these who are clothed in white? Where did they come from?"

¹⁴And I said to him, "Sir, you are the one who knows."

Then he said to me, "These are the ones who died in* the great tribulation.* They have washed their robes in the blood of the Lamb and made them white.

¹⁵ "That is why they stand in front of God's
throne
and serve him day and night in his
Temple.
And he who sits on the throne
will give them shelter.
¹⁶ They will never again be hungry or thirsty;
they will never be scorched by the heat
of the sun.
¹⁷ For the Lamb on the throne*
will be their Shepherd.
He will lead them to springs of life-giving
water.
And God will wipe every tear from
their eyes."

The Lamb Breaks the Seventh Seal

8 When the Lamb broke the seventh seal on the scroll,* there was silence throughout heaven for about half an hour. ²I saw the seven angels who stand before God, and they were given seven trumpets.

³Then another angel with a gold incense burner came and stood at the altar. And a great amount of incense was given to him to mix with the prayers of God's people as an offering on the gold altar before the throne. ⁴The smoke of the incense, mixed with the prayers of God's holy people, ascended up to God from the altar where the angel had poured them out. ⁵Then the angel filled the incense burner with fire from the altar and threw it down upon the earth; and thunder crashed, lightning flashed, and there was a terrible earthquake.

The First Four Trumpets

⁶Then the seven angels with the seven trumpets prepared to blow their mighty blasts.

⁷The first angel blew his trumpet, and hail and fire mixed with blood were thrown down on the earth. One-third of the earth was set on fire, one-third of the trees were burned, and all the green grass was burned.

7:14a Greek *who came out of.* **7:14b** Or *the great suffering.* **7:17** Greek *on the center of the throne.* **8:1** Or *book.*

⁸Then the second angel blew his trumpet, and a great mountain of fire was thrown into the sea. One-third of the water in the sea became blood, ⁹one-third of all things living in the sea died, and one-third of all the ships on the sea were destroyed.

¹⁰Then the third angel blew his trumpet, and a great star fell from the sky, burning like a torch. It fell on one-third of the rivers and on the springs of water. ¹¹The name of the star was Bitterness.* It made one-third of the water bitter, and many people died from drinking the bitter water.

¹²Then the fourth angel blew his trumpet, and one-third of the sun was struck, and one-third of the moon, and one-third of the stars, and they became dark. And one-third of the day was dark, and also one-third of the night.

¹³Then I looked, and I heard a single eagle crying loudly as it flew through the air, "Terror, terror, terror to all who belong to this world because of what will happen when the last three angels blow their trumpets."

The Fifth Trumpet Brings the First Terror

9 Then the fifth angel blew his trumpet, and I saw a star that had fallen to earth from the sky, and he was given the key to the shaft of the bottomless pit.* ²When he opened it, smoke poured out as though from a huge furnace, and the sunlight and air turned dark from the smoke.

³Then locusts came from the smoke and descended on the earth, and they were given power to sting like scorpions. ⁴They were told not to harm the grass or plants or trees, but only the people who did not have the seal of God on their foreheads. ⁵They were told not to kill them but to torture them for five months with pain like the pain of a scorpion sting. ⁶In those days people will seek death but will not find it. They will long to die, but death will flee from them!

⁷The locusts looked like horses prepared for battle. They had what looked like gold crowns on their heads, and their faces looked like human faces. ⁸They had hair like women's hair and teeth like the teeth of a lion. ⁹They wore armor made of iron, and their wings roared like an army of chariots rushing into battle. ¹⁰They had tails that stung like scorpions, and for five months they had the power to torment people. ¹¹Their king is the angel from the bottomless pit; his name in Hebrew is *Abaddon,* and in Greek, *Apollyon*—the Destroyer.

¹²The first terror is past, but look, two more terrors are coming!

The Sixth Trumpet Brings the Second Terror

¹³Then the sixth angel blew his trumpet, and I heard a voice speaking from the four horns of the gold altar that stands in the presence of God. ¹⁴And the voice said to the sixth angel who held the trumpet, "Release the four angels who are bound at the great Euphrates River." ¹⁵Then the four angels who had been prepared for this hour and day and month and year were turned loose to kill one-third of all the people on earth. ¹⁶I heard the size of their army, which was 200 million mounted troops.

¹⁷And in my vision, I saw the horses and the riders sitting on them. The riders wore armor that was fiery red and dark blue and yellow. The horses had heads like lions, and fire and smoke and burning sulfur billowed from their mouths. ¹⁸One-third of all the people on earth were killed by these three plagues—by the fire and smoke and burning sulfur that came from the mouths of the horses. ¹⁹Their power was in their mouths and in their tails. For their tails had heads like snakes, with the power to injure people.

²⁰But the people who did not die in these plagues still refused to repent of their evil deeds and turn to God. They continued to worship demons and idols made of gold, silver, bronze, stone, and wood—idols that can neither see nor hear nor walk! ²¹And they did not repent of their murders or their witchcraft or their sexual immorality or their thefts.

The Angel and the Small Scroll

10 Then I saw another mighty angel coming down from heaven, surrounded by a cloud, with a rainbow over his head. His face shone like the sun, and his feet were like pillars of fire. ²And in his hand was a small scroll* that had been opened. He stood with his right foot on the sea and his left foot on the land. ³And he gave a great shout like the roar of a lion. And when he shouted, the seven thunders answered.

⁴When the seven thunders spoke, I was about to write. But I heard a voice from heaven saying, "Keep secret* what the seven thunders said, and do not write it down."

⁵Then the angel I saw standing on the sea and on the land raised his right hand toward heaven. ⁶He swore an oath in the name of the one who lives forever and ever, who created the heavens and everything in them, the earth and everything in it, and the sea and everything in it. He said, "There will be no more delay. ⁷When the seventh angel blows his trumpet, God's mysterious plan will be fulfilled. It will happen just as he announced it to his servants the prophets."

⁸Then the voice from heaven spoke to me again: "Go and take the open scroll from the hand of the angel who is standing on the sea and on the land."

⁹So I went to the angel and told him to give me the small scroll. "Yes, take it and eat it," he said.

8:11 Greek *Wormwood.*   **9:1** Or *the abyss,* or *the underworld;* also in 9:11.   **10:2** Or *book;* also in 10:8, 9, 10.   **10:4** Greek *Seal up.*

"It will be sweet as honey in your mouth, but it will turn sour in your stomach!" ¹⁰So I took the small scroll from the hand of the angel, and I ate it! It was sweet in my mouth, but when I swallowed it, it turned sour in my stomach.

¹¹Then I was told, "You must prophesy again about many peoples, nations, languages, and kings."

The Two Witnesses

11 Then I was given a measuring stick, and I was told, "Go and measure the Temple of God and the altar, and count the number of worshipers. ²But do not measure the outer courtyard, for it has been turned over to the nations. They will trample the holy city for 42 months. ³And I will give power to my two witnesses, and they will be clothed in burlap and will prophesy during those 1,260 days."

⁴These two prophets are the two olive trees and the two lampstands that stand before the Lord of all the earth. ⁵If anyone tries to harm them, fire flashes from their mouths and consumes their enemies. This is how anyone who tries to harm them must die. ⁶They have power to shut the sky so that no rain will fall for as long as they prophesy. And they have the power to turn the rivers and oceans into blood, and to strike the earth with every kind of plague as often as they wish.

⁷When they complete their testimony, the beast that comes up out of the bottomless pit* will declare war against them, and he will conquer them and kill them. ⁸And their bodies will lie in the main street of Jerusalem,* the city that is figuratively called "Sodom" and "Egypt," the city where their Lord was crucified. ⁹And for three and a half days, all peoples, tribes, languages, and nations will stare at their bodies. No one will be allowed to bury them. ¹⁰All the people who belong to this world will gloat over them and give presents to each other to celebrate the death of the two prophets who had tormented them.

¹¹But after three and a half days, God breathed life into them, and they stood up! Terror struck all who were staring at them. ¹²Then a loud voice from heaven called to the two prophets, "Come up here!" And they rose to heaven in a cloud as their enemies watched.

¹³At the same time there was a terrible earthquake that destroyed a tenth of the city. Seven thousand people died in that earthquake, and everyone else was terrified and gave glory to the God of heaven.

¹⁴The second terror is past, but look, the third terror is coming quickly.

The Seventh Trumpet Brings the Third Terror

¹⁵Then the seventh angel blew his trumpet, and there were loud voices shouting in heaven:

"The world has now become the Kingdom of our Lord and of his Christ,*
and he will reign forever and ever."

¹⁶The twenty-four elders sitting on their thrones before God fell with their faces to the ground and worshiped him. ¹⁷And they said,

"We give thanks to you, Lord God, the Almighty,
the one who is and who always was,
for now you have assumed your great power
and have begun to reign.
¹⁸ The nations were filled with wrath,
but now the time of your wrath has come.
It is time to judge the dead
and reward your servants the prophets,
as well as your holy people,
and all who fear your name,
from the least to the greatest.
It is time to destroy
all who have caused destruction on the earth."

¹⁹Then, in heaven, the Temple of God was opened and the Ark of his covenant could be seen inside the Temple. Lightning flashed, thunder crashed and roared, and there was an earthquake and a terrible hailstorm.

The Woman and the Dragon

12 Then I witnessed in heaven an event of great significance. I saw a woman clothed with the sun, with the moon beneath her feet, and a crown of twelve stars on her head. ²She was pregnant, and she cried out because of her labor pains and the agony of giving birth.

³Then I witnessed in heaven another significant event. I saw a large red dragon with seven heads and ten horns, with seven crowns on his heads. ⁴His tail swept away one-third of the stars in the sky, and he threw them to the earth. He stood in front of the woman as she was about to give birth, ready to devour her baby as soon as it was born.

⁵She gave birth to a son who was to rule all nations with an iron rod. And her child was snatched away from the dragon and was caught up to God and to his throne. ⁶And the woman fled into the wilderness, where God had prepared a place to care for her for 1,260 days.

⁷Then there was war in heaven. Michael and his angels fought against the dragon and his angels. ⁸And the dragon lost the battle, and he and his angels were forced out of heaven. ⁹This great dragon—the ancient serpent called the devil, or Satan, the one deceiving the whole world—was thrown down to the earth with all his angels.

¹⁰Then I heard a loud voice shouting across the heavens,

11:7 Or *the abyss,* or *the underworld.*   11:8 Greek *the great city.*   11:15 Or *his Messiah.*

"It has come at last—
 salvation and power
and the Kingdom of our God,
 and the authority of his Christ.*
For the accuser of our brothers and sisters*
 has been thrown down to earth—
the one who accuses them
 before our God day and night.
¹¹ And they have defeated him by the blood of
 the Lamb
 and by their testimony.
And they did not love their lives so much
 that they were afraid to die.
¹² Therefore, rejoice, O heavens!
 And you who live in the heavens, rejoice!
But terror will come on the earth and the sea,
 for the devil has come down to you in great
 anger,
 knowing that he has little time."

¹³When the dragon realized that he had been thrown down to the earth, he pursued the woman who had given birth to the male child. ¹⁴But she was given two wings like those of a great eagle so she could fly to the place prepared for her in the wilderness. There she would be cared for and protected from the dragon* for a time, times, and half a time.

¹⁵Then the dragon tried to drown the woman with a flood of water that flowed from his mouth. ¹⁶But the earth helped her by opening its mouth and swallowing the river that gushed out from the mouth of the dragon. ¹⁷And the dragon was angry at the woman and declared war against the rest of her children—all who keep God's commandments and maintain their testimony for Jesus.

¹⁸Then the dragon took his stand* on the shore beside the sea.

The Beast out of the Sea

13 Then I saw a beast rising up out of the sea. It had seven heads and ten horns, with ten crowns on its horns. And written on each head were names that blasphemed God. ²This beast looked like a leopard, but it had the feet of a bear and the mouth of a lion! And the dragon gave the beast his own power and throne and great authority.

³I saw that one of the heads of the beast seemed wounded beyond recovery—but the fatal wound was healed! The whole world marveled at this miracle and gave allegiance to the beast. ⁴They worshiped the dragon for giving the beast such power, and they also worshiped the beast. "Who is as great as the beast?" they exclaimed. "Who is able to fight against him?"

⁵Then the beast was allowed to speak great blasphemies against God. And he was given au-

thority to do whatever he wanted for forty-two months. ⁶And he spoke terrible words of blasphemy against God, slandering his name and his dwelling—that is, those who dwell in heaven.* ⁷And the beast was allowed to wage war against God's holy people and to conquer them. And he was given authority to rule over every tribe and people and language and nation. ⁸And all the people who belong to this world worshiped the beast. They are the ones whose names were not written in the Book of Life before the world was made—the Book that belongs to the Lamb who was slaughtered.*

⁹ Anyone with ears to hear
 should listen and understand.
¹⁰ Anyone who is destined for prison
 will be taken to prison.
Anyone destined to die by the sword
 will die by the sword.

This means that God's holy people must endure persecution patiently and remain faithful.

The Beast out of the Earth

¹¹Then I saw another beast come up out of the earth. He had two horns like those of a lamb, but he spoke with the voice of a dragon. ¹²He exercised all the authority of the first beast. And he required all the earth and its people to worship the first beast, whose fatal wound had been healed. ¹³He did astounding miracles, even making fire flash down to earth from the sky while everyone was watching. ¹⁴And with all the miracles he was allowed to perform on behalf of the first beast, he deceived all the people who belong to this world. He ordered the people to make a great statue of the first beast, who was fatally wounded and then came back to life. ¹⁵He was then permitted to give life to this statue so that it could speak. Then the statue of the beast commanded that anyone refusing to worship it must die.

¹⁶He required everyone—small and great, rich and poor, free and slave—to be given a mark on the right hand or on the forehead. ¹⁷And no one could buy or sell anything without that mark, which was either the name of the beast or the number representing his name. ¹⁸Wisdom is needed here. Let the one with understanding solve the meaning of the number of the beast, for it is the number of a man.* His number is 666.*

The Lamb and the 144,000

14 Then I saw the Lamb standing on Mount Zion, and with him were 144,000 who had his name and his Father's name written on their foreheads. ²And I heard a sound from

12:10a Or *his Messiah.* **12:10b** Greek *brothers.* **12:14** Greek *the serpent;* also in 12:15. See 12:9. **12:18** Greek *Then he took my stand; some manuscripts read Then I took my stand.* Some translations put this entire sentence into 13:1. **13:6** Some manuscripts read *and his dwelling and all who dwell in heaven.* **13:8** Or *not written in the Book of Life that belongs to the Lamb who was slaughtered before the world was made.* **13:18a** Or *of humanity.* **13:18b** Some manuscripts read *616.*

heaven like the roar of mighty ocean waves or the rolling of loud thunder. It was like the sound of many harpists playing together.

³This great choir sang a wonderful new song in front of the throne of God and before the four living beings and the twenty-four elders. No one could learn this song except the 144,000 who had been redeemed from the earth. ⁴They have kept themselves as pure as virgins,* following the Lamb wherever he goes. They have been purchased from among the people on the earth as a special offering* to God and to the Lamb. ⁵They have told no lies; they are without blame.

The Three Angels

⁶And I saw another angel flying through the sky, carrying the eternal Good News to proclaim to the people who belong to this world—to every nation, tribe, language, and people. ⁷"Fear God," he shouted. "Give glory to him. For the time has come when he will sit as judge. Worship him who made the heavens, the earth, the sea, and all the springs of water."

⁸Then another angel followed him through the sky, shouting, "Babylon is fallen—that great city is fallen—because she made all the nations of the world drink the wine of her passionate immorality."

⁹Then a third angel followed them, shouting, "Anyone who worships the beast and his statue or who accepts his mark on the forehead or on the hand ¹⁰must drink the wine of God's anger. It has been poured full strength into God's cup of wrath. And they will be tormented with fire and burning sulfur in the presence of the holy angels and the Lamb. ¹¹The smoke of their torment will rise forever and ever, and they will have no relief day or night, for they have worshiped the beast and his statue and have accepted the mark of his name."

¹²This means that God's holy people must endure persecution patiently, obeying his commands and maintaining their faith in Jesus.

¹³And I heard a voice from heaven saying, "Write this down: Blessed are those who die in the Lord from now on. Yes, says the Spirit, they are blessed indeed, for they will rest from their hard work; for their good deeds follow them!"

The Harvest of the Earth

¹⁴Then I saw a white cloud, and seated on the cloud was someone like the Son of Man.* He had a gold crown on his head and a sharp sickle in his hand.

¹⁵Then another angel came from the Temple and shouted to the one sitting on the cloud, "Swing the sickle, for the time of harvest has come; the crop on earth is ripe." ¹⁶So the one

sitting on the cloud swung his sickle over the earth, and the whole earth was harvested.

¹⁷After that, another angel came from the Temple in heaven, and he also had a sharp sickle. ¹⁸Then another angel, who had power to destroy with fire, came from the altar. He shouted to the angel with the sharp sickle, "Swing your sickle now to gather the clusters of grapes from the vines of the earth, for they are ripe for judgment." ¹⁹So the angel swung his sickle over the earth and loaded the grapes into the great winepress of God's wrath. ²⁰The grapes were trampled in the winepress outside the city, and blood flowed from the winepress in a stream about 180 miles* long and as high as a horse's bridle.

The Song of Moses and of the Lamb

15 Then I saw in heaven another marvelous event of great significance. Seven angels were holding the seven last plagues, which would bring God's wrath to completion. ²I saw before me what seemed to be a glass sea mixed with fire. And on it stood all the people who had been victorious over the beast and his statue and the number representing his name. They were all holding harps that God had given them. ³And they were singing the song of Moses, the servant of God, and the song of the Lamb:

"Great and marvelous are your works,
 O Lord God, the Almighty.
Just and true are your ways,
 O King of the nations.*
⁴ Who will not fear you, Lord,
 and glorify your name?
For you alone are holy.
All nations will come and worship before
 you,
 for your righteous deeds have been
 revealed."

The Seven Bowls of the Seven Plagues

⁵Then I looked and saw that the Temple in heaven, God's Tabernacle, was thrown wide open. ⁶The seven angels who were holding the seven plagues came out of the Temple. They were clothed in spotless white linen* with gold sashes across their chests. ⁷Then one of the four living beings handed each of the seven angels a gold bowl filled with the wrath of God, who lives forever and ever. ⁸The Temple was filled with smoke from God's glory and power. No one could enter the Temple until the seven angels had completed pouring out the seven plagues.

16 Then I heard a mighty voice from the Temple say to the seven angels, "Go your ways and pour out on the earth the seven bowls containing God's wrath."

²So the first angel left the Temple and poured out his bowl on the earth, and horrible, malignant sores broke out on everyone who had the mark of the beast and who worshiped his statue.

³Then the second angel poured out his bowl on the sea, and it became like the blood of a corpse. And everything in the sea died.

⁴Then the third angel poured out his bowl on the rivers and springs, and they became blood. ⁵And I heard the angel who had authority over all water saying,

"You are just, O Holy One, who is and who always was,
because you have sent these judgments.
⁶ Since they shed the blood
of your holy people and your prophets,
you have given them blood to drink.
It is their just reward."

⁷And I heard a voice from the altar,* saying,

"Yes, O Lord God, the Almighty,
your judgments are true and just."

⁸Then the fourth angel poured out his bowl on the sun, causing it to scorch everyone with its fire. ⁹Everyone was burned by this blast of heat, and they cursed the name of God, who had control over all these plagues. They did not repent of their sins and turn to God and give him glory.

¹⁰Then the fifth angel poured out his bowl on the throne of the beast, and his kingdom was plunged into darkness. His subjects ground their teeth in anguish, ¹¹and they cursed the God of heaven for their pains and sores. But they did not repent of their evil deeds and turn to God.

¹²Then the sixth angel poured out his bowl on the great Euphrates River, and it dried up so that the kings from the east could march their armies toward the west without hindrance. ¹³And I saw three evil* spirits that looked like frogs leap from the mouths of the dragon, the beast, and the false prophet. ¹⁴They are demonic spirits who work miracles and go out to all the rulers of the world to gather them for battle against the Lord on that great judgment day of God the Almighty.

¹⁵"Look, I will come as unexpectedly as a thief! Blessed are all who are watching for me, who keep their clothing ready so they will not have to walk around naked and ashamed."

¹⁶And the demonic spirits gathered all the rulers and their armies to a place with the Hebrew name *Armageddon.**

¹⁷Then the seventh angel poured out his bowl into the air. And a mighty shout came from the throne in the Temple, saying, "It is finished!" ¹⁸Then the thunder crashed and rolled, and lightning flashed. And a great earthquake struck–the worst since people were placed on the earth. ¹⁹The great city of Babylon split into three sections, and the cities of many nations fell into heaps of rubble. So God remembered all of Babylon's sins, and he made her drink the cup that was filled with the wine of his fierce wrath. ²⁰And every island disappeared, and all the mountains were leveled. ²¹There was a terrible hailstorm, and hailstones weighing as much as seventy-five pounds* fell from the sky onto the people below. They cursed God because of the terrible plague of the hailstorm.

The Great Prostitute

17 One of the seven angels who had poured out the seven bowls came over and spoke to me. "Come with me," he said, "and I will show you the judgment that is going to come on the great prostitute, who rules over many waters. ²The kings of the world have committed adultery with her, and the people who belong to this world have been made drunk by the wine of her immorality."

³So the angel took me in the Spirit* into the wilderness. There I saw a woman sitting on a scarlet beast that had seven heads and ten horns, and blasphemies against God were written all over it. ⁴The woman wore purple and scarlet clothing and beautiful jewelry made of gold and precious gems and pearls. In her hand she held a gold goblet full of obscenities and the impurities of her immorality. ⁵A mysterious name was written on her forehead: "Babylon the Great, Mother of All Prostitutes and Obscenities in the World." ⁶I could see that she was drunk—drunk with the blood of God's holy people who were witnesses for Jesus. I stared at her in complete amazement.

⁷"Why are you so amazed?" the angel asked. "I will tell you the mystery of this woman and of the beast with seven heads and ten horns on which she sits. ⁸The beast you saw was once alive but isn't now. And yet he will soon come up out of the bottomless pit* and go to eternal destruction. And the people who belong to this world, whose names were not written in the Book of Life before the world was made, will be amazed at the reappearance of this beast who had died.

⁹"This calls for a mind with understanding: The seven heads of the beast represent the seven hills where the woman rules. They also represent seven kings. ¹⁰Five kings have already fallen, the sixth now reigns, and the seventh is yet to come, but his reign will be brief.

¹¹"The scarlet beast that was, but is no longer, is the eighth king. He is like the other seven, and

16:7 Greek *I heard the altar.* **16:13** Greek *unclean.* **16:16** Or *Harmagedon.* **16:21** Greek *1 talent* [34 kilograms]. **17:3** Or *in spirit.* **17:8** Or *the abyss,* or *the underworld.*

he, too, is headed for destruction. ¹²The ten horns of the beast are ten kings who have not yet risen to power. They will be appointed to their kingdoms for one brief moment to reign with the beast. ¹³They will all agree to give him their power and authority. ¹⁴Together they will go to war against the Lamb, but the Lamb will defeat them because he is Lord of all lords and King of all kings. And his called and chosen and faithful ones will be with him."

¹⁵Then the angel said to me, "The waters where the prostitute is ruling represent masses of people of every nation and language. ¹⁶The scarlet beast and his ten horns all hate the prostitute. They will strip her naked, eat her flesh, and burn her remains with fire. ¹⁷For God has put a plan into their minds, a plan that will carry out his purposes. They will agree to give their authority to the scarlet beast, and so the words of God will be fulfilled. ¹⁸And this woman you saw in your vision represents the great city that rules over the kings of the world."

The Fall of Babylon

18 After all this I saw another angel come down from heaven with great authority, and the earth grew bright with his splendor. ²He gave a mighty shout:

"Babylon is fallen—that great city is fallen!
    She has become a home for demons.
She is a hideout for every foul* spirit,
    a hideout for every foul vulture
    and every foul and dreadful animal.*
³ For all the nations have fallen*
    because of the wine of her passionate
        immorality.
The kings of the world
    have committed adultery with her.
Because of her desires for extravagant luxury,
    the merchants of the world have
        grown rich."

⁴Then I heard another voice calling from heaven,

"Come away from her, my people.
    Do not take part in her sins,
    or you will be punished with her.
⁵ For her sins are piled as high as heaven,
    and God remembers her evil deeds.
⁶ Do to her as she has done to others.
    Double her penalty* for all her evil deeds.
She brewed a cup of terror for others,
    so brew twice as much* for her.
⁷ She glorified herself and lived in luxury,
    so match it now with torment and sorrow.
She boasted in her heart,
    'I am queen on my throne.
I am no helpless widow,
    and I have no reason to mourn.'

⁸ Therefore, these plagues will overtake her in
        a single day—
    death and mourning and famine.
She will be completely consumed by fire,
    for the Lord God who judges her is
        mighty."

⁹And the kings of the world who committed adultery with her and enjoyed her great luxury will mourn for her as they see the smoke rising from her charred remains. ¹⁰They will stand at a distance, terrified by her great torment. They will cry out,

"How terrible, how terrible for you,
    O Babylon, you great city!
In a single moment
    God's judgment came on you."

¹¹The merchants of the world will weep and mourn for her, for there is no one left to buy their goods. ¹²She bought great quantities of gold, silver, jewels, and pearls; fine linen, purple, silk, and scarlet cloth; things made of fragrant thyine wood, ivory goods, and objects made of expensive wood; and bronze, iron, and marble. ¹³She also bought cinnamon, spice, incense, myrrh, frankincense, wine, olive oil, fine flour, wheat, cattle, sheep, horses, chariots, and bodies—that is, human slaves.

¹⁴ "The fancy things you loved so much
        are gone," they cry.
"All your luxuries and splendor
        are gone forever,
        never to be yours again."

¹⁵The merchants who became wealthy by selling her these things will stand at a distance, terrified by her great torment. They will weep and cry out,

¹⁶ "How terrible, how terrible for that great city!
    She was clothed in finest purple and
        scarlet linens,
    decked out with gold and precious stones
        and pearls!
¹⁷ In a single moment
    all the wealth of the city is gone!"

And all the captains of the merchant ships and their passengers and sailors and crews will stand at a distance. ¹⁸They will cry out as they watch the smoke ascend, and they will say, "Where is there another city as great as this?" ¹⁹And they will weep and throw dust on their heads to show their grief. And they will cry out,

"How terrible, how terrible for that great city!
    The shipowners became wealthy
    by transporting her great wealth on
        the seas.
In a single moment it is all gone."

18:2a Greek *unclean;* also in each of the two following phrases. **18:2b** Some manuscripts condense the last two lines to read *a hideout for every foul [unclean] and dreadful vulture.* **18:3** Some manuscripts read *have drunk.* **18:6a** Or *Give her an equal penalty.* **18:6b** Or *brew just as much.*

²⁰ Rejoice over her fate, O heaven
and people of God and apostles and
prophets!
For at last God has judged her
for your sakes.

²¹Then a mighty angel picked up a boulder the size of a huge millstone. He threw it into the ocean and shouted,

"Just like this, the great city Babylon
will be thrown down with violence
and will never be found again.
²² The sound of harps, singers, flutes, and
trumpets
will never be heard in you again.
No craftsmen and no trades
will ever be found in you again.
The sound of the mill
will never be heard in you again.
²³ The light of a lamp
will never shine in you again.
The happy voices of brides and grooms
will never be heard in you again.
For your merchants were the greatest in
the world,
and you deceived the nations with
your sorceries.
²⁴ In your* streets flowed the blood of the
prophets and of God's holy people
and the blood of people slaughtered all
over the world."

Songs of Victory in Heaven

19 After this, I heard what sounded like a vast crowd in heaven shouting,

"Praise the Lord!*
Salvation and glory and power belong to
our God.
² His judgments are true and just.
He has punished the great prostitute
who corrupted the earth with her immorality.
He has avenged the murder of his servants."

³And again their voices rang out:

"Praise the Lord!
The smoke from that city ascends forever
and ever!"

⁴Then the twenty-four elders and the four living beings fell down and worshiped God, who was sitting on the throne. They cried out, "Amen! Praise the Lord!"

⁵And from the throne came a voice that said,

"Praise our God,
all his servants,
all who fear him,
from the least to the greatest."

⁶Then I heard again what sounded like the shout of a vast crowd or the roar of mighty ocean waves or the crash of loud thunder:

"Praise the Lord!
For the Lord our God,* the Almighty,
reigns.
⁷ Let us be glad and rejoice,
and let us give honor to him.
For the time has come for the wedding feast
of the Lamb,
and his bride has prepared herself.
⁸ She has been given the finest of pure white
linen to wear."
For the fine linen represents the good
deeds of God's holy people.

⁹And the angel said to me, "Write this: Blessed are those who are invited to the wedding feast of the Lamb." And he added, "These are true words that come from God."

¹⁰Then I fell down at his feet to worship him, but he said, "No, don't worship me. I am a servant of God, just like you and your brothers and sisters* who testify about their faith in Jesus. Worship only God. For the essence of prophecy is to give a clear witness for Jesus.*"

The Rider on the White Horse

¹¹Then I saw heaven opened, and a white horse was standing there. Its rider was named Faithful and True, for he judges fairly and wages a righteous war. ¹²His eyes were like flames of fire, and on his head were many crowns. A name was written on him that no one understood except himself. ¹³He wore a robe dipped in blood, and his title was the Word of God. ¹⁴The armies of heaven, dressed in the finest of pure white linen, followed him on white horses. ¹⁵From his mouth came a sharp sword to strike down the nations. He will rule them with an iron rod. He will release the fierce wrath of God, the Almighty, like juice flowing from a winepress. ¹⁶On his robe at his thigh* was written this title: King of all kings and Lord of all lords.

¹⁷Then I saw an angel standing in the sun, shouting to the vultures flying high in the sky: "Come! Gather together for the great banquet God has prepared. ¹⁸Come and eat the flesh of kings, generals, and strong warriors; of horses and their riders; and of all humanity, both free and slave, small and great."

¹⁹Then I saw the beast and the kings of the world and their armies gathered together to fight against the one sitting on the horse and his army. ²⁰And the beast was captured, and with him the false prophet who did mighty miracles on behalf of the beast—miracles that deceived all who had accepted the mark of the beast and

18:24 Greek *her.* **19:1** Greek *Hallelujah;* also in 19:3, 4, 6. *Hallelujah* is the transliteration of a Hebrew term that means "Praise the Lord." **19:6** Some manuscripts read *the Lord God.* **19:10a** Greek *brothers.* **19:10b** Or *is the message confirmed by Jesus.* **19:16** Or *On his robe and thigh.*

who worshiped his statue. Both the beast and his false prophet were thrown alive into the fiery lake of burning sulfur. ²¹Their entire army was killed by the sharp sword that came from the mouth of the one riding the white horse. And the vultures all gorged themselves on the dead bodies.

The Thousand Years

20 Then I saw an angel coming down from heaven with the key to the bottomless pit* and a heavy chain in his hand. ²He seized the dragon—that old serpent, who is the devil, Satan—and bound him in chains for a thousand years. ³The angel threw him into the bottomless pit, which he then shut and locked so Satan could not deceive the nations anymore until the thousand years were finished. Afterward he must be released for a little while.

⁴Then I saw thrones, and the people sitting on them had been given the authority to judge. And I saw the souls of those who had been beheaded for their testimony about Jesus and for proclaiming the word of God. They had not worshiped the beast or his statue, nor accepted his mark on their foreheads or their hands. They all came to life again, and they reigned with Christ for a thousand years.

⁵This is the first resurrection. (The rest of the dead did not come back to life until the thousand years had ended.) ⁶Blessed and holy are those who share in the first resurrection. For them the second death holds no power, but they will be priests of God and of Christ and will reign with him a thousand years.

The Defeat of Satan

⁷When the thousand years come to an end, Satan will be let out of his prison. ⁸He will go out to deceive the nations—called Gog and Magog—in every corner of the earth. He will gather them together for battle—a mighty army, as numberless as sand along the seashore. ⁹And I saw them as they went up on the broad plain of the earth and surrounded God's people and the beloved city. But fire from heaven came down on the attacking armies and consumed them.

¹⁰Then the devil, who had deceived them, was thrown into the fiery lake of burning sulfur, joining the beast and the false prophet. There they will be tormented day and night forever and ever.

The Final Judgment

¹¹And I saw a great white throne and the one sitting on it. The earth and sky fled from his presence, but they found no place to hide. ¹²I saw the dead, both great and small, standing before God's throne. And the books were opened, including the Book of Life. And the dead were

judged according to what they had done, as recorded in the books. ¹³The sea gave up its dead, and death and the grave* gave up their dead. And all were judged according to their deeds. ¹⁴Then death and the grave were thrown into the lake of fire. This lake of fire is the second death. ¹⁵And anyone whose name was not found recorded in the Book of Life was thrown into the lake of fire.

The New Jerusalem

21 Then I saw a new heaven and a new earth, for the old heaven and the old earth had disappeared. And the sea was also gone. ²And I saw the holy city, the new Jerusalem, coming down from God out of heaven like a bride beautifully dressed for her husband.

³I heard a loud shout from the throne, saying, "Look, God's home is now among his people! He will live with them, and they will be his people. God himself will be with them.* ⁴He will wipe every tear from their eyes, and there will be no more death or sorrow or crying or pain. All these things are gone forever."

⁵And the one sitting on the throne said, "Look, I am making everything new!" And then he said to me, "Write this down, for what I tell you is trustworthy and true." ⁶And he also said, "It is finished! I am the Alpha and the Omega—the Beginning and the End. To all who are thirsty I will give freely from the springs of the water of life. ⁷All who are victorious will inherit all these blessings, and I will be their God, and they will be my children.

⁸"But cowards, unbelievers, the corrupt, murderers, the immoral, those who practice witchcraft, idol worshipers, and all liars—their fate is in the fiery lake of burning sulfur. This is the second death."

⁹Then one of the seven angels who held the seven bowls containing the seven last plagues came and said to me, "Come with me! I will show you the bride, the wife of the Lamb."

¹⁰So he took me in the Spirit* to a great, high mountain, and he showed me the holy city, Jerusalem, descending out of heaven from God. ¹¹It shone with the glory of God and sparkled like a precious stone—like jasper as clear as crystal. ¹²The city wall was broad and high, with twelve gates guarded by twelve angels. And the names of the twelve tribes of Israel were written on the gates. ¹³There were three gates on each side— east, north, south, and west. ¹⁴The wall of the city had twelve foundation stones, and on them were written the names of the twelve apostles of the Lamb.

¹⁵The angel who talked to me held in his hand a gold measuring stick to measure the city, its gates, and its wall. ¹⁶When he measured it, he found it was a square, as wide as it was long. In

20:1 Or *the abyss,* or *the underworld;* also in 20:3.   **20:13** Greek *and Hades;* also in 20:14.   **21:3** Some manuscripts read *God himself will be with them, their God.*   **21:10** Or *in spirit.*

fact, its length and width and height were each 1,400 miles.* [17]Then he measured the walls and found them to be 216 feet thick* (according to the human standard used by the angel).

[18]The wall was made of jasper, and the city was pure gold, as clear as glass. [19]The wall of the city was built on foundation stones inlaid with twelve precious stones:* the first was jasper, the second sapphire, the third agate, the fourth emerald, [20]the fifth onyx, the sixth carnelian, the seventh chrysolite, the eighth beryl, the ninth topaz, the tenth chrysoprase, the eleventh jacinth, the twelfth amethyst.

[21]The twelve gates were made of pearls—each gate from a single pearl! And the main street was pure gold, as clear as glass.

[22]I saw no temple in the city, for the Lord God Almighty and the Lamb are its temple. [23]And the city has no need of sun or moon, for the glory of God illuminates the city, and the Lamb is its light. [24]The nations will walk in its light, and the kings of the world will enter the city in all their glory. [25]Its gates will never be closed at the end of day because there is no night there. [26]And all the nations will bring their glory and honor into the city. [27]Nothing evil* will be allowed to enter, nor anyone who practices shameful idolatry and dishonesty— but only those whose names are written in the Lamb's Book of Life.

22 Then the angel showed me a river with the water of life, clear as crystal, flowing from the throne of God and of the Lamb. [2]It flowed down the center of the main street. On each side of the river grew a tree of life, bearing twelve crops of fruit,* with a fresh crop each month. The leaves were used for medicine to heal the nations.

[3]No longer will there be a curse upon anything. For the throne of God and of the Lamb will be there, and his servants will worship him. [4]And they will see his face, and his name will be written on their foreheads. [5]And there will be no night there—no need for lamps or sun—for the Lord God will shine on them. And they will reign forever and ever.

[6]Then the angel said to me, "Everything you have heard and seen is trustworthy and true. The Lord God, who inspires his prophets,* has sent his angel to tell his servants what will happen soon.*"

Jesus Is Coming

[7]"Look, I am coming soon! Blessed are those who obey the words of prophecy written in this book.*"

[8]I, John, am the one who heard and saw all these things. And when I heard and saw them, I fell down to worship at the feet of the angel who showed them to me. [9]But he said, "No, don't worship me. I am a servant of God, just like you and your brothers the prophets, as well as all who obey what is written in this book. Worship only God!"

[10]Then he instructed me, "Do not seal up the prophetic words in this book, for the time is near. [11]Let the one who is doing harm continue to do harm; let the one who is vile continue to be vile; let the one who is righteous continue to live righteously; let the one who is holy continue to be holy."

[12]"Look, I am coming soon, bringing my reward with me to repay all people according to their deeds. [13]I am the Alpha and the Omega, the First and the Last, the Beginning and the End."

[14]Blessed are those who wash their robes. They will be permitted to enter through the gates of the city and eat the fruit from the tree of life. [15]Outside the city are the dogs—the sorcerers, the sexually immoral, the murderers, the idol worshipers, and all who love to live a lie.

[16]"I, Jesus, have sent my angel to give you this message for the churches. I am both the source of David and the heir to his throne.* I am the bright morning star."

[17]The Spirit and the bride say, "Come." Let anyone who hears this say, "Come." Let anyone who is thirsty come. Let anyone who desires drink freely from the water of life. [18]And I solemnly declare to everyone who hears the words of prophecy written in this book: If anyone adds anything to what is written here, God will add to that person the plagues described in this book. [19]And if anyone removes any of the words from this book of prophecy, God will remove that person's share in the tree of life and in the holy city that are described in this book.

[20]He who is the faithful witness to all these things says, "Yes, I am coming soon!"

Amen! Come, Lord Jesus!

[21]May the grace of the Lord Jesus be with God's holy people.*

Join the Team

There are thousands of hockey players, their families and fans who are struggling to find meaning in life. Maybe you are one of them. Possibly you are really caught up in the game. Hockey is great but it is, after all, just a game. It isn't able to permanently satisfy or to offer eternal hope, supernatural peace or victory over the challenges of life. It's important to think about where you place your trust and the truths upon which you are building your life. Jesus is the answer to life and promises eternal life and help in this life to all who believe in Him. We encourage you to read through this special Hockey Player's New Testament. Also please take time to consider the following paragraphs which provide a brief outline on how to join Christ's winning team and discover true purpose in life through a personal relationship with God.

1. God Has a Goal for Each One of Our Lives

God has a goal for each of us. He wants us to live full and meaningful lives by loving and serving Him. The apostle Paul explained it this way:

"God has made us what we are, and in union with Christ Jesus he has created us for a life of good deeds, which he has already prepared for us to do." (Ephesians 2:10)

2. We Have All Broken God's Rules

Just like there are rules when you step onto the ice to play, there are rules to the game of life. It's God's game, it's his rink and we play by his rules . . . or at least we're supposed to! But we all take shortcuts with the playbook. Sometimes we want to get ahead and sometimes we just think we know better than the coach. God calls our breaking the rules by a word we don't use much anymore.

" . . . everyone has sinned and is far away from God's presence." (Romans 3:23)

3. We All Deserve God's Penalty

When you break the rules on the ice . . . there's a penalty. When you break God's rules for life, there's also a penalty, but the consequences are much more serious. Sin pulls us away from God's perfect presence . . . far away and separated from God forever. The Bible sometimes calls this death.

"For sin pays its wages—death; but God's free gift is eternal life in union with Christ Jesus our Lord." (Romans 6:23)

Hey, that sounded like good news at the end of that verse. What's that about a free gift?

4. Our penalty has been served by a "Teammate" . . .

You probably already know that when a goalie breaks the rules, one of his teammates serves his time in the penalty box. Jesus, your Teammate, has served your penalty.

When the officials looked at Christ's on-ice performance it turns out he had never broken the rules, not a single time! Because he didn't have to serve a penalty for himself, he served yours. That's exactly what happened when Jesus died on the Cross 2000 years ago. He took your place in the penalty box.

"But God has shown us how much he loves us—it was while we were still sinners that Christ died for us!" (Romans 5:8)

"For Christ died for sins once and for all, a good man on behalf of sinners, in order to lead you to God." (1 Peter 3:18)

The added piece of good news is that after Jesus served your penalty, he came out of the box, just to prove that the penalty was paid in full. Because Jesus was raised from the dead after paying the penalty for our sins, we know that God accepted His death on our behalf and that Jesus is alive forever to skate beside us in the game of life.

5. We Have to Accept the Offer

As you consider joining God's team please understand that it does not involve a fierce struggle or competition with other players in an effort to earn a position on the team.

"For it is by grace you have been saved, through faith—and this not from yourselves, it is the gift of god—not by works, so that no one can boast." (Ephesians 2:8,9)

God is offering forgiveness and eternal life as a gift. You can become a part of His team by accepting His gift of forgiveness and salvation.

It's really no more complicated than telling God that you know you need Him because you can't pull this off on your own. If you have never spoken to God in prayer before, you might not quite know how to go about it. But it's really rather simple. Some people approach it like this:

> *Heavenly Father,*
>
> *I know you sent Your Son, Jesus Christ, into the world to be my substitute. I know I need to be forgiven. I believe that Jesus died for my sins, paid my penalty in full and rose again from the dead. I accept Him as my personal Savior and invite him to be Lord of my life. Help me turn away from wrong and learn to surrender my life to you and to live in a way that pleases you, as the Bible teaches.*

If you've decided to join the team, we'd love to hear about it. Please contact the person who gave you this New Testament or our staff at *Hockey Ministries International*. We would be pleased to send a copy of the booklet, The Bible and the Game of Life.

When the Puck Drops

When you became a player on Christ's team, Jesus became a part of your life. He will give you strength to live a life that wins and is pleasing to Him. Here are some ideas from the coach to help in your development as player:

Find Teammates

You will struggle if you try to grow in your faith on your own. We all need friends to encourage and spur us on. Seek out a Christian church in your community that teaches the truths of the Bible. Establish friendships with like-minded believers and get involved in Bible studies and fellowship groups. (See Hebrews 10:24)

Talk to the Coach

Christians need to communicate with the "Head Coach" (God) through prayer. This is an essential part of the Christian life. The New Testament reminds us to always keep on praying. We can pray anywhere, anytime about anything. (See Philippians 4:6,7)

Trust the Coach

Just like players have to learn to trust the coach and his game plan so we have to trust the Lord and His plan for our lives. (See Ephesians 2:10)

Know the Playbook

God has given us His playbook (the Bible) to guide us through life. He wants us to read and study it each day and to apply its truths to our lives. It is the best way to get to know God and find peace. (See 2 Timothy 2:15)

Draw Strength from the Holy Spirit

When a person accepts Jesus, the Holy Spirit comes to live within him. He will strengthen and enable you to live a strong Christian life. Learn to be sensitive to His presence within you and to walk in step with His leading. (See Galatians 5:16)

Tell Others

Take every opportunity to tell others, especially family members, teammates and friends, about your personal faith in Jesus Christ. (See 2 Corinthians 5:18-20)

The Playbook

The Bible is our playbook for life. Benefitting from it requires planning and discipline, writes Ryan Walter: "During my 15 years in the NHL I had to continuously practice my skills to stay sharp. That meant planning and discipline. The same is true in our spiritual lives. We have to plan to set time aside daily to be in God's Word."

Practice these skills to better understand God's Playbook:

Learn . . . AS YOU STUDY THE BIBLE

In Acts 17:11 and 2 Timothy 2:15 we are taught to study making sure we understand what the Bible says. It helps to ask: "who wrote the passage? to whom was it written and what is the lesson or theme?" Taking notes and memorizing important verses anchors our understanding.

Listen . . . AS GOD SPEAKS THROUGH THE BIBLE

We can improve our spiritual ears by setting aside time daily to read in a quiet location as Jesus did in Matthew 1:35, developing a thirst for righteousness (Matthew 5:6), desiring spiritual truth (1 Peter 2:1,2), putting God first in our lives (Matthew 6:33).

Live . . . AS YOU PRATICE WHAT YOU LEARN

Jesus said: " . . . everyone who hears these words of mine and puts them into practice is like a wise man who built his house upon the rock."

By putting what we learn into action we build a solid foundation for the trials of life.

Lean . . . AS YOU TRUST GOD'S PROMISES

The Lord wants us to trust His promises and lean on Him through life's challenges. Jesus promises to give us rest as we come to Him (Matthew 11:28).

Lead . . . AS YOU SHARE BIBLE TRUTHS WITH OTHERS

Paul urged his young friend Timothy to tell others about the important truths he was learning. (2 Timothy 2:2)